Reagents for Organic Synthesis

Reagents for Organic Synthesis

VOLUME 2

Mary Fieser

Research Fellow in Chemistry
Harvard University

Louis Fieser

Sheldon Emery Professor of Organic Chemistry, Emeritus
Harvard University

WILEY-INTERSCIENCE

A DIVISION OF JOHN WILEY & SONS

NEW YORK · LONDON · SYDNEY · TORONTO

10 9 8 7 6 5 4 3 2 1

Library of Congress Catalogue Card Number: 66–27894

SBN 471 25876 8

Printed in the United States of America

PREFACE

Favorable comments expressed both in formal reviews and personally have en-
couraged us to present this second volume of *Reagents*, the size of which measures
the amount of new material that has accumulated in the two and a half years since
the closing date of August 23, 1966, for Volume 1. This second volume contains
1320 additional references to 390 reagents discussed in the first volume and 550
references to 226 reagents reviewed by us now for the first time. Most of the latter
were introduced since the first volume was written, but a few are old reagents recently reintroduced into modern research. It is interesting that in this period more new
oxidizing agents (17) and reducing agents (11) were discovered. However, it appears
that the biggest field for new reagents is that of the organometallic compounds. Thus
we have discussed in this volume 34 new organometallic reagents, compared with a
total of only 50 in the larger first volume. New organophosphorous and organosulfur
compounds are also proving increasingly useful.

We are indebted to Research Corporation for a grant in support of the project and
to colleagues for help in the preparation of this volume. Many have sent us useful
information or have checked sections pertaining to their own work. Some have
sent us contributions for which we are most grateful.

The formulas were drawn by Miss Theodora S. Lytle, who also typed the manu-
script. Of the twin Siamese cats whose photographs graced the preface of Volume
1, Shio Pooh is still full of life and good health at an age of more than twenty-four.
His photograph is one used previously in a book that included a review of the
chemistry of nepetalactone.

Cambridge, Massachusetts   MARY FIESER
February 18, 1969   LOUIS F. FIESER

Shio Pooh

CONTENTS

Reagents for Organic Synthesis

Introduction

Arrangement. Suppliers mentioned in the text are listed in a section placed before the indexes and easily located by an indenture.

For enhanced usefulness the book is provided not only with a subject and an author index but also with an index of types, that is, types of reactions or types of compounds, for example: acetylation, bromination, characterization (of a, b, c, etc.), decarboxylation, or: π-acids, benzyne precursors, carbene precursors, diimide precursors. Listed alphabetically under each such entry are all the reagents which figure in the operation or group cited, whether as prime reactant, catalyst, solvent, scavenger, etc. A given reagent may fit appropriately in two or more categories. When a reagent does not fit easily into a reasonable category, we leave it unclassified rather than make a forced assignment. With no less than 109 reagents available as oxidants and 115 for use as reducing reagents, it seemed out of the question to attempt to indicate in the index of types further details about these general reactions. In a few instances a procedure cited for the preparation of one reagent provides a good example of the use of another one. For example, a preferred route to allene is by reaction of 2,3-dichloropropene with zinc dust and ethanol; in the index of types the entries under "dechlorination" include "Zinc dust − ethanol, *see* Allene, preparation."

Names and spelling. One guideline we have followed is the rule recently adopted by *Organic Syntheses* that when an ester, ether, or peroxide contains two or more alkyl, aryl, or acyl groups the name must indicate the number of such groups:

Formula	Correct	Incorrect
$(CH_3)_2O$	Dimethyl ether	Methyl ether
$(C_2H_5O)_2SO_2$	Diethyl sulfate	Ethyl sulfate
$(C_6H_5)_2O$	Diphenyl ether	Phenyl ether
$(CO_2CH_3)_2$	Dimethyl oxalate	Methyl oxalate
$CH_2(CO_2C_2H_5)_2$	Diethyl malonate	Ethyl malonate
$(C_6H_5COO)_2$	Dibenzoyl peroxide	Benzoyl peroxide
$HC(OC_2H_5)_3$	Triethyl orthoformate	Ethyl orthoformate
$(C_2H_5O)_4C$	Tetraethyl orthocarbonate	Ethyl orthocarbonate

That the situation previously was highly confused is evident from the following entries in the index of *Org. Syn., Coll. Vol.*, **4**: "Diethyl oxalate" and "Diethyl malonate" (both correct), but "Ethyl orthoformate" and "Ethyl orthocarbonate" (both incorrect). The following entry is describable as a double error: "Triethyl orthoformate, *see* Ethyl orthoformate." To locate all references to a given ester, it is thus necessary to search under two names. We urge suppliers to revise their catalogs in accordance with the rule cited. In this book we do not even list, with cross references, names which we consider to be incorrect.

Similar reform in the nomenclature of polyhalogen compounds may come some day, but for the present we consider it imprudent to do more than make a start.

Thus the correct names for BF_3 and for $ClCH_2CH_2Cl$ surely are boron trifluoride and ethylene dichloride, and we feel no restraint from using them. However, although the names methylene chloride for CH_2Cl_2 and aluminum chloride for $AlCl_3$ seem incorrect, we cannot bring ourselves to break with tradition and employ other names.

As explained in our *Style Guide for Chemists* (p. 77), we disapprove of the weak-sounding dioxăn, furăn, tryptophăn, and urethăn and add the letter *e* to these words to produce the strong pronunciations dioxāne, furāne, tryptophāne, and urethāne. For the same reason we favor desoxo- and desoxy- over deoxo- and deoxy-.

Abbreviations. Short forms of abbreviations of journal titles are as follows:

Journal of the American Chemical Society
Angewandte Chemie
Angewandte Chemie, international Edition in English
Annalen der Chemie
Annales de chimie (Paris)
Australian Journal of Chemistry
Chemische Berichte (formerly Berichte der deutschen chemischen Gesellschaft)
Bulletin de la société chimique de France
Canadian Journal of Chemistry
Chemical Communications
Chemical and Pharmaceutical Bulletin
Acta Chemica Scandinavica
Collection of Czechoslovak Chemical Communications
Comptes rendus hebdomadaires des séances de l'académie des sciences
Gazzetta chimica italiana
Helvetica Chimica Acta
Journal of the Chemical Society (London)
Journal of Heterocyclic Chemistry
Journal of Organic Chemistry
Journal of Organometallic Chemistry
Monatshefte für Chemie
Organic Syntheses
Organic Syntheses, Collective Volume
Recueil des travaux chimique des Pays-Bas (The Netherlands)

The book by one of us, *Organic Experiments*, 2nd Ed., D. C. Heath and Co., Boston (1968), is referred to as *Org. Expts.*

Abbreviations

Ac	Acetyl
AcOH	Acetic acid
BuOH	Butanol
Bz	Benzoyl
Cathyl	Carboethoxy
Cb	Carbobenzoxy
DCC	Dicyclohexylcarbodiimide
DDQ	2,3-Dichloro-5,6-dicyano-1,4-benzoquinone

Diglyme	Diethylene glycol dimethyl ether
DMF	Dimethylformamide
DMSO	Dimethyl sulfoxide
DNF	2,4-Dinitrofluoro-benzene
DNP	2,4-Dinitrophenyl-hydrazone
EtOH	Ethanol
Glyme	1,2-Dimethoxyethane
HMPT	Hexamethylpolyphosphoric triamide
MeOH	Methanol
Ms	Mesyl, CH_3SO_2
NBS	N-Bromosuccinimide
Ph	Phenyl
Phth	Phthaloyl
PPA	Polyphosphoric acid
Py	Pyridine
THF	Tetrahydrofurane
Triglyme	Triethylene glycol dimethyl ether
Trityl	$(C_6H_5)_3C-$
Ts	Tosyl, $p\text{-}CH_3C_6H_4SO_2-$
TsCl	Tosyl chloride
TsOH	Tosic acid, $p\text{-}CH_3C_6H_4SO_3H$

A

Acetaldehyde dimethylacetal (1,1-Dimethoxyethane), $CH_3CH(OCH_3)_2$ [**1**, 3, before **Acetaldoxime**]. Mol. wt. 90.12, b.p. 63–65°. Suppliers: B, C, E, F. Fl. (Fluka), K.-L. (Koch-Light), Sch. (Schuchardt).

O'Meara and Shepherd[1] found the reagent useful for the conversion of aldopyranoses into ethylidene derivatives. Thus 2.5 ml. of concd. sulfuric acid was added dropwise to a stirred suspension of 58 g. of methyl β-D-glucopyranoside (1) in 250 ml. of acetaldehyde dimethylacetal. The mixture was shaken for 48 hrs., filtered, and the solid product (2) collected and crystallized twice from ethanol. Methyl 4 : 6-

O-ethylidene-β-D-glucopyranoside (2) was obtained thus in a high state of purity in 65% yield. This transformation previously had been accomplished by treating paraldehyde with the glucoside in the presence of sulfuric acid,[2] but the yields were variable owing to a side reaction which gives methyl 4 : 6-O-ethylidene-2 : 3-O-oxidodiethylidene-β-D-glucopyranoside. A second British group[3] has confirmed the observation that the side reaction can be eliminated by use of acetaldehyde dimethylacetal.

[1]D. O'Meara and D. M. Shepherd, *J. Chem. Soc.*, 4232 (1955)
[2]B. Helferich and H. Appel, *Ber.*, **64**, 1841 (1931); J. Dewar and G. Fort, *J. Chem. Soc.*, 492 (1944)
[3]J. Honeyman and T. C. Stening, *ibid.*, 3316 (1957)

Acetamidomethanol, $CH_3CONHCH_2OH$ [**1**, 3, before **Acetic anhydride**]. Mol. wt. 89.10, m.p. 50–52°.

Preparation from acetamide and formaldehyde.[1]

Protection of cysteine.[2] The reagent reacts with L-cysteine in hydrochloric acid at pH 0.5 at 25° to give S-acetamidomethyl-L-cysteine hydrochloride from which the free base can be obtained by treatment with Ag_2O and then H_2S. The S-acetamidomethyl group is stable to acidic reagents commonly used for removal of acid-labile substituents: CF_3COOH, HBr, HCl, HF; but it is removed in high yield by 2 equiv. of Hg(II) salts at pH 4 at room temperature, conditions that do not affect such groups as carbobenzoxy, N-*t*-butyloxycarbonyl, and S-benzyl. The solubility

$$\underset{\underset{H_2NCHCOOH}{|}}{CH_2SH} \quad + \quad CH_3CONHCH_2OH \quad \xrightarrow[-H_2O]{HCl, \; pH \; 0.5} \quad \underset{\underset{Cl^-}{\overset{+}{H_3N}-CHCOOH}}{CH_2SCH_2NHCOCH_3}$$

$$\downarrow Ag_2O, \; H_2S$$

$$\underset{H_2N-CHCOOH}{CH_2SCH_2NHCOCH_3}$$

characteristics of this group make it suitable for peptide synthesis in both anhydrous and aqueous media. The blocking group is stable to conditions used in the azide peptide synthesis.

The Merck[3] total synthesis of ribonuclease involved coupling various peptide units to form a tetrahectapeptide (104 residues) known as S-protein. This polypeptide contains 8 cysteine and 3 methionine residues. The acetamidomethyl blocking group proved invaluable for protection of the cysteine units.

[1]A. Einhorn and C. Ladisch, *Ann.*, **343**, 265 (1905)

[2]D. F. Veber, J. D. Milkowski, R. G. Denkewalter, and R. Hirschmann, *Tetrahedron Letters*, 3057 (1968)

[3]R. G. Denkewalter, D. F. Veber, F. W. Holly, and R. Hirschmann, *Am. Soc.*, **91**, 502 (1969)

Acetic acid, CH_3CO_2H [1, 3, before **Acetic anhydride**]. Mol. wt. 60.05, b.p. 118°. An acetylation can sometimes be modified to advantage by use of acetic acid as a diluent. An efficient method of enzymic resolution illustrated for the case of DL-alanine (1) involves conversion to the DL-N-acetate (2) and enzymic hydrolysis to natural L-acetyl-N-alanine, an alcohol-soluble product easily separated from alcohol-insoluble L-alanine. The acetylation step presents the difficulty that, if the conditions are too severe, the N-acetyl derivative (2) may be converted in part through the enol (3) into the azlactone (4). A procedure for the precise control of the reaction[1] calls for heating 2 g. of DL-alanine and 5 ml. of acetic acid in a test tube to a little above 100°, and adding 3 ml. of acetic anhydride. The temperature falls (91–95°, cooling by added reagent), rises (100–103°, exothermal, acetylation), and begins to fall. Work-up affords DL-acetylalanine in nearly quantitative yield.

A procedure by Burgstahler and Worden[2] for the preparation of benzofurane (6) from o-formylphenoxyacetic acid (5) calls for refluxing for 8 hrs. a mixture of 0.5 mole of (5), 2.2 moles of sodium acetate, 450 ml. of acetic anhydride, and 450 ml. of acetic acid; benzofurane (6), the product of cyclodehydration and decarboxyla-

$$\underset{(1)}{\underset{\underset{NH_2}{|}}{DL\text{-}CH_3CHCO_2H}} \xrightarrow{(CH_3CO)_2O} \underset{(2)}{\underset{\underset{NHCOCH_3}{|}}{DL\text{-}CH_3CHCO_2H}} \rightleftharpoons \underset{(3)}{\underset{\underset{CH_3}{|}}{CH_3CHCO_2H}}$$

$$\xrightarrow{-H_2O} \underset{(4)}{CH_3CH-C=O}$$

$$\text{(salicylaldehyde)} + \text{NaOH} + \text{H}_2\text{O} + \text{ClCH}_2\text{CO}_2\text{H} \xrightarrow{82-83\%} \text{(5)}$$

1 mole   2 moles   200 ml.   1 mole

(6) 30-31%   +   (7) 45%   (6) 65.7%

tion, was obtained in 65.7% yield. When no acetic acid was used, the yield of benzofurane was cut in half and coumarilic acid (7) was obtained in yield of 45%.

[1]L. F. Fieser, *Org. Expts.*, 138, D. C. Heath, second edition 1968
[2]A. W. Burgstahler and L. R. Worden, *Org. Syn.*, **46**, 28 (1966)

Acetic acid, 80% [**1, 3**, before **Acetic anhydride**]. Lewbart is credited by Reichstein *et al.*[1] with originating use of this reagent in an efficient and generally applicable method for the cleavage of acetonides, as illustrated by the Swiss workers in elucidating the structure of strogoside, a cardiac glycoside related to ouabain (1). Ouabain, a rhamnoside, had afforded only resins or extensive degradation products on attempted acid hydrolysis. Then Mannich and Siewart[2] found that although the glycoside is only sparingly soluble in acetone, when a suspension in acetone containing hydrogen chloride is shaken in the cold, the solid soon dissolves in the form of a

$$\text{Ouabain (1)} \xrightarrow[93\%]{(\text{CH}_3)_2\text{CO}-\text{HCl}} (2) \xrightarrow[90\%]{\text{Ac}_2\text{O}}$$

$$(3) \xrightarrow[80\%]{80\% \text{ AcOH}} (4)$$

monoacetonide in which the group introduced is in the sugar residue. On standing for 1 or 2 weeks the solution deposits crystals of the 1,3-monoacetonide of ouabain. The Reichstein group applied this procedure to 24.25 g. of ouabain and obtained 14.44 g. of the 1,19-acetonide (2), and this on acetylation afforded the acetate-acetonide (3). Then a solution of 6 g. of (3) in 250 ml. of 80% acetic acid was let stand at 20° for 3 days and evaporated in vacuum; crystallization of the residue from water gave ouabagenin 3,11-diacetate (4) in 80% yield.

More recently, Lewbart[3] reported selective hydrolysis of the acetonide group of 17,20α-isopropylidenedioxy-5β-pregnane-3α,21-diol diacetate (5) with retention of the primary and secondary acetoxy groups.

$$\xrightarrow[\text{70. 5\%}]{\substack{\text{80\% AcOH}\\ \text{12 hrs. at 65°}}}$$

(5)   (6)

[1]U. P. Geiger, Ek. Weiss, and T. Reichstein, *Helv.*, **50**, 194 (1967)
[2]C. Mannich and G. Siewart, *Ber.*, **75**, 737 (1942).
[3]M. L. Lewbart, *J. Org.*, **33**, 1695 (1968)

Acetic anhydride [bottom of **1**, 3].

Polonovski reaction.[1] This reaction consists in the reaction of the N-oxide of a tertiary amine (1) with acetic anhydride to form the N-acylated secondary amine (2) as the major product and the deaminated ketone (3) as minor product:

(1)   (2)   (3)

The mechanism of the Polonovski reaction has been studied without conclusive results.[2] Recently a French group[3] interested in steroidal alkaloids reasoned that trifluoroacetic anhydride might be more reactive and applied the reaction to (4), the N-oxide of N-methyldihydro-5α-paravallarine. NMR data provided evidence for the formation of the immonium salts (5) and (6). Hydrolysis with aqueous sodium bicarbonate leads to (7) and (8).

Thiele reaction. In a typical Thiele reaction,[4,5] 1,4-benzoquinone (1) is added with stirring at room temperature or below to a solution of a catalyst such as concentrated sulfuric acid in acetic anhydride; 1,4-addition to (2) is followed rapidly by enolization (3) and acetylation to give 1,2,4-triacetoxybenzene (4) in high yield. In a few cases Thiele used zinc chloride as catalyst but without apparent advantage. Boron trifluoride etherate would appear to be a more satisfactory Lewis acid since

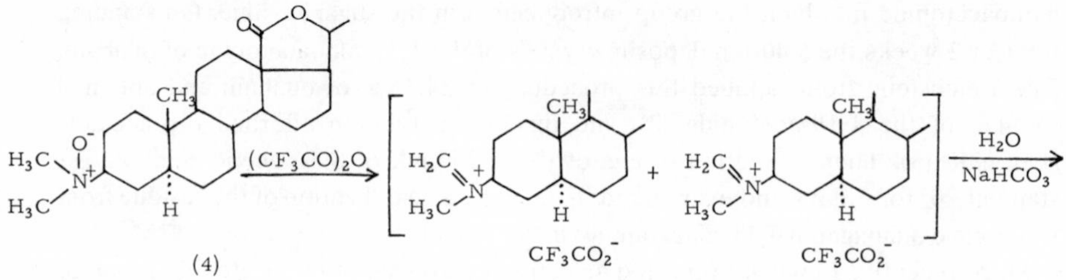

(4)   (5) 60%   (6) 40%

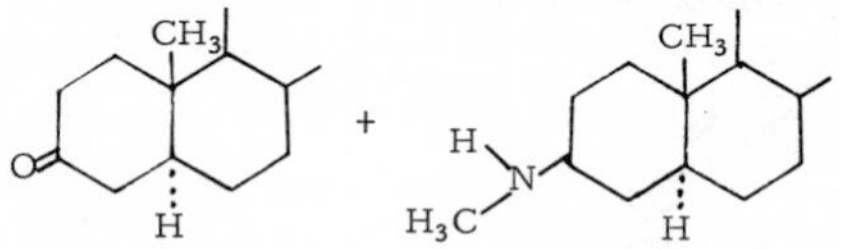

(7) 60%   (8) 40%

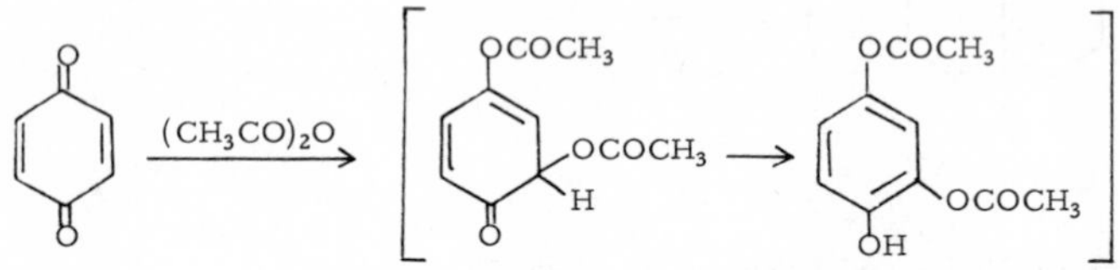

(1)   (2)   (3)

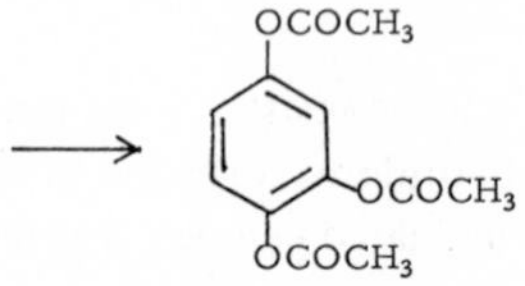

(4)

it is a liquid miscible with acetic anhydride; in one comparison a batch of 1,4-naphthoquinone gave 1,2,4-triacetoxynaphthalene in 81% yield with boron trifluoride etherate and in 74.5% yield with sulfuric acid as catalyst (Fieser[6] and *Reagents*, 1, 72).

The following discussion of catalysts and yields includes new observations by Wilgus and Gates[7] of the Eastman Kodak Co. Thus these investigators report that toluquinone (1) on reaction with acetic anhydride and sulfuric acid gives in 90% yield a mixture shown by VPC analysis to represent a yield of 78% of the 2,4,5-triacetoxy derivative (2) and a 14.5% yield of 2,3,5-isomer (3). Thus the reaction

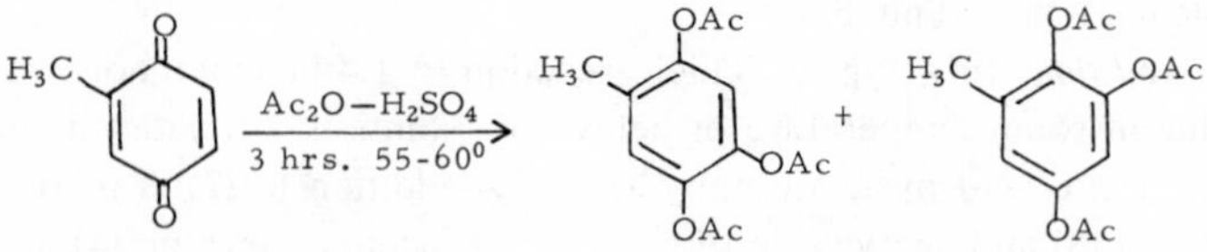

(1)   (2) 2, 4, 5-Isomer   (3) 2, 3, 5-Isomer
                  78%   14. 5%

involves attack by a new acetoxyl group in the positions *para* and *meta* to the methyl group originally present.

Data already summarized (*see* **1**, 71) show that with α-naphthoquinone, which is unhindered, BF_3-etherate is a more satisfactory catalyst for Thiele acetoxylation than sulfuric acid, but that with hindered quinones BF_3-etherate is a less potent catalyst than H_2SO_4. Thus 2,5-dimethyl-1,4-benzoquinone adds acetic anhydride smoothly in the presence of BF_3-etherate but 2,6-dimethyl-1,4-benzoquinone does not; on the other hand, 2,6-dimethyl-1,4-benzoquinone undergoes the H_2SO_4-catalyzed Thiele reaction. Fieser and Fieser's *Advanced Organic Chemistry*, p. 855, presents theoretical interpretations of the relationships noted and of the fact that 2-methyl-1,4-naphthoquinone is relatively inert to acetic anhydride–sulfuric acid. Wilgus and Gates[7] found that with BF_3-etherate catalysis 2-methyl-1,3,4-triacetoxynaphthalene is produced in 27% yield in a reaction period of 18 hrs. and in 52% yield in a period of 120 hrs. Burton and Praill (**1**, 801) found that perchloric acid is a more effective Thiele catalyst and that in the presence of this acid the hindered quinone reacts to give 2-methyl-1,3,4-triacetoxynaphthalene in moderate yield. A study of samples of 1,4-naphthoquinone of various grades of purity (**1**, 715–716) further demonstrated the efficacy of perchloric acid as catalyst for Thiele acetoxylation of the *p*-quinone. 1,2-Naphthoquinone shows about the same reactivity to Ac_2O—H_2SO_4 as does 1,4-naphthoquinone to Ac_2O—BF_3 (*Adv. Org. Chem.*,

p. 855). Thiele acetylation proceeds in good yield in spite of the presence of a methyl group adjacent to one of the quinonoid carbonyl groups.[8]

M. Lounasmaa,[9] of the Technical University of Helsinki, Otaniemi, Finland, refluxed for several hours a solution of 2,6-dimethoxy-1,4-benzoquinone in acetic anhydride in the presence of sodium acetate, added water, and isolated by extraction with chloroform and crystallization from acetic acid a colorless product melting at 149–150° which, on the basis of analysis ($C_{14}H_{16}O_8$), mass spectrography, and IR and NMR spectroscopy, was assigned the structure (6).

[1]M. Polonovski and M. Polonovski, *Bull. soc.*, [4] **39**, 147 (1926); **41**, 1190 (1927)

[2]E. Wenkert, *Experientia*, **10**, 346 (1954); R. Huisgen *et al.*, *Ber.*, **92**, 3223 (1959); **93**, 363 (1960); *idem*, *Tetrahedron Letters*, 783 (1965); S. Oae, T. Kitao, and Y. Kitaoka, *Am. Soc.*, **84**, 3366 (1962)

[3]A. Cavé, C. Kan-Fan, P. Potier, and J. Le Men, *Tetrahedron*, **23**, 4681 (1967)

[4]J. Thiele, *Ber.*, **31**, 1247 (1898)

$$CH_3\overset{O}{\overset{\|}{C}}O^- + CH_3\overset{O}{\overset{\|}{C}}-O-\overset{O}{\overset{\|}{C}}CH_3 \longrightarrow CH_3\overset{O}{\overset{\|}{C}}OH + CH_2\overset{O}{\overset{\|}{C}}-O-\overset{O}{\overset{\|}{C}}CH_3$$

(1)

(2)   (3)   (4)

(5)   (6)

[5]J. Thiele and E. Winter, *Ann.*, **311**, 341 (1899)
[6]L. F. Fieser, *Am. Soc.*, **70**, 3165 (1948)
[7]H. S. Wilgus, III, and J. W. Gates, Jr., *Canad. J. Chem.*, **45**, 1975 (1967)
[8]L. F. Fieser and A. M. Seligman, *Am. Soc.*, **56**, 2690 (1934). The yield here reported is that obtained by L. F. F. on repeating the experiment with 492 mg. of the quinone and a cold solution of 0.5 g. of sulfuric acid in 30 ml. of iced acetic anhydride. The product precipitated on addition of water amounted to 500 mg. (85%); crystallization from acetic acid gave white needles, m.p. 159°.
[9]M. Lounasmaa, *Tetrahedron Letters*, 91 (1968); *idem, Chem. Scand.*, **22**, 70 (1968)

Acetic–formic anhydride [1, 4] Mol. wt. 88.06.

[Line 16]: An improved preparatory procedure stated to be essentially that of Muramatsu *et al.*[4] is described as follows by Krimen.[6] A 2-l. three-necked flask equipped with stirrer, thermometer, reflux condenser with calcium chloride tube, and dropping tube is charged with 300 g. (4.41 moles) of finely ground sodium formate and 250 ml. of anhydrous ether (a slight excess of sodium formate ensures

$$CH_3COCl + HCOONa \longrightarrow CH_3\overset{O}{\overset{\|}{C}}-O-\overset{O}{\overset{\|}{C}}H + NaCl$$

a product free of acetyl chloride). The dropping tube is charged with 294 g. (266 ml., 3.75 moles) of acetyl chloride, a cooling bath (20–24°) is put in place to control the mildly exothermal reaction, and the acetyl chloride is run in in about 5 min. at a temperature controlled to 23–27°. The mixture is then stirred at 23–27° for 5.5 hrs. to ensure complete reaction. The mixture is then filtered by suction and the salt residue rinsed with ether. The ether is removed by distillation at reduced pressure, and distillation of the residue at reduced pressure gives 212 g. (65%) of colorless acetic–formic anhydride, b.p. 27–28°/10 mm., or 38–38.5°/39 mm., n_D^{20} 1.388.

The mixed anhydride may be stored at 4° in a standard round-bottomed flask fitted with a 24/40 polyethylene stopper. Since moisture catalyzes decomposition of the product to acetic acid and carbon monoxide, it must not be stored in a sealed container.

Spectrographic characterization.[6] The infrared spectrum of the mixed anhydride shows bands in the carbonyl region at 1765 and 1791 cm^{-1} and carbon–oxygen–carbon stretching absorption at 1050 cm^{-1} (a band at 1180 cm^{-1} could also be due to C—O—C). The NMR spectrum shows singlets at $\delta = 2.25$ (acetyl protons), and at $\delta = 9.05$ (formyl proton).

If the product is not pure, the following peaks may be observed from the impurity indicated:

$\underline{H}$COOH, $\delta = 8.05$; ($\underline{H}$CO)$_2$O, $\delta = 8.85$; C$\underline{H}_3$, $\delta = 2.05$;

CH$_3$CO$_2$H, $\delta = 2.05$; C$\underline{H_3}$COCl, $\delta = 2.68$; (C$\underline{H_3}$CO)$_2$O, $\delta = 2.20$.

Reaction with Grignard reagents. Edwards and Kammann[7] studied the reaction of phenylmagnesium bromide in ether at $-70°$ with one equivalent of formic–acetic anhydride and found that the less hindered carbonyl group of the mixed anhydride reacts preferentially, with the result that the aldehydic product (5) predominates strongly over the methyl ketone (6). With ether as solvent, the ratio

(a)	Ether $-70°$	82.9	17.1
(b)	THF $-70°$	53.5	46.5
(c)	Ether $0°$	84.0	16.0

mole percent

of products was nearly the same at $0°$ as at $-70°$. Use of tetrahydrofurane as solvent eliminated the preference, and the mole percent of aldehyde and that of methyl ketone were about the same. Aldehydes predominated strongly over ketones in the products obtained with four other aromatic Grignard reagents; less strongly with aliphatic reagents.

Blocking group in peptide synthesis. The conversion of an amino acid into its N-formyl derivative does not require preformed acetic–formic anhydride. Sheehan and Yang[5] added 83 ml. of acetic anhydride dropwise to a mixture of 0.10 mole of the amino acid in 250 ml. of 88% formic acid at a rate to maintain a temperature of 50–60°. The mixture was stirred at room temperature for 1 hr. and 80 ml. of ice water was added. The mixture was concentrated at reduced pressure and the crystalline residue could be crystallized easily from water or aqueous ethanol.

Formylation of amines and alcohols. Béhal,[8] discoverer of the reagent, found that it reacts unidirectionally with simple alcohols to produce alkyl formates free from acetates. Hurd *et al.*[9] found that acetic–formic anhydride (prepared from formic acid and ketene) reacts quantitatively with aniline to give formanilide. Another study[10] established that acetic-formic anhydride mixes endothermally with 2-nitro-2-methyl-1-propanol, exothermally with 2-nitro-2-methyl-1,3-propanediol, and displays no appreciable temperature effect with either 2-nitro-1-butanol or tris-(hydroxymethyl)-nitromethane. Formic esters are favored by avoiding a high reaction temperature and by not using sulfuric acid as catalyst. The mixed anhydride has been used for the preparation of formyl fluoride.[11]

Unhindered phenols are converted into formates in satisfactory yields.[12]

[6]L. I. Krimen, procedure submitted to *Org. Syn.*, 1967
[7]W. R. Edwards, Jr., and K. P. Kammann, Jr., *J. Org.*, **29**, 913 (1964)
[8]A. Béhal, *Compt. rend.*, **128**, 1460 (1900)
[9]C. D. Hurd and A. S. Roe, *Am. Soc.*, **61**, 3355 (1939)
[10]C. D. Hurd, S. S. Drake, and O. Fancher, *ibid.*, **68**, 789 (1946)
[11]G. A. Olah and S. J. Kuhn, *ibid.*, **82**, 2380 (1960)
[12]S. Sófuku, I. Muramatsu, and A. Hagitani, *Bull. Chem. Soc. Japan*, **40**, 2942 (1967)

Acetic-phosphoric anhydride, $HO-\overset{O}{\underset{OH}{P}}-O-\overset{O}{C}CH_3$. [**1**, 4, before **Acetoacetyl fluoride**].

Mol. wt. 136.01. Anhydrous phosphoric acid is available from Matheson Co., Chicago, or can be prepared by dissolving 113 g. of phorphorus pentoxide in 150 g. of ortho-phosphoric acid at 60–70°.[1] The resulting product is a liquid that crystallizes on standing (m.p. 42°). The crystalline material can be liquefied by brief heating at 60° (prolonged heating or higher temperatues lead to formation of polyphosphoric acid).

The mixed anhydride, useful as an acetylating reagent,[1] is prepared just before use by adding 1 ml. of anhydrous phosphoric acid to 4 ml. of acetic anhydride (mole ratio, 1:1.7) in a graduated cylinder and stirring until a homogeneous solution is obtained. The temperature usually rises to 50–55°.

Acetylation. Inositol (1), which has five equatorial and one axial hydroxyl group, was acetylated by stirring 20 g. with 200 ml. of the reagent at 85° for 15 min. followed by treatment with ice-water. This afforded 47 g. (97%) of almost pure

(1) $(HO)_2\overset{O}{P}-O-\overset{O}{C}CH_3$ 15 min. 85°   (2)

inositol hexaacetate (2). Previously known methods of acetylation, including the powerful Fritz-Schenk reagent[2] (acetic anhydride and perchloric acid in ethyl acetate) had failed to provide an acetate from croconic acid (3). The new reagent, acetic–phosphoric anhydride, affords croconic acid diacetate (4) in good yield by the procedure formulated.

The reagent can be used also for the Thiele reaction, that is, acid-catalyzed addition of acetic anhydride to a quinone with further conversion into the hydroquinone

(3) 1 g.   (4)

triacetate.[1] Usual catalysts are concentrated sulfuric acid and boron trifluoride etherate; perchloric acid is still more powerful. The procedure indicated in the formulation is that used in the only experiment on record. Since the new reagent is very

mild because of the nonoxidizing character of phosphoric acid, the yield seems surprisingly low.

[1]A. J. Fatiadi, *Carbohydrate Res.*, **6**, 237 (1968)
[2]J. S. Fritz and G. H. Schenk, *Anal. Chem.*, **31**, 1808 (1959)

Acetone, CH_3COCH_3, [**1**, 5, before **Acetone cyanohydrin**]. Mol. wt. 58.05, b.p. 56–57°. For commercial sources of pure acetone, *see* **1**, 1110. For the purification of reagent required for the preparation of carbohydrate acetonides, Whistler and Wolfrom[1] recommend that technical-grade acetone be refluxed with small amounts of permanganate until the purple color persists, distilled, and dried for 2 days over anhydrous potassium carbonate or calcium sulfate, filtered, and distilled.,

[1]R. L. Whistler and M. L. Wolfrom, "Methods in Carbohydrate Chemistry," II, 319 (1963)

Acetonitrile, CH_3CN, b.p. 81.6° [**1**, 7, before *a*-**Acetoxyacrylonitrile**]. Aprotic, water-miscible Diels-Alder solvent (**1**, 239). Supplier of pure solvent, **1**, 1110. For polarographic use, Moe[1] notes that the main impurity is acrylonitrile, which differs from it in b.p. by only 4.2°, and recommends separation by distillation of the ternary and secondary azeotropes which the two liquids form with ethanol and with water. Ethanol (95%) is added to practical acetonitrile and the mixture is distilled through an H. Stedman column of 60–65 theoretical plates. The purified material is suitable also for UV spectroscopy.

[1]N. S. Moe, *Chem. Scand.*, **21**, 1389 (1967)

α-Acetoxyacrylonitrile [**1**,7, after first formulation].
    Acetoxyacrylonitrile has also been prepared[1a] by the reaction of chloroacetaldehyde (1) in aqueous solution with sodium cyanide at −10–0°. 2-Chloro-1-cyanoethyl acetate (2) is obtained in 90% yield by way of the postulated intermediates (a) and (b). Formation of the cyanohydrin (a) is believed to be the first step, followed by loss of hydrogen chloride and ketonization to give acetyl cyanide (b); the latter intermediate is considered to acetylate the cyanohydrin (a) to give 2-chloro-1-

$$ClCH_2CHO \xrightarrow{NaCN} \left[ClCH_2\overset{OH}{\underset{CN}{CH}} \xrightarrow[-HCl]{} CH_3COCN \right] \xrightarrow[90\%]{} ClCH_2\overset{OH}{\underset{CN}{CH}}$$

(1)   (a)   (b)   (a)

$$ClCH_2\overset{OCOCH_3}{\underset{CN}{CH}} \xrightarrow[91\%]{(C_2H_5)_3N} CH_2{=}C\overset{OCOCH_3}{\underset{CN}{}}$$

(2)   (3)

cyanoethyl acetate (2), the first isolated product. Dehydrohalogenation of (2) with triethylamine gives α-acetoxyacrylonitrile (3).

[1a]R. M. Nowak, *J. Org.*, **28**, 1182 (1963)

Acetyl *p*-toluenesulfonate, $CH_3\overset{O}{\overset{\|}{C}}{-}O{-}\overset{O}{\underset{O}{\overset{\|}{\underset{\|}{S}}}}{-}\langle\!\bigcirc\!\rangle{-}CH_3$ [1,14, before **Acrylonitrile**].
Mol. wt. 214.24, m.p. 54–56° (not pure).

Preparation.[1] This mixed sulfonic–carboxylic anhydride is prepared in quantitative yield by refluxing anhydrous *p*-toluenesulfonic acid with an excess of acetyl chloride until the evolution of hydrogen chloride ceases (3–5 hrs.); the excess acetyl chloride is removed to give the colorless crystalline anhydride. It can also be prepared from acetic anhydride (excess) and anhydrous *p*-toluenesulfonic acid.

Cleavage of ethers.[1] Ethers are cleaved by the reagent under relatively mild conditions (25–130°, 2–48 hrs., acetonitrile usually used as solvent). The third and fifth examples are particularly interesting because they demonstrate that this reagent

(1) $(\underline{n}\text{-}C_4H_9)_2O \xrightarrow[50\%]{} \underline{n}\text{-}C_4H_9O\overset{O}{\overset{\|}{C}}CH_3 \ + \ \underline{n}\text{-}C_4H_9OTs$

(2) [cyclic ether] $\xrightarrow[82\%]{} CH_3\overset{O}{\overset{\|}{C}}O(CH_2)_4OTs$

(3) [methyl cyclic ether] $\xrightarrow[95\%]{} CH_3\overset{O}{\overset{\|}{C}}O(CH_2)_3\overset{CH_3}{\underset{OTs}{CH}}$

(4) [dioxane] $\xrightarrow[87\%]{} CH_3\overset{O}{\overset{\|}{C}}OCH_2CH_2OCH_2CH_2OTs$

(5) $CH_3\overset{O}{\overset{\|}{C}}CH_2CH_2OCH_2CH_2OTs \xrightarrow[45\%]{} CH_3\overset{O}{\overset{\|}{C}}OCH_2CH_2OTs$

shows a greater specificity of cleavage than other reagents. Since the sulfonate group of the product is subject to ready nucleophilic displacement, synthesis of novel substituted acetates can be achieved. The procedure for carrying out the cleavage of dioxane (4) is described in further detail in an *Organic Syntheses* procedure.[2]

[1]M. H. Karger and Y. Mazur, *Am. Soc.*, **90**, 3878 (1968)
[2]*Idem*, procedure submitted to *Org. Syn.* (1969)

Acrolein, CH_2=CHCHO [1, 14, before **Acrylonitrile**]. Mol. wt. 56.06, b.p. 51–53°, sp. gr. 0.841. Suppliers: A, B, C, E, F, MCB; Fl., Sch.

A trialkylborane, for example (3) resulting from reaction of hexene-1 (1) with diborane (2, generated from $NaBH_4 + BF_3$), undergoes remarkably fast 1,4-addition to acrolein to produce the enol borinate (4), which on hydrolysis gives the aldehyde (5).[1] The Brown group found it more convenient to add water to a solution of the

$$6\ CH_2{=}CHCH_2CH_2CH_2CH_3\ +\ B_2H_6\ \longrightarrow\ 2\ B(CH_2CH_2CH_2CH_2CH_2CH_3)_3$$

$$(1)\qquad\qquad (2)\qquad\qquad (3)$$

$$\xrightarrow{CH_2{=}CHCHO}\ CH_3CH_2CH_2CH_2CH_2CH_2CH_2CH{=}CHOBR_2\ \xrightarrow[77\%]{H_2O}$$

$$(4)$$

$$CH_3CH_2CH_2CH_2CH_2CH_2CH_2CH_2CHO$$

$$(5)$$

organoborane in tetrahydrofurane; introduction of acrolein then results in concurrent 1,4-addition and simultaneous hydrolysis to produce the aldehyde (5). In the case cited, gas chromatography indicated the following yields after 10, 25, and 60 min.: 65, 71, and 77%.

Other examples:

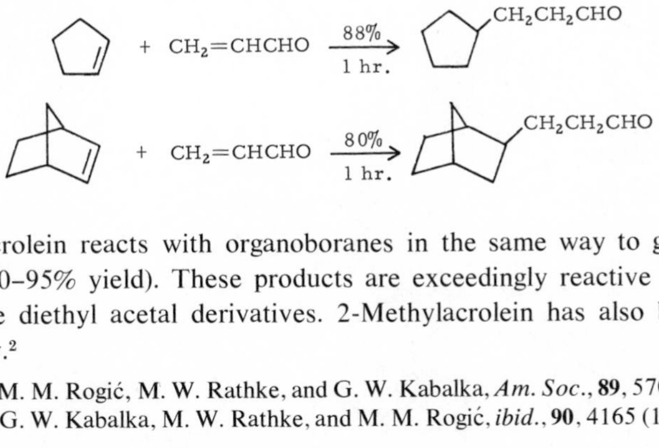

2-Bromoacrolein reacts with organoboranes in the same way to give α-bromo aldehydes (60–95% yield). These products are exceedingly reactive and are best stored as the diethyl acetal derivatives. 2-Methylacrolein has also been used in the same way.[2]

[1]H. C. Brown, M. M. Rogić, M. W. Rathke, and G. W. Kabalka, *Am. Soc.*, **89**, 5709 (1967)
[2]H. C. Brown, G. W. Kabalka, M. W. Rathke, and M. M. Rogić, *ibid.*, **90**, 4165 (1968)

Adamantane-1-carboxylic acid chloride [1, 15, before **1-Adamantyl chloroformate**]. Mol. wt. 198.69, m.p. 54 –56°. Supplier: A.

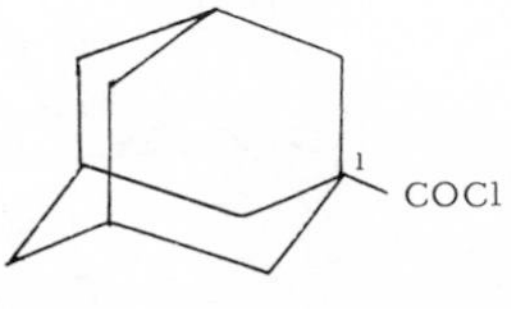

Adamantane, prepared according to Schleyer[1] and supplied by Aldrich Chemical Co., can be converted into the 1-carboxylic acid by carboxylation with formic acid, *t*-butanol, and 96% sulfuric acid,[2] or from 1-bromoadamantane, formic acid, and 96% sulfuric acid.[3]

Rapala *et al.*[4] of the Eli Lilly Research Laboratories prepared 17β-adamantantoate esters of steroids by the action of the acid chloride on the alcohol in benzene containing 1 equivalent of pyridine. The adamantoic ester of 19-nortestosterone has significantly higher anabolic potency than other esters.

This hindered acid chloride has been suggested also for use in nucleoside synthesis for the protection of the 5'-primary hydroxyl group.[5] 1-Adamantoyl chloride reacts in benzene–pyridine solution with 2'-desoxy-5-fluorouridine (3) to give a crystalline ester in which the group introduced must be at either the 3'- or the 5'-position. A distinction between these possibilities was provided by acetylation experiments. Monoadamantoylation of (3) attacks the primary 5'-position preferentially. The product of tritylation and acetylation followed by partial hydrolysis is 3'-O-acetyl-2'-desoxy-5-fluorouridine (1), and this substance on adamantoylation to (2) and deacetylation gives 5'-adamantoyl-2'-desoxy-5-fluorouridine (4) identical with the product of direct adamantoylation. The isomeric 3'-adamantoyl-2'-desoxy-5-fluoro-uridine (6) was obtained for comparison from 2'-desoxy-5-fluorouridine (3) by trityla-tion of the 5'-hydroxyl group, adamantoylation of the 3'-hydroxyl group to give (5), and treatment of the fully protected derivative (5) with aqueous acetic acid to remove the trityl group. The product (6) indeed proved to be the 3'-isomer of (4). The isomers differ in melting point, in chromatographic behavior, and in spectral qualities. Note that the trityl group of (5) was removed selectively with aqueous acetic acid without disturbance of an adamantoyl group. On the other hand, mildly alkaline conditions (0.025 N NaOH) permit the preferential removal of the 3'-acetyl group of (2). The 5'-adamantoate group is cleaved readily by stronger base (0.25 N).

[1]P. von R. Schleyer, M. M. Donaldson, R. D. Nicholas, and C. Cupas, *Org. Syn.*, **42**, 8 (1962)
[2]H. Stetter, M. Schwarz, and A. Hirschhorn, *Ber.*, **92**, 1629 (1959)
[3]L. F. Fieser, M. Z. Nazer, S. Archer, D. A. Berberian, and R. G. Slighter, *J. Med. Chem.*, **10**, 517 (1967)
[4]R. T. Rapala, R. J. Kraay, and K. Gerzon, *ibid.*, **8**, 580 (1965)
[5]K. Gerzon and D. Kau, *ibid.*, **10**, 189 (1967)

Alumina for dehydration of alcohols [bottom of **1**, 19].

Barrett and Büchi[3a] dehydrated the epimeric alcohol mixture (1) by grinding 6.6 g. with 21 g. of neutral Woelm alumina (activity I) mixed with 2% w/v of anhy-

(1)

(2)   (3)

drous pyridine and pyrolyzed the mixture at 230°. The resulting oil (5.4 g.) was shown by glpc to be a 3:1 mixture of triene (2), $\lambda 277$ mμ (ϵ 4600), and triene (3), $\lambda 233, 239, 246$ mμ.

[3a]H. C. Barrett and G. Büchi, *Am. Soc.*, **89**, 5665 (1967)

Alumina for selective hydrolysis of primary acetates [**1**, 20, before **Aluminum amalgam**].
Johns and Jerina[1] found that selective hydrolysis of acetates of primary alcohols in the presence of acetates of secondary alcohols can be achieved easily by use of untreated alumina (Merck, Alcoa) in a modified chromatographic technique.

[1]W. F. Johns and D. M. Jerina, *J. Org.*, **28**, 2922 (1963)

Alumina–Potassium hydroxide ("Basic alumina") [**1**, **20**, before **Aluminum amalgam**]. Castells and Fletcher[1] prepared this reagent by shaking for 2 hrs. a mixture of 1 kg. of alumina with a solution of 100 g. of potassium hydroxide in 75 ml. of water. A reasonably homogeneous adsorbate results and can be poured into a chromatographic tube for elution with ether. Baird and Winstein[2] used Harshaw activated powder, catalyst grade, 90% Al_2O_3. Passage of a benzene solution of a 3,5-dinitrobenzoate through a column of this reagent effects cleavage. A reaction is evident from an instantaneous violet coloration.

Alumina–potassium hydroxide can be used for the generation of dichlorocarbene or dibromocarbene from chloroform or bromoform, respectively.[3] A 3:1 molar mixture of cyclohexene and the haloform is adsorbed on basic alumina and kept at room temperature for 4 days and then eluted with ether. The 7,7-dihalonorcarane was obtained in 12–15% yield (calculated on the basis of the base in the alumina).

Baird and Winstein[2] isolated the extremely sensitive spiro [2.5] octadiene-3-one (4) as a crystalline solid by passage of a solution of 2-p-hydroxyphenyl-1-ethyl-bromide (3) through basic alumina.

E. R. H. Jones et al.[4] investigated the dehydrohalogenation of (5) and found that usual reagents [KOH, K_2CO_3, $(C_2H_5)_3N$, $NaNH_2$] are ineffective but that alumina–potassium hydroxide gives (6) in about 17% yield. The product ultimately desired was the fully conjugated decayne (7) and, surprisingly, it was found that this sub-

stance can be made directly from (5) by Eglinton-Galbraith[5] coupling (**1**, 159) without preparation of (6).

[1]J. Castells and G. A. Fletcher, *J. Chem. Soc.*, 3245 (1956)
[2]R. Baird and S. Winstein, *Am. Soc.*, 79, 4238 (1957); *idem, ibid.*, 85, 567 (1963)
[3]F. Serratosa, *J. Chem. Ed.*, 41, 564 (1964)
[4]E. R. H. Jones, H. H. Lee, and M. C. Whiting, *J. Chem. Soc.*, 3483 (1960)
[5]G. Eglinton and A. R. Galbraith, *ibid.*, 889 (1959)

Aluminum [1, 20, before **Aluminum amalgam**]. At. wt. 26.98. Supplier of purified 6×6-in. foil and of powder: B, MCB.

In an improvement over Karrer's synthesis of β-carotene and lycopene, a German industrial group[1] used aluminum and a trace of mercuric chloride for the condensation of 2 moles of propargyl bromide with 1,2-dichloro-1,2-diethoxyethane to give

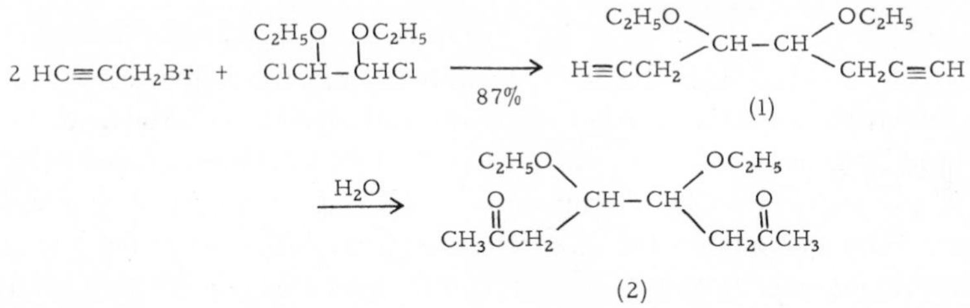

the diethoxydiacetylene derivative (1), required for hydration to the diethoxydiketone (2).

Schneider and Weedon[2] found this metal superior to zinc for the Reformatsky condensation of propargyl bromide with acetone; the product (3) was observed to be

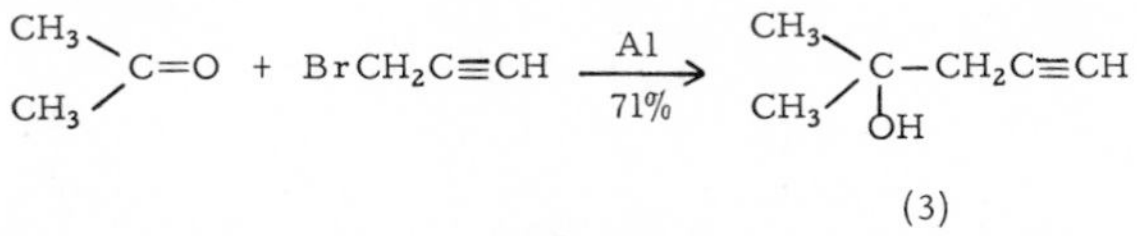

free from allenic impurities, whereas such impurities were present when zinc was used.

[1]H.-J. Kabbe, E. Truscheit, and K. Eiter, *Ann*, 684, 14 (1965)
[2]D. F. Schneider and B. C. L. Weedon, *J. Chem. Soc.*, (C), 1686 (1967)

Aluminum bromide [1, 22-23, before references].

Friedel-Crafts intramolecular cyclization. Huisgen and Ugi[7] report that aluminum bromide is superior to aluminum chloride for intramolecular Friedel-Crafts cyclization of ω-phenylalkanoic acid chlorides (1) to paracyclophanes (2). In both cases high dilution was used (CS_2 solvent), but in the case of aluminum bromide the acid

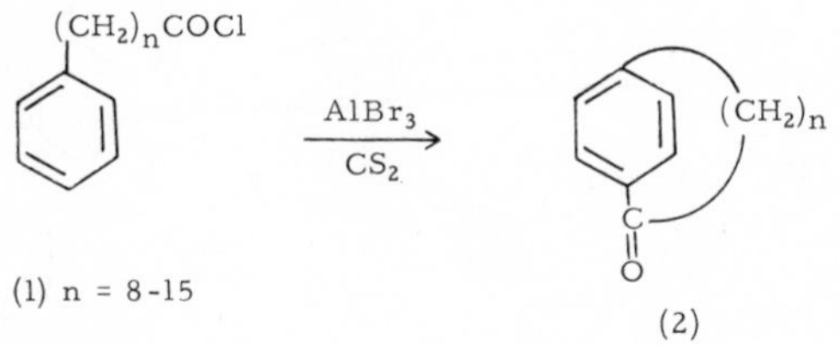

(1) n = 8-15

(2)

chloride can be added more rapidly. Another advantage is that yields are usually doubled with AlBr$_3$. As usual, yields are negligible in the case of medium sized cyclophanes but, when $n = 15$, (2) is obtained in yield of 70% with AlBr$_3$ as catalyst and in yield of 30% in the case of AlCl$_3$.

Still more striking is the result in the cyclization leading to the tetralinocyclenones.[8] Only with AlBr$_3$, not with AlCl$_3$, reasonable yields were obtained through the whole range of ring size ($n = 6$–22), as a few examples show:

Ring size, n =	6	8	9	10	11	12	14	16	18	22
Yield, %	93	68	51	18	32	47	64	58	64	55

Catalyst for adamantane synthesis. Schleyer *et al.*[9] found that certain tricyclic hydrocarbons having 10–12 carbon atoms are rearranged at 50° to adamantane or its bridgehead alkyl derivatives in yields as high as 19% by a large amount of AlBr$_3$ as catalyst, *sec.*-butyl bromide as promoter, and HBr as cocatalyst. A more effective aluminum bromide complex has been prepared from AlBr$_3$, HBr, and a mixture of dimethylcyclohexanes.[10] Robinson and Tarrat[11] prepared an effective catalyst by adding *t*-butyl bromide to a stirred suspension of aluminum bromide to the hydrocarbon to be rearranged; yields are 25–65%. This catalyst apparently is similar to an "AlBr$_3$ sludge" catalyst prepared from AlBr$_3$ and *t*-BuBr but so far described only in a thesis.[12] This catalyst has been used for the rearrangement of a hydrocarbon (1) C$_{18}$H$_{24}$, regarded as heptacyclic, to triamantane (2).[13]

$$C_{18}H_{24} \xrightarrow[2.5\%]{AlBr_3}$$
(1)

(2) Triamantane C$_{18}$H$_{24}$

Isomerization. A Netherlands group[14] found that diphenylacetylene can be dimerized to 1,2,3-triphenylazulene in 10–15% yield by aluminum bromide purified by sublimation or zone melting. The reaction is remarkable: $2\ C_{14}H_{10} \longrightarrow C_{28}H_{20}$ and is not clarified by writing the structural formulas out in full; one of four original benzenoid rings is expanded to a seven-membered ring, a second is contracted by one carbon atom, and three six-membered rings remain. Yields up to 41% were obtained by addition of transition-state metal ions (V^{2+} or Ni^{2+}). For example, a

2
(1)

Catalyst

(2)

mixture of vanadium tetrachloride and zinc dust is effective, since zinc reduces the vanadium compound to the divalent state.

Assony and Kharasch[15] effected the dimerization of diphenylacetylene (1) to 1,2,3-triphenylazulene (2) in about 25% yield with 2,4-dinitrobenzenesulfenyl chloride and aluminum chloride.

[7] R. Huisgen and I. Ugi, *Ber.*, **93**, 2693 (1960)
[8] R. Huisgen, V. J. Trescher, and H. Oertel, Ph.D. Thesis, V. J. Trescher, Munich, 1956; Ph.D. Thesis, H. Oertel, Munich, 1958
[9] P. von R. Schleyer and M. M. Donaldson, *Am. Soc.*, **82**, 4645 (1960); R. C. Fort, Jr., and P. von R. Schleyer, *Chem. Rev.*, **64**, 277 (1964)
[10] A. Schneider, R. W. Warren, and E. J. Janoski, *J. Org.*, **31**, 1617 (1966)
[11] M. J. T. Robinson and H. J. F. Tarrat, *Tetrahedron Letters*, 5 (1968)
[12] V. Z. Williams, Jr., A.B. Thesis, Princeton University (1965)
[13] V. Z. Williams, Jr., P. von R. Schleyer, G. J. Gleicher, and L. B. Rodewald, *Am. Soc.*, **88**, 3862 (1966)
[14] H. J. de Liefde Meijer, U. Pauzenga, and E. Jellinek, *Rec. trav.*, **85**, 634 (1966)
[15] S. J. Assony and N. Kharasch, *Am. Soc.*, **80**, 5978 (1958)

Aluminum *t*-butoxide [1, 24, before *Condensation catalyst*].

Meerwein-Ponndorf reduction. This method is the reverse of the Oppenauer oxidation. A ketone is reduced to an alcohol by treatment with an alcohol and a base. Engel[3a] was interested in the reduction of 3-ketosteroids of the 5β-series to the axial 3β-alcohol, a system present in the active cardiotonic steroids. After exploring catalytic reductions with limited success, he turned to the Meerwein-Ponndorf method using *sec.*-butyl alcohol and aluminum *t*-butoxide in refluxing absolute benzene. One interesting observation is that the reduction is complete in about 15 min; furthermore, yields of 60% of the axial alcohol can be obtained if the reaction is stopped at this point. Prolonged reaction leads to an increase in the yield of the thermodynamically more stable equatorial alcohol.

[3a] G. Bach, J. Capitaine, and C. R. Engel, *Canad. J. Chem.*, **46**, 733 (1968); R. Bouchard and C. R. Engel, *ibid.*, **46**, 2201 (1968)

Aluminum chloride [1, 24–34]

Reaction techniques [after Fig. A-1]. A refined method of adding a solid reagent (Fig. A-1) utilizes a Tom Teflon Joint Connector, Rho Scientific, Inc., Commack, N.Y. 11725.

Diels-Alder catalyst [1, 31–32, after line 8]. Ciganek (Du Pont) found that aluminum chloride strongly accelerates the Diels-Alder reaction of benzene with dicyanoacetylene.[33a] In the presence of this Lewis acid the reaction proceeded at room temperature to furnish the adduct (1) in 63% yield and smaller amounts of the Friedel-Crafts products phenylmaleonitrile (2) and phenylfumaronitrile (3). In the absence of aluminum chloride the adduct (1) was produced in yield of only 14% after a reaction period of 2 days at 180°.

(1) 63%   (2) 11%   (3) 4%

In a review of Diels-Alder reactions, Sauer[33b] notes that no catalysis with Lewis acids has been observed in the case of dienophiles with no polar substituents (CO, CN). IR spectra show that the Lewis acid forms a complex with the polar group.

Aluminum chloride strongly catalyzes the Diels-Alder addition of dienes to acrylic acid derivatives.[33c] In this case other Lewis acids have much less or no catalytic activity.

Sauer and Kredel[33d] studied the addition of cyclopentadiene to methyl acrylate and found that Lewis acids not only catalyze the reaction but also increase the proportion of the *endo* product (I). In the absence of catalyst the *endo* and *exo* products were

formed in a ratio of 82:18 (total yield 22–51%); in the presence of $AlCl_3$ the ratio was 98:2 (total yield 79–81%).

Preparation of β-chloroglycosides[38] [1, 33, before references]. In work carried out in 1953 at the University of Adelaide, South Australia, and presented in 1954 in a Ph.D. thesis, J. Gagolski[39] found that β-D-glucopyranose pentaacetate (1) reacts with anhydrous aluminum chloride in cold chloroform to give in good yield a product identical with "β-acetochloroglucose" (3) obtained by reaction of tetra-O-acetyl-α-D-glucopyranosyl chloride with "active" silver chloride.[40] A similar observation was made at about the same time by Zemplén, Mester, and Eckhart.[41] At the University of Adelaide the observations of Gagolski were extended by Korytnyk and Mills,[42] who assumed that the reaction involves participation of the neighboring 2-acetoxyl group and pictured the intermediate complex as having the boat conformation (2). Transfer of chlorine to the 1-position proceeds with fission of the

(1)
β-D-Glucose pentaacetate

(2)

(3)

C_1-acetoxyl bond. The reaction is applicable to fully acetylated aldopyranoses of 1:2-*trans* configuration and gives stereospecifically acetyl glycosyl chlorides of 1:2-*trans* configuration (the less stable anomers).

Trimerization of alkynes [1, 33, before references]. 2-Butyne (1) is bicyclotrimerized by about 10 mole percent anhydrous aluminum chloride (or alkylaluminum dichloride) in benzene or methylene dichloride at 25–35° to a hydrocarbon (3) identified with accuracy and described by the picturesque name hexamethyl Dewar benzene and defined by the systematic name hexamethyltricyclo [2.2.0] hexa-2,5-

diene (yield 60–70%).[43,44] An intermediate complex (2) of $AlCl_3$ and trimethylmethylenecyclobutene solvated with benzene may be involved.[45] The reaction provides the first large-scale preparation of a Dewar benzene derivative. Reaction of one half mole of anhydrous aluminum chloride with one mole of 2-butyne in cyclohexane at 0° results in a tricyclotetramerization of 2-butyne to octamethyl-*syn*-tricyclo[4.2.0.0$^{2.5}$] octa-3,7-diene (4). The yield is said to be 56%. Formation of (4) probably involves a dimerization step of the complex compound (2).

(4)

[33a]E. Ciganek, *Tetrahedron Letters*, 3321 (1967)
[33b]J. Sauer, *Angew. Chem., internat. Ed.*, **6**, 16 (1967).
[33c]T. Inukai and M. Kasai, *J. Org.*, **30**, 3567 (1965); T. Inukai and T. Kojima, *ibid.*, **31**, 2032 (1966)
[33d]J. Sauer and J. Kredel, *Tetrahedron Letters*, 731 (1966)
[38]Topic suggested by Peter M. Barna, Calbiochem.
[39]J. Gagolski, Ph.D. Thesis, Adelaide, 1954
[40]H. H. Schlubach, P. Stadler, and I. Wolf, *Ber.*, **61**, 287 (1928)
[41]G. Zemplén, L. Mester, and E. Eckhart, *Acta Chim. Acad. Sci. Hungaricae*, **4**, 53 (1954)
[42]W. Korytnyk and J. A. Mills, *J. Chem. Soc.*, 636 (1959)
[43]W. Schäfer, *Angew Chem., internat. Ed.*, **5**, 669 (1966)
[44]W. Schäfer and H. Hellmann, *ibid.*, **6**, 518 (1967)
[45]W. Schäfer, personal communication
[46]H. M. Rosenberg and E. C. Eimutis, *Canad. J. Chem.*, **45**, 2263 (1967)

Aluminum hydride [1, 34–35, before references]

Yoon and Brown[4] find that satisfactory results can also be obtained by using the heterogeneous mixture formed by dissolving a weighed amount of $LiAlH_4$ in THF followed by addition of 100% sulfuric acid to form the aluminum hydride. In further exploration of applications of aluminum hydride they find that this reducing agent is much less active than $LiAlH_4$ toward halogen and nitro groups and hence useful for selective reduction of other groups. It is also an excellent reagent for reduction of ketoximes and amides to amines. It is superior to $LiAlH_4$ or mixed hydride for reduction of nitriles to amines, especially in cases where the α-hydrogen is relatively acidic.

[4]N. M. Yoon and H. C. Brown, *Am. Soc.*, **90**, 2927 (1968)

p-**Aminobenzoic acid** [**1**, 37, before **1-Aminobenzotriazole**]. Mol. wt. 137.14, m.p. 188–189°. Suppliers: A, B, C, E, F, MCB. The amine condenses readily with aldoses to give *p*-N-glycosylaminobenzoic acids useful for identification.[1]

[1]G. P. Ellis, *Chem. Ind.*, 902 (1966)

2-**Amino-2-methyl-1,3-propanediol,**

$$CH_2\overset{\overset{\displaystyle CH_3}{|}}{\underset{\underset{\displaystyle NH_2}{|}}{C}}{-}CH_2OH.$$
$$\overset{|}{OH}$$

[**1**, 37, before **1-Amino-2-methyl-1-propanol**]. Mol. wt. 105.14, b.p. 111–112.5°. Suppliers: A, E, F, B, MCB, Fl, K-L, Sch.

Loeblich and Lawrence[1] describe a method for isolating neoabietic acid from pine oleoresin or rosin in 8–12% yield by recrystallization of the 2-amino-2-methyl-1,3-propanediol salt.

[1]V. M. Loeblich and R. V. Lawrence, *J. Org.*, **21**, 610 (1956). *Correction to this paper*: On p. 611, right-hand column, lines 12 and 20, *for* 3 lbs. of amine *read* 1.5 lbs of amine.

t-**Amyl chloroformate** [**1**, 40]. *Correction*: Delete (crude) and replace by: (b.p. not recorded in ref. 1).

[**1**, 40, before reference]. Further examples of use of the reagent in peptide synthesis have been reported by Sakakibara.[2,3] However, in some cases ureides are formed as by-products. This side reaction can be suppressed almost completely by use of N,N-diethylglycine ethyl ether in place of triethylamine as the base.[4]

Use of *t*-amyl chloroformate to give the *t*-amyloxycarbonylamino acids has some limitations since strictly anhydrous conditions are required. Sakakibara[5] has converted the reagent into the more useful *t*-amyl azidoformate (b.p. 81.5–82°/51–53 mm.) by reaction with anhydrous hydrazine to give *t*-amyl carbazate followed by reaction with sodium nitrite (compare synthesis of *t*-butyl azidoformate [*see* **1**, 84]). The azidoformate reacts with amino acids in aqueous dioxane in the presence of triethylamine to give N-*t*-amyloxycarbonylamino acids in yields of 70–95%.

[2]S. Sakakibara and M. Fujino, *Bull. Chem. Soc. Japan*, **39**, 947 (1966)
[3]S. Sakakibara and N. Inukai, *ibid.*, **39**, 1567 (1966); S. Sakakibara and M. Itoh, *ibid.*, **40**, 646 (1967)

[4]R. Willstätter, *Ber.*, **35**, 584 (1902)
[5]I. Honda, Y. Shimonishi, and S. Sakakibara, *Bull. Chem. Soc. Japan*, **40**, 2415 (1967)

i-Amyl nitrate [**1**, 40, after formulas].

Mononitration of ketones can be effected by use of equivalent amounts of nitrate ester and ketone and a 50% excess of sublimed potassium *t*-butoxide in THF. The reaction also leads to cleavage products which, in the case of cyclic ketones, are ω-nitrocarboxylic esters.[1a]

[Before references]: Hassner[4] has shown that a carbonyl group can be transposed to an adjacent carbon atom in fair yield *via* the α-nitro ketone. Thus cholestanone-3 was converted into cholestanone-2 as shown in the formulation.

[1a]H. Feuer and P. M. Pivawer, *J. Org.*, **31**, 3152 (1966)
[4]A. Hassner, J. M. Larkin, and J. E. Dowd, *ibid.*, **33**, 1733 (1968)

Aryldiazonium tetrahaloborates [**1**, 43–44, before references].

Caution: An explosion of 3-pyridyldiazonium fluoroborate has been reported.[12] Although the majority of diazonium fluoroborates are stable at room temperature, those that decompose below 100° should be handled with care.[13] If decomposition occurs near room temperature, the salt should be allowed to dry completely and used as soon as possible.

[12]*Chem. Eng. News*, **45**, Oct. 16, p. 44 (1967)
[13]G. O. Doak and L. D. Freedman, *ibid.*, **45**, Dec. 18, p. 8 (1967)

B

Benzenediazonium-2-carboxylate [**1**, 46, before references].

Stiles[4] found that flash photolysis of benzenediazonium-2-carboxylate led to the formation of N_2, CO_2, biphenylene, and triphenylene. Biphenylene predominated over triphenylene. Yields were low. Friedman[5] obtained biphenylene in yields as high as 30% by heating benzenediazonium-2-carboxylate in gently boiling, stirred 1,2-dichloroethane (b.p. 83–84°).

[4]R. S. Berry, G. N. Spokes, and M. Stiles, *Am. Soc.*, **84**, 3570 (1962)
[5]F. M. Logullo, A. H. Seitz, and L. Friedman, *Org. Syn.*, **48**, 12 (1968)

β-Benzoylpropionic acid, $C_6H_5COCH_2CH_2COOH$ [**1**, 51, before **Benzylamine**]. Mol. wt. 178.18, m.p. 116–119°. *Preparation* succinoylation of benzene. Supplier: A.

Blocking of OH groups.[1] The reagent reacts with OH groups in the presence of DCC to give β-benzoylpropionyl derivatives. Unblocking is accomplished at room temperature by treatment with hydrazine hydrate in pyridine buffered with acetic acid. The keto function serves as a trigger for the cleavage since it reacts selectively with hydrazine. The combination of pyridine–acetic acid is used because it does not attack acid-sensitive methoxytrityl ethers or base-sensitive cyanoethylphosphoric esters and because it does not attack the pyrimidine ring of deoxycytidine and thymine. The blocking group has been used in oligonucleotide synthesis; it was also found useful in synthesis on insoluble polymer supports.

[1]R. L. Letsinger, M. H. Caruthers, P. S. Miller, and K. K. Ogilvie, *Am. Soc.*, **89**, 7146 (1967); *see also* R. L. Letsinger, P. S. Miller, and G. W. Grams, *Tetrahedron Letters*, 2621 (1968)

Benzyl chloromethyl ether [**1**, 52].

Preparation. A modified procedure[1a] avoids the use of a large excess of formaldehyde and provides a considerably simplified work-up.

[1a]D. S. Connor, G. W. Klein, and G. N. Taylor, procedure submitted to *Org. Syn.*, 1968

Benzylthiocarbonyl chloride, $C_6H_5CH_2SCOCl$ [**1**, 53, before **Benzyltrimethylammonium chloride**]. Mol. wt. 176.66, m.p. 12°, b.p. 65°/0.01 mm. Suppliers: A, K and K.

The reagent is prepared by the reaction of benzylthiol with phosgene.[1] Amino acids and peptides are smoothly acylated by the reagent in water–dioxane at 0° in the presence of magnesia, sodium bicarbonate, or sodium carbonate. The protective group has been used successfully in several peptide syntheses.[2] It has also been used for protection of hydroxyl groups in carbohydrate synthesis.[3]

[1]J. Kollonitsch, V. Gábor, and A. Hajós, *Nature*, **177**, 841 (1956)
[2]J. Kollonitsch, A. Hajós, and V. Gábor, *Ber*, **89**, 2289, 2293 (1956); D. J. McCorquodale and G. C. Mueller, *Archives Biochem. Biophys.*, **77**, 13 (1958)
[3]J. J. Willard, *Canad. J. Chem.*, **40**, 2035 (1962); J. J. Willard, J. Sadowski, and W. Vitale, *ibid.*, **41**, 1223 (1963)

Benzylthiomethyl chloride, $C_6H_5CH_2SCH_2Cl$ [1, 53 before **Benzyltrimethylammonium chloride**]. Mol. wt. 172.68, b.p. 78°/0.2 mm.

Preparation.[1] The reagent is obtained by the reaction of benzyl mercaptan with polyoxymethylene catalyzed by hydrogen chloride. The unpleasant odor can be in large part suppressed by washing used apparatus immediately with alkaline permanganate.

Protection of the thiol group of cysteine. The S-benzyl group has been generally used for protection of cysteine groups in peptide synthesis; however, it now appears that undesirable side reactions can occur in the removal by means of sodium in liquid ammonia. Young *et al.*[1,2] recommend the S-benzylthiomethyl group, which can be removed by mercuric acetate in 80% formic acid (ethanediol is added to reduce formation of thiazolidine-4-carboxylic acid). The blocking group was used for the synthesis of analytically pure glutathione in near-quantitative yield.

[1]P. J. E. Brownlee, M. E. Cox, B. O. Handford, J. C. Marsden, and G. T. Young, *J. Chem. Soc.*, 3832 (1964)
[2]R. Camble, R. Purkayastha, and G. T. Young, *ibid.*, (C), 1219 (1968)

Birch reduction [1, 54–56].

Aniline as co-solvent [before references]. Strel'tsova and Shilov[9] have observed the conversion of diphenylacetylene into 1,2-diphenylethane by sodium in liquid ammonia containing aniline or *p*-toluidine, reactions probably involving stilbene as an intermediate. Metal-ammonia reagents probably reduce styrenoid systems by the successive addition of electrons from the metal and protons from the ammonia. Aniline may assist the process by increasing the availability of protons in the reaction medium. British investigators,[10] on experiencing difficulty in effecting complete reduction of 9-dehydro-D-homoestrone derivatives (1), found a reliable method in Birch reduction with aniline as co-solvent. Johns[11] used the aniline-cosolvent method

to advantage for the reduction of the conjugated diene (3) to $\Delta^{8(14)}$-dehydroestradiol (4).

(3) → Na, NH₃, C₆H₅NH₂ → (4)

Birch reduction of phenols [1, 56, before references]. Although free phenols are regarded as generally not reducible under Birch conditions, Fried et al.[12] noted some reduction in the case of 2-hydroxy-7-methoxyfluorene (1). They then noted that if the concentration of lithium is increased from 1.5 to 4 M essentially complete reduction of the phenolic ring occurs. Thus estrone (4) furnishes (5) in 75% yield.

(1) → Li–NH₃ → (2) + (3)

(4) → Li–NH₃, 75% → (5)

Reduction of amines. Birch[13] noted that N,N-dimethylanilines are reducible by lithium and liquid ammonia, but Stork and White[14] made the more significant observation that the primary amine precursors of the tertiary amines are also reducible in satisfactory yields. In a careful study of the reduction of o-toluidine, the highest yields were obtained with the combination lithium–liquid ammonia–t-butanol. One advantage of using an amine as substrate is that the unreduced basic amine is readily separated from neutral ketonic products. In all cases examined the desired unsatura-

→ Na, NH₃, (CH₃)₂COH → → H⁺ → 50% + 18%

ted ketone was contaminated with the saturated ketone. However, the two can be separated by taking advantage of the fact that piperidine adds quantitatively to the unsaturated ketone and not at all to the saturated ketone. The unsaturated ketone is recovered from the piperidino ketone by conversion into the methiodide, crystallization from n-butanol, and cleavage with pyridine.

[9]S. G. Strel'tsova and E. A. Shilov, *C.A.*, **51**, 4330 (1957)
[10]G. H. Douglas, J. M. H. Graves, D. Hartley, G. A. Hughes, B. J. McLoughlin, J. Siddall, and H. Smith, *J. Chem. Soc.*, 5072 (1963)
[11]W. F. Johns, *J. Org.*, **31**, 3780 (1966)
[12]J. Fried, N. A. Abraham, and T. S. Santhanakrishnan, *Am. Soc.*, **89**, 1044 (1967)
[13]A. J. Birch, *J. Chem. Soc.*, 593 (1946)
[14]G. Stork and W. N. White, *Am. Soc.*, **78**, 4604 (1956)

Bis-(2,4-dinitrophenyl)carbonate [1, 56, before reference]

Gante[2] used the reagent for the synthesis of peptides and azapeptides.

[2]J. Gante, *Ber.*, **99**, 1576 (1966)

Bis-3-methyl-2-butylborane ("Disiamylborane") [1, 57–59, before references].

This was found to be the best reagent for reduction of the steroidal lactone (1) to the corresponding hemiacetal (2).[7] No improvement was noted when tri-*t*-butoxyaluminum hydride was employed.

(1)   (2)

[7]R. W. Kierstead and A. Faraone, *J. Org.*, **32**, 704 (1967)

Bis-(*p*-nitrophenyl)hydrogen phosphate.

$HOP(OC_6H_4NO_2-p)_2$ [1, 60, before **Bis-*o*-phenylene pyrophosphite**]. Mol. wt. 328.18, m.p. 176–179°.

Preparation. *p*-Nitrophenol is treated with $POCl_3$ in acetonitrile,[1] or tris-(*p*-nitrophenyl)phosphate is partially hydrolyzed by sodium hydroxide.[2]

Nucleoside synthesis.[3] This reagent is superior to *p*-toluenesulfonic acid, ethyl polyphosphate, or zinc chloride for the preparation of nucleosides by fusion of purines with fully acetylated pentoses or hexoses. An example of the method[4] is the fusion of purine (1) with tetra-O-acetyl-D-ribofuranose (2) at 174–180° (at the water pump vacuum) to give the two nucleosides (3) and (4). The main product (3) is the triacetyl derivative of a naturally occurring nucleoside antibiotic nebularine.

(1)   (2)

(3) 30%   (4) 20%

[1]T. Hashizume, Jap. pat. 18132 (1964) [*C.A.*, **62**, 5229 (1965)]
[2]T. Hashizume and K. Hirohisa, Jap. pat. 15982 (1964) [*C.A.*, **62**, 6432 (1965)]
[3]T. Hashizume and H. Iwamura, *Tetrahedron Letters*, 3095 (1965)
[4]*Idem, J. Org.*, **33**, 1796 (1968)

Bis-*o*-phenylene pyrophosphite [1, 60, before references]. The reagent is superior to dicyclohexylcarbodiimide for cyclization of model penta- and hexapeptides; it is less satisfactory in the case of tripeptides.[3]

[3]A. W. Miller and P. W. G. Smith, *J. Chem. Soc.*, (C), 2140 (1967)

Bis(tribromomethyl)mercury, $(Br_3C)_2Hg$ [1, 60, before **O,N-Bis-(trifluoroacetyl)-hydroxylamine**]. Mol. wt. 704.12, m.p. 148° dec.

This organometallic reagent is prepared in 85–95% yield by the reaction of mercuric chloride and sodium tribromoacetate in the molar proportion 1:2.5–3.0 in monoglyme. The reagent is a convenient source of dibromocarbene. Thus it reacts with cyclohexene in refluxing benzene (N_2) to give dibromonorcarane in 54% yield.[1]

54%

Bis(trichloromethyl)mercury has been prepared in the same way; it has been used as a precursor of dichlorocarbene. In this case temperatures of 170–190° are required and the yields of dichlorocyclopropanes obtained are around 25%.[2]

[1]R. Robson and I. E. Dickson, *J. Organometallic Chem.*, **15**, 7 (1968)
[2]T. J. Logan, *J. Org.*, **28**, 1129 (1963)

Bis(trimethylsilyl)acetamide [1, 61]. Supplier: Aldrich.

Bis(trimethylsilyldichloromethyl)mercury $[(CH_3)_3SiCCl_2]_2Hg$ [1, 61, before **Bistriphenylphosphinedicarbonylnickel**]. Mol. wt. 488.62, m.p. 151–153°.
    Preparation.[1]

$$[(CH_3)_3SiCCl_2]Hg + C_6H_5Li \xrightarrow{-165°} (CH_3)_3SiCCl_2Li + C_6H_6 (\text{"high yield"})$$

$$(CH_3)_3SiCCl_2Li + HgBr_2 \xrightarrow[35\%]{-135°} [(CH_3)_3SiCl_2]_2Hg + LiBr$$

Use.[1] The reagent when heated (115°) decomposes to give trimethylsilylchlorocarbene:

$$[(CH_3)_3SiCCl_2]_2Hg + (C_6H_5)_2Hg + 2 \quad \overset{118°}{\longrightarrow} \quad 2 \quad \overset{Cl}{\underset{Si(CH_3)_3}{}} \quad + 2 C_6H_5HgCl$$

62%   82%

The diphenylmercury is added to effect utilization of both $(CH_3)_3SiCCl_2$ groups. When heated to higher temperatures the reagent gives rise to the trimethylsilyldichloromethyl radical.

[1] D. Seyferth and E. M. Hanson, *Am. Soc.*, **90**, 2438 (1968)

9-Borabicyclo[3.3.1]nonane (9-BBN) [**1**, 63, before **Boric acid**]. Mol. wt. 122.02, m.p. 140–142°.

Preparation.[1] The reagent (1) is prepared by the reaction of 1,5-cyclooctadiene with diborane in THF:

(1)

The reagent possesses remarkable thermal stability at 200°, but, more unexpectedly, is unusually stable to air (for at least 2 months).

Hydroboration.[2] The reagent is as selective as disiamylborane for hydroboration of olefins. Thus 1-hexene is converted into 1-hexanol (99%) and 2-hexanol (1%); styrene into 2-phenylethanol (98%) and 1-phenylethanol (2%). The reactions are usually complete within 5 min. except in the case of highly hindered olefins (2,3-dimethyl-2-butene requires 24 hrs. at 25°).

Synthesis of 9-alkylbicyclo[3.3.1]nonanols-9.[3] The reaction of the reagent (1) with olefins, followed by carbonylation, produces a 9-alkylbicyclo[3.3.1]nonanol-9 in overall yield of 85–95%.

[1] E. F. Knights and H. C. Brown, *Am. Soc.*, **90**, 5280 (1968)
[2] *Idem, ibid.*, **90**, 5281 (1968)
[3] *Idem, ibid.*, **90**, 5283 (1968)

Boric acid [1, 63–66, before references].

Condensation catalyst. Boric acid (also boron oxide and 10-hydroxy-10,9-boroxarophenanthrene)[12a] has been used as catalyst for aldol condensation and subsequent dehydration. The reaction is carried out in refluxing *m*-xylene under a Dean-Stark trap for removal of water. Examples[12b]:

$$2 \overset{7}{C}H_3CH_2CH_2CH_2CH_2CH_2\overset{1}{C}HO \ + \ H_3BO_3 \ + [CH_3C_6H_4CH_3(\underline{m})]$$

37. 6 g.   12. 5 g.   220 g.

$$\xrightarrow[100\%]{\text{Refl. 18 hrs.}} \overset{7}{C}H_3\overset{6}{C}H_2\overset{5}{C}H_2\overset{4}{C}H_2\overset{3}{C}H_2\overset{2}{C}H_2\overset{1}{C}H=\overset{2'}{C}-\overset{1'}{C}HO$$

$$\underset{7'\ \ 6'\ \ 5'\ \ 4'\ \ 3'}{CH_3CH_2CH_2CH_2CH_2}$$

$$C_6H_5CHO \ + \ CH_3COC_6H_5 \ + \ H_3BO_3 \ + [CH_3C_6H_4CH_3(\underline{m})] \cdot$$

10. 6 g.   12. 0 g.   6. 2 g.   100 g.

$$\xrightarrow[74\%]{\text{Refl. 65 hrs.}} C_6H_5CH=CHCOC_6H_5$$

[12a] M. J. S. Dewar and R. Dietz, *Tetrahedron Letters*, **14**, 21 (1959)
[12b] R. D. Offenhauer and S. F. Nelsen, *J. Org.*, **33**, 775 (1968)

p-**Boronobenzoic acid,** *p*-HO$_2$CC$_6$H$_4$B(OH)$_2$ [1, 66, before **Boron tribromide**]. Mol. wt. 135.97, m.p. 225°. Prepared by oxidation of *p*-tolylboronic acid with permanganate in alkaline solution.[1]

$$\underline{p}\text{-}CH_3C_6H_4B(OH)_2 \ \xrightarrow{KMnO_4-NaOH; \ neut.} \ HO_2CC_6H_4B(OH)_2$$

(1)   (2)

This reagent was used by Agosta[2] as resolving agent in the demonstration of optical activity of a novel type. Letsinger and Gilpin[3] had condensed 1,8-dilithionaphthalene with acenaphthenequinone and obtained the diol (3) as a crystalline solid melting at 319–321° and converted by oxidation with lead tetraacetate into 1,8-naphthalylnaphthalene (4). Examination of a model shows that in 1,8-naphthalyl-

(3)   (4)

naphthalene (4) there is available a single, rather rigid, bent conformation (5) free of distorted bond angles and in which the carbonyl bonds lie in a plane at an angle to both aromatic rings. This conformation, in which the carbonyl groups are only 2.5 Å

apart, favors transannular reaction of the diketone, as examplified by photoreduction.
Irradiation of a dilute solution of the compound
in isopropanol gives the pinacol (6) = (3) in
55% yield. A transannular reaction leading to
oxygen bridging occurs most simply on hydra-

(5) X = H   (6) X = H

tion. Brief heating of an acetic acid solution of the diketone (5) containing
dilute hydrochloric acid converts it virtually quantitatively into the glycol (7).
Agosta[2] nitrated the glycol (6), X = H, and obtained as the sole product a substance

Refl. AcOH–
dil. HCl

(5)   (7)

characterized as the 4-nitro derivative (6), X = NO$_2$.
If the molecule is indeed bent out of a plane the nitro
substituent should produce the potentiality for molecular asymmetry. Hence the nitro derivative was
treated with p-boronobenzoic acid in benzene under a
water separator to yield the cyclic boronate ester carboxylic acid (8), a derivative directly suitable for optical
resolution. As a carboxylic acid, (8) gave a crystalline
salt with quinine which, after four recrystallizations
(αD − 37.4°), liberation of the organic acid, and hydrolysis
gave optically active nitroglycol (6), X = NO$_2$. Lead
tetraacetate cleavage of the dextrorotatory (6), X = NO$_2$,

(8)

gave optically active (5), X = NO$_2$, the racemization of which was followed by
polarimetry in a chloroform solution.

[1] A. Michaelis, Ann., 315, 19 (1901)
[2] W. C. Agosta, Am. Soc., 89, 3505 (1967); 89, 3926 (1967)
[3] R. L. Letsinger and J. A. Gilpin, J. Org., 29, 243 (1964)

Boron tribromide [1, 66–67, ref. 3]. Definitive paper: J. F. McOmie, M. L. Watts,
and D. E. West, Tetrahedron, 24, 2289 (1968).

Mechanism of ether cleavage.

$$\text{ArOCH}_3 + \text{BBr}_3 \longrightarrow \left[\text{ArO}^{+} \overset{\text{CH}_3}{\underset{\text{BBr}_3}{\diagdown}} \right] \xrightarrow[-\text{CH}_3\text{Br}]{} \text{ArOBBr}_2$$

$$\xrightarrow{3\ \text{H}_2\text{O}} \text{ArOH} + \text{H}_3\text{BO}_3 + 2\ \text{HBr}$$

Since the reaction probably proceeds via a complex formed between the reagent and the ethereal oxygen atom, it is advisable to use one mole of BBr_3 per ether group together with an extra mole of reagent for each potentially basic group present (e.g. $-CHO, -CN, -CO_2H$).

The final step in the synthesis of DL-zearalenone (2) involved removal of the protecting groups of the dimethyl ether (1). Treatment with boron trifluoride etherate or

(1)   (2)

with sodium diphenylphosphide[3a] gave only mono ethers. Complete cleavage was effected with boron tribromide in dichloromethane in 34% yield.[3b]

1,3-Dibromo-adamantane [**1**, 66, after citation of refs. 4 and 5]: Talaty *et al*[5a] were unable to repeat Baughman's preparation of 1,3-dibromoadamantane by bromination of adamantane with boron tribromide and a trace of aluminum bromide. However, they found that 1,3-dibromoadamantane could be prepared in 86% yield by bromination in the presence of boron tribromide–aluminum bromide in the molar ratio 125 : 1.

Tetrabromocyclopropene [**1**, 67, before references 1–6]: Tetrachlorocyclopropene (1) reacts exothermally with boron tribromide to give tetrabromocyclopropene (2) and gaseous boron trichloride in almost quantitative yields.[7] The reaction is unusual since Lewis acids normally convert (1) into trichlorocyclopropenium ion salts. The

(1)   (2)

reaction is considered to proceed through initial formation of $C_3Cl_3{}^+BBr_3Cl^-$ and exchange of halogen within the solvent cage to give $C_3Br_3{}^+BCl_4{}^-$; reaction of the latter ion pair with BBr_3 would give the observed products.

[3a]F. G. Mann and M. J. Pragnell, *J. Chem. Soc.*, 4120 (1965)
[3b]I. Vlattas, I. T. Harrison, L. Tökés, J. H. Fried, and A. D. Cross, *J. Org.*, **33**, 4176 (1968)
[5a]E. R. Talaty, A. E. Cancienne, Jr., and A. E. Dupuy, *J. Chem. Soc.*, (C), 1902 (1968)
[7]S. W. Tobey and R. West, *Am. Soc.*, **88**, 2481 (1966)

Boron trichloride [**1**, 67–68, before references]. Boron trichloride effects selective demethylation of a methoxy group *ortho* to a carbonyl group.[9] The neat reagent, cooled to $-70°$, is added to the second reactant in cold methylene chloride; after reaction has occurred the methylene chloride is washed with water to free it from hydrochloric acid and boric acid. A six-membered coordinate ring is postulated. Yields generally are in the range 75–95%.

[9]F. M. Dean, J. Goodchild, L. E. Houghton, J. A. Martin, R. B. Morton, B. Parton, A. W. Price, and N. Somvichien, *Tetrahedron Letters*, 4153 (1966)

Boron trifluoride etherate [1, 70–72, before references].

Intramolecular acylation. This reaction is the key step in a new synthesis of the twistane ring system by a Canadian group.[14] The starting material, decalin-2,7-dione (3), can be prepared easily in quantity by hydrogenation of 2,7-dihydroxynaphthalene to a mixture of isomeric diols (2) and chromic acid oxidation of the mixture.[15,16] Treat-

ment with acetic ahnydride, acetic acid, and boron trifluoride etherate effects acetylative cyclization to 8-acetoxy-4-twistanone (4) = (4a). Ketalization at C_4 with ethylene glycol, hydrolysis of the acetate to the alcohol with $LiAlH_4$, reaction with thionyl bromide to yield the bromo ketal, hydrogenolysis with Raney nickel, and deketalization afforded 4-twistanone (5).

Cleavage of oxides. Shoppee *et al.*[17] found that cleavage of the oxide (1) with pyridine hydrochloride proceeded poorly but could be effected cleanly with BF_3-

etherate in acetic anhydride (10 min. at 20°) to give the enol acetate (2) which on brief alkaline hydrolysis gives (4), presumably through loss of formaldehyde from (3).

Alkoxy displacement.[18] When diazoacetophenone in ether or benzene solution is treated with BF_3-etherate, nitrogen is evolved at room temperature but the product is a dark tar. When methanol is used as solvent, α-methoxyacetophenone is formed. This appears to be a general route to α-alkoxy ketones.

$$C_6H_5COCHN_2 \; + \; CH_3OH \; \xrightarrow[79\%]{BF_3 \cdot O(C_2H_5)_2} \; C_6H_5COCH_2OCH_3 \; + \; N_2$$

Fission-rearrangement of epoxides. Following his suggestion that epoxy-acids may be important intermediates in biosynthesis,[19] Gunstone with Conacher [20] found that when the unsaturated epoxy ester methyl vernolate (1) is treated with boron trifluoride etherate in cold benzene solution it is converted into a number of products, two of which cannot be separated from each other but, together, account for a yield of 34%. On the basis of chemical properties, infrared, NMR, and mass spectra they are believed to be the *cis* and *trans* forms of the ketocyclopropane ester (2).

$$CH_3(CH_2)_4\overset{O}{\overset{\diagup\diagdown}{CH}}\!\!-\!\!CHCH_2CH_2CH\!=\!CH(CH_2)_7CO_2CH_3 \; \xrightarrow{BF_3}$$

(1)

$$CH_3(CH_2)_4COCH_2\overset{\overset{\displaystyle CH_2}{\diagup\diagdown}}{CH}\!\!-\!\!CH(CH_2)_7CO_2CH_3$$

(2)

Peptide cleavage. In the presence of BF_3-etherate the Cb group of methionine-containing peptides can be removed quantitatively by hydrogenolysis catalyzed by palladium catalyst.[21]

[14]A. Bélanger, J. Poupart, and P. Deslongchamps, *Tetrahedron Letters*, 2127 (1968)
[15]J. Gauthier and P. Deslongchamps, *Canad. J. Chem.*, **45**, 297 (1967)
[16]A. G. Anderson and D. O. Barlow, *Am. Soc.*, **77**, 5165 (1955)
[17]C. W. Shoppee, N. W. Hughes, and R. E. Lack, *Tetrahedron Letters*, 5235 (1966)
[18]M. S. Newman and P. F. Beal, III, *Am. Soc.*, **72**, 5161 (1950)
[19]F. D. Gunstone, *Chem. Ind.*, 1551 (1966)
[20]H. B. S. Conacher and F. D. Gunstone, *Chem. Commun.*, 984 (1967)
[21]M. Okamoto, S. Kimoto, T. Oshima, Y. Kinomura, K. Kawesaki, and H. Yajima, *Chem. Pharm. Bull.*, **15**, 1618 (1967)

Boron trifluoride etherate–Acetic anhydride [1, 72–73, before references].

The combination reagent was used for selective cleavage of 1-methyl-7-oxabicyclo[2.2.1]heptane-2,3-dicarboxylic acids.[3] Thus the ether (1), obtained by reaction of 2-methylfurane with maleic anhydride followed by hydrogenation, when warmed with the reagents afforded (2) and the product of hydrolysis (3). Both reagents are necessary for the cleavage.

(1)   (2)   (3)

[3]Y. Kitahara, T. Kato, N. Ototani, A. Inoue, and H. Izumi, *J. Chem. Soc.*, (C), 2508 (1968)

Boron trifluoride (see 1, 68)–Hydrogen fluoride (see 1, 455).

Isomerization of alkylbenzenes [1, 73, before **Boron trifluoride–Methanol**]. Pearson *et al.*[1] give full details for use of a liquid mixture of the two reagents for effecting isomerization of *p*-cymene to *m*-cymene at −78°. Anhydrous hydrogen fluoride is

liquefied by passing the gas through a spiral of copper tubing surrounded by an iso-propyl alcohol–dry ice bath and the liquid is delivered into a 500-ml. Nalgene poly-ethylene bottle provided with a magnetic stirring bar and surrounded by dry ice. *p*-Cymene precooled to −60° is added and boron trifluoride is then bubbled in with stirring and cooling. Work-up and fractionation through a 1-ft. helices-packed column gave *m*-cymene of 98% purity (VPC) in yield of 75–80%.

[1]D. E. Pearson, R. D. Wysong, and J. M Finkel, *Org. Syn.*, **47**, 40 (1967)

Bromine azide, Br—N$\overset{+}{=}$N$\overset{-}{=}$N [1, 73, before **Bromine chloride**]. Mol. wt. 121.94.

Preparation in solution.[1] Hydrochloric acid (30%, 25 ml.) followed by bromine (8.0 g.) is added to an ice-cooled and well stirred mixture of 32.5 g. of sodium azide and 100 ml. of methylene chloride. After 30--60 min. the organic layer containing bro-mine azide is decanted and used as such. Although the reagent has been reported to have explosive properties,[2] no explosions have been experienced in use of the above procedure.

Addition to olefins.[1] Depending upon the polarity of the solvent, bromine azide adds to olefins by ionic or free radical processes. Ionic additions are achieved in nitromethane–methylene chloride; free radical addition predominates in pentane:

Bromine azide adds stereospecifically to *cis-* and *trans*-2-butene under ionic conditions.

[1]A. Hassner and F. Boerwinkle, *Am. Soc.*, **90**, 216 (1968)
[2]D. A. Spencer, *J. Chem. Soc.*, **127**, 216 (1925)

Bromine chloride [1, 73]. Bromine chloride has been generated *in situ* from NBA and HCl.[1] The addition of bromine chloride to cholesterol and derivatives gives the 5α-bromo-6β-chloro dihalide in good yield.[1] However, Havinga[2] reported that in the case of 1-methylcyclohexene the combination NBA-concd. hydrochloric acid led to a dibromide, a bromochloride, and a bromohydrin. Use of NBS-HCl in methylene chloride gave only a bromochloride. In the case of alkylcyclohexenes the addition leads to mixtures of isomeric *trans*-bromochlorides. The results are interpreted by a mechanism in which a cyclic bromonium ion is formed followed by a *trans*-diaxial opening to give the bromochloride.

[1]J. B. Ziegler and A. C. Shabica, *Am. Soc.*, **74**, 4891 (1952)
[2]H. J. Hageman and E. Havinga, *Rec. trav.*, **85**, 1141 (1966)

Bromine (chlorine) dipyridine nitrate, $[Br(C_5H_5N)_2]^+NO_3^-$ [1, 73, before **Bromine–Silver acetate**]. Mol. wt. Br: 300.13 (Cl: 255.67), m.p. (Cl) 77–78°. These are stable compounds prepared by the action of bromine[1,2] or chlorine[3] on silver nitrate and pyridine in chloroform solution. Silver halide precipitates and the complex is isolated from the solution. Thus Carlsohn[2] dissolved 5.4 g. of bromine in 30 ml. of chloroform, cooled the solution to 15–20°, and added a cooled solution of 5.2 g. of silver nitrate in 10 g. of pyridine and 15 ml. of chloroform. Most of the silver bromide was removed by centrifugation and the rest by filtration through a fritted-glass funnel. Addition of ether precipitated the complex, which separated as an oil and then solidified. J. S. Mills[4] of the National Gallery, London, used reagent prepared *in situ* for reaction with cholesteryl acetate. Silver nitrate (0.11 mole) was dissolved in pyridine (18.7 ml.) and chloroform (250 ml.). Cholesteryl acetate (0.1 mole) was added and the solution cooled in ice-salt and stirred. A solution of chlorine in carbon tetrachloride (100 ml. of 1.2 *M*, calcd., 90 ml.) was added dropwise during 30 min. The mixture was allowed to warm to room temperature during 30 min. and filtered to remove silver chloride. The filtrate was combined with chloroform washings and washed with aqueous potassium iodide and sodium thiosulfate, followed by water. After drying and evaporating, crystallization from methylene chloride–methanol gave the nitrate ester (2), 5α-chlorocholestane-3 β,6β-diol 3-acetate 6-nitrate, of reasonable purity (m.p. 139–141°) in 59% yield.

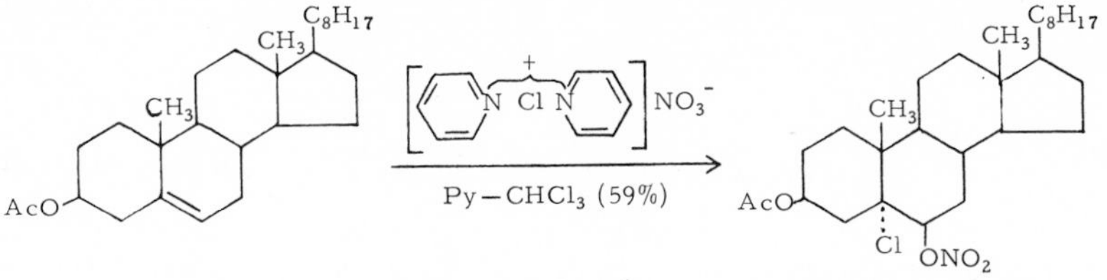

(1)   (2) M. p. 142-143°

Py–CHCl$_3$ (59%)

[1]M. I. Uschakow and W. O. Tchistow, *Ber.*, **68**, 824 (1935)
[2]H. Carlsohn, *ibid.*, **68**, 2209 (1935)
[3]M. I. Uschakow and W. O. Tchistow, *Bull. soc.* [5] **3**, 2142 (1936)
[4]J. S. Mills, *J. Chem. Soc.*, (C), 2261 (1966)

N-Bromoacetamide [1, 74, before references].

Reaction with olefins. Study of the reaction of cyclohexene with N-bromoacetamide in carbon tetrachloride solution under ultraviolet illumination established that the initial product is *trans*-acetamidocyclohexyl bromide.[12] There was no evidence of allylic bromination.

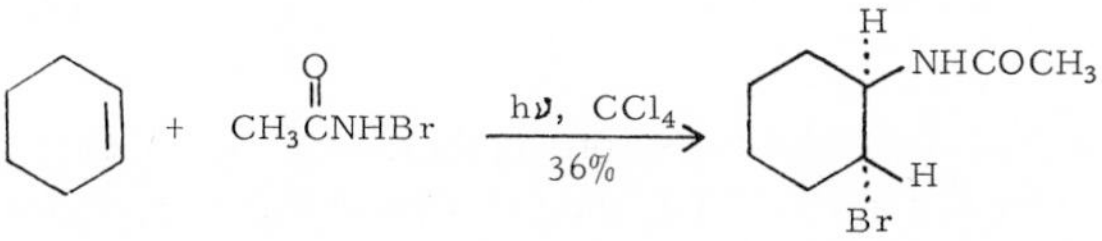

Bromination. A Merck, Sharp and Dohme group[13] reports that NBA (slightly more than 1 equiv.) in ethanol is the most satisfactory reagent for the bromination of estradiol. Probably 2- and 4-bromoestradiol are formed in about equal amounts but the 2-bromo compound is difficult to isolate because of solubility factors. Use of

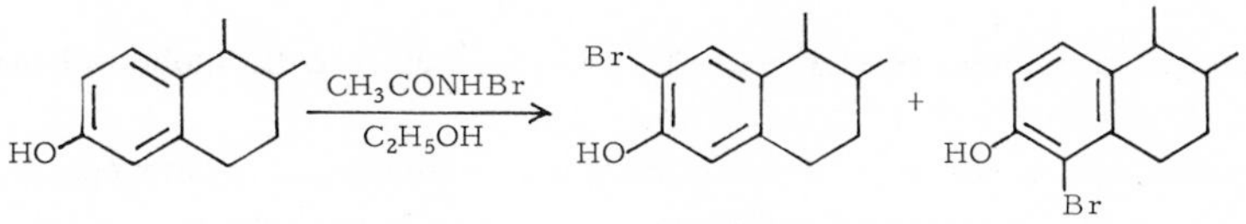

25-40%   5.5%

more than 2 equivalents of NBA gives 2,4-dibromoestradiol in essentially quantitative yield.[14]

[12]S. Wolfe and D. V. C. Awang, *Am. Soc.*, **89**, 5287 (1967)
[13]T. Utne, R. B. Jobson, and F. W. Landgraf, *J. Org.*, **33**, 1654 (1968)
[14]R. B. Woodward, *Am. Soc.*, **62**, 1625 (1940)

N-Bromoacetamide–Hydrogen fluoride [1, 75, before references].

The reaction of "BrF" generated from these reactants has been extended to terminal aliphatic alkenes to give *vic.*-fluorobromides.[4] An example is the preparation of 1-bromo-2-fluoroheptane.[5] The products are convertible, as shown for the case of 1-bromo-2-fluoroheptane,[6] into α-fluoroalkanoic acids.[7]

$$CH_3(CH_2)_4CH{=}CH_2 \xrightarrow[60-77\%]{CH_3CONHBr,\ HF} (CH_3)_2(CH_2)_4CHFCH_2Br$$

$$\xrightarrow{NaOAc,\ NaI} CH_3(CH_2)_4CHFCH_2OCOCH_3 \xrightarrow{HNO_3,\ HOAc} CH_3(CH_2)_4CHFCOOH$$

[4]F. L. M. Pattison, D. A. V. Peters, and F. H. Dean, *Canad. J. Chem.*, **43**, 1689 (1965)
[5]F. H. Dean, J. H. Amin, and F. L. M. Pattison, *Org. Syn.*, **46**, 10 (1966)
[6]*Idem, ibid.*, **46**, 37 (1966)
[7]F. L. M. Pattison, R. L. Buchanan, and F. H. Dean, *Canad. J. Chem.*, **43**, 1700 (1965)

(−)-α-Bromocamphor-π-sulfonic acid (1) [**1**, 76, before **N-Bromocaprolactam**]. Mol. wt. 311.21, m.p. 44–46°, αD −92° (H_2O). This resolving agent is available as the ammonium salt from Aldrich.

In a total synthesis of natural (*levo*) prostaglandian E_1 (2), Corey et al.[1] resolved the intermediate racemic amine (3) as the salt with (−)-α-bromocamphor-π-sulfonic acid. One crystallization from methanol–ethyl acetate afforded essentially a single diastereomeric salt, m.p. 157–159°, $[\alpha]_{578} - 59.6°$. The maximum rotation observed after further crystallizations was $[\alpha]_{578} - 59.65°$.

[1]E. J. Corey, I. Vlattas, and K. Harding, *Am. Soc.*, **91**, 535 (1969)

α-Bromocyanoacetamide, $N{\equiv}CCHCONH_2$ (Br) [**1**, 77, before **α-Bromofluorobenzene**]. Mol. wt. 162.99, m.p. 116–117°.

Preparation.[1] A solution of dibromocyanoacetamide and cyanoacetamide in ethanol is refluxed for 5 hrs. in the presence of boron trifluoride etherate, yield 74%.

Use in phosphorylation.[1-3]

[1]T. Hata and T. Mukaiyama, *Bull. Chem. Soc. Japan*, **35**, 1106 (1962)
[2]O. Mitsunobu, T. Onato, and T. Mukaiyama, *J. Org.*, **30**, 1071 (1965)
[3]T. Obata, M. Ueki, and T. Mukaiyama, *Bull. Chem. Soc. Japan*, **39**, 1040 (1966)

N-Bromosuccinimide [**1**, 78–80].

Allylic bromination. [**1**, 79, after citation of ref. 8]. N-Bromosuccinimide reacts with isolapachol (1) in refluxing CCl_4 by vinylic substitution to give (2); N-iodosuccinimide reacts in the same way.[8a] β-Isopropylfurano-1,4-naphthoquinone (3) was obtained by cyclization of the vinylic bromide (2) with NIS and also by the action of two equivalents of NIS on (1). Even when the unsaturated side chain has a primary or secondary hydrogen in the allylic position, for example (4), the same vinylic substitution was observed (5).

(1) → NBS–CCl₄ → (2)

(2) → NIS → (3)

(1) → 2 NIS → (3)

(4) → NBS → (5)

Bromohydrins [**1**, 80, after line 3]. The preparation of bromohydrins from olefins by the combination of NBS with water has been hampered by the limited solubility of olefins in water. Dalton *et al.*[12a] report that the reaction can be carried out in good yield in DMSO containing a small quantity of water. In a special experiment, 10 moles of cyclohexene was allowed to dissolve in 50 ml. of dry dimethyl sulfoxide and and 25 mmoles of water was added. Under a nitrogen atmosphere, 20 mmoles of NBS was added with cooling below 20°. After 15 min. the reaction mixture was quenched in a large volume of water and the product removed by ether extraction.

$$\text{cyclohexene} \xrightarrow[\substack{15 \text{ min. } 20° \\ 78\%}]{\text{NBS} + H_2O \text{ in DMSO}} \text{bromohydrin}$$

A study of the stereospecificity of the reaction as applied to *trans*-stilbene in the presence of O-18 enriched water and unenriched DMSO resulted in the suggestion of one possible mechanism.[12b]

Dehydrogenation of aromatic aldoximes to nitrile oxides [**1**, 80, before references]. N-Bromosuccinimide in dimethylformamide is an excellent reagent for the dehydrogenation of aromatic aldoximes to the corresponding nitrile oxides.[17] Triethylamine serves well as base required to bind the hydrogen bromide eliminated; since it is

$$\text{ArCH=NOH} + \text{NBS} + (C_2H_5)_3N \xrightarrow[90\%]{\text{DMF}} \text{ArC}\equiv\text{N}\rightarrow\text{O} + (C_2H_5)_3\text{NHBr}$$

attacked by NBS, it is added to the reaction mixture only after the NBS has been added and had a chance to react, but at 5–15° the reaction is always complete within 1 hr. Dilution with water then precipitates the nitrile oxide. The procedure is superior to an earlier one using sodium hypobromite in aqueous alkali.[18]

Oxidation of α-hydroxy ketones [1, 80, before references]. Aliphatic α-hydroxy ketones are oxidized in good yield to α-diketones by NBS either in anhydrous carbon tetrachloride or in aqueous dioxane; the yields are higher in the latter case.[19]

[8a]K. H. Dudley and H. W. Miller, *Tetrahedron Letters*, 571 (1968)
[12a]D. R. Dalton, J. B. Hendrickson, and D. G. Jones, *Chem. Commun.*, 591 (1966)
[12b]D. R. Dalton and D. G. Jones, *Tetrahedron Letters*, 2875 (1967)
[17]C. Grundmann and R. Richter, *J. Org.*, **33**, 476 (1968)
[18]C. Grundmann and J. M. Dean, *ibid.*, **30**, 2809 (1965)
[19]R. Heilmann and P. Baret, *Compt. rend.*, **267** (C), 579 (1968)

Bromotrichloromethane [1, 80].

Preparation (simplified procedure).[1a] A mixture of 168.5 g of anhydrous aluminum bromide and 940 g. of dry aluminum chloride is refluxed for 45 min. and let cool. Solid material is removed by filtration and the liquid is shaken with 170 ml. of 5% sodium carbonate solution and then with two 170-ml. portions of water. After drying with calcium chloride, fractionation with a 70-cm. Vigreux column gave a fore-run of 480 ml. of CCl_4 and then 193 g. (51.4%) of pure bromotrichloromethane, b.p. 102–106°, $n^{20}D$ 1.5063.

[1a]G. Lehmann and B. Lücke, *J. pr. Chem.*, [4], **22**, 230 (1963)

Bromotrifluoromethane, BrF_3C [1, 81, before 4-Bromo-2,5,7-trinitrofluorenone].

Mol. wt. 148.93, b.p. −59°, f.p. −168°, density, gas at b.p. 8.71 g./l. Suppliers: Imperial Smelting Corp., Ltd. as "Isceon 13Bl"; Matheson Co., Inc., as "Freon 13Bl."

Uses (other than as refrigerant or fire extinguisher):

(a) Source of difluorocarbene:[1]

$$BrCF_3 + C_4H_9Li +$$

(b) Brominating agent:[2]

$$LiNH_2 - liq. NH_3$$
$$CF_3Br$$

[1]V. Franzen and L. Fikentscher, *Ber.*, **95**, 1958 (1962); V. Franzen, *ibid.*, 95, 1964 (1962)
[2]C. Burgess, G. Cooley, P. Feather, and V. Petrow, *Tetrahedron*, **22**, 4111 (1967)

t-Butoxycarbonyl-N-hydroxysuccinimide ester, [1, 82, before *t*-Butyl acetate]. Mol. wt. 215.20, m.p. 98–100°.

Preparation by reaction of N-hydroxysuccinimide (1, 487) with *t*-butyl chloro-

***t*-BOC amino acids**. Several N-*t*-BOC amino acids are supplied by Koch-Light. The *t*-butoxycarbonyl (*t*-BOC) moiety since its introduction in peptide synthesis as an amino protecting group has become second in use only to the carbobenzoxy group, but previous methods for the preparation have suffered from serious disadvantages. A new method which is rapid and tidy consists in aminolysis of *t*-butoxycarbonyl-N-hydroxysuccinimide ester by the sodium salt of an amino acid; the corresponding *t*-butoxycarbonyl amino acid is formed in good yield and the by-product N-hydroxy-succinimide, being water soluble, is easily separated from the *t*-BOC derivatives. The aminolysis is carried out at 90° for 1½–2 hrs.

The related ester, N-(*t*-butoxycarbonyloxy)-phthalimide (1), mol. wt. 263.24, m.p. 118°, dec., has been prepared and used in the same way.[2] This reagent is available from EGA-Chemie KG.

I

[1]M. Frankel, D. Ladkany, C. Gilon, and Y. Wolman, *Tetrahedron Letters*, 4765 (1966)
[2]H. Gross and L. Bilk, *Angew. Chem., internat. Ed.*, **6**, 570 (1967)

***t*-Butylamine** [1, 84, before references].

o-**Bromination of Phenols**. The procedure that follows was kindly made available to us by Dr. D. E. Pearson, Vanderbilt University, and is essentially the same as one already published.[3] The principle is that bromination of phenol in toluene solution gives the hypobromite (2), which undergoes α,γ-shift of bromine to give (3), which by α,γ-shift of hydrogen in the opposite direction gives (4), the first stable product. Then (5), the bond-isomer of (4), is converted via the hypobromite (6) and the product of its rearrangement (7) into 2,6-dibromophenol (8).

1. Procedure

In a 5-l. three-necked flask fitted with a powerful mechanical stirrer (Note 1), a low temperature thermometer, and an addition funnel topped with a drying tube is placed 2.5 l. of dry toluene and 147 g. (2 moles) of *t*-butylamine (Note 2). The flask is surrounded by a suitable container to act as an isopropanol–dry ice cooling bath. The stirrer is started and the container is charged with isopropanol and dry ice until the inside temperature is −20° to −30°, and 160 g. (1 mole) of bromine is added over a period of 10 min. The solution is then cooled to −70° to −75° by addition of more dry ice, and 47 g. (0.5 mole) of anhydrous phenol dissolved in 100 ml. of methylene chloride is added over a period of 5 min.; the temperature of the solution increases about 10° during this addition. The reaction mixture is allowed to warm to room temperature over a period of 5–6 hrs., and the reaction mixture is transferred to a 5-l. separatory funnel and washed with 500 ml. of water. The organic phase is then extracted with a 300 ml. and a 200 ml. portion of 10% aqueous sodium hydroxide. The combined alkaline solution is cooled with ice (Note 3) and acidified with 20% aqueous sulfuric acid. The product separates as an oil. It is isolated by extraction with a 200-ml. and a 100-ml. portion of methylene chloride. The combined extract is dried over magnesium sulfate, filtered, and evaporated at room temperature. The yield of 2,6-dibromophenol, m.p. 50-53°, is 110 g. (87%). Recrystallization from 200 ml. of hexane, using refrigeration, affords 94 g. (75%) in two crops, m.p. 55–56° (Note 4).

2. Notes

1. The bromination occurs between −70° and room temperature with precipitation of a large amount of *t*-butylamine hydrobromide.

2. Isopropylamine can also be used. Triethylamine also gives almost exclusive *ortho* -substitution, but more polyhalogenation occurs.

3. Acidification after ice cooling gives a colorless product. If the heat of acidification is not controlled, an off-white to brown product with inferior melting point results.

4. For the preparation of *o*-bromophenol the amount of phenol is doubled, the amounts of phenol and of *t*-butylamine are halved, and the work-up is as follows: The brominated reaction mixture is extracted with a 425 ml. and a 200 ml. portion of 10% aqueous sodium hydroxide. The total extract is acidified in a 2-l. separatory funnel and the oil which separates is transferred to another 2-l. separatory funnel. The remaining aqueous solution is then washed with two 500-ml. portions of hexane and the washings added to the oil in the separatory funnel. The resulting mixture of oil and hexane is then washed thoroughly with four 500-ml. portions of de-ionized water which removes the unreacted phenol (a step of importance since in the preparation of *o*-bromophenol a large excess of phenol is necessary to reduce the extent of dibromination).

[3]D. E. Pearson, R. D. Wysong, and C. V. Breder, *J. Org.*, **32**, 2358 (1967)

t-Butyl azidoformate [1, 84–85].

[**1**, 84, After Supplier: Aldrich]: *Caution*: Inhalation of small amounts of vapor causes severe headaches.

Preparation (contd.). In a convenient alternative[1a] to the Carpino procedure,[1] a 300-ml. three-necked flask fitted with a mechanical stirrer is charged with 120 ml. of dimethyl sulfoxide and 8.1 g. (0.1 mole) of crushed potassium azide (preferred to

$$(CH_3)_3C-O\overset{O}{\overset{\|}{C}}-O-\overset{O}{\overset{\|}{P}}(OC_2H_5)_2 \ + \ KN_3 \ \xrightarrow{\text{DMSO}} \ (CH_3)_3C-O\overset{O}{\overset{\|}{C}}N_3$$

sodium azide because of greater solubility). The mixture is stirred until most of the salt is dissolved (about 30 min.) and then stirred in a cooling water bath at room temperature, and 25.4 g. (0.1 mole) of *t*-butylcarbonic diethylphosphoric anhydride (a new reagent, p. 46) is added slowly. After stirring for 1 hr. more below 25°, 120 ml. of distilled water is added with cooling and the solution is extracted with three 120-ml. portions of ether. The combined ether extract is extracted with three 6-ml. portions of distilled water and then with 20 ml. of saturated sodium chloride solution. The ether solution is dried with magnesium sulfate, the latter is removed by filtration, and the ether is removed at room temperature under water-pump vacuum. The product is 11–14 g. of a slightly yellow liquid which can be distilled at water-pump vacuum from a Claisen flask with indentures in the side arm.

N-Protection of amino acids [before references]. For the preparation of N-*t*-butoxycarbonylamino acids, DeTar[4] recommends use of 1 equivalent of the amino acid, 1.10 equivalents of the reagent, and 4 equivalents of triethylamine.

Carpino and Barr[5] used the carbo-*t*-butoxy group for protection of the nitrogen atom of pyrrole during Diels-Alder addition to benzyne for the preparation of 7-azabenzonorbornadiene (5). A solution of pyrrole in tetrahydrofurane was stirred under nitrogen and treated at room temperature with 1 equivalent of potassium to

form the potassium salt (2), which on reaction with *t*-butyl azidoformate afforded *t*-butyl pyrrolecarboxylate (3). Benzyne was then generated in the presence of this protected derivative from magnesium and *o*-bromofluorobenzene in THF, with production of the Diels-Alder adduct (4) in 35–41% yield. Careful treatment with hydrochloric acid at 0° removed the protective group and gave the free base (5), 7-azabenzonorbornadiene. Attempted cleavage with hydrogen chloride at 25° gave mainly α-naphthylamine hydrochloride (6). As expected for a system with a strained double bond, the protected derivative (4) reacted readily with phenyl azide to give an adduct (7), which on pyrolysis yielded 1-phenyl-1,2,3-triazole (8).

[1a]D. S. Tarbell and M. A. Insalaco, *Proc. Natl. Acad. Sci.*, **57**, 233 (1967)
[4]N. F. Estrin, A. A. Alemany, and D. F. DeTar, procedure submitted to *Org. Syn.*, 1967
[5]L. A. Carpino and D. E. Barr, *J. Org.*, **31**, 764 (1966)

t-**Butyl carbazate** [**1**, 85]. Suppliers: Aldrich; EGA-Chemie KG, Steinheim, Germany; Fl.; K.-L.; E. Merck.

t-**Butylcarbonic diethylphosphoric anhydride** (3) [**1**, 86, before *t*-**Butyl chloride**]. Oil, mol. wt. 223.24.

    Preparation.[1] Potassium *t*-butoxide in THF is treated with dry ice to form potassium *t*-butylcarbonate (1); diethyl phosphorochloridate (2, Stauffer Chemical Co.)

$$(CH_3)_3COK \xrightarrow[\text{THF}]{CO_2} (CH_3)_3CO\overset{O}{\overset{\|}{C}}OK \xrightarrow[\text{THF}]{(C_2H_5O)_2\overset{O}{\overset{\|}{P}}Cl\,(2)} (CH_3)_3CO\overset{O}{\overset{\|}{C}}-O-\overset{O}{\overset{\|}{P}}(OC_2H_5)_2$$

$$(1) \qquad\qquad\qquad\qquad\qquad (3)$$

in THF is then added slowly with stirring to form the product (3) as an oil.

    N-Protection of amino acids.[1] The reagent reacts with an amino acid ester hydrochloride, for example that of glycine (4) in chloroform containing triethyl-

$$(CH_3)_3CO\overset{O}{\overset{\|}{C}}-O-\overset{O}{\overset{\|}{P}}(OC_2H_5)_2 \;+\; ClH\cdot H_2NCH_2CO_2C_2H_5 \xrightarrow[71\%]{(C_2H_5)_3N-CHCl_3}$$

$$(3) \qquad\qquad\qquad\qquad\qquad (4)$$

$$(CH_3)_3CO\overset{O}{\overset{\|}{C}}-NHCH_2CO_2C_2H_5 \xrightarrow[\text{aq. THF}]{OH^-} (CH_3)_3CO\overset{O}{\overset{\|}{C}}-NHCH_2CO_2H$$

$$(5) \qquad\qquad\qquad\qquad\qquad (6)$$

amine to give the N-*t*-butoxycarbonyl derivative (5). The free acid (6) can be obtained by saponification in aqueous THF.

[1] D. S. Tarbell and M. A. Insalaco, *Proc. Natl. Acad. Sci.*, **57**, 233 (1967); *idem.*, procedure submitted to *Org. Syn.*

t-**Butyl chloride** [**1**, 86, after *Preparation*]. In the presence of a group of catalytically active Lewis acids which includes Al_2Cl_6, BCl_3, $FeCl_3$, and $SnCl_4$, interaction of cycloheptatriene and *t*-butyl chloride gives a tropylium salt, for example:[1]

Ferric chloride (16.2 g.) was added with stirring to a mixture of 18.4 g. of cycloheptatriene and 19 g. of *t*-butyl chloride. Hydrogen chloride was evolved, and the temperature was kept below 50°. After stirring at 65° for 5 hrs. the mixture was cooled and pentane was stirred in. Unchanged ferric chloride separated and the supernatant suspension was decanted. The procedure was repeated twice more and the first yellow suspension of complex was washed with ethanol and finally with pentane; yield 3.0 g. (5%).

    The complex (2) from *t*-butyl chloride and aluminum chloride transforms 1,5-diketones (1) into pyryllium salts (3).[2]

(1)   (3)

[1]D. Bryce-Smith and N. A. Perkins, *J. Chem. Soc.*, 2320 (1961)
[2]A. T. Balaban, *Compt. rend.*, **256**, 4239 (1963); A. T. Balaban, A. R. Katritzky and B. M. Semple, *Tetrahedron*, **23**, 4001 (1967)

i-**Butyl chloroformate**, $(CH_3)_2CHCH_2COCl$ [**1**, 86]. Mol. wt. 136.58, b.p. 123–126°. Supplier: Eastman.

The isobutyloxycarbonyl group has been used to block the 5'-hydroxyl function

of desoxyribosides in oligonucleotide synthesis.[1] The reagent shows a good selectivity for the 5'-hydroxyl group, as is evident in the high yield in (1) → (2). The blocking group is removed smoothly by alkaline hydrolysis: (3) → (4).

[1]K. K. Ogilvie and R. L. Letsinger, *J. Org.*, **32**, 2365 (1967)

i- and *sec.*-**Butyl chloroformate** [**1**, 86, before references]. In a study of the mixed anhydride peptide synthesis, Vaughan[6] noticed some slight advantage of *i-* and *sec*-butyl chloroformate over other simple derivatives tried. Anderson *et al.*[7] state that "Since yields are a little better if isobutyl chloroformate is the reagent" (reference to a paper of 1952), "we have subsequently used this compound routinely." They note that is has the advantage of being stable on storage.

[6]J. R. Vaughan, Jr., and R. L. Osata, *Am. Soc.*, **74**, 676 (1952)
[7]G. W. Anderson, J. E. Zimmerman, and F. M. Callahan, *ibid.*, **88**, 1338 (1966); **89**, 5012 (1967)

t-Butyl chloroformate [1, 86].

Preparation (cont'd). In one step of a total synthesis of cephalosporin C (1), Woodward et al.[1] prepared *t*-butyl chloroformate *in situ* from *t*-butanol, phosgene,

(1)

and pyridine in methylene chloride at $-74°$ and used it to form the *t*-butoxycarbonyl derivative of an amino acid. The protective group was later removed by treatment with trifluoroacetic acid.

Yajima and Kawatani[2] prepared *t*-butyl chloroformate according to Woodward's conditions and treated the solution directly with hydrazoic acid in ether and triethylamine to obtain *t*-butyl azidoformate directly in 35% yield. The method is probably the most convenient route to *t*-butyl azidoformate.

[1]R. B. Woodward et al., Am. Soc., **88**, 852 (1966)
[2]H. Yajima and H. Kawatani, Chem. Pharm. Bull., **16**, 183 (1968)

t-Butyl chromate [1, 86–87, before references].

Oxidation of α-ionone (1) with *t*-butyl chromate yields, in addition to the expected product (2), some 1-hydroxy-4-keto-α-ionone (3). By using nonpolar solvents,

(1)   (2)   +

(3)   (4)

particularly *t*-butanol, yields of 23–27% of (3) can be obtained. This oxidation was useful because (3) is readily transformed into abscisic acid (4), a plant hormone involved in leaf and flower abscision.[9]

[9]D. L. Roberts, R. A. Heckman, B. P. Hege, and S. A. Bellin, J. Org., **33**, 3566 (1968)

t-Butyl fluoroformate, $(CH_3)_3COCOF$ [**1**, 88, before **t-Butyl hydroperoxide**]. Mol. wt. 120.12, b.p. 4°/15 mm.

The reagent is prepared from *t*-butanol and carbonyl chlorofluoride:

$$(CH_3)_3COH + ClCOF \rightarrow (CH_3)_3COCOF + HCl.$$

In contrast to the very unstable *t*-butyl chloroformate, this reagent can be stored for months at 0–20°. It reacts readily with amino acids to give *t*-butyloxycarbonyl (BOC) derivatives.[1]

[1]E. Schnabel, H. Herzog, P. Hoffmann, E. Klauke, and I. Ugi, *Angew. Chem., internat. Ed.,* **7**, 380 (1968)

t-Butyl hydroperoxide [1, 88–89].

[**1**, 88, after the first paragraph]: Meinwald *et al.*[11a] applied the Wiberg method of decarboxylation to the acid (1) and obtained the crystalline alcohol (5) in 15% overall yield.

For an efficient procedure by Sheng and Zajacek for the oxidation of a tertiary amine to the amine oxide, *see* **Vanadium oxyacetylacetonate** (this volume).

Mono- and diepoxy-1,4-benzoquinones [**1**, 89, before references]. A general method for the preparation of monoepoxy-1,4-benzoquinones described by H. W. Moore[13] is as follows. A solution of 0.1 mole of 1,4-benzoquinone in 100 ml. of 1:1 mixture of absolute ethanol and dioxane is treated with 0.11 mole of *t*-butyl hydroperoxide and cooled to 5–10°, and 2 ml. of Triton B (30% methanolic benzyl-trimethylammonium hydroxide) was added. Aliquots of the solution were monitored

by gas chromatography; the results showed the reactions to be complete in 1–3 hrs. and monoepoxides were obtained by dilution with water and crystallization in yields of 30–80%. Diepoxides were obtained in the same way with a ratio of oxidant to quinone of 2:1. Duroquinone (1) gave a sharp-melting product and only one isomer was detected by gas chromatography. This was characterized as the *trans* isomer.[14]

[11a]J. Meinwald, J. C. Shelton, G. L. Buchanan, and A. Courtin, *J. Org.*, **33**, 99 (1968)
[13]H. W. Moore, *ibid.*, **32**, 1996 (1967)
[14]H. W. Moore, private communication

t-Butyl hypochlorite [1, 90–94]

Preparation [**1**, 90, before *Halogenation of hydrocarbons*]. A new preparative procedure[1a] which eliminates the dangers in working with compressed chlorine and the danger from explosion due to poor temperature control during the addition of chlorine uses commercial bleach solution (Clorox) and has advantages of simplicity of equipment needed, shortness of time required, and high purity of the product.

Photochlorination of ethers [**1**, 93, after *Diazoalkanes*] with *t*-butyl hypochlorite at low temperatures leads to facile α-substitution, often in satisfactory yield.[20]

[1a]M. J. Mintz and C. Walling, procedure submitted to *Org. Syn.*, 1968
[20]C. Walling and M. J. Mintz, *Am. Soc.*, **89**, 1515 (1967)

t-Butyl hypoiodite [1, 94–95 before references].

Iodination of hydrocarbons. Tanner and Gidley[4] prepared the reagent by treatment of *t*-butyl hypochlorite in carbon tetrachloride or Freon 113 with mercuric iodide:

$$2\ (CH_3)_3COCl\ +\ HgI_2\ \longrightarrow\ 2\ (CH_3)_3COI\ +\ HgCl_2$$

Such solutions on irradiation in the presence of a hydrocarbon give iodinated hydrocarbons in yields of 30–50%.

$$Cyclohexane\ \xrightarrow{\ 51\%\ }\ Cyclohexyl\ iodide$$

$$\underline{n}\text{-Butane}\ \xrightarrow{\ 35\%\ }\ CH_3CH_2CH_2CH_2I\ +\ CH_3CH_2\underset{\underset{I}{|}}{C}HCH_3$$

[4]D. D. Tanner and G. C. Gidley, *Am. Soc.*, **90**, 808 (1968).

t-Butyl isocyanide, $(CH_3)_3CN{\equiv}C$ [1, 95, before *n*-Butyllithium]. Mol. wt. 83.13, b.p. 91–92°/720 mm. Supplier: Fl.

Preparation.[1] Ethyl formate (3.52 moles) is added slowly with cooling to 4 moles of *t*-butylamine and, after the exothermal reaction has ceased, the solution is refluxed for 2 hrs.; fractionation then affords *t*-butylformamide in high yield. Dehydration of the formamide to *t*-butyl isocyanide is accomplished by stirring with

$$(CH_3)_3CNH_2\ +\ HCO_2C_2H_5\ \xrightarrow[90\%]{-HOC_2H_5}\ (CH_3)_3C\overset{H}{\underset{|}{N}}-\overset{H}{\underset{|}{C}}=O$$

$$(CH_3)_3C\overset{H}{\underset{|}{N}}-\overset{H}{\underset{|}{C}}=O\ +\ POCl_3\ +\ 4\ Py\ \xrightarrow[68\%]{}\ (CH_3)_3CN{\equiv}C\ +\ Py\cdot HCl\ +\ Py\cdot HPO_3$$

ice cooling and dropping in phosphoryl chloride ($POCl_3$). Pyridine is used to neutralize the acids formed. Addition of ice water, extraction with petroleum ether, and distillaton then afford *t*-butyl isocyanide.

New indole synthesis. One of six syntheses reported by Zeeh[2] without explanation but said to afford yields of 15–40% is formulated as follows:

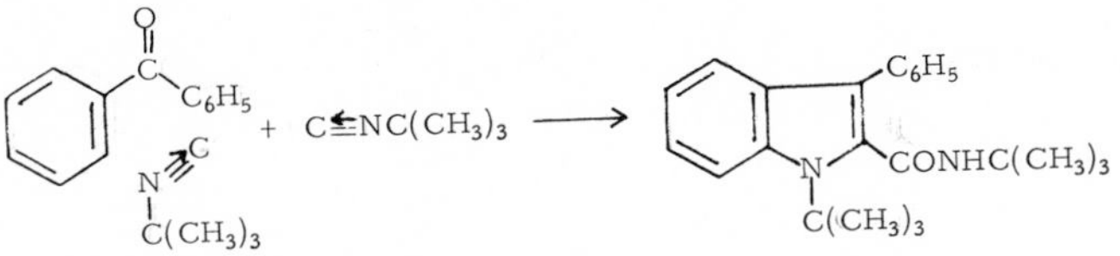

[1] I. Ugi, R. Meyr, M. Lipinski, F. Bodesheim, and F. Rosendahl, *Org. Syn.*, **41**, 13 (1961)
[2] B. Zeeh, *Tetrahedron Letters*, 3881 (1967)

n-Butyllithium [1, 95–96].

[Before Suppliers]: *Caution*: The reagent is highly corrosive and should be handled with protection from rubber gloves and safety glasses.

Metalating agent [1, 95, after the formulation]. As the first example of intramolecular addition of an organolithium to a triple bond, Dessy and Kandil[4a] found that when an ethereal solution of 1-phenylethynyl-8-bromonaphthalene (1) was

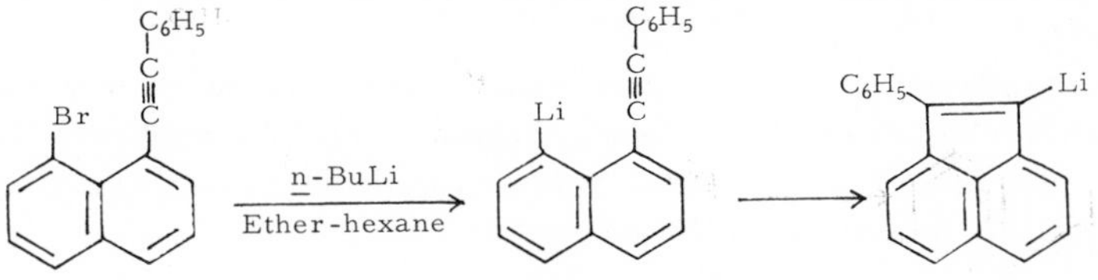

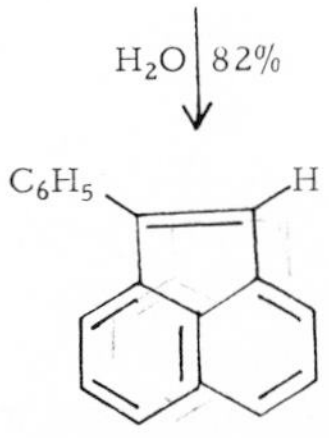

treated with *n*-butyllithium in hexane at room temperature, followed by hydrolysis, 1-phenylacenaphthylene (4) was obtained as the only identifiable product in 82% yield. Similarly, the diphenyl (5) yields the fluorene derivative (6).

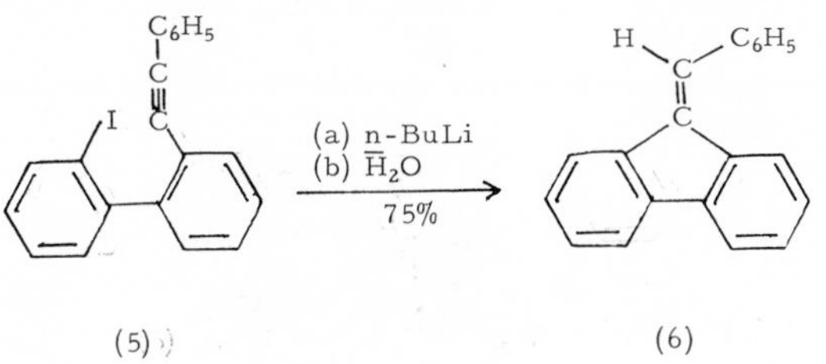

In both of these examples the organometallic group is locked in close proximity to the triple bond, but Ward[4b] has shown that such steric coercion is not necessary for the reaction. Thus 6-bromo-1-phenyl-1-hexyne (7) is converted into benzylidene-cyclopentane (8) in 60% yield. Ward suggests that the cyclizing species is a radical and not a carbanion:

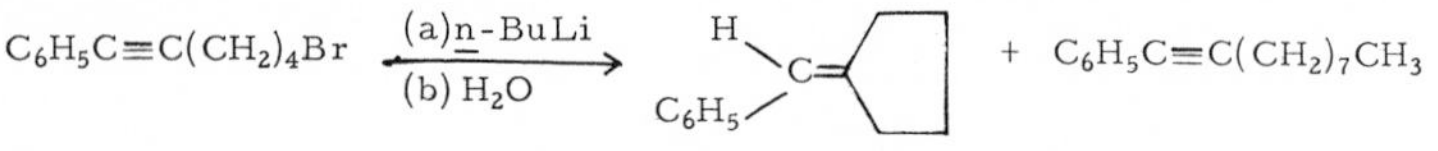

$$C_6H_5C{\equiv}C(CH_2)_4Br \xrightarrow[\text{(b) } H_2O]{\text{(a)} \underline{n}\text{-BuLi}} \quad \underset{C_6H_5}{\overset{H}{>}}C{=}\!\!\!\bigcirc \quad + \quad C_6H_5C{\equiv}C(CH_2)_7CH_3$$

$$\text{(7)} \qquad\qquad\qquad \text{(8) } 60\% \qquad\qquad\qquad 20\%$$

$$C_6H_5C{\equiv}C(CH_2)_4Br \xrightarrow{\underline{n}\text{-BuLi}} C_6H_5C{=}C(CH_2)_3\dot{C}H_2 \;+\; \underline{n}\text{-}\dot{B}u \;+\; LiBr$$

$$\underset{C_6H_5}{\overset{\cdot}{>}}\dot{C}{=}\!\!\!\bigcirc \xrightarrow{\underline{n}\text{-}Bu} \underset{C_6H_5}{\overset{H}{>}}C{=}\!\!\!\bigcirc \;+\; \text{1-Butene}$$

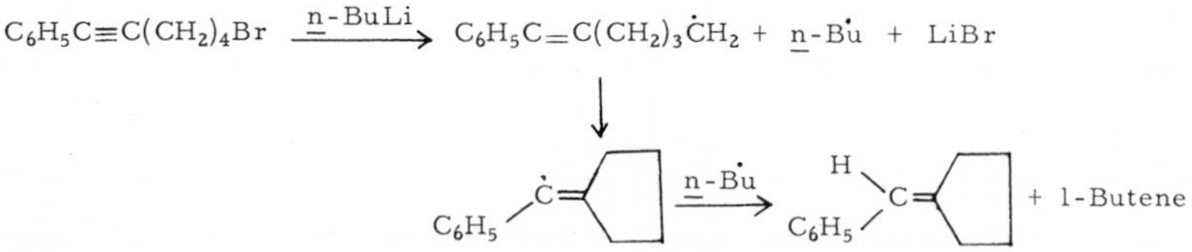

As in metalation with *n*-butyllithium, ether and THF accelerate the reaction markedly over the rate observed with hydrocarbon solvents. Eastham *et al.*[4c] suggest that in a hydrocarbon solvent the reagent exists as a polymer and that this dissociates in ether or THF.

Lithium alkynes [1, 96, before references]. Pattison and Dear[9] found the reagent convenient for the conversion of terminal alkynes into lithium alkynes. They also found that the reaction of this reagent with dihydropyrane provides the simplest and best synthesis of *trans*-1-hydroxy-4-nonene yet found:

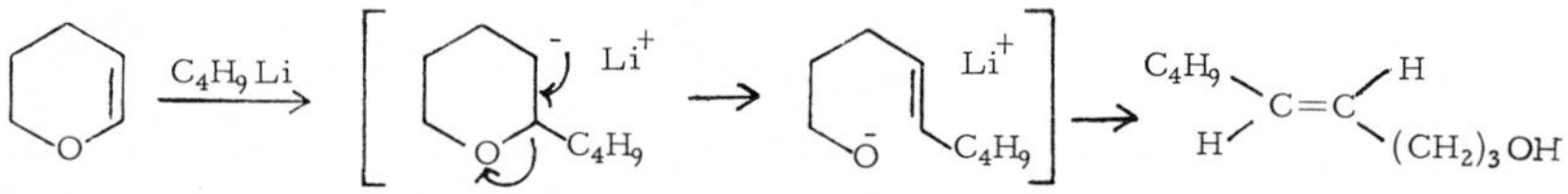

Li alkynes are generally more convenient to handle than Na alkynes because the Li compounds are soluble in dioxane. ω-Fluoro-1-alkynes can be prepared conveniently from ω-fluoroalkyl halides and the acetylenic function undergoes further reactions without loss of fluorine.

Synthesis of allenes [1, 96, before references]. Tetramethoxyallene (3), the diacetal of carbon suboxide, has been prepared by the following sequence:[10]

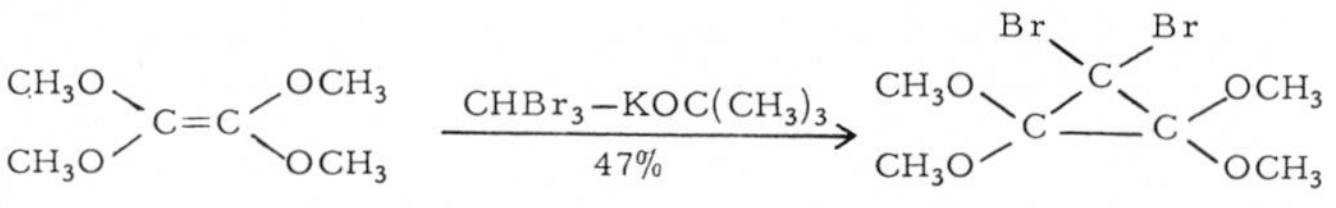

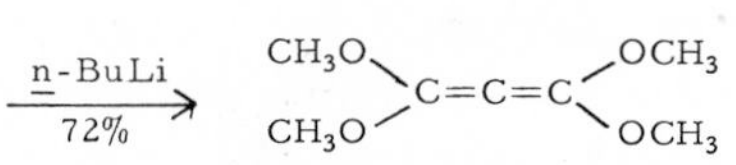

$$\text{(3) M. p. } 65\text{-}67^0$$

Reaction with active-hydrogen compounds [**1**, 96, before references]. Hauser[11] reports that *n*-butyllithium can afford dilithio salts from active-hydrogen compounds when use of potassium amide in liquid ammonia is ineffective. Thus acetanilide (1) reacts with *n*-butyllithium in THF or ether to form a dilithio derivative formulated as (2). This disalt on alkylation with benzyl chloride gives (3).

$$CH_3\overset{O}{\underset{\|}{C}}-NHC_6H_5 \quad \xrightarrow[\text{THF}]{2\ BuLi} \quad LiCH_2\overset{O}{\underset{\|}{C}}\overset{Li}{\underset{}{N}}C_6H_5 \quad \xrightarrow{C_6H_5CH_2Cl} \quad C_6H_5CH_2CH_2\overset{O}{\underset{\|}{C}}-\overset{H}{\underset{|}{N}}C_6H_5$$

(1)   (2)   (3)

Dioxolane olefin synthesis [**1**, 96, before references]. The benzylidine derivative of *trans*-cyclooctane-1,2-diol (1) when treated with *n*-butyllithium in hexane at 20° for 14 hours is converted into *trans*-cyclooctene in 75% yield.[12] None of the

(1)

cis-isomer is formed. The reaction is general, and affords an alternative to Corey's thionocarbonate synthesis of olefins (see **Trimethyl phosphite**, in both volumes).

[4a]R. E. Dessy and S. A. Kandil, *J. Org.*, **30**, 3857 (1965); *idem, Am. Soc.*, **88**, 3027 (1966)

[4b]H. R. Ward, *Am. Soc.*, **89**, 5517 (1967)

[4c]J. F. Eastham and G. W. Gibson, *ibid*, **85**, 2171 (1963); C. G. Screttas and J. F. Eastham, *ibid.*, **88**, 5668 (1966)

[9]F. L. M. Pattison and R. E. A. Dear, *Canad. J. Chem.*, **41**, 2600 (1963)

[10]R. W. Hoffman and U. Bressel, *Angew. Chem. internat. Ed.*, **6**, 808 (1967)

[11]R. L. Gay, S. Boatman and C. R. Hauser, *Chem. Ind.*, 1789 (1965)

[12]J. N. Hines, M. J. Peagram, G. H. Whitham, and M. Wright, *Chem. Communun.*, 1593 (1968)

n-Butyl mercaptan. [**1**, 97, before **n-Butyl nitrite**]. Mol. wt. 90.19, b.p. 96–98°. Suppliers: Aldrich, Eastman, Fl., K.-L.

Ireland[1] found certain advantages in converting a hydroxymethylene derivative of type (1) into the *n*-butylthiomethylene derivative (2) prior to alkylation by acid-catalyzed azeotropic distillation with *n*-butyl mercaptan in benzene. The derivative (2) can be methylated efficiently (3) and the blocking *n*-butylthiomethylene group removed with aqueous sodium hydroxide in diethylene glycol (4). The *n*-butylthio-methylene group can also be reduced to a methyl group (5) by Raney nickel de-sulfurization. If a readily reducible double bond is present, as in the derivative of *trans*-Δ^6-decalone-1, the desired reduction to a methyl group can be effected with sodium in liquid ammonia (34% yield). The derivative (3) also can be converted by reduction (6) and acid-catalyzed rearrangement into the α,β-unsaturated aldehyde (7).

$$\underset{(1)}{-CH\overset{\overset{\textstyle O}{\|}}{C}-\underset{|}{C}=CHOH} \xrightarrow[-H_2O]{n\text{-}C_4H_9SH} \underset{(2)}{-CH\overset{\overset{\textstyle O}{\|}}{C}-\underset{|}{C}=CHSC_4H_9\text{-}n} \xrightarrow{CH_3I,\,OH^-}$$

$$\underset{(3)}{-\overset{\overset{\textstyle CH_3}{|}}{C}-\overset{\overset{\textstyle O}{\|}}{C}-\underset{|}{C}=CHSC_4H_9\text{-}n}$$

OH⁻ → $\underset{(4)}{-\overset{\overset{\textstyle CH_3}{|}}{C}-\overset{\overset{\textstyle O}{\|}}{C}-CH_2}$

Ni → $\underset{(5)}{-\overset{\overset{\textstyle CH_3}{|}}{C}-\overset{\overset{\textstyle O}{\|}}{C}-CHCH_3}$

NaBH₄ → $\underset{(6)}{-\overset{\overset{\textstyle CH_3}{|}}{C}-\overset{\overset{\textstyle OH}{|}}{CH}C=CHSC_4H_9\text{-}n} \xrightarrow{H^+} \underset{(7)}{-\overset{\overset{\textstyle CH_3}{|}}{C}-CH=CCHO}$

[1] R. E. Ireland and J. A. Marshall, *J. Org.*, **27**, 1615, 1620 (1962).

t-**Butyloxycarbonyl fluoride** [**1**, 98, before *t*-**Butyloxycarbonylimidazole**]. Mol. wt. 120.13, b.p. 4°/15 mm.

The reagent is prepared[1] by the reaction of carbonyl chlorofluoride[2] with *t*-butanol. Like *t*-butyl azidoformate, the reagent reacts with amino acids to give *t*-butyloxycarbonylamino acids (BOC-amino acids).[1]

$$\underset{\overset{\textstyle \|}{\textstyle O}}{F\overset{}{C}Cl} \; + \; HOC(CH_3)_3 \longrightarrow \underset{\overset{\textstyle \|}{\textstyle O}}{F-\overset{}{C}OC(CH_3)_3}$$

[1] E. Schnabel, H. Herzog, P. Hoffmann, E. Klauke, and I. Ugi, *Ann.*, **716**, 175 (1968)
[2] H. J. Emeléus and J. F. Wood, *J. Chem. Soc.*, 2183 (1948)

t-**Butyl pentachlorophenyl carbonate**, $C_6Cl_5O\overset{\overset{\textstyle O}{\|}}{C}C(CH_3)_3$ [**1**, 98, before *t*-**Butyl perbenzoate**]. Mol. wt. 366.46, m.p. 116–117°.

The reagent is prepared by reaction of pentachlorophenyl chloroformate (m.p. 58°) with *t*-butanol in benzene in the presence of pyridine. Like *t*-butyl azidoformate and *t*-butyl *p*-nitrophenyl carbonate, it reacts with amino acids to give *t*-butyloxycarbonylamino acids in yields of 60–85%.[1]

[1] M. Fujino and C. Hatanaka, *Chem. Pharm. Bull.*, **15**, 2015 (1967)

t-**Butyl perbenzoate** [**1**, 98–101].

Additional suppliers: Fl., K.-L.

Reaction with unsaturated compounds [**1**, after citation of ref. 7]. A detailed example of the reaction first described by Kharasch, Sosnovsky, and Yang[7] is the reaction of cyclohexene to give 3-cyclohexenylbenzoate.[7a]

$$\text{(cyclohexene)} + C_6H_5\overset{O}{\overset{\|}{C}}OOC(CH_3)_3 \xrightarrow[79-81\%]{Cu_2Br_2,\ N_2,\ 80-82^\circ} \text{(product)} \begin{array}{c} H \quad OCOC_6H_5 \end{array} + (CH_3)_3COH$$

[7a]K. Pedersen, P. Jakobsen, and S.-O. Lawesson, *Org. Syn.*, **48**, 18 (1968).

t-**Butylperoxy isopropyl carbonate**, $(CH_3)_3C\overset{O}{\overset{\|}{-O}}CO-CH(CH_3)_2$ [**1**, 101, before **γ-Butyrolactone**]. Mol. wt. 160.21. Supplier: Pittsburgh Plate Glass Co. Like diisopropyl peroxydicarbonate, the reagent converts alkylbenzenes into alkyl-phenols.[1]

[1]P. Kovacic and M. E. Kurz, *J. Org.*, **31**, 2459 (1966)

t-**Butyl 2,4,5-trichlorophenyl carbonate** (3) [**1**, 101, before **γ-Butyrolactone**]. Mol. wt. 297.57, m.p. 67–68.5°. Supplier: A.

Preparation.[1] Suppliers of 2,4,5-trichlorophenol: A, B, C, E, F, MCB. A solution of 100 g. of phosgene in 375 ml. of toluene was stirred at −10° and treated

$$\underset{(1)}{\text{Cl}\text{-aryl-}OH} \xrightarrow[60\%]{COCl_2;\ C_6H_5N(CH_3)_2} \underset{(2)}{\text{Cl}\text{-aryl-}O\overset{O}{\overset{\|}{C}}Cl} \xrightarrow[55-65\%]{Quinoline;\ HOC(CH_3)_3}$$

$$\underset{(3)}{\text{Cl}\text{-aryl-}O\overset{O}{\overset{\|}{C}}OC(CH_3)_3}$$

with 0.86 mole of 2,4,5-trichlorophenol, followed by 0.87 mole of dimethylaniline, added at such a rate as to maintain a temperature of 5–10° during the addition (20 min.). After stirring at 22–24° overnight, 100 g. of ice was added and the bis-(2,4,5-trichlorophenyl)carbonate which separated (9.5 g.) was removed by filtration. The organic layer in the filtrate was separated, washed with 2 *N*-hydrochloric acid and with 10% brine. Evaporation then afforded 134.5 g. (60%) of pure 2,4,5-trichlorophenyl chloroformate (2), b.p. 93–95°/0.4–0.6 mm., m.p. 62–63°. In the next step a solution of the crude chloroformate (2, from 3.6 moles of 2,4,5-trichloro-phenol) in 400 ml. of methylene chloride was added over 1 hr. at 30–32° to a stirred solution of 3.6 mole each of *t*-butanol and quinoline in 900 ml. of methylene chloride. The mixture was stirred overnight at 22–24°; then ice-water was added and the suspension was filtered from bis-(2,4,5-trichlorophenyl)carbonate (189 g., 25%). The organic layer in the filtrate was separated, washed with water, 2 *N* hydrochloric acid, and water, dried and evaporated. Crystallization of the residue from a mixture of methanol and water (charcoal) gave 610 g. (65%) of colorless plates of *t*-butyl 2,4,5-trichlorophenyl carbonate (3).

Peptide Synthesis.[1] In the presence of triethylamine the reagent reacts with an amino acid to give the N-*t*-butoxycarbonylamino acid and 2,4,5-trichlorophenol. The two products can be extracted together by ethyl acetate, and if DCC is added the 2,4,5-trichlorophenyl ester of N-*t*-butoxycarbonylamino acid is obtained in high yield. This is an active ester suitable for peptide synthesis (**1**, 1196).

[1]W. Broadbent, J. S, Morley, and B. E. Stone, *J. Chem. Soc.*, (C), 2632 (1967)

C

Calcium borohydride, $Ca(BH_4)_2$ [**1**, 103, before **Calcium carbonate**]. Mol. wt. 69.79.

Preparation.[1] Calcium borohydride can be obtained in solid form by the reaction of anhydrous calcium chloride and sodium borohydride in THF, 4–8 hrs., thorough stirring. After removal of sodium chloride by centrifugation and evaporation of solvent a crystalline addition compound of calcium borohydride and THF is obtained. The reagent can be prepared *in situ* by the reaction of calcium iodide and sodium borohydride in THF.

Reduction. The reagent is useful for reduction of carboxylic acid esters to primary alcohols. For example, the following esters have been reduced to the corresponding carbinols: ethyl *p*-nitrobenzoate (96% yield), ethyl phenylacetate (90% yield), ethyl glycinate (70% yield).[1] The reaction has some useful features: Hydroxylic solvents (ethanol, water) can be used, the selectivity is higher than in the case of lithium aluminum hydride, and the reagent is nearly neutral. The reagent was found to be satisfactory for reduction of the dimethyl ester of 4,4′-dinitro-2,2′-diphenic acid (1a) to the corresponding alcohol (1b, 51% yield).[2]

1 a R = COOCH$_3$
1 b R = CH$_2$OH

The reagent is also suitable for reduction of aldehydes and ketones.[3] Thus the stereoselective reduction of the acetamino ketone (2) to the *threo* diol (3) was effected by means of calcium borohydride in 70% yield:[4]

(2)   (3)

Sodium borohydride gave a mixture of the *threo* diol (25% yield) and the *erythro* diol (47% yield).

[1] J. Kollonitsch, O. Fuchs, and V. Gábor, *Nature*, **175**, 346 (1955)
[2] L. V. Dvorken, R. B. Smyth, and K. Mislow, *Am. Soc.*, **80**, 486 (1958)
[3] J. Kollonitsch, O. Fuchs, and V. Gábor, *Nature*, **173**, 4949 (1954)
[4] L. Léval, G. Fodor, K. Ritvay-Emandity, O. Fuchs, and A. Hajós, *Ber.*, **93**, 387 (1960)

Calcium carbonate [**1**, 103–104].

Tosylate rearrangement [before references]. In an approach to a synthesis of prostaglandins, Orr and Johnson[6] have investigated a route in which the five-membered ring of the prostaglandin skeleton is generated by modification of a six-membered ring. The starting material is 1,4-cyclohexanedione (7), which is transformed by standard procedures into a mixture of epimeric ditosylates (8).

(7)   (8)   (9)

The mixture was then refluxed with calcium carbonate in DMF for $2\frac{1}{2}$ hrs. The desired product (9) was obtained in 88% yield. One advantage of this route is that a keto function is generated in a position suitable for later introduction of an allylic hydroxyl group in the side chain.

[6]D. E. Orr and F. B. Johnson, *Canad. J. Chem.*, **47**, 47 (1969)

Calcium hydride [**1**, 105–106]. Suppliers: Alfa Inorganics, British Drug Houses, Ventron Corp., Fl., E. Merck, Riedel-de-Haën, Sch.

Acylation of tertiary alcohols[6] [**1**, 106, before references]. Tertiary alcohols can be esterified with carboxylic acids or anhydrides in good yield in the presence of calcium hydride or calcium carbide. *t*-Butyl acetate is obtained in 80% yield from *t*-butanol and acetic anhydride. 17α-Methyltestosterone is acetylated in 89–96% yield.

[6]R. V. Oppenauer, *Monatshefte*, **97**, 62 (1966)

Calcium–Liquid NH₃ [**1**, 106–107, before references]. Deacetoxylation of (1) was effected by reaction with calcium in liquid ammonia but could not be brought about with zinc in refluxing acetic anhydride.[3]

(1)   (2)

[3]A. W. Burgstahler and R. E. Sticker, *Tetrahedron*, **24**, 2435 (1968).

***d*-10-Camphorsulfonic acid** [**1**, 109, after line 2].

A new method for the resolution of ketones depends upon the formation of an iminium salt containing an optically active anion.[2] A ketone of one type, exemplified by (1), is converted into the pyrrolidine enamine (2), which is then treated with *d*-10-camphorsulfonic acid (3) to give the salt (4), which was resolved by systematic crystallization. Each enantiomeric salt was then crystallized and hydrolyzed to a pure enantiomeric ketone (1).

The *dl*-ketone (5) did not form an enamine readily but was resolved by dissolving 7.7 g. in hot absolute ethanol (45 ml.) and adding 6.4 g. of pyrrolidine perchlorate[3] and 2 drops of pyrrolidine. The enamine perchlorate that crystallized was collected and treated with potassium *d*-camphor-10-sulfonate in absolute methanol. Crystallization then gave enantiomeric salts and from them the (+) and (−) ketones were recovered.

[2] W. R. Adams, O. L. Chapman, J. B. Sieja, and W. J. Welstead, Jr., *Am. Soc.*, **88**, 162 (1966)
[3] N. J. Leonard and J. V. Paukstelis, *J. Org.*, **28**, 3021 (1963)

Carbobenzoxy chloride (benzyl chloroformate) [1, 109–110]. Additional suppliers: Fl., K.-L., E. Merck, Sch.

Peptide synthesis [1, 109–110]. DeTar[6a] has reported a procedure for the preparation of bis-benzyloxycarbonyl-L-histidine based essentially on one by Patchornik, Berger, and Katchalski.[6b]

[6a] A. A. Wieland, R. J. Albers, and D. F. DeTar, procedure submitted to *Org. Syn.* (1967)
[6b] A. Patchornik, A. Berger, and E. Katchalski, *Am. Soc.*, **79**, 6416 (1957)

Carbomethoxymethylenetriphenylphosphorane [1, 112–114, after citation of reference 3].

The reaction of 3β-acetoxy-20-keto-21-iodo-Δ⁵-pregnene (1) with carbomethoxymethylenetriphenylphosphorane provides a convenient synthesis of methyl 3β-acetoxy-20-keto-21-nor-5,-*trans*-22-choladienate (2). The reaction was used in a synthesis of isocardenolides.[3a]

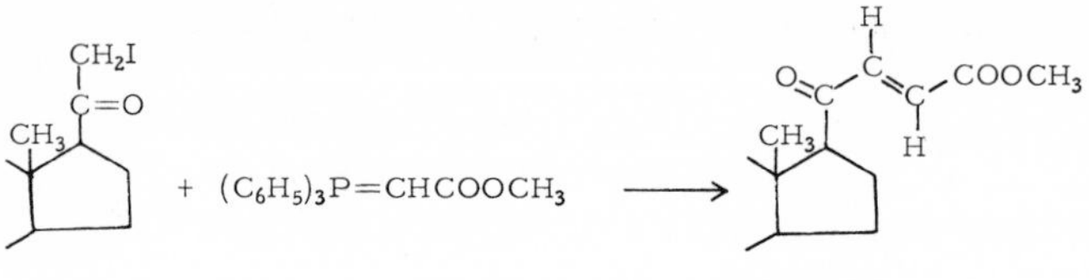

(1)   (2)

[3a]G. R. Pettit, B. Green, A. K. Das Gupta, P. A. Whitehouse, and G. V. Yardly, *J. Org.*, in press.

Carbon monoxide, CO [1, 114, before **Carbonyl chloride**]. Mol. wt. 18.01, b.p. −191.5°. Supplier: *See* Gases (this volume).

Reaction with trialkylboranes. Carbon monoxide added to a solution of a trialkylborane formed *in situ* in diglyme solution reacts at 100° at atmospheric pressure; the resulting organoboron intermediate is oxidized by hydrogen peroxide to a trialkylcarbinol in excellent yield.[1] *t*-Carbinols with highly branched alkyl groups

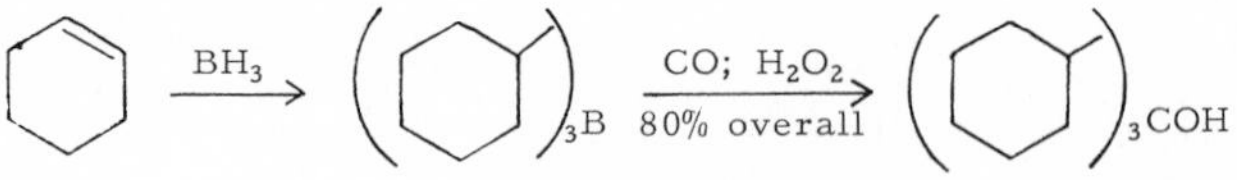

which are difficultly accessible by Grignard reagents are thus readily obtained. If a little water is present, migration of the third alkyl group from boron to carbon is inhibited and the product is a dialkyl ketone:

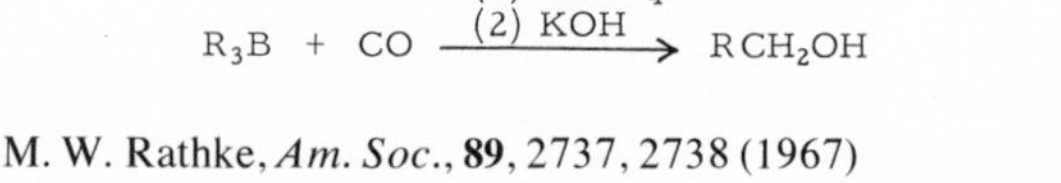

In the presence of sodium or lithium borohydride the reaction of carbon monoxide with a trialkylborane gives the homologated alcohol.[2]

$$R_3B \ + \ CO \ \xrightarrow[\text{(2) KOH}]{\text{(1) NaBH}_4} \ RCH_2OH$$

[1]H. C. Brown and M. W. Rathke, *Am. Soc.*, **89**, 2737, 2738 (1967)
[2]M. W. Rathke and H. C. Brown, *ibid.*, **89**, 2740 (1967)

Carbonyl cyanide, O=C(CN)₂ [1, 114, before **N,N′-Carbonyldiimidazole**]. Mol. wt. 80.05, m.p. −38°, b.p. 65–66°. *Caution*: Reacts with water with explosive violence to form hydrogen cyanide and carbon dioxide.

Preparation. Martin[1] has devised a convenient, high-yield procedure for the preparation of this reagent by dropwise addition of di-*n*-butyl sulfide to a flask charged with diethyl phthalate and tetracyanoethylene oxide and kept at 50°.

$$\underset{NC}{\overset{NC}{>}}C\underset{O}{-}C\underset{CN}{\overset{CN}{<}} + (\underline{n}\text{-}C_4H_9)_2S \xrightarrow[86-91\%]{} \underset{NC}{\overset{NC}{>}}C{=}O + \underset{\underline{n}\text{-}C_4H_9}{\overset{n\text{-}C_4H_9}{>}}S{=}C\underset{CN}{\overset{CN}{<}}$$

Uses. Carbonyl cyanide reacts with alcohols and phenols to form cyanoformate esters, with primary and secondary amines to give cyanoformamides, with N,N-dimethylaniline to give $[p\text{-}(CH_3)_2NC_6H_4]_2C(CN)_2$ and with pyrrole to form 2-cyanoformylpyrrole. It reacts with olefins of the type C=C—CH and undergoes Diels-Alder reaction with some conjugated dienes to give dicyanodihydropyranes.

[1]E. L. Martin, procedure submitted to *Org. Syn.*, 1968

N,N'-Carbonyldiimidazole [**1**, 114–116]. Suppliers: K and K., Fl., Sch. The preparation in 80–94% yield has been described in detail.[1a]

[**1**, 116, before references]. The reagent has been used to introduce the carbonyl group in the preparation of five-membered heterocyclic systems starting with derivatives of *o*-phenylenediamine (I), ethylenediamine (II), and 2-anilinoethanol (III). The reaction proceeds in good to excellent yields in THF or THF and benzene

at 25–65°.[12] Phosgene (highly toxic) has been used previously for such syntheses, but requires higher temperatures for cyclizations.

[1a]H. A. Staab and K. Wendel, *Org. Syn.*, **48**, 44 (1968)
[12]W. B. Wright, Jr., *J. Heterocyclic Chem.*, **2**, 41 (1965)

1,1-Carbonyldi-1,2,4-triazole (1) [**1**, 116]. Mol. wt. 164.13. This reagent was incorrectly named N,N'-carbonyldi-*s*-triazine in Vol. **1**. The structure has been established by NMR spectroscopy.[2]

[2]K. T. Potts and T. H. Crawford, *J. Org.*, **27**, 2631 (1962)

N-Carbonylsulfamic acid chloride (N-Carbonylsulfamyl chloride) [**1**, 117]. Review: R. Graf, *Angew. Chem., internat. Ed.*, **7**, 172 (1968). The reagent is now supplied by Aldrich.

p-**Carboxybenzenediazonium** **chloride,**[1] $p\text{-}HO_2CC_6H_4\overset{+}{N}\equiv N\overset{-}{Cl}$ [**1**, 118, before **4-(4-Carboxyphenyl)semicarbazide**].

Prepared *in situ* by diazotization of *p*-aminobenzoic acid with sodium nitrite in an acid medium, the reagent reacts with an active methylene compound (at pH < 6 to avoid formation of a formazan derivative) to give a *p*-carboxyphenylhydrazone, which can be titrated with 0.1 *N* NaOH as a monobasic acid.

$$HO_2CC_6H_4\overset{+}{N}\equiv N\overset{-}{Cl} + H_2C\!\!\big< \xrightarrow{HCl} HO_2CC_6H_4N=N-CH\!\!\big< \; \rightleftharpoons \; HO_2CC_6H_4NHN=C\!\!\big<$$

[1]A. Friediger, J. H. Vestergaard, and S. Veibel, *Monatshefte*, **98**, 1234 (1967).

p-**Carboxybenzenesulfonyl azide**, $p\text{-}HOOCC_6H_4SO_2N_3$ [**1**, 118, before **4-(4-Carboxyphenyl)semicarbazide**]. Mol. wt. 227.20.

Preparation.[1] The monopotassium salt of *p*-carboxybenzenesulfonic acid (Aldrich) is treated with chlorosulfonic acid and the resultant *p*-carboxybenzenesulfonyl chloride is then treated with sodium azide.

Diazo transfer.[1] *p*-Toluenesulfonyl azide (*which see*) is commonly used for diazo-transfer reactions; however, it has the disadvantage that the *p*-toluenesulfonamide formed as one product is difficult to separate from the diazo compound. Hendrickson and Wolf[1] found that the lithium and triethylamine salts of *p*-carboxybenzenesulfonyl azide are soluble in THF and acetonitrile, respectively, and that the triethylamine salt of *p*-carboxybenzenesulfonamide is essentially insoluble in acetonitrile. In a standard procedure a solution of the carboxy azide is prepared in acetonitrile by addition of triethylamine. The active methylene reactant is added and the carboxyamide salt separates within an hour. It is removed by filtration and the diazo product isolated by usual procedures. 2-Diazodimedone (2) was obtained by this procedure in 86% yield (the yield with tosyl azide is 42%). Several varia-

(1)   + $HOOCC_6H_4SO_2N_3$ →   (2)   + $HOOCC_6H_4SO_2NH_2$

tions are possible. For example, the active methylene group can be formylated and the ion of the resultant derivative treated with the reagent:

$$\xrightarrow{\quad} \quad \text{(CHOH)} \quad \xrightarrow[\displaystyle HOOCC_6H_4SO_2N_3]{\displaystyle OH^- \atop 52\%} \quad (N_2)$$

An acetoacetic ester can be monoalkylated and then submitted to the diazo-transfer reaction with cleavage of acetyl:

$$CH_3COCH_2COOR' \longrightarrow \underset{R}{CH_3COCHCOOR'} \longrightarrow \underset{N_2}{R\overset{\text{O}}{\underset{\|}{C}}COOR'}$$

[1]J. B. Hendrickson and W. A. Wolf, *J. Org.*, **33**, 3610 (1968).

Catechyl phosphorus tribromide, PBr_3 [1, 120, before **Catechyl phosphorus**

trichloride]. Mol. wt. 347.84, m.p. 67–70°.

The reagent is prepared just as the corresponding trichloride is prepared by reaction of catechol with PBr_3 and then bromine. It reacts with formic acid esters to give α,α-dibromomethyl alkyl ethers:[1]

The reagent reacts with carboxylic acids or anhydrides to give the corresponding acid bromides in 80–94% yields.[2]

[1] H. Gross and U. Karsch, *J. pr. Chem.*, **29**, 315 (1965)
[2] J. Gloede and H. Gross, *Ber.*, **100**, 1770 (1967)

Catechyl phosphorus trichloride [1, 120]. Supplier: Sch.

[Before reference]: The reagent has been used to convert amines into isothiocyanates.[2] The amine is converted into the dithiocarbamate alkyl ammonium salt

by reaction with carbon disulfide. The salt is then heated in benzene with catechyl phosphorus trichloride. Phosphoryl chloride has been used, but yields are somewhat lower.

The reagent was found to be superior to phosphorus pentachloride for conversion of cyclic ketones (8–12 membered rings) into 1-chlorocycloalkenes.[3]

$$n = 6\text{-}10$$

[2] D. Martin, E. Beyer, and H. Gross, *Ber.*, **98**, 2425 (1965)
[3] K. Schank, B. Eistert, and J. H. Felzmann, *ibid.*, **99**, 1414 (1966)

Ceric ammonium nitrate (CAN). [1, 120–121, before references]. In an acid medium (acetic, formic, perchloric, nitric acid), the reagent oxidizes a single aromatic methyl group in high yield to an aldehyde group but oxidizes a second methyl group only under much more drastic conditions.[3]

In a new route to 19-norsteroids,[4] a $\Delta^{1,4,6}$-3-ketosteroid (1) is subjected to the dienone-phenol rearrangement by treatment with a catalytic amount of concentrated sulfuric acid in acetic anhydride. The 3-acetoxy group of the product is hydrolyzed

$$\text{CH}_3\text{-}C_6H_4\text{-}CH_3 \xrightarrow[\text{quant.}]{\substack{\text{CAN}\\ 50\%\ \text{CH}_3\text{CO}_2\text{H},\ 90^0,\ 90\ \text{min.}}} \text{CHO-}C_6H_4\text{-}CH_3$$

$$\text{CH}_2\text{CH}_3\text{-}C_6H_5 \xrightarrow[\text{77\%}]{\substack{\text{CAN}\\ 3.5\ \underline{N}\ \text{HNO}_3,\ 90^0,\ 70\ \text{min.}}} \text{COCH}_3\text{-}C_6H_5$$

$$\xrightarrow[\text{76\%}]{\substack{\text{CAN}\\ 3.5\ \underline{N}\ \text{HNO}_3,\ 30^0,\ 90\ \text{min.}}}$$

and the resulting phenol methylated (2). The 5,6 double bond is then eliminated by hydrogenation (3), and the l-methyl group is oxidized by CAN to give the l-aldehyde (4). Decarbonylation with tris(triphenylphosphine)chlororhodium gives the ring A phenol methyl ether (5) suitable for Birch reduction.

$$(1) \xrightarrow[\substack{3)\ (\text{CH}_3)_2\text{SO}_4\text{-KOH}}]{\substack{1)\ \text{H}^+,\ \text{Ac}_2\text{O}\\ 2)\ \text{H}_2\text{O}}} (2) \xrightarrow{\text{H}_2}$$

$$(3) \xrightarrow{\text{CAN}} (4) \xrightarrow{[(\text{C}_6\text{H}_5)_3\text{P}]\text{RhCl}} (5)$$

This reagent oxidizes cyclopropanemethanol to the corresponding aldehyde in 5–15 min. at 75° in 64% isolated yield.[5] This reaction is probably the most convenient route to the aldehyde.

$$\triangleright\text{-CH}_2\text{OH} \xrightarrow[\text{64\%}]{2\ (\text{NH}_4)_2\text{Ce(NO}_3)_2} \triangleright\text{-CH=O}$$

Arylcyclopropanes are cleaved by ceric ammonium nitrate (CAN) to dinitrates and nitrate acetates as summarized in the formulas.[6]

Reaction of Ceric Ammonium Nitrate (CAN) with Cyclopropanes:

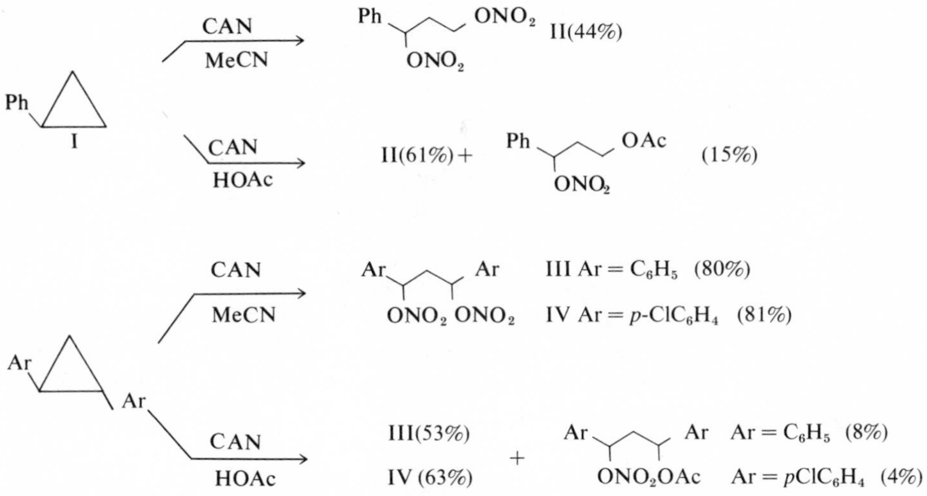

Oximes and semicarbazones are oxidized by ceric ammonium nitrate to the parent carbonyl compound in yields of 70–80%. Aqueous alcohols, acetonitrile, and acetic acid are suitable solvents, and the reaction is rapid at 0°.[7]

[2]*Add:* W. S. Trahanovsky, L. B. Young, and G. L. Brown, *J. Org.*, **32**, 3865 (1967)
[3]L. Syper, *Tetrahedron Letters*, 4493 (1966)
[4]S. B. Laing and P. J. Sykes, *J. Chem. Soc.*, (C), 2915 (1968)
[5]L. B. Young and W. S. Trahanovsky, *J. Org.*, **32**, 2349 (1967)
[6]L. B. Young, *Tetrahedron Letters*, 5105 (1968)
[7]J. W. Bird and D. G. M. Diaper, *Canad. J. Chem.*, **47**, 145 (1969)

Ceric sulfate, $Ce(SO_4)_2 \cdot 4 H_2O$ [**1**, 121, before **Cerous hydroxide**]. Mol. wt. 404.32. Suppliers: Riedel-de Haën, Alfa Inorganics.

Oxidation of catechol. *o*-Benzoquinone was first prepared by Willstätter and Pfannenstiel by oxidation of catechol with silver oxide (**1**, 1011–1012) under strictly anhydrous conditions. But Brockhaus[1] has reported that *o*-benzoquinone is stable in aqueous medium at pH 1–3 and can be prepared by adding 1 g. of catechol in 65 ml. of chloroform to 130 ml. of 20% sulfuric acid containing 7.34 g of oxidant and ice, shaking vigorously for a few seconds, shaking again with 10% of the theoretical amount of ceric sulfate solution at 0°, and then washing with 0.01 *N* sulfuric acid, and drying over sodium sulfate. Yield in solution: 86%.

[1]R. Brockhaus, *Ann.*, **712**, 214 (1968)

Chloramine [**1**, 122–125].

Ring expansion of phenols [**1**, 124, after line 4]. In the ring expansion of a phenol with chloramine, the phenol was taken in excess because of ready availability and to serve as solvent. Paquette and Farley[17a] found that if chloramine is used in excess the phenol is oxidatively dimerized:

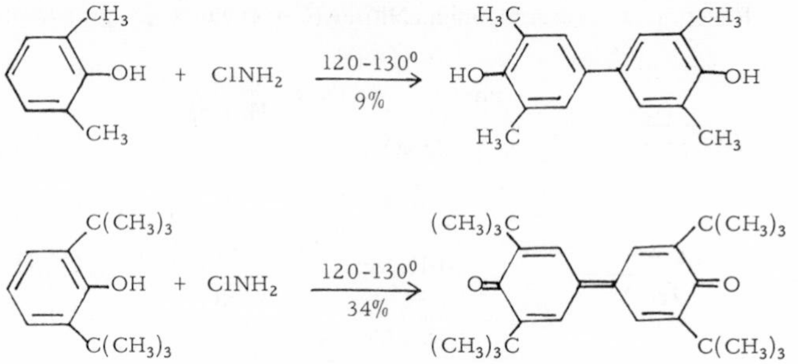

The reaction is regarded as proceeding through a radical mechanism.

Diaziridines [**1**, 124, after formula (4)]. Schmitz *et al.*[19a] found that chloramine reacts with the Schiff base derived from an aldehyde, ketone, or cyclic ketone to give a diaziridine in 20–70% yield. He presented evidence that the reaction involves direct nucleophilic addition of chloramine:

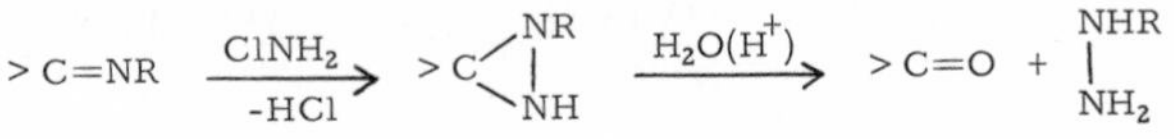

The diaziridine (1) is hydrolyzed by aqueous oxalic acid to the carbonyl compound (2) and an alkylhydrazine (3). Chloramine can be replaced by N-chloromethylamine or the N-chloro derivative of another primary aliphatic amine.[19b]

[13]Definitive paper: M. P. Cava and B. R. Vogt, *J. Org.*, **30**, 3775 (1965)

[15]*Add*: L. A. Paquette and W. C. Farley, *Am. Soc.*, **89**, 3595 (1967)

[17a]L. A. Paquette and W. C. Farley, *J. Org.*, **32**, 2718 (1967)

[19a]E. Schmitz and D. Habisch, *Ber.*, **95**, 680 (1962); E. Schmitz, *Angew. Chem., internat. Ed.*, **3**, 333 (1964)

[19b]E. Schmitz and K. Schinkowski, *Ber.*, **97**, 49 (1964)

Chloranil [**1**, 125–127].

Dehydrogenation [**1**, 127, at end.] The hydrocarbon (3) was obtained by condensation of tetraphenylcyclopentadienyl sodium (1) with tropylium bromide (2).[8a] Dehydrogenation to tetraphenylsesquifulvalene (4) was accomplished by refluxing with chloranil. An initial deep red solution deposited greenish black needles having a metallic luster, m.p. 250°, dec.

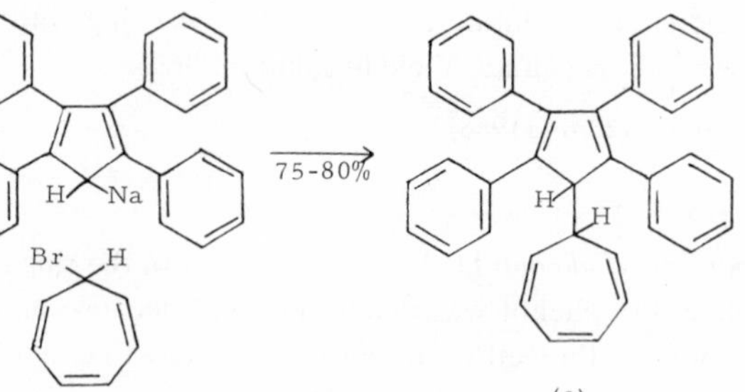

$$CCl_4 \; + \; \begin{array}{c} Cl \quad Cl \\ Cl \quad Cl \end{array}$$

$$\xrightarrow[\;64\%\;]{}$$

(4)

[8a]H. Prinzbach, D. Seip, L. Knothe, and W. Faisst, *Ann*, **698**, 34 (1966)

1-Chlorobenzotriazole (1) [**1**, 130, before **Chlorodiazomethane**] Mol. wt. 153.57, m.p. 105–106°. Supplier: A. The reagent is prepared in 90% yield by the reaction of benzotriazole in 50% aqueous acetic acid with aqueous sodium hypochlorite.[1]

This positive halogen compound oxidizes alcohols to aldehydes or ketones and hydrazo compounds to azo compounds under mild conditions and in high yields. The oxidant is converted into benzo-triazole hydrochloride. It also oxidizes 1-amino-benzotriazole to benzyne (80% yield, 2 moles of oxidant required) and 2-amino-benzotriazole to *cis,cis*-1,4-dicyanobutadiene-1,3.[1]

(1)

[1]C. W. Rees and R. E. Storr, *Chem. Commun.*, 1305 (1968)

Chlorocarbonylbis(triphenylphosphine)rhodium, $[P(C_6H_5)_3]_2Rh(CO)Cl$ [**1**, 130, before **Chlorodiazomethane**]. Mol. wt. 459.63. This is an efficient catalyst for the decarbonylation of aroyl halides to aryl halides.[1] *See also* **Tris(triphenylphosphine)-chlororhodium** (This volume).

[1]J. Tsuji and K. Ohno, *Tetrahedron Letters*, 4713 (1966)

N-Chloro-N-cyclohexylbenzenesulfonamide, $C_6H_5SO_2NClC_6H_{11}$. [**1**, 130, before **Chlorodiazomethane**]. Mol. wt. 273.78, m.p. 89°. This pseudo halogen is obtained as an oil which slowly crystallizes after digestion with petroleum ether.

Preparation.[1]

$$C_6H_5SO_2Cl \; + \; H_2NC_6H_{11} \; \xrightarrow[\text{quant.}]{Py} \; C_6H_5SO_2NHC_6H_{11} \; \xrightarrow{HClO} \; C_6H_5SO_2NClC_6H_{11}$$

Allylic chlorination.[1] The reagent is useful for chlorination of olefins; the reaction is catalyzed by benzoyl peroxide. Yields are in the range 40–80%. 1-Methyl-naphthalene is converted into 1-chloromethylnaphthalene in 63% yield.

[1]W. Theilacker and H. Wessel, *Ann.*, **703**, 34 (1967)

Chloroiridic acid and iridium trichloride [**1**, 131–132, before references]. Henbest *et al.*[1] introduced chloroiridic acid as catalyst, in combination with aqueous iso-propanol and trimethyl phosphite, for reduction of a ketone to form a high proportion of an axial alcohol. For reduction of 4-*t*-butylcyclohexanone to the *cis*-alcohol, Eliel and Doyle[2] used iridium trichloride with initially favorable results (as noted,

1, 132). Eventually, however, Eliel[3] found that "the original procedure did not work well because the commercially available iridium trichloride is not of reproducible solubility in HCl; if insoluble, it does not work." He then found that iridium tetrachloride can be substituted for the trichloride and that it "works every time." For the new procedure, *see* **Iridium tetrachloride** (this volume).

[3]E. L. Eliel, private communication

m-Chloroperbenzoic acid [1, 135–139]. Suppliers: also Aldrich.

Preparation[1a] [**1**, 135, at end]. Since a glass surface catalyzes the decomposition of the peracid, the reaction of *m*-chlorobenzoyl chloride with hydrogen peroxide in the presence of magnesium sulfate heptahydrate, aqueous sodium hydroxide, and dioxane is carried out in a polyethylene beaker (Nalgene). The product obtained contains 80–85% active oxygen.

Epoxidation [**1**, 137, after citation of ref 6]. Whereas epoxidation of an α,β-unsaturated ester usually requires a basic medium, ethyl α-phenyl-*cis*-cinnamate

(1) can be epoxidized directly with *m*-chloroperbenzoic acid in slight excess in methylene chloride.[6a]

Baeyer-Villiger oxidation [**1**, 137, after the formulation]. The acetate (2) was obtained from the methyl ketone (1) in 91% yield by oxidation with *m*-chloroper-

benzoic acid.[2a] Thus a solution of 1.0 g. of (1) in 3 ml. of chloroform was added to a stirred solution of 1.89 g. of *m*-chloroperbenzoic acid in 10 ml. of chloroform and the progress of the reaction was followed by VPC analysis; it was complete in 20 hrs. at room temperature in the dark.

Cleavage of the tetrahydrochromane, [**1**, 137, last paragraph, and **1**, 138, formulation]. This original write-up incorporated errors in a preliminary communication by I. J. Borowitz and G. Gonis, *Tetrahedron Letters*, 1151 (1964), but corrected in the definitive paper by I. J. Borowitz, G. Gonis, R. Kelsey, R. Rapp, and G. J. Williams, *J. Org.*, **31**, 3032 (1966). A corrected version of the formulation as given in *Reagents* is:

(1) $\xrightarrow[\text{51\%}]{\text{Li}-\text{C}_2\text{H}_5\text{NH}_2-(\text{CH}_3)_2\text{NH}}$ (2) $\xrightarrow[\text{30\%}]{\begin{array}{c}\text{Perphthalic}\\\text{acid}\end{array}}$ (3)

$\text{CH}_2\text{Cl}_2 \downarrow \text{ClC}_6\text{H}_4\text{CO}_3\text{H}$ $\text{Pb(OAc)}_4 \downarrow 83\%$

(4) $\xrightarrow[\text{92\%}]{\text{ArCO}_2\text{H}}$ (5)

The tetrahydrochromane (2) is oxidized by *m*-chloroperbenzoic acid to 6-ketonon-anolide (5) under carefully controlled conditions (2.8 equiv. of peracid, methylene chloride, room temperature). The reaction is postulated to involve the hydroxy peracid (4) as an intermediate which undergoes fragmentation. Use of perphthalic acid gives the glycol (3), which on cleavage with lead tetraacetate gives (5).

3-Phenyl-2-n-alkyloxaziridines can be prepared in yields of more than 60% by oxidation of imines by *m*-chloroperbenzoic acid.[6b] The use of peracetic acid in this case is usually unsuccessful.

$$\text{C}_6\text{H}_5\text{CH}=\text{NR} \longrightarrow \text{C}_6\text{H}_5\text{CH}\text{—NR}$$

[1a]R. N. McDonald, R. N. Steppel, and J. E. Dorsay, procedure submitted to *Org. Syn.*, 1968
[2a]J. Meinwald, J. J. Tufariello, and J. J. Hurst, *J. Org.*, **29**, 2914 (1964)
[6a]V. R. Valente and J. L. Wolfhagen, *ibid.*, **31**, 2509 (1966)
[6b]R. G. Pews, *ibid.*, **32**, 1628 (1967)

N-Chlorosuccinimide [**1**, 139, before references].

Chlorination. In a study of the monochlorination of 1,3-dihydro-2H-azepine-2-ones (parent system, **1**), Paquette[4] found that N-chlorosuccinimide gives higher yields than other chlorinating agents, *t*-butyl hypochlorite, chloramine, and chlorine.

(1)   (2) $\xrightarrow[\text{95\%}]{\text{NCS, CH}_2\text{Cl}_2}$ (3)

The site of chlorination in these cyclic dienamides is at C_4 or C_6 depending on the substitution at N, C_3, or C_7. The related 2-pyridone (2) gives 5-chloro-2-pyridone (3) in 95% yield. Paquette considers that direct electrophilic substitution is the most probable pathway and notes that the position of chlorination is consistent with Hine's principle of least motion,[5] which states that "those elementary reactions will be favored that involve the least change in atomic position and electronic configuration."

[4]L. A. Paquette and W. C. Farley, *J. Org.*, **32**, 2725 (1967)
[5]J. Hine, *ibid.*, **31**, 1236 (1966)

Chlorosulfonic acid [1, 140–141, before references].

Ester decarbonylation. When ethyl 1,2-dimethylcyclopropene-3-carboxylate (1) is dissolved in chlorosulfonic acid (or fluorosulfuric acid) at room temperature, carbon monoxide is evolved and the dimethylcyclopropenium ion (2) is formed in

nearly quantitative yield as judged by the NMR.[6] This procedure is simpler than and superior to the use of perchloric acid, originally suggested for the preparation of the diphenylcyclopropenium ion.[7]

[6]D. G. Farnum, G. Mehta, and R. G. Silberman, *Am. Soc.*, **89**, 5048 (1967)
[7]D. G. Farnum and M. Burr, *ibid.*, **82**, 2651 (1960)

Chlorosulfonyl isocyanate, $ClSO_2NCO$ **[1**, 140 before **Chlorotris(triphenylphosphine)-rhodium**]. Mol. wt. 141.54, b.p. 54–56°/100 mm. Suppliers: A, Hoechst.

Caution: The isocyanate is highly corrosive and reacts violently with water.

Preparation.[1]

Synthesis of nitriles.[2] The reagent reacts with aromatic hydrocarbons that under-go ready electrophilic substitution (e.g., anthracene) to give carboxamine-N-sulfo-chlorides. These are converted into nitriles by loss of SO_3 and HCl when treated

with DMF. The reagent also reacts with acids to give carboxamine-N-sulfochlorides as shown by the reaction with cinnamic acid.

[1]R. Graf, *Org. Syn.*, **46**, 23 (1966)
[2]G. Lohaus, *Ber*, **100**, 2719 (1967); *idem*; procedure submitted to *Org. Syn.*, 1968

Chromic acid [1, 142–144].

Jones reagent **[1**, 143, after citation of ref. 7] Lavie *et al.*[7a] treated the steroidal lactone (1) with the Jones reagent expecting to obtain the corresponding enone. In-stead they obtained the epoxy diketone (2). The same product was also obtained from the isomeric allylic alcohol (3). Further investigation established that epoxi-dation occurs only if the hydroxyl group is axial, and if the oxidation is slower than

(1)   (2)   (3)

epoxidation of the double bond. The epoxidation reaction is stereospecific; it gives a product with the epoxide group on the same side of the molecule as the hydroxyl group.

Two-phase oxidation [1, 143, last paragraph]. Allylic alcohols (1) are oxidized to the corresponding vinyl ketones (2) in acceptable yields by the procedure of Brown and Garg.[11] A 30–40% excess of oxidant is required because of concurrent oxidation at the double bond.[11a] The Jones reagent is less satisfactory.

The two-phase system has been used for selective oxidation of an alkylborane group in the presence of a double bond.[11b] Thus the cyclic diene (3) was treated with 1 equiv. of diborane to give the alkylborane (4), which was then oxidized by aqueous chromic acid–diethyl ether to give 8-cyclohexadecene-1-one (5), a musk compound.

(3)   (4)   (5)

Oxidation in the presence of manganous nitrate, $Mn(NO_3)_2$ [1, 144, before references]. The oxidation of the secondary-tertiary *vic*-glycol (1) by chromic acid

(1)   (2)

in acetic acid-water containing some sulfuric acid leads predominantly to cleavage to the 17-ketone (74%). However, if manganous nitrate is added cortisone acetate (2) can be obtained as the predominant product.[15]

[7a]E. Glotter, S. Greenfield, and D. Lavie, *J. Chem. Soc.*, (C), 1646 (1968)
[11a]A. E. Vanstone and J. S. Whitehurst, *ibid.*, (C), 1972 (1966)
[11b]L. G. Wideman, *J. Org.*, **33**, 4541 (1968)
[15]B. H. Walker, *ibid.*, **32**, 1098 (1967)

Chromic anhydride [**1**, 144–147].

Aqueous acetic acid (preparative procedures) [**1**, 145, after (d)].

(e) In what apparently is the first example of the oxidative cleavage of a ditertiary 1,2-diglycol to a diketone, Uskokovic *et al.*[4a] treated the substrate, a *D*-homo-17α, 17aα-diol (1), in 80% aqueous acetic acid–methylene chloride with chromic anhydride and shook the two-phase system at room temperature for 72 hrs., when the acetic acid layer had a violet color. The diketone (2) was isolated from the methylene chloride solution.

(1) 100 mg.   (2) 45 mg.

Aqueous acetic acid (rate of oxidation) [**1**, 145, after citation of ref. 5]. Roček and Westheimer[5a] reported that the oxidation of *cis*-1,2-dimethyl-1,2-cyclopentanediol (1) by chromic acid in water or 90% acetic acid to 2,6-heptanedione (2) is much faster than oxidation of the *trans* isomer (3). In water the oxidation of (1) to (2) is 17,000

(1)   (2)   (3)

times faster than that of the *trans* isomer; in 90% acetic acid the factor is 800. They suggest that the *cis*-diol forms a cyclic ester with chromic acid and that the rate-determining step is decomposition of this ester. The *trans* isomer presumably is oxidized by a noncyclic mechanism.

Anhydrous CrO₃-Acetic acid (Fieser reagent) [**1**, 145, after citation of ref. 8]. The protection of an alcohol group by conversion into the methyl ether is a reaction of limited synthetic utility owing to the low yields generally encountered in the subsequent ether-cleavage reaction. Workers at Syntex Research Institute[8a] found that Fieser's anhydrous chromium trioxide in acetic acid converts a methyl ether into the corresponding formate, hydrolyzable by base to the alcohol, in yields of 50–60%. For example, hexadecyl methyl ether (I, 200 mg.) oxidized by a suspension of chromium trioxide (1 g.) in a mixture of acetic acid (10 ml.) and methylene chloride (10 ml.) for 1 hr. at 20° gave, after chromatography on silica gel, hexadecyl formate (II) in 48% yield.

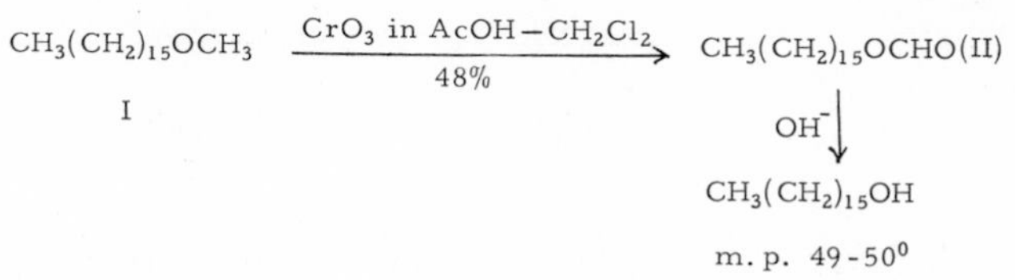
CH3(CH2)15OCH3
I
CrO3 in AcOH–CH2Cl2
48%
CH3(CH2)15OCHO(II)
OH⁻
CH3(CH2)15OH
m. p. 49-50°

In another example the steroid 3-methyl ether (III) is cleaved by oxidation after first protecting the double bond by bromination.

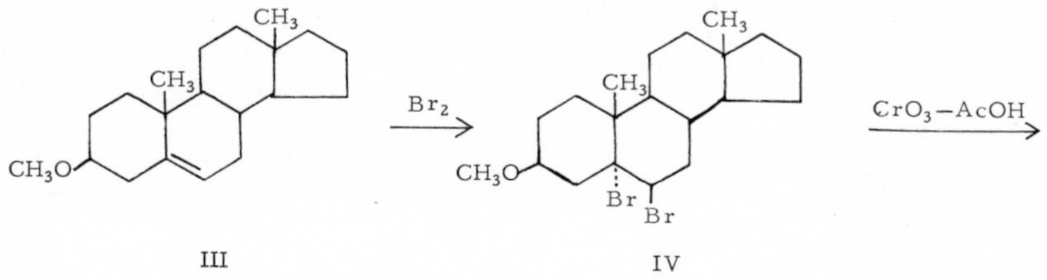
CH3
CH3
CH3O
Br2
Br
Br
CrO3–AcOH
III
IV

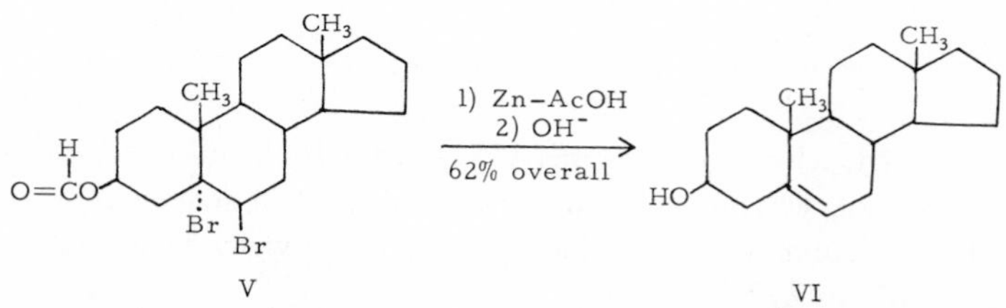
CH3
CH3
H
O=CO
Br
Br
1) Zn–AcOH
2) OH⁻
62% overall
HO
V
VI

Boekelheide and Phillips[8b] achieved the synthesis of the interesting *trans*-15,16-dimethyldihydropyrene (17) and found that by all criteria, including both spectral properties and chemical reactivity, this hydrocarbon having substituents within the cavity of the $(4n+2)$ electron cloud is an aromatic molecule. In their synthesis, indicated briefly in the formulation, one *meta* link between two molecules of (8) is established by reaction with magnesium in the presence of ferric chloride to produce the bibenzyl derivative (9). Reaction of the diiodide (14) with finely divided sodium and tetraphenylethylene in tetrahydrofurane establishes the second *meta* link

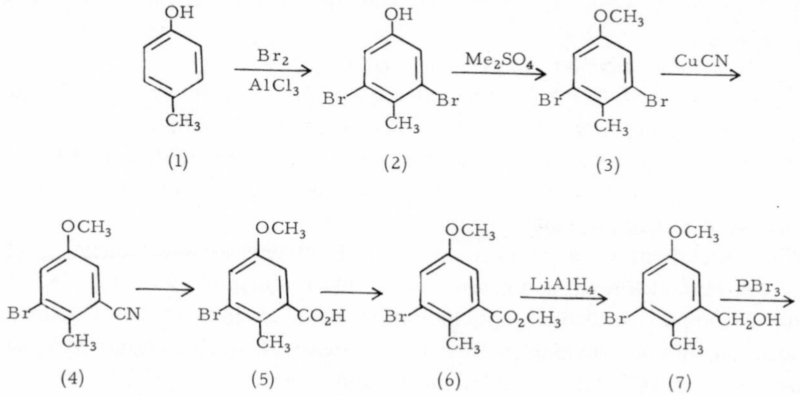
OH
CH3
(1)
Br2
AlCl3
Br
Br
(2)
Me2SO4
OCH3
(3)
CuCN
CN
(4)
CO2H
(5)
CO2CH3
(6)
LiAlH4
CH2OH
(7)
PBr3

(8) → (9) → (10) X = CN

(11) CH$_2$N$_2$
(12) CH$_2$OH
(13) CH$_2$Br
(14) CH$_2$I
} X

Na
(C$_6$H$_5$)$_2$C=C(C$_6$H$_5$)$_2$

(15)
(a) FeCl$_3$-CHCl$_3$ (93%)
(b) CrO$_3$-CH$_3$COCH$_3$
(100%)
(16)
Several steps
(17)

to give the tricyclic dimethyl ether (15). This 8,16-dimethyl-5,13-dimethoxy[2.2]-metacyclophane was obtained initially in the 14-step sequence in yield of 1.9%, but a shorter and more convenient route was found which in ten steps afforded (15) in overall yield of 5.1%.

Then another difficulty arose: Application to the diether (15) of usual methods of demethylation proved ineffective. However, accumulating NMR evidence made it clear that the synthetic goal was near, and so further attempts to cleave the methoxyl groups of (15) were monitored by testing the reaction mixture for ferric chloride-phenol color. It was soon found that ferric chloride demethylates the bis-dienone in high yield! With anhydrous reagent in chloroform solution a yield of 93% can be realized (this reaction was cited on **1**, 391). Of other oxidizing agents tried, chromic acid effects the conversion in quantitative yield at room temperature.

The oxidative demethylation of methyl ethers by ferric chloride is probably limited to cases where a concomitant coupling reaction occurs as in the given example.

CrO$_3$-pyridine complex (Sarett reagent) [**1**, 145–146, after citation of ref. 11]. Collins, Hess, and Frank[11a] prepared the complex essentially according to the original procedure of Sarett, but continued stirring the yellow form at 15° until it was converted into a deep red macrocrystalline form (polymorphism?) that could be washed with petroleum ether, filtered, and dried at 10 mm. This form can be stored with protection from moisture. The use of various solvents was explored and chlorocarbons were found to be superior solvents for the reagent. Excellent yields of both aldehydes and ketones were obtained merely by mixing a 6:1 mole-ratio of complex to alcohol in dichloromethane at 25° in 5–15 min. Cholesterol is oxidized to Δ^5-cholestenone (64% yield) together with small amounts of Δ^4-choles-tene-3,6-dione (10%) and Δ^4-cholestene-3β-ol-6-one(8%).

The reagent has been found capable of oxidizing steroidal tertiary amines to N-formyl derivatives, in some cases in good yield.[11b] Such an oxidation may be of

preparative interest when it leads to an N-formyl derivative hydrolyzable to a secondary amine.

[4a]M. Uskokovic, M. Gut, E. N. Trachtenberg, W. Klyne, and R. I. Dorfman, *Am. Soc.*, **82**, 4965 (1960)

[5a]J. Roček and F. H. Westheimer, *ibid.*, **84**, 2241 (1962)

[8a]I. T. Harrison and S. Harrison, *Chem. Commun.*, 752 (1966)

[8b]V. Boekelheide and J. B. Phillips, *Am. Soc.*, **85**, 1545 (1963); **89**, 1695 (1967)

[11a]J. C. Collins, W. W. Hess, and F. J. Frank, *Tetrahedron Letters*, 3363 (1968)

[11b]A. Cavé, C. Kan-Fan, P. Potier, J. Le Men, and M.-M. Janot, *Tetrahedron*, **23**, 4691 (1967)

Chromous acetate [1, 147–149].

Deiodination of an iodoketone [**1**, 148, after formulas (4)–(6)]. A variety of conditions (irradiation, catalytic hydrogenation) were useless for deiodination of

the iodolactone (7). The desired reduction was accomplished satisfactorily by the method of Barton and Basu[2,5] using chromous ion in DMSO in the presence of ethanethiol. The reaction occurs with inversion.[5a]

Reductive dehalogenation [**1**, 149, before references]. Reduction of 1,2,3,4,7,7-hexachloro-5-*endo*-acetoxybicyclo[2.2.1]-2-heptene (1) with chromous acetate

leads mainly to replacement of the chlorine atom *anti* to the double bond to give
(2) in 78% yield.[7] The same preference is shown in zinc-acetic acid reduction, but

(1)   (2) 78%   (3) 18%

in this case the reaction is not so clean since four products are obtained. Reaction
with palladium on charcoal leads to reduction and dechlorination of the vinyl system.

[5a]M. D. Bachi, J. W. Epstein, Y. Herzberg-Minzly, and H. J. E. Loewenthal, *J. Org.*, **34**,
126 (1969)

[7]K. L. Williamson, Y. F. L. Hsu, and E. I. Young, *Tetrahedron*, **24**, 6007 (1968)

Chromous chloride [1, 149–150].

Reduction [**1**, 150, after formula (4)]. Reduction of a 9α-bromo-11β-acetoxy-
$\Delta^{1,4}$-3-ketosteroid with chromous chloride does not lead to the expected 1,4,9(11)-
triene, but rather to a 5,9-cyclosteroid:[10a]

Treatment of 6-nitrocholesteryl acetate with 8 equivalents of 0.1 N chromous
chloride in refluxing tetrahydrofurane under nitrogen (3 hrs.) gives the oxime of
3β-acetoxy-5α-hydroxy-6-ketocholestane.[10b]

[**1**, 150, after formula (6)]: When 5α-chloro-6β-nitrocholestane-3β-ol (7) is
reduced with 4 equivalents of chromous chloride in refluxing THF, the corresponding 5α-hydroxy-6-oxime (10) is obtained in 86% yield.[11a] Intermediates (8) and (9)
are postulated; the mechanism predicts the *anti* arrangement of the 5-OH and of the
oxime-OH.

Elimination of an acetoxyl group [**1**, 150, before references]. In an efficient new
synthesis of $\Delta^{4,6}$-3-keto-19-norsteroids Kalvoda and Anner[13] oxidized (1) to the 10-
acetoxysteroid (2) by means of lead tetraacetate and calcium carbonate. The 10-
acetoxy group was eliminated by treatment with chromous chloride in acetic acid

to give (3), which was isomerized by short warming in acetic acid to give the 19-nordienone (4). Reduction of (2) with zinc dust gave a nonhomogeneous product.

[10a]C. H. Robinson, O. Gnoj, E. P. Oliveto, and D. H. R. Barton, *J. Org.*, **31**, 2749 (1966)
[10b]J. R. Hanson and E. Premuzic, *Tetrahedron Letters*, 5441 (1966)
[11a]J. R. Hanson and E. Premuzic, *Tetrahedron*, **23**, 4105 (1967)
[13]J. Kalvoda and G. Anner, *Helv.*, **50**, 269 (1967)

Chromous sulfate [1, 150–151].

Preparation [**1**, 150]. In an improved procedure[3] 300 g. of hydrous chromium sulfate is mixed with 2 l. of water, 75 g. of mossy zinc, and 4 ml. of mercury and stirred in a stream of nitrogen and warmed for about 30 hrs. until the originally green solution is converted into a clear, deep sky blue. Filtration is thus eliminated.

Reduction [**1**, 151]. α,β-Unsaturated esters, acids, and nitriles are reduced, usually to give equal amounts of *meso* and *dl* products. The reductions are carried out in homogeneous mixtures of water and DMF. Example:[4]

Certain olefins are also reduced at room temperature by the reagent in aqueous

DMF. Tetrasubstituted olefins are reduced to an equal mixture of *meso-* and *dl-*alkanes. On the other hand, dimethyl 2,3-dimethylmaleate is reduced entirely in a *cis* fashion to yield dimethyl *meso-*2,3-dimethylsuccinate. A number of unsaturated compounds were found to be inert (e.g., ethyl cinnamate, isoprene, styrene).

[3]C. E. Castro, procedure submitted to *Org. Syn.*, 1968
[4]A. Zurqiyah and C. E. Castro, *ibid.*; *see also* C. E. Castro, R. D. Stephens, and S. Mojé, *Am. Soc.*, **88**, 4964 (1966)

Chromyl acetate [**1**, 151, before references].

In investigations of the photoisomerization of *cis,cis*-1,5-cyclooctadiene (1), Srinivasan[3] had characterized a transformation product as the interesting tricyclo-[3.3.0.0^{2,6}]octane (2) and raised the yield from 1% to about 30%. In investigating the oxidation of the hydrocarbon with chromyl acetate, Meinwald and Kaplan[4] effected a further increase in yield to about 50%. The oxidizing agent was prepared by adding 40 g. of chromic anhydride to a mixture of 200 ml. each of acetic acid and acetic anhydride, stirring for 1 hr., and then cooling to 0°, adding the hydrocarbon to be oxidized, and stirring at 0–3°. Workup included dilution with water, heating to 100°, addition of enough sodium hydroxide solution to neutralize 90% of the acetic acid, and exhaustive extraction with ether.

3,5-Cycloandrostane (5) is oxidized by this reagent to the three ketones shown (30% of the starting material was recovered).[5] The same three products were ob-

tained in a total yield of 20% when chromic anhydride was used. Only a few examples of oxidation α to a cyclopropane ring have been reported.

The oxidation of alkenes with chromyl acetate has been reviewed by Wiberg.[6]

3β-Acetoxy-5α,6β-dichloroandrostanone-17 (9) is oxidized by chromyl acetate to the corresponding 14α-hydroxy compound (10) in 25% yield.[7] This method is superior to oxidation with chromic anhydride, a method introduced by André et al.[8] The latter reagent apparently requires catalysis by hydrogen bromide or perchloric acid.

[3]R. Srinivasan, Am. Soc., **85**, 3048 (1963); **86**, 3318 (1964)
[4]J. Meinwald and B. E. Kaplan, ibid., **89**, 2611 (1967)
[5]R. Beugelmans and R. Toubiana, Compt. rend., **264** (C), 343 (1967)
[6]K. B. Wiberg, "Oxidation in Organic Chemistry, Part A," 131–135 Academic Press, New York, 1965
[7]P. J. Sykes and R. W. Kelly, J. Chem. Soc., (C), 2346 (1968)
[8]A. F. St. André, H. B. MacPhillamy, J. A. Nelson, A. C. Shabica, and C. R. Scholz, Am. Soc., **74**, 5506 (1952)

Chromyl chloride [1, 151–152]. Suppliers: for Alfa, read Alfa Inorganics.

[1, 152, before references]: The reaction takes a different course with 2,4,4-trimethyl-1-pentene (1), a terminal alkene.[8] The hydrocarbon (Aldrich; Phillips) is

dissolved in methylene chloride that has been pretreated with the reagent, reagent is added, the mixture is stirred at 0–5°, and then treated with zinc dust to decompose a complex. The product is 4,4-dimethyl-2-neopentylpentanal (3).

2,3-Dimethyl-2-butene is oxidized to pinacolone in 50% yield.

Chromyl chloride oxidation of tetraphenylethylene (4) results in cyclization to give 9,10-diphenylphenanthrene (5) in 70% yield.[9] The major product of the oxidation of 1,1,2,2-tetraphenylethanol by chromyl chloride is also (5).[10]

(4)   (5)

[8]F. Freeman, P. J. Cameron, and R. H. DuBois, J. Org., **33**, 3970 (1968); F. Freeman and R. H. DuBois, procedure submitted to Org. Syn., 1968
[9]A. L. Gatzke, R. A. Stairs, and D. G. M. Diaper, Canad. J. Chem., **46**, 3695 (1968)
[10]C. D. Nenitzescu, Bull. soc., 1349 (1968)

Cobalt (II) acetate, $Co(OCOCH_3)_2$ [**1**, 154 before **Cobalt acetate bromide**]. Mol. wt. 201.05. Supplier: Alfa Inorganics.

Oxidative cleavage of 1,2-diols. The reagent catalyzes the cleavage of 1,2-glycols by oxygen in an aprotic, polar solvent (benzonitrile, DMF, sulfolane). Yields of aldehydes are 60–81%. Further oxidation to carboxylic acids is possible.[1]

$$C_8H_{17}\underset{\underset{OH}{|}}{CH}CH_2OH \xrightarrow{\;O_2\;} C_8H_{17}COOH \;+\; CH_2O \;+\; H_2O$$

[1]G. de Vries and A. Schors, *Tetrahedron Letters*, 5689 (1968)

Cobalt hydrocarbonyl [**1**, 154–155, before references].

In the hydroformylation of 1-pentene with cobalt hydrocarbonyl, addition of benzonitrile greatly enhances the yield of aldehyde; various other nucleophiles were less effective.[4] In addition, benzonitrile suppresses isomerization of 1-pentene to 2-pentene.

[4]L. Roos and M. Orchin, *J. Org.*, **31**, 3015 (1966)

Copoly(ethylene-N-hydroxymaleimide), II [**1**, 155, before **Copper–Ascorbic acid**].
Introduced by Blout *et al.*[1] for use in peptide synthesis, the reagent is prepared as shown in Chart I by condensing copoly(ethylenemaleic anhydride) (I, Monsanto DX840) with hydroxylamine hydrochloride in DMF. BOC-α-amino derivatives of alanine, phenylalanine, threonine, methionine, leucine, etc., were synthesized in

Chart I. Preparation and Reactions of Copoly(ethylene-N-hydroxymaleimide) in Peptide Synthesis

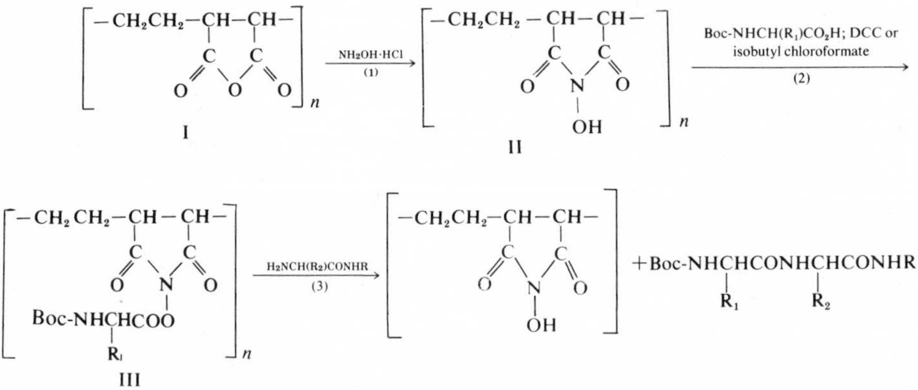

yields of *ca.* 70% by either the mixed anhydride or the DCC method. Then polymeric NHS (N-hydroxysuccinimide) esters (III) were used as intermediates in the synthesis of peptides in ethyl acetate solution. Insoluble by-products were removed by filtration or centrifugation, and flash evaporation of the supernatant gave chromatographically pure peptides.

[1]D. A. Loufer, T. M. Chapman, D. I. Marlborough, V. M. Vaidya, and E. R. Blout, *Am. Soc.*, **90**, 2696 (1968)

Copper (II) acetylacetonate, $Cu(C_5H_7O_2)_2 \cdot H_2O$ [1, before **Copper–Ascorbic acid**]. Supplier: Alfa Inorganics.

Decomposition of azo compounds to carbenes (*see also* **Diazoacetaldehyde**, this volume). Huisgen[1] was able to stabilize benzoylcarbene (generated from diazoacetophenone) sufficiently to observe 1,3-dipolar cycloadditions by addition of various copper compounds, of which copper (I) cyanide and copper (II) acetylacetonate appeared to be the most effective.

Japanese chemists[2] have also reported cases in which the addition of the copper chelate modifies the reactions of carbenes. Thus diphenylcarbene (thermal decomposition of diphenyldiazomethane, 1) is converted mainly into benzophenone azine (2) when generated in an aprotic medium and into 1,1,2,2-tetraphenylethane (3) when generated in a protic medium. The second reaction is considered to proceed by abstraction of hydrogen from the solvent to form benzhydryl radicals which then

dimerize. When the carbene is generated in the presence of copper powder in a protic or aprotic medium, the azine (2) is the main product. When the copper chelate is present, (3) is completely absent, and the azine and tetraphenylethylene (4) are the two products, the ratios depending on the solvent. The Japanese investigators

suggest that the effect of the copper chelate is due to coordination of the diazoalkane as a fifth ligand to give a complex which decomposes to a carbene-copper complex, which then gives the observed reactions.

[1] R. Huisgen, G. Binsch, and L. Ghosez, *Ber.*, **97**, 2628 (1964)
[2] H. Nozaki, H. Takaya, S. Moriuti, and R. Noyori, *Tetrahedron*, **24**, 3655 (1968)

Copper chromite, $Cu_2Cr_2O_5$ (or, more commonly, $2\ CuO \cdot Cr_2O_3$) [1, 156–157].

Dr. S. L. Stafford (Alfa Inorganics) writes that "I am unable to tell the difference from the method of preparation between the Lazier catalysts and the Adkins catalysts. They seem to be essentially identical and both are made in the same way as the material which we offer. Our copper chromate is a fine black powder of the formula indicated plus small amounts of barium chromate which may or may not be essential as the activator. The catalyst is stable to both air and moisture."

A similar catalyst is also supplied by Girdler Catalysts, Chemical Products Division, Chemetron Corp., Louisville, Kentucky 40201.

Copper powder [1, 157–158].

[After citation of ref. 4]: Pelletier and Hawley [4a] worked out a procedure for the large-scale preparation of 2-furoic acid involving the synthesis of furanetetracarboxylic acid from Eastman's diethyl oxaloacetate and decarboxylation with Baker's copper powder and quinoline in a nitrogen atmosphere.

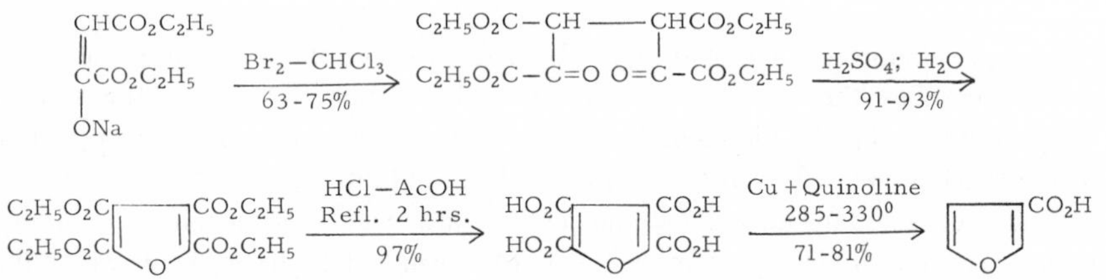

Diazoketones [1, 158, before references]. Šorm[9] found that an α-diazoketone decomposes in the presence of copper bronze to give an intermediate which reacts with an olefin to produce a ketocyclopropane:

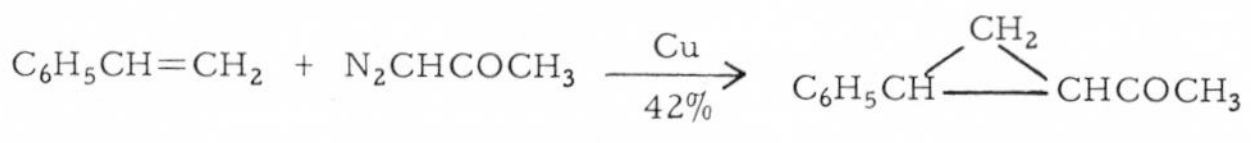

Stork and Ficini[10] found that intramolecular cyclization of α-diazoketones furnishes interesting possibilities for synthesis: thus (1) was cyclized in good yield to bicyclo-[4.1.0]heptanone-2 (2) in good yield:

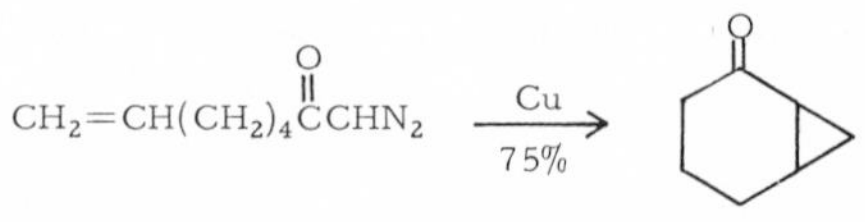

$$CH_2=CH(CH_2)_4\overset{\overset{\text{O}}{\|}}{C}CHN_2 \xrightarrow[75\%]{Cu}$$

(1)   (2)

Doering et al.[11] extended this application to the synthesis of tricyclic ketones from monocyclic diazoketones, using as catalyst copper powder, cupric sulfate, or cuprous iodide with apparently equal success. A sketchy advance report,[12] claims the synthesis of 8,9-dehydroadamantane-2-one (5, m.p. 206.5–207.5°) via the acid chlorides (3) and (4) and the derived diazoketones.

Fawzi and Gutsche[13] examined the intramolecular cyclization of a series of olefinic diazoketones of structure (6) and found that the highest yields were obtained when $n = 2$ and consequently concluded that the proximity of the double bond to the

diazoalkyl group is important. The reaction is applicable also to unsaturated esters of diazoacetic acid (8), and in this instance House and Blankley noted[14] that the de-

composition exhibits an induction period during which an active copper catalyst probably is formed.

Monahan[15] used the intramolecular cyclization of diazoketones to prepare the highly hindered 1,5,6-triphenyltricyclo[3.1.0.0²,⁶]hexane-3-one (13) from 1-(1,2,3-triphenylcycloprop-2-enyl)-3-diazopropane-2-one (12). The starting material was prepared by the reaction of triphenylcyclopropenyl bromide (10) with ethyl bromo-acetate to give (11) followed by conversion to the diazoketone (12) by standard procedures. Cyclization to (13) was carried out in 57% yield with copper powder in refluxing benzene under nitrogen.

[4a]S. W. Pelletier and L. B. Hawley, Jr., procedure submitted to *Org. Syn.*, 1967
[9]F. Šorm *et al.*, *Coll. Czech.*, **22**, 1836 (1957); **23**, 467, 1126 (1958)
[10]G. Stork and J. Ficini, *Am. Soc.*, **83**, 4678 (1961)
[11]W. von E. Doering, E. T. Fossel, and R. L. Kaye, *Tetrahedron*, **21**, 25 (1965)
[12]J. E. Baldwin and W. D. Fogelsong, *Tetrahedron Letters*, 4089 (1966)
[13]M. M. Fawzi and C. D. Gutsche, *J. Org.*, **31**, 1390 (1966)
[14]H. O. House and C. J. Blankley, *ibid.*, **33**, 53 (1968)
[15]A. S. Monahan, *ibid.*, **33**, 1441 (1968)

Cupric acetate [**1**, 159, before references].

Cupric acetate (anhydrous) markedly catalyzes the oxidative decarboxylation of carboxylic acids by lead tetraacetate to alkenes:[7]

$$C_6H_5CH_2(CH_2)_3CO_2H \ + \ Pb(OAc)_4 \ \xrightarrow[65\%]{Cu(OAc)_2} \ C_6H_5CH_2CH=CH_2 \ + \ CO_2 \ +$$

$$Pb(OAc)_2 \ + \ 2 \ CuOAc$$

In the absence of the catalyst, only decarboxylation was observed but the alkane was not obtained in good yield and high purity.

Under catalysis by cupric acetate monohydrate, air oxidation of phenylacetylene and a secondary amine can be effected to give ynamines.[8]

$$C_6H_5C\equiv CH + HN(CH_3)_2 \ \xrightarrow[\text{ca. }40\%]{\substack{Cu(OAc)_2, \ O_2 \\ \text{benzene}}} \ C_6H_5C\equiv C-N(CH_3)_2$$

[7]J. D. Bacha and J. K. Kochi, *Tetrahedron*, **24**, 2215 (1968)
[8]L. I. Peterson, *Tetrahedron Letters* 5357 (1968)

Cupric bromide [**1**, 161–162].

Bromination of carbonyl compounds [**1**, 162, end of first paragraph]. Jemison[8a] has reported instances in which nuclear bromination of several aryl methyl ketones predominates over side chain bromination.

[8a]R. W. Jemison, *Australian J. Chem.*, **21**, 217 (1968)

Cupric chloride [**1**, 163, before references].

Oxidation of hydrazo compounds. In an improved synthesis of bicyclo[2.1.0]-cyclopentane (6) from the Diels-Alder adduct (1) of cyclopentadiene and diethyl azodicarboxylate (**1**, 245), Gassman and Mansfield[4] hydrogenated (1) to (2), hydro-

(1)

(2)   (3)

(4)   (5)   (6)

+ N≡N

lyzed the diester with potassium hydroxide in ethylene glycol, and stirred a solution of the product (3) into 2 N cupric chloride solution. The blue-green color of the cupric chloride was rapidly discharged and a brick red coloration appeared, followed by precipitation of bright red crystals of the cuprous ligand of 2,3-diazobicyclo-[2.2.1]heptene-2 (4). Treatment with sodium hydroxide liberated the free azo compound (5) and, in the completing step, (5) on pyrolysis lost nitrogen to form (6).

Halogenation of ketones. Kochi[5] reported that acetone reacts with cupric chloride in aqueous acetone in the presence of lithium chloride (which increases the rate of reaction) according to the equation:

$$2\ CuCl_2\ +\ CH_3COCH_3\ \longrightarrow\ 2\ CuCl\ +\ ClCH_2COCH_3\ +\ HCl$$

Kosower[6] developed the reaction into a useful preparative procedure for chlorination of ketones. DMF was chosen as solvent; it is a good solvent for organic compounds and inorganic salts and it neutralizes the hydrogen chloride formed (which decreases the reaction rate). The chlorination of propiophenone is typical:

$$C_6H_5COCH_2CH_3\ +\ 2\ CuCl_2\ \xrightarrow[\substack{\text{LiCl (1.8 m.)}\\ \text{DMF(900 ml.)}\\ \text{72\% pure}}]{}\ C_6H_5COCHClCH_3$$

1. 5 m.   3. 6 m.

Cyclic α,β-unsaturated ketones, for example 2-cyclohexenone, are usually converted into phenols, but acyclic unsaturated ketones can be chlorinated:

$$CH_2{=}CHCOCH_3\ \longrightarrow\ CH_2{=}CClCOCH_3$$

Phenol is chlorinated to a mixture of *p*- and *o*-chlorophenol, with the para isomer definitely preferred (6:1 to 10:1).

Johnson[7] used this procedure for chlorination of the dione (1).

(1)   (2)

Oxidative ring closure. Wynberg and co-workers[8,9] at the University of Gronin-gen synthesized all six of the cyclopentadithiophenes, that is, analogs of fluorene (m.p. 116–117°) in which both benzene rings are replaced by thiophene rings. The synthesis of one of the six isomers (4) is summarized as follows. 3,3′-Dithienyl-

(1)   (2)

(3)   (4)

carbinol (1) on reduction with lithium aluminum hydride and aluminum chloride in ether afforded dithienylmethane (2) in 88% yield. Addition of a CCl_4 solution of (2) to aqueous bromine caused rapid decolorization and gave the 3,3′-thienylmethane (3, m.p. 43°). The dibromide (3) was converted by metal-halogen interchange followed by intramolecular oxidative coupling into (4), 4*H*-cyclopenta-[2.1-b:3.4-b′]-dithiophene. The oxidative ring closure method worked well in all other instances tried.

Coupling of 9-methoxy-10-methylanthracene.[10] Both cupric chloride and cupric bromide convert 9-methoxy-10-methylanthracene (1) into the coupled product (4). It is suggested that the reaction proceeds by attack on the methyl group to give

(1)   (2)   (3)

(4)

the radical (2) which dimerizes to (3). Partial demethylation by the hydrogen halide and ketonization give the coupled product (4).

[4]P. G. Gassman and K. T. Mansfield, procedure submitted to *Org. Syn.*, 1966
[5]J. K. Kochi, *Am. Soc.*, **77**, 5274 (1955)
[6]E. M. Kosower, W. J. Cole, G.-S. Wu, D. E. Cardy, and G. Meisters, *J. Org.*, **28**, 630 (1963); E. M. Kosower and G.-S. Wu, *ibid.*, **28**, 633 (1963)
[7]W. S. Johnson, K. Wiedhaup, S. F. Brady, and G. L. Olsen, *Am. Soc.*, **90**, 5277 (1968); *see also* W. S. Johnson, T. Li, D. J. Faulkner, and S. F. Campbell, *ibid.*, **90**, 6225 (1968)
[8]H. Wynberg and A. Kraak, *J. Org.*, **29**, 2455 (1964)
[9]A. Kraak, A. K. Wiersema, P. Jordens, and H. Wynberg, *Tetrahedron*, **24**, 3381 (1968)
[10]D. C. Nonhebel and J. A. Russell, *Chem. Ind.*, 1841 (1968)

Cupric chloride (bromide)–Nitric oxide, $CuX_2 \cdot 2H_2O$–NO [**1**, 163, before **Cupric nitrate–Acetic anhydride**]. The one-step displacement of a primary aromatic amino group by chlorine or bromine can be achieved as follows:[1]

$$ArNH_2 + CuCl_2 \cdot NO \longrightarrow ArCl + 2\,CuCl + H_2O + N_2$$

A solution of the amine in acetonitrile is added to a solution of cupric chloride (bromide) in acetonitrile under an atmosphere of NO at room temperature. Yields generally are in the range 30–90%. The reaction is, in effect, a one-step Sandmeyer reaction. Ice cooling is not required.

[1]W. Brackman and P. J. Smit, *Rec. trav.*, **85**, 857 (1966)

Cupric nitrate–Acetic anhydride [bottom of **1**, 163].

Sondheimer *et al.*[4] have used this reagent to effect electrophilic substitution of annulenes. Thus 1,8-bisdehydro[14]annulene (1) on nitration with cupric nitrate in acetic anhydride at room temperature was attacked at the position adjacent to the triple bond to yield the 3-mononitro compound (2) as black needles which on heating

(1)   (2)

decomposed above 200°. Of more significance is the finding that [18]annulene (3) can be nitrated by this reagent,[5] because nitration under the usual conditions is unsuccessful. The new method of nitration was applied also to 1,6-oxido[10]annulene

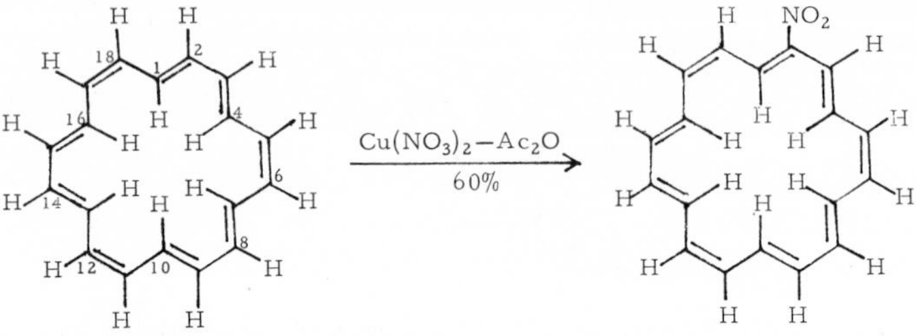

[18]Annulene
(3)

Nitro[18]annulene
(4)

(10),[6] an interesting compound available from naphthalene by sodium–ammonia reduction to (6), selective monoepoxidation (7), bromination (8), and dehydro-

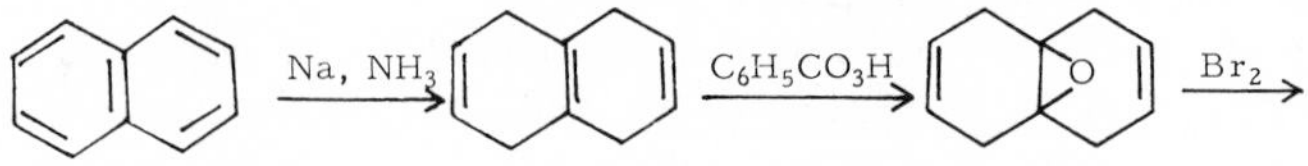

(5)   (6)   (7)

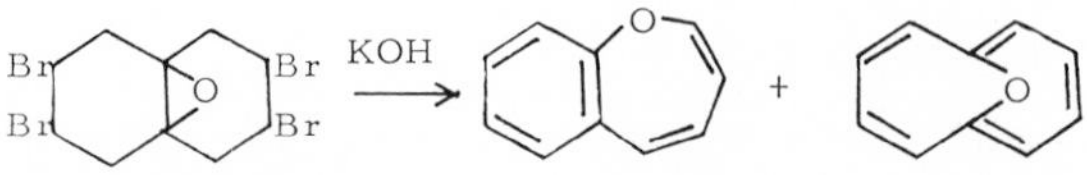

(8)   (9) 20%   (10) 50%

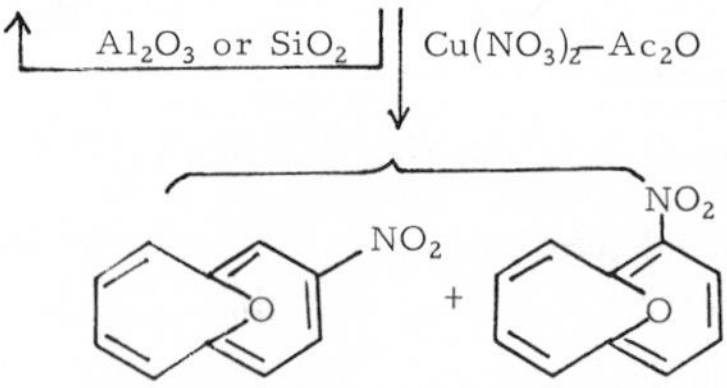

(11) 30%   (12) 30%

bromination with a large excess of potassium hydroxide in ethanol. The major product proved to be 1,6-oxido[10]annulene (10), while the minor product (yellow liquid) was 1-benzoxepin (9). Nitration of 1,6-oxido[10]annulene (10) with cupric nitrate–acetic anhydride gave the 2- and 3-mononitro derivatives.

[4]Y. Gaoni and F. Sondheimer, *Am. Soc.*, **86**, 521 (1964)
[5]I. C. Calder, P. J. Garrett, H. C. Longuet-Higgins, F. Sondheimer, and R. Wolovsky, *J. Chem. Soc.*, (C), 1041 (1967)
[6]A. Shani and F. Sondheimer, *Am. Soc.*, **89**, 6310 (1967)

Cupric sulfate, anhydrous, $CuSO_4$ [**1**, 165, before **Cuprous ammonium bromide**]. Mol. wt. 159.60. Suppliers: B, F, Fl., MCB.

Formation of acetonides (isopropylidene derivatives). Levene and Tipson[1] prepared the 2′,3′-O-acetonide (2) of uridine (1) in practically quantitative yield by reaction with acetone and cupric sulfate in the presence of a catalytic amount of sulfuric acid. The reaction requires at least 48 hrs. at room temperature.

Dehydration. Chromanol-4 (1) is converted into Δ^3-chromene (3) in 76% yield when heated with anhydrous copper sulfate at 160° at 20 mm. It is suggested that the unshared pair of electrons of the oxygen are bonded to the incomplete $3d$ orbital of copper (2). Attempted dehydration with *p*-toluenesulfonic acid gave resinous products.[2]

[1] P. A. Levene and R. S. Tipson, *J. Biol. Chem.*, **106**, 113 (1934); R. S. Tipson, *Syn. Proc. Nucleic Acid Chemistry*, **1**, 431 (1968)
[2] F. Baranton, G. Fontaine, and P. Maitte, *Bull. soc.*, 4203 (1968)

Cuprous acetate, CuOAc [**1**, 165, before **Cuprous ammonium chloride**]. Mol. wt. 122.58.

Cuprous compounds form stable complexes with acetonitrile. Kochi[1] prepared colorless stable complexes of cuprous acetate in acetonitrile–acetic acid solution either by heating cupric acetate with copper powder in these solvents or by the reaction of cuprous oxide with acetic acid in acetonitrile:

$$Cu_2O + 2\ HOAc \xrightarrow{CH_3CN} 2\ CuOAc + H_2O.$$

The complex is effective at low temperatures for homolytic chain decomposition of diacyl peroxides and alkyl hydroperoxides.

[1] J. K. Kochi and A. Bemis, *Tetrahedron*, **24**, 5099 (1968)

Cuprous bromide [1, 165–166].

Homologization [**1**, 166, after citation of ref. 5]. Phenanthrene affords dibenznor-caradiene (4) as the major product together with a hydrocarbon which is either (5a)

(4)   (5a)   (5b)

or (5b).[5a] The reaction with anthracene is more complex.[5b] Homologization of hexamethyl Dewar benzene (6) gives (7) and (8), with (7) predominating even with a large excess of diazomethane.[5c]

(6)   (7)   (8)

Reductive coupling [**1**, 166, before references]. The synthesis of octabromoful-valene (3) by the reductive coupling of hexabromocyclopentadiene (2) with cuprous bromide is reported by West and Kwitowski.[7] The immediate precursor (2) was pre-

(1)   (2)   (3)

pared from hexachlorocyclopentadiene and boron tribromide. In a typical coupling experiment 10.90 g. of (2) in 27 ml. of 90% 1,2-dimethoxyethane–10% water was chilled to $-80°$ and 5.75 g. of copper (I) bromide was added. The mixture was allowed to warm to 0° with stirring. Reaction took place as the water melted and within 3 min. the reagent was consumed. Immediate filtration through sintered glass separated the crude violet solid which on chromatography in chloroform–hexane on silicic acid yielded 0.50 g. of (3) as dark blue crystals, m.p. 170°, dec.

Meerwein reaction [**1**, 166, before references]. The arylation of olefinic com-pounds by diazonium halides with copper salt catalysis was discovered by Meerwein (1939).[8] Cupric chloride has been usually employed. Cleland,[9] however, prefers cuprous bromide (MCB reagent grade) and recommends that the salt (light green) be washed with acetone until the washings are colorless and then with benzene and then with hexane. The resulting solid is dried at 120° and is only faintly colored. He also recommends that the reaction media should have a low water content. The preparation of *p*-acetyl-α-bromohydrocinnamic acid is typical.

$$CH_3CO-\!\!\langle\!\!\langle\ \rangle\!\!\rangle\!-\overset{+}{N_2}Br^- \ + \ CH_2=CHCOOH \xrightarrow[59-66\%]{\overset{Cu_2Br_2}{HBr,\ acetone}} CH_3CO-\!\!\langle\!\!\langle\ \rangle\!\!\rangle\!-CH_2CHBrCOOH$$

[5a]E. Müller, H. Kessler, and H. Suhr, *Tetrahedron Letters*, 423 (1965)
[5b]E. Müller and H. Kessler, *Ann.*, **692**, 58 (1966)
[5c]*Idem, Tetrahedron Letters*, 3037 (1968)
[7]P. T. Kwitowski and R. West, *Am. Soc.*, **88**, 4541 (1966); R. West and P. T. Kwitowski, *ibid.*, **90**, 4697 (1968)
[8]C. S. Rondestvedt, Jr., *Organic Reactions*, **11**, 189 (1960)
[9]G. H. Cleland, *J. Org.*, **26**, 3362 (1961); *idem*, procedure submitted to *Org. Syn.*, 1968

Cuprous chloride [1, 166–169].

Catalyst for (conjugate) Grignard additions [1, 168, after the last formulation]. Eliel *et al.*[10a] treated an ethereal solution of methylmagnesium iodide with cuprous chloride and then added an ethereal solution of diethyl isopropylidenemalonate

$$(CH_3)_2C=C(COOC_2H_5)_2 \ + \ CH_3MgI \xrightarrow[\quad]{Cu_2Cl_2} \xrightarrow[87-94.5\%]{H_2O;\ H_2SO_4} (CH_3)_3CCH(COOC_2H_5)_2$$

dropwise with stirring and ice cooling. Work-up afforded diethyl *t*-butylmalonate in yield of 82–94.5%. The reaction had been run without use of cuprous chloride, and the yield was 37–64%.[10b]

Coupling of terminal acetylenes [top of 1, 169, after the formulation]. Miller[17a] has described a procedure for the cuprous chloride-catalyzed coupling of an alkynyl Grignard reagent (1) with propargyl bromide to produce a skipped 1,4-diyne (2) and its isomerization under mild conditions to a conjugated 1,3-diyne (3).

$$C_6H_5C\equiv CH \xrightarrow[THF,\ N_2]{C_2H_5MgBr} C_6H_5C\equiv CMgBr \xrightarrow[65\%]{CH\equiv CHCH_2Br(Cu_2Cl_2)}$$
$$(1)$$

$$C_6H_5C\equiv CCH_2C\equiv CH \xrightarrow[75\%]{C_2H_5ONa-C_2H_5OH(N_2)} C_6H_5C\equiv CC\equiv CCH_3$$
$$(2) \qquad\qquad\qquad\qquad\qquad (3)$$

Synthesis of dienes [1, 169, before references]. Tetrahydrofurane solutions of vinylmagnesium halides are readily accessible from vinyl halides by the method of Normant.[19] Kauffmann and Sahm[20] found that when a THF solution of the vinyl-magnesium compound (1) is treated at −60° to −40° under nitrogen with a suspension of cuprous chloride an intensely green or red solution is obtained which presumably contains a vinylcopper compound. When the mixture is warmed to

$$2\ \overset{R}{\underset{R}{>}}C=CHMgCl \ + \ 2\ Cu_2Cl_2 \longrightarrow 2\left[\overset{R}{\underset{R}{>}}C=CH-Cu\right] \xrightarrow[-2\ Cu]{} \overset{R}{\underset{R}{>}}C=CH-CH=C\overset{R}{\underset{R}{<}}$$
$$(1) \qquad\qquad\qquad\qquad (2) \qquad\qquad\qquad\qquad (3)$$

+20°, a conjugated diene (3) is formed, the intense color disappears, and elemental copper separates.

Examples:

$$2\ CH_2{=}CHMgCl\ +\ Cu_2Cl_2 \xrightarrow[60.5\%]{\text{Green intermediate}} CH_2{=}CHCH{=}CH_2$$

$$2\ CH_3\overset{\displaystyle CH_3}{\underset{\displaystyle |}{C}}{=}CH{-}MgBr\ +\ Cu_2Cl_2 \xrightarrow[97\%]{\text{Green intermediate}} CH_3\overset{CH_3}{\underset{|}{C}}{=}CHCH{=}\overset{CH_3}{\underset{|}{C}}CH_3$$

$$\left.\begin{array}{c} CH_3\overset{H}{\underset{|}{C}}{=}\overset{H}{\underset{|}{C}}{-}MgBr \\[2mm] CH_3\overset{H}{\underset{|}{C}}{=}\underset{|}{\overset{|}{C}}{-}MgBr \\ \underset{H}{} \end{array}\right\}_2 \xrightarrow[81\%]{\text{Red intermediates}} \left\{\begin{array}{ll} CH_3\overset{H}{\underset{}{C}}{=}\overset{H}{\underset{}{C}}{-}\overset{H}{\underset{}{C}}{=}\overset{H}{\underset{}{C}}CH_3 & 14.4 \\[3mm] CH_3\overset{H}{C}{=}\overset{H}{C}{-}\overset{H}{\underset{\underset{H}{|}}{C}}{=}CCH_3 & 7.3 \\[3mm] CH_3\overset{H}{C}{=}C{-}\overset{H}{\underset{\underset{H}{|}}{C}}{=}CCH_3 & 3.1 \end{array}\right.$$

[10a]E. L. Eliel, R. O. Hutchins, and Sr. M. Knoeber, procedure submitted to *Org. Syn.*

[10b]S. Widequist, *Arkiv Kemi, B23*, No. 4, 1 (1946); G. M. Lampman, K. E. Apt, E. J. Martin, and L. E. Wangen, *J. Org.*, **32**, 3950 (1967)

[17a]S. I. Miller, procedure submitted to *Org. Syn.*, 1966; *see also* H. Taniguchi, I. M. Mathai and S. I. Miller, *Tetrahedron*, **22**, 867 (1966)

[19]H. Normant, *Bull. soc.*, 728 (1957)

[20]Th. Kauffmann and W. Sahm, *Angew. Chem.*, *internat. Ed.*, **6**, 85 (1967)

Cuprous iodide [**1**, 169, before reference].

Grignard reaction. Under catalysis by cuprous iodide, isopropenylmagnesium bromide effects efficient conjugate addition to cyclohexenone:[2]

This route to (2) is more satisfactory than dehydration of (3), which gives mainly the more stable conjugated ketone (4).

[2]H. O. House, R. A. Latham, and C. D. Slater, *J. Org.*, **31**, 2667 (1966)

Cyanogen azide, $\overset{-}{N}{=}\overset{+}{N}{=}N{-}C{\equiv}N$ [**1**, 173–174, before reference]. Cyanogen azide reacts with an alkane at 40° to give a primary alkylcyanamide with loss of nitrogen.[2] Presumably cyanonitrene (NCN) is formed and inserted into a C—H bond:

$$N_3CN + RH \longrightarrow RNHCN + N_2$$

[2]A. G. Anastassiou, H. E. Simmons, and F. D. Marsh, *Am. Soc.*, **87**, 2296 (1965)

Cyanogen bromide [**1**, 174–176]. Supplier (of "Bromcyan"): Sch.
Synthesis of heterocycles [before references]. Examples:

1.[10]

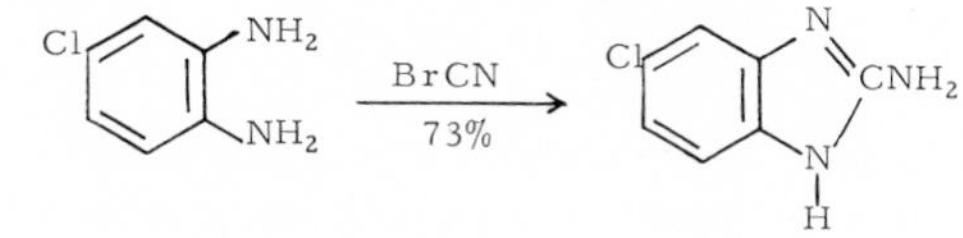

2.[11]

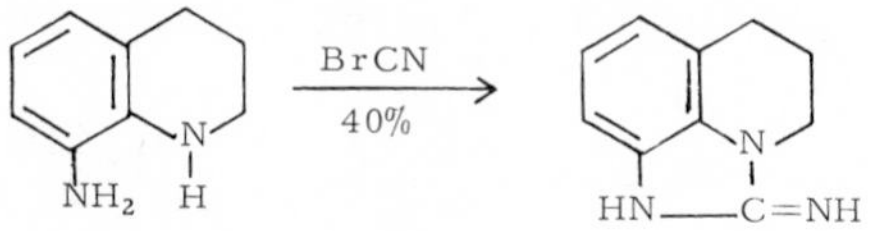

3.[12]

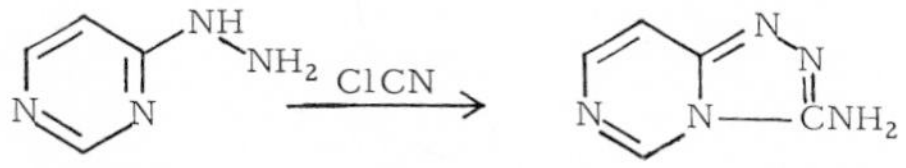

4.[13]

20 g.   21 g.

5.[14]

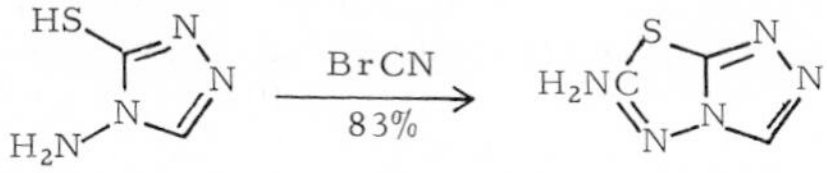

6.[15]

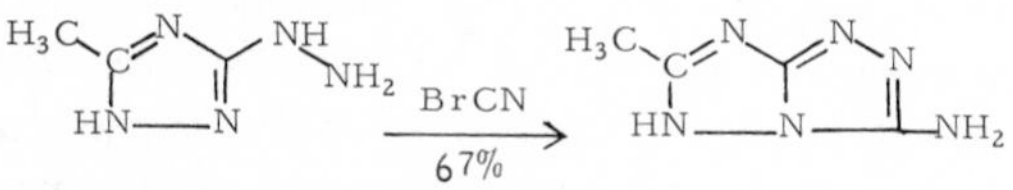

[10]N. J. Leonard, D. Y. Curtin, and K. M. Beck, *Am. Soc.*, **69**, 2459 (1947)
[11]A. Richardson, Jr., *J. Org.*, **28**, 2581 (1963)
[12]G. W. Miller and F. L. Rose, *J. Chem. Soc.*, 5642 (1963)
[13]N. K. Basu and F. L. Rose, *ibid.*, 5660 (1963)
[14]K. T. Potts and R. M. Husby, *J. Org.*, **31**, 3528 (1966)
[15]K. T. Potts and C. Hirsch, *ibid.*, **33**, 143 (1968)

1,2-Cyclohexanedione [**1**, 178, before **Cyclohexane-1,3-dione**]. Mol. wt. 112.12, m.p. 39°, b.p. 75–79°/16 mm. Suppliers: A, B, Fl., K.-L.
Preparation.[1,2]

1.[1]

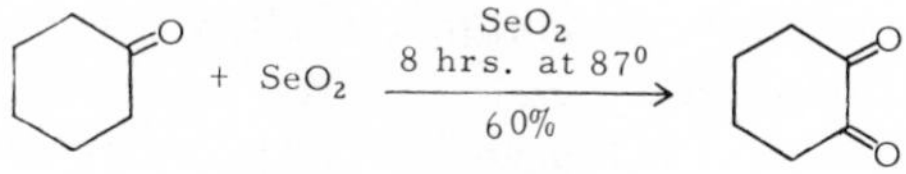

2.[2]

$$+ (CH_3)_2SO + BF_3 \cdot Et_2O \xrightarrow{76\%} \quad \xrightarrow[76\%]{\overset{3.^3}{FeCl_3-2\,\underline{N}\,HCl}}$$

Chemical modification of arginine.[4] A new α-amino acid prepared by the reaction of 1,2-cyclohexanedione (1) with L-arginine (2) in aqueous 0.2 N NaOH was shown to be N⁵-(-4-oxo-1,3-diazaspiro[4.4]non-2-ylidene-L-ornithine (3) by an independent synthesis. It is concluded that, in a tryptic digestion, 1,2-cyclohexanedione reacts

specifically with the guanidino group of arginine and that this reaction restricts tryptic hydrolysis of a protein to lysyl bonds.

[1]C. C. Hach, C. V. Banks, and H. Diehl, *Org. Syn., Coll. Vol.*, **4**, 229 (1963)

[2]T. Cohen and T. Tsuji, *J. Org.*, **26**, 1681 (1961)

[3]L. DeBorger, M. Anteunis, H. Lammens, and M. Verzele, *Bull. soc. chim. Belg.*, **73**, 73 (1964)

[4]K. Toi, E. Bynum, E. Norris, and H. A. Itano, *J. Biol. Chem.*, **240**, PC3455 (1965); *idem, ibid.*, **242**, 1036 (1967)

Cyclopentadienone ketals (dimethyl, diethyl, trimethylene, and ethylene) [1, 182, before **Cyclopentanol**].

Preparation. Cyclopentadienone itself undergoes spontaneous dimerization even at very low temperatures and has but fleeting existence. With the expectation that the ketals of the ketone should be less reactive, Eaton and Hudson[1] undertook their preparation. Treatment of the appropriate ketal of cyclopentanone with 2 molar

equivalents of pyridinium hydrobromide perbromide gives good yields of the corresponding ketals of 2,5-dibromocyclopentanone as oils. Treatment with potassium *t*-butoxide in DMSO at 18–20° effects double dehydrobromination; the reaction is quenched with ice-water and the unsaturated ketal is extracted into cold pentane. These ketals are more stable than the parent ketone, but even so can be used only in dilute solution and as formed.

Diels-Alder reactions. The dimethyl, diethyl, and trimethylene ketals of cyclopentadienone, but not the ethylene ketal, react readily with reactive dienophiles, such as maleic anhydride, tetracyanoethylene, or *p*-benzoquinone, to give norbornenone derivatives. Less reactive dienophiles can be used if present in large excess. The masking ketal group is removed by acid treatment.[1]

When cyclobutadiene is liberated as a transient species by oxidative decomposition of cyclobutadieneiron tricarbonyl (lead tetraacetate in pyridine) in the presence of cyclopentadienone diethyl ketal the adduct I is obtained. Irradiation of I in acetone gives 9,9-diethoxyhomocubane, which on hydrolysis gives homocubanone, II. The corresponding alcohol, homocubanol, is of interest because the derived cation is a fluctional molecule.[2]

I   II

[1]R. E. Eaton and R. A. Hudson, *Am. Soc.*, **87**, 2769 (1965)
[2]J. C. Barborak and R. Pettit, *ibid.*, **89**, 3080 (1967)

Cyclopropyltriphenylphosphonium bromide (2) [**1**, 182, after **Cyclopentyl chloroformate**]. Mol. wt., 383.26, m.p. 189–190°.

The reagent (2) has been prepared in several ways, but the most convenient method involves intramolecular cyclization of 3-bromopropyltriphenylphosphonium bromide (1, available from Aldrich) by sodium hydride in THF.[1]

In the presence of phenyllithium the reagent reacts with carbonyl compounds to give cyclopropylidene derivatives:[2]

$$(2) \xrightarrow{C_6H_5Li} \quad \overset{-}{\underset{(3)}{\triangleright}}\overset{+}{P}(C_6H_5)_3$$

$$\xrightarrow[60\%]{C_6H_5CHO} \quad \triangleright\!\!=\!\!CHC_6H_5 \quad (4)$$

$$\xrightarrow{47\%} \quad \triangleright\!\!=\!\!\bigcirc \quad (5)$$

The reagent reacts with the sodium salt of salicylaldehyde (6) to give 2,3-dihydro-7-benzoxepine (7) and 2-methyl-3-chromene (8).

$$\text{(6)} \; + \; (3) \; \longrightarrow \; \left[\text{OCH}_2\text{CH}_2\overset{-}{\text{CH}}\overset{+}{\text{P}}(C_6H_5)_3 \right] \xrightarrow{60\%}$$

(7)   (8)

¹E. E. Schweizer, J. G. Thompson, E. T. Shaffer, and H. K. Hanson, procedure submitted to *Org. Syn.*, 1968
²E. E. Schweizer, C. J. Berninger, and J. G. Thompson, *J. Org.*, **33**, 336 (1968)

D

DABCO [1, 183, before **Dehydroabietylamine**]. See **1,4-Diazabicyclo[2.2.2]octane** this volume.

Dehydroabietylamine [1, 183]. Supplier: A.

Diacetyl–Trimethyl phosphite adduct   (2,2,2-Trimethoxy-4,5-dimethyl–1,3-dioxaphospholene) (1) [1, 186, before **Diacyl peroxides**]. Mol. wt. 210.17.

(1)

Mol. wt. 86.09   Mol. wt. 124.08

b.p. 88°   b.p. 111° (1, 1233)   b.p. 45–53°/0.2–0.5 mm.

Preparation. The reagent is obtained in 95% yield from freshly distilled diacetyl (2,3-butanedione; suppliers: A. B. Columbia, E, MCB) and trimethyl phosphite (1, 1233–1235).

Reaction with aldehydes.[1] The reagent (1) reacts with propionaldehyde to form one diastereoisomeric form of a cyclic saturated oxyphosphorane structure with the 1,3-dioxaphospholane ring system (2). The product is hydrolyzed by water in benzene solution to give an erythro-α,β-dihydroxy ketone (3). Compare **1**, 1233.

Reaction with acid chlorides.[2] The adduct reacts with aliphatic and aromatic acid chlorides to give phosphate esters of α-hydroxy-β-diketones (1) in yields of 70–90%. The reaction is considered to involve nucleophilic substitution at the carbonyl group of the acid chloride. The esters are hydrolyzed to α-hydroxy-β-diketones readily by refluxing aqueous benzene (12 hrs.).

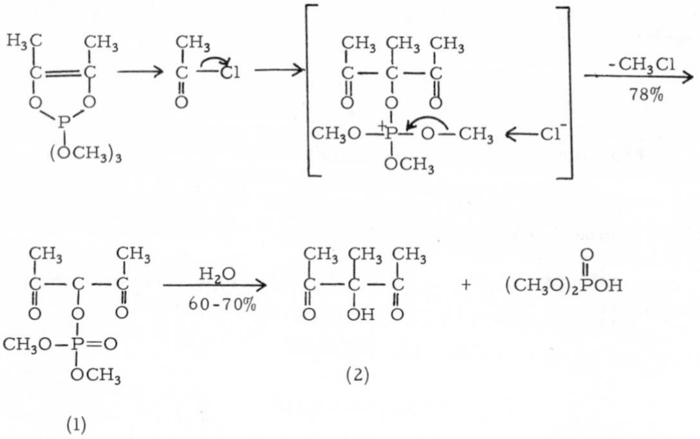

(1)

(2)

[1]F. Ramirez, A. V. Patwardhan, N. Ramanathan, N. B. Desai, C. V. Greco, and S. R. Heller, *Am. Soc.*, **87**, 543 (1966)
[2]F. Ramirez, S. B. Bhatia, A. J. Bigler, and C. P. Smith, *J. Org.*, **33**, 1192 (1968)

1,2-Dianilinoethane [1, 187]. Suppliers: A, Columbia, E. Merck, Sch.

[Before reference]: In the preparation of an aldehyde from a thiolester (1) by desulfurization with Raney nickel, 1,2-dianilinoethane is added to trap the aldehyde as the 1,3-diphenyltetrahydroimidazole derivative (2) and so prevent its reduction.

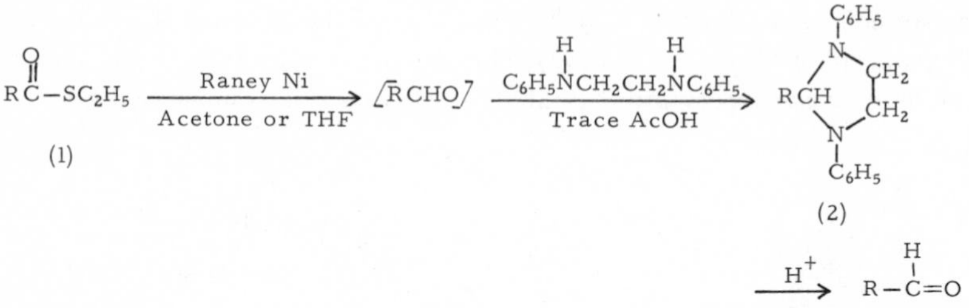

The reagent has been shown capable of trapping an aldehyde formed on hydrogenation of a nitrile, but in this case the yield is not so good as that obtainable with semicarbazide as a trapping agent.[2]

[2]H. J. Bestmann and H. Schulz, *Ber.*, **92**, 530 (1959)

1,5-Diazabicyclo[4.3.0]nonene-5 (DBN) [1, 189–190]. Now supplied by Aldrich. Note the correction in nomenclature.

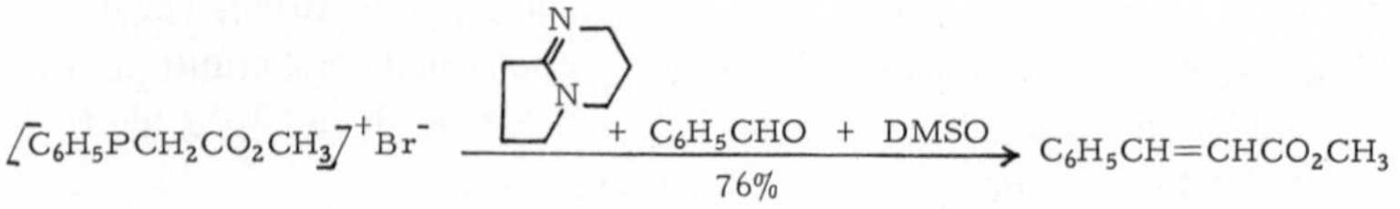

Wittig reaction [before references]. The paper by Oediger, Kabbe, Möller, and Eiter[5] also reports that the reagent is useful for the dehydrobromination of phosphonium salts for Wittig reaction with alkali-sensitive aldehydes. DMSO is used as solvent.

Dehydrohalogenation. Vogel and Klärner[6] were able to prepare 1,2-naphthalene oxide (3) for the first time by bromination of 1,2-dihydronaphthalene oxide (1) with NBS followed by dehydrohalogenation with this base at 0° in THF. Other bases were tried without success. The oxide (3) is highly unstable and rearranges in the solid state–sometimes explosively – to α-naphthol.

$$\underset{(1)}{\text{[structure]}} \xrightarrow[23\%]{\text{NBS}} \underset{(2)}{\underset{\text{Br}}{\text{[structure]}}} \xrightarrow[83\%]{\text{[structure]}} \underset{(3)}{\text{[structure]}}$$

Cyclodehydration.[7] In one step in the total synthesis of prostaglandins, Corey *et al.* effected cyclodehydration of the keto aldehyde (1) by treatment with 0.1 equivalent of this reagent; the cyclopentanol was isolated as the acetate (2) in 45% yield.

$$\underset{(1)}{\text{[structure]}} \xrightarrow[45\%]{\begin{array}{l}\text{1) DBN}\\ \text{2) Ac}_2\text{O—Py}\end{array}} \underset{(2)}{\text{[structure]}}$$

[6]E. Vogel and F.-G. Klärner, *Angew. Chem. internat. Ed.*, **7**, 374 (1968)
[7]E. J. Corey, N. H. Andersen, R. M. Carlson, J. Paust, E. Vedejs, I. Vlattas, and R. E. K. Winter, *Am. Soc.*, **90**, 3245 (1968)

1,4-Diazabicyclo [2.2.2] octane (DABCO, sometimes known as "triethylenediamine")[**1**, 190 before **9-Diazofluorene**]. Mol. wt. 112.18, b.p. 156–160° Suppliers: Houdry Process Co., Marcus Hook, Pa., 19061; E; Fl.; Sch.

Complexes with organometallic compounds. See observations of Screttas and Eastham under **Triethylenediamine, 1**, 1203.

The reagent is reported[1] to form a very stable complex with bromine. This complex oxidizes sulfides to sulfoxides in high yield:

$$C_6H_5SC_6H_5 \xrightarrow[H_2O]{C_6H_{12}N_2-Br_2} C_6H_5\overset{O^-}{\underset{}{\overset{+}{S}}}C_6H_5$$

Metalation. Corey and Seebach[2] treated thioanisole and *n*-butyl bromide and the reagent in THF at 0° and obtained phenylthiomethyllithium in 97% yield.

$$n\text{-BuLi} + C_6H_5SCH_3 + \text{DABCO} \xrightarrow[97\%]{\text{THF, 0}^0} C_6H_5SCH_2Li$$

Dehydrohalogenation. Zaugg et al.[3] report dehydrohalogenation of the bromo-amide (1) to the imidate (2) by the reagent in methanol or DMF. Hassner and Fowler[4]

added iodine azide to ethyl crotonate (3) to form ethyl 3-azido-2-iodopropionate (4) and treated this with DABCO. The vinyl azide (5) was formed, as evidenced by the IR and NMR spectra, but it lost nitrogen at room temperature, giving the azirine (6).

Cyclization catalyst. Newman and Courduvelis[5] used the reagent as catalyst for the condensation of *o*-benzoylbenzoic acid methyl ester (1) with methyl chloro-carbonate. The product (2) decomposes on heating to give the pseudo ester (3).

Newman suggests that the decomposition proceeds through the [3.2.1]bicyclic path indicated by the arrows.

Ethylene diisocyanate reacts with active-hydrogen compounds to form 1-sub-stituted 2-imidazolidones in high yield.[6] The order of reactivity is $R_2NH > RNH_2 > ROH > RSH$; in the last case, catalysis by DABCO ("triethylenediamine") is required.

Quenching of singlet oxygen. DABCO (and other tertiary aliphatic amines) deactivate singlet oxygen ($^1O_2$).[7]

[1]S. Oae, Y. Ohnishi, S. Kozuka, and W. Tagaki, *Bull. Chem. Soc. Japan*, **39**, 364 (1966)

[2]E. J. Corey and D. Seebach, *J. Org.*, **31**, 4097 (1966)

[3]H. E. Zaugg, R. J. Michaels, A. D. Schaefer, A. M. Wenthe, and W. H. Washburn, *Tetrahedron*, **22**, 1257 (1966)

[4]A. Hassner and F. W. Fowler, *J. Org.*, **33**, 2686 (1968); *see also* F. W. Fowler, A. Hassner and L. A. Levy, *Am. Soc.*, **89**, 2077 (1967)

[5]M. S. Newman and C. Courduvelis, *ibid.*, **88**, 781 (1966)

[6]J. N. Tilley and A. A. R. Sayigh, *J. Org.*, **29**, 3347 (1964)

[7]C. Ouannès and T. Wilson, *Am. Soc.*, **90**, 6527 (1968)

1,5-Diazabicyclo [5.4.0] undecene-5 (DBU), see (4), [**I**, 190, before 9-**Diazofluorene**]. Mol. wt. 152.14, liquid. Preparation from caprolactam (1) and acrylonitrile via intermediates (2) and (3).[1] Supplier: A.

(1)   (2)   (3)   (4)

Dehydrohalogenation.[1] A mixture of equimolar amounts of a bromoalkane and the base is warmed to 80–90° and the alkene formed is distilled off. A solvent such as dimethyl sulfoxide may be added. As shown in the table, yields of alkenes are improved considerably over those obtained with DBN (1,5-diazabicyclo[4.3.0]-nonene-5).

		Yield, %	
Bromoalkane	Alkene	DBN	DBU
4-Bromoheptane	2-Heptene	60	91
2-Bromoheptane	1- and 2-Heptene (1:4)	36	78
2-Bromooctane	1- and 2-Octene (1:4)	40	84

[1]H. Oediger and Fr. Möller, *Angew. Chem., internat. Ed.*, **6**, 76 (1967)

Diazoacetaldehyde, $N{\equiv}\overset{+}{N}{-}\overset{-}{C}HCHO \longleftrightarrow \bar{N}{=}\overset{+}{N}{=}CHCHO$ [1, 190, before **9-Diazofluorene**]. Mol. wt. 70.06, b.p. 40°/10 mm. *Caution*: Diazoacetaldehyde detonates violently when overheated.

Preparation[1] from β-N-methylanilinoacraldehyde by heating it with excess *p*-toluenesulfonyl azide (**1**, 1178) *in vacuo* to about 70–80°; the diazoacetaldehyde distils off as soon as it is formed.

Precursor of formylcarbene.[1] In the presence of various catalysts, of which copper (II) acetylacetonate (this volume) proved most efficient, diazoacetaldehyde decomposes to give formylcarbene, trapped with tetramethylethylene:

$$(CH_3)_2C{=}C(CH_3)_2 \quad + \quad \xrightarrow{:CHCHO} \quad (CH_3)_2C\underset{\underset{CHO}{|}}{\overset{}{\diagdown}}\overset{}{\diagup}C(CH_3)_2$$

[1]Z. Arnold, *Chem. Commun.*, 299 (1967)

Diazomethane [**1**, 191–195].

(b) *Preparation from* **p-**-*toluenesulfonylmethylnitrosamide* [**1**, 191]. *Correction.* Ethanol (95%, 25 ml.) should be added at the beginning to the solution of potassium hydroxide in water. No diazomethane is generated in the absence of the alcohol (Dr. J. P. Dusza, personal communication).

Esterification of acids [**1**, 192, at end]. In the routine preparation of methyl esters for characterization by gas chromatography by ether extraction and treatment with diazomethane, the extraction step is troublesome in the case of water-soluble acids (e.g., diacids, hydroxy acids). A simple expedient is as follows:[14a]

Assuming that the fatty acid solution is alkaline and free of neutral materials, acidify to pH 3–4 with hydrochloric acid (excess would be converted into methyl chloride), cool (to prevent loss of diazomethane by volatilization), and cautiously (bubbling) add an ethereal solution of diazomethane.

Methylation of alcohols [**1**, 193, after citation of ref. 18]. Diazomethane–boron trifluoride etherate is useful for the methylation of carbohydrates containing base-

labile substituents (for example, acetyl groups). Thus 6-O-methyl-D-glucose (4) has been prepared by methylation of 1,2,3,4-tetra-O-acetyl-β-D-glucopyranoside (1) with diazomethane-BF_3 to give (2) followed by deacetylation with sodium methoxide in methanol. Use of Purdie's reagent (CH_3I—Ag_2O) is often accompanied by acetyl migration to give methyl 2,3,4,6-tetra-O-acetyl-β-D-glucopyranoside (3).[18a]

Arndt-Eistert reaction [**1**, 194, after citation of ref. 29]. The procedure here described for the preparation of ethyl 1-naphthylacetate[29a] represents a modified Arndt-Eistert reaction as developed by Newman and Beal.[29b] The use of triethylamine in the formation of the diazoketone makes possible the use of only one equivalent of diazomethane.[29b]

$$1\text{-}C_{10}H_7COCl + CH_2N_2 + (C_2H_5)_3N \longrightarrow 1\text{-}C_{10}H_7CN{=}\overset{+}{N}{=}\overset{-}{N} + (C_2H_5)_3\overset{+}{N}HC\overset{-}{l}$$

A solution of 30.5 g. of 1-naphthoyl chloride in 50 ml. of dry ether is added during 30 min. to a magnetically stirred and ice-cooled solution of 1 equiv. each of diazo-methane and triethylamine in 900 ml. of dry ether. After stirring for 3 hrs. at 0° the triethylamine was removed and washed with ether (yield, 90% of theory). Removal of solvent from filtrate and washings gives yellow crystals of 1-diazo-acetylnaphthalene (a powerful skin irritant).

A solution of 15.7 g. of this substance in 50 ml. of absolute ethanol is placed in a 150-ml. two-necked flask equipped with a Teflon coated magnetic stirrer bar, a serum stopper cap and a distillation-reflux condenser connected at the top with a gas-collecting device. After heating to reflux, 1 ml. of a freshly prepared catalyst solution made by dissolving 1 g. of silver benzoate in 10 ml. of triethylamine is added by injection through the serum cap. When the evolution of nitrogen almost stops, a second milliliter of catalyst solution is added. Usually 3–4 additions are required. The reaction time should not be more than 45 min. The mixture is refluxed for 1 hr., cooled, and filtered, and the solvents are removed from the filtrate on a rotatory evaporator at reduced pressure. The residue is taken up in ether and the solution washed twice each with 10% sodium carbonate, water, and saturated salt solution, filtered through a cone of anhydrous magnesium sulfate, evaporated. Distillation gave ethyl 1-naphthylacetate, b.p. 100–105°, 0.1–0.2 mm., 84–92% yield.

Reaction with chloromethanesulfonyl chloride [1, 195, before references]. Diazo-alkanes react with alkylsulfenes ($RCH{=}SO_2$), produced by dehydrochlorination of primary alkanesulfonyl chlorides with triethylamine, to form episulfones.[32] The reaction is illustrated by a procedure for the preparation of 2-chlorothiirane-1,1-dioxide

(4).[33] A slurry of 210 g. of s-trithiane (Eastman, m.p. 218°) in 1 l. of acetic acid and 210 ml. of water is stirred mechanically and chlorinated at 40–50° over a period of several hours, with stirring at $-10°$ in a system blanketed with nitrogen, an ethereal solution of diazomethane is added, followed by triethylamine to effect dehydrohalogenation of (2).

Synthesis of olefins. The reaction described above for syntheses of episulfones is part of a general synthesis of olefins.[32] For example, D-2-oxo-7,7-dimethyl-1-vinylbicyclo[2.2.1]heptane (4) has been prepared as indicated from D-camphor-10-

(1)   (2)   (3)

(4)

sulfonyl chloride (1).[34] Thus (1) is treated with triethylamine and diazomethane in a single operation. The crude episulfone when heated to 90° loses sulfur dioxide to form the olefin (4). In general, yields of olefins by this procedure range from 35% to 97%.

Addition to ketenes.[35] When a cold ($-78°$) methylene chloride solution of diazomethane is added to an excess of ketene, cyclopropanone can be identified as the product by various spectral properties and chemical reactions. In the same way,

$$CH_2=C=O \ + \ CH_2N_2 \ \xrightarrow[-N_2]{CH_2Cl_2, \ -78°} \ \triangle{=}O$$

90%

solutions of methylcyclopropanone, 2,2-dimethylcyclopropanone, and tetramethylcyclopropanone have been prepared. The mechanism is not clear; methylene is probably not an intermediate.

[14a]Contributed by E. J. Eisenbraun, Oklahoma State Univ.

[18a]E. G. Gros and S. M. Flematti, *Chem. Ind.*, 1556 (1966); I. O. Mastronardi, S. M. Flematti, J. O. Deferrari, E. G. Gros, *Carbohydrate Research*, **3**, 177 (1966); J. O. Deferrari, E. G. Gros, and I. O. Mastronardi, *ibid.*, **4**, 432 (1967)

[29a]V. Lee and M. S. Newman, procedure submitted to *Org. Syn.*, 1968

[29b]M. S. Newman and P. F. Beal, III, *Am. Soc.*, **71**, 1506 (1949); *ibid.*, **72**, 5163 (1950)

[32]G. Opitz and Klaus Fischer, *Z. Naturforsch.*, **18b**, 775 (1963); *idem, Angew. Chem., internat. Ed.*, **4**, 70 (1965)

[33]L. A. Paquette, L. S. Wittenbrook, and V. V. Kane, *Am. Soc.*, **89**, 4487 (1967); L. A. Paquette and L. S. Wittenbrook, procedure submitted to *Org. Syn.*, 1967

[34]N. Fischer and G. Opitz, *Org. Syn.*, **48**, 106 (1968)

[35]N. J. Turro and W. B. Hammond, *Tetrahedron*, **24**, 6017 (1968)

2-Diazopropane **(Dimethyldiazomethane)**, $(CH_3)_2C\!\!=\!\!\overset{+}{N}\!\!=\!\!\overset{-}{N} \leftrightarrow (CH_3)_2\overset{-}{C}\!\!-\!\!\overset{+}{N}\!\!\equiv\!\!N$
[**1**, 195, before *trans*-**1,2-Dibenzoylethylene**]. Mol. wt. 70.10.

Preparation. Acetone hydrazone is oxidized in dry xylene with freshly prepared yellow mercuric oxide.[1,2]

$$(CH_3)_2C\!\!=\!\!NNH_2 \;+\; HgO \;\longrightarrow\; (CH_3)_2\overset{-}{C}\!\!-\!\!\overset{+}{N}\!\!\equiv\!\!N$$

Synthesis of gem-dimethylcyclopropanes.[3] The reagent reacts with butenolides (1) to give pyrazolines (2) in good yield. These can be converted into *gem*-dimethyl-cyclopropanes (3) by pyrolysis but preferably by photolysis, particularly in the presence of benzophenone as sensitizer.

(1)   (2)   (3)

[1]H. Staudinger and A. Gaule, *Ber.*, **49**, 1897 (1916); P. C. Guha and D. K. Sankaran, *ibid.*, **70**, 1688 (1937)
[2]A. C. Day, P. Raymond, and M. C. Whiting, procedure submitted to *Org. Syn.*, 1966
[3]M. Franck-Neumann, *Angew. Chem., internat. Ed.*, **7**, 65 (1968)

1,3-Dibenzyl-2-methyl-1,3,2-diazaphospholidine (2) [**1**, 198, before **Dibenzyl phosphonate**]. Mol. wt. 284.34, b.p. 135°/0.04 mm.

Preparation.[1] Methylphosphonous dichloride reacts with diethylamine to give N,N,N′,N′-tetraethyl methylphosphonous diamide (1). This is then treated with N,N′-dibenzylethylenediamine to give the reagent (2).

(1)

(2)

Olefin synthesis. This reagent has an advantage over trialkyl phosphites (*see* **Trimethyl phosphite**, **1**, 1233, and this volume) for stereospecific generation of olefins from trithio- and thionocarbonates in that the conditions are mild (30°).[2] Thus optically active *trans*-cyclooctene (6) has been prepared from *cis*-cyclooctene in the following way.[3] Addition of thiocyanogen to *cis*-cyclooctene (3) affords *trans*-1,2-dithiocyanocyclooctane (4), which when refluxed with 47% hydrobromic acid affords the iminodithiocarbonate (5). This was resolved via the salt with (−)-1-phenyl-ethanesulfonic acid by thirteen recrystallizations from 2-butanone. The (+)-(5) was

(3)   (4)   (5)
(+)-antipode

(6)   (7)
(−)-antipode   (+)-antipode

then converted into the trithiocarbonate (6) by treatment with hydrogen sulfide. Elimination to *trans*-cyclooctene was effected by treatment with 1,3-dibenzyl-2-methyl-1,3,2-diazaphospholidine. The product was 96% optically pure. This route is an alternative to the thionocarbonate route described in this volume (*see* **Methyl-phosphoric acid bis(dimethylamide)**).

[1]E. J. Corey and C. C. Cumbo, unpublished
[2]E. J. Corey, *Pure Appl. Chem.*, **14**, 19 (1967)
[3]E. J. Corey and J. I. Shulman, *Tetrahedron Letters*, 3655 (1968)

Diborane [1, 199–207].
    Reduction [**1**, 201, after citation of ref. 9]. Whereas ketoximes themselves are reduced by diborane to hydroxylamines, ketoxime acetates or tosylates are reduced to amines in 60–75% yield by diborane in THF at room temperature:[9a]

$$R_2C\text{=}NO\text{-}COR \rightarrow R_2CHNH_2.$$

[**1**, 202, after citation of ref. 15]: The amide (1) is reduced to the amine (2) satisfactorily with diborane; attempted reduction with $LiAlH_4$ failed.[15a]

An amide functional group can often be selectively reduced by diborane in the presence of an ester group:[15b]

[**1**, 202, after citation of ref. 16]: Jackson[16a] has observed some differences in the reduction of aromatic aldehydes and ketones bearing electron-releasing groups between diborane generated externally from boron trifluoride–sodium borohydride and then passed into the carbonyl compound and diborane generated *in situ* in the presence of the carbonyl compound. Thus the aldehyde (1) is completely reduced by

$$CH_3 \xleftarrow[\;72\%\;]{\substack{B_2H_6 \\ (internal)}} CHO \xrightarrow[\;95\%\;]{\substack{B_2H_6 \\ (external)}} CH_2OH$$

(2)　　　　　　　　　(1)　　　　　　　　　(3)

diborane generated internally to give (2) and by diborane generated externally to the alcohol (3). Electron-releasing substituents on the aromatic ring are necessary for complete reduction of the carbonyl group.

Reduction of the N-methylamide (1) to (2) was achieved with a large excess of diborane; (3) was obtained when diborane was used in smaller amounts.[16b] $LiAlH_4$ did not effect this reduction.

(1)　　　　　　　　　(2)

(3)

[9a] A. Hassner and P. Catsoulacos, *Chem. Commun.*, 590 (1967)
[15a] R. D. Schuetz, G. P. Nilles, and R. L. Titus, *J. Org.*, **33**, 1556 (1968)
[15b] M. J. Kornet, P. A. Thio, and S. I. Tan, *ibid.*, **33**, 3637 (1968)
[16a] K. M. Biswar, L. E. Houghton, and A. H. Jackson, *Tetrahedron*, **22**, Suppl. 7, 261 (1966)
[16b] J. W. Daly, J. Benigni, R. Minnis, Y. Kanaoka, and B. Witkop, *Biochemistry*, **4**, 2513 (1965)

Diborane–Boron trifluoride [1, 207, before Dibromodifluoromethane].

Reduction of epoxides.[1] Styrene oxide and similar aryl epoxides undergo rapid anti-Markownikov opening when reduced with diborane in the presence of boron

$$C_6H_5CH\!-\!\!-\!\!-\!CH_2 \xrightarrow[\;98\%\;]{B_2H_6-BF_3} C_6H_5CH_2CH_2OH$$

82%　　　　　　18%

trifluoride. The aryl group is necessary. Note that aliphatic and alicyclic epoxides are reduced in the same way by diborane–sodium borohydride (*which see*, in this volume).

[1]H. C. Brown and N. M. Yoon, *Chem. Commun.*, 1549 (1968)

Diborane–Sodium(lithium) borohydride [1, 207, before Dibromodifluoromethane].

Reduction of epoxides. The reaction of diborane alone with epoxides is complicated. Thus 1,2-butylene oxide requires 48 hrs. and gives a mixture of butanols (96% 2-butanol and 4% 1-butanol) in only 48% yield. The reaction with trisubstituted epoxides is even more complicated and only trace amounts of simple alcohols are formed. Brown and Yoon[1] found that the presence of trace amounts of sodium or lithium borohydride greatly enhances the rate of reaction and modifies the course to give predominantly anti-Markownikov opening of the epoxide ring. Thus 1-methylcyclohexene oxide is reduced mainly to *cis*-2-methylcyclohexanol:

2-Methyl-2-butene oxide gives predominantly 3-methyl-2-butanol:

Lower overall yields and a complex mixture are obtained with mixed hydride ($AlH_3 \cdot 2 AlCl_3$).

[1]H. C. Brown and N. M. Yoon, *Am. Soc.*, **90**, 2686 (1968)

1,3-Dibromo-5,5-dimethylhydantoin [1, 208, before references].

Secondary aromatic alcohols are oxidized by this reagent and by NBA; yields were slightly higher with the former reagent.[3]

Japanese chemists[4] have converted Δ^{16}-pregnenes into $\Delta^{14,16}$-pregnadienes by treatment with dibromodimethylhydantoin. Yields have not been reported.

[3]R. A. Corral and O. O. Orazi, *Chem. Commun.*, 5 (1965)
[4]M. Fukuoka and H. Mitsuhashi, *Chem. Pharm. Bull.*, **15**, 2007 (1967); *idem, ibid.*, **16**, 1634 (1968)

Dibromoisocyanuric acid (DBI) (1) [**1**, 208, before **Dibromomalonamide**]. Mol. wt. 268.89, m.p. 307–309°.

The reagent is prepared[1] by the reaction of dilithium cyanurate with excess bromine (yield 88%). DBI in conc. sulfuric acid is a powerful brominating agent for aromatic compounds, even deactivated ones.[2] Yields are higher than those obtained with bromine-iron or NBS in sulfuric acid.

(1)

[1]W. Gottardi, *Monatshefe*, **98**, 507 (1967)
[2]*Idem, ibid.*, **99**, 815 (1968)

2,6-Di-*t*-butylpyridine [**1**, 212]. Brown and Kanner[1] also noticed that the reagent does not combine with SO_3.

1,3-Dichloroacetone, $ClCH_2COCH_2Cl$ [**1**, 214, before **1,3-Dichloro-2-butene**]. Mol. wt. 126.97; m.p. 41–43°. Suppliers: B, E, Fl., Sch.

DePuy synthesis of 1-arylcyclopropanols.[1] In the example of the synthesis illustrated,[2] a solution of 0.2 mole of 1,3-dichloroacetone in ether is added over a 1-hr. period to an ethereal solution of the Grignard reagent from 0.205 mole of *p*-bromo-

$$\begin{array}{c}ClCH_2\\ \\ ClCH_2\end{array}\!\!C{=}O \;+\; CH_3C_6H_4MgBr \longrightarrow \begin{array}{c}ClCH_2\\ \\ ClCH_2\end{array}\!\!C\!\!\begin{array}{c}OMgBr\\ \\ C_6H_4CH_3\text{-}\underline{p}\end{array} \xrightarrow[FeCl_3]{C_2H_5MgBr}$$

(1)

$$\begin{array}{c}CH_2\\ |\\ CH_2\end{array}\!\!C\!\!\begin{array}{c}OMgBr\\ \\ C_6H_4CH_3\text{-}\underline{p}\end{array} \xrightarrow[HCl]{NH_4Cl} \begin{array}{c}CH_2\\ |\\ CH_2\end{array}\!\!C\!\!\begin{array}{c}OH\\ \\ C_6H_4CH_3\text{-}\underline{p}\end{array}$$

(2)   (3)

toluene to form the adduct (1). In a separate flask a solution is prepared from 1.18 moles of ethyl bromide, magnesium, and ether, and the solution is forced under nitrogen pressure into a 1-l. addition funnel. In a 250-ml. addition funnel is placed a filtered solution of 0.0154 mole of anhydrous ferric chloride in 200 ml. of ether. With resumed stirring of the reaction flask, the two solutions are run simultaneously in 2 hrs. into the solution of the adduct (1). In this step the cyclopropane ring is closed with formation of (2) and possibly C_2H_4, C_2H_6, and MgBrCl. The reaction mixture is added to a slurry of ice and hydrochloric acid containing ammonium chloride. Work-up and distillation affords 51–57% of crude 1-*p*-tolylcyclopropanol (3) and crystallization from pentane affords the pure alcohol, m.p. 38–39°.

[1]C. H. DePuy, G. M. Dappen, K. L. Eilers, and R. A. Klein, *J. Org. Chem.*, **29**, 2813 (1964)
[2]C. H. DePuy and R. A. Klein, *Org. Syn.*, **47**, 108 (1967)

Di-μ-chloro-π-allyldipalladium (1) [**1**, 214, before **1,3-Dichloro-2-butene**]. Mol. wt. 366.45, m.p. 160°, dec.

Preparation.[1] This π-allylic palladium chloride complex is formed in high yield by the action of carbon monoxide on a solution of allyl chloride in methanol containing sodium chloropallidate.

Decomposition of ethyl diazoacetate.[2] This complex (1) decomposes ethyl diazoacetate (2) under very mild conditions (0–5°) to a carbene or related intermediate, which can be trapped by an alkene or alkyne. Thus the decomposition in the presence of cyclohexene gives ethyl bicyclo[4.1.0]heptane-3-carboxylate (3) in 47% yield.

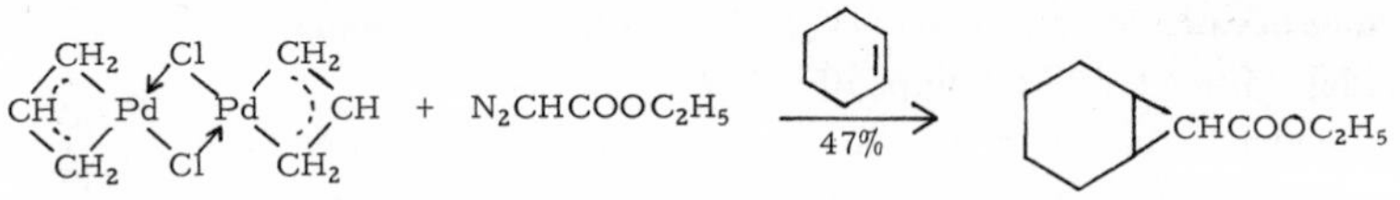

[1]W. T. Dent, R. Long, and A. J. Wilkinson, *J. Chem. Soc.*, 1585 (1964)
[2]R. K. Armstrong, *J. Org.*, **31**, 618 (1966)

Dichlorobis(triphenylphosphine)nickel, $[(C_6H_5)_3P]_2NiCl_2$ [**1**, 214, before **1,3-Dichloro-2-butene**]. Mol. wt. 654.15, dark blue crystals.

Preparation.[1] The reagent is prepared in 84% yield by the reaction of nickel chloride hexahydrate with triphenylphosphine in glacial acetic acid.

Reaction of allylic alcohols with Grignard reagents. The reaction of *n*-propyl-magnesium bromide with allylic alcohols in the presence of catalytic amounts of dichlorobis(triphenylphosphine)nickel leads to a mixture of olefins derived from the alcohol;[2] for example:

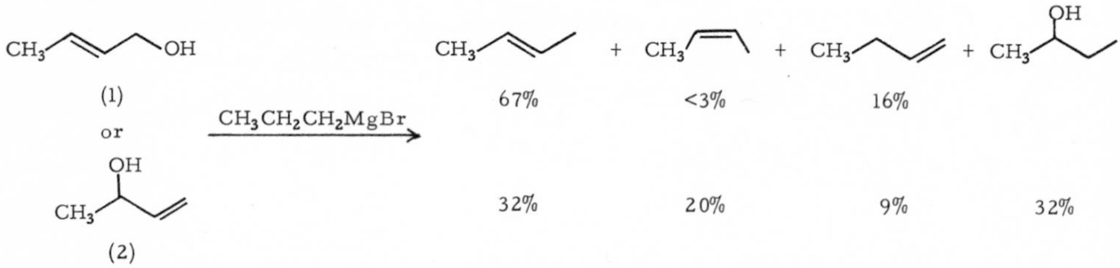

It is interesting that isomeric allylic alcohols give a different proportion of olefins. If the Grignard reagent has no β-hydrogen, the reaction leads to carbon-carbon bond formation:[3]

$$CH_2{=}CHCH_2OH \;+\; CH_3MgBr \xrightarrow[91\%]{} CH_2{=}CHCH_2CH_3$$

$$CH_2{=}CHCH_2OH \;+\; C_6H_5CH_2MgBr \xrightarrow[90\%]{} CH_2{=}CHCH_2CH_2C_6H_5$$

$$C_6H_5CH{=}CHCH_2OH \;+\; CH_3MgBr \xrightarrow[81\%]{} C_6H_5CH{=}CH_2CH_2CH_3$$

The last example shows that there is a marked propensity to form a terminal olefin.

[1]L. M. Venanzi, *J. Chem. Soc.*, 719 (1958)
[2]H. Felkin and G. Swierczewski, *Compt. rend.*, **266** (C), 1611 (1968)
[3]C. Chuit, H. Felkin, C. Frajerman, G. Roussi, and G. Swierczewski, *Chem. Commun.*, 1604 (1968)

1,3-Dichloro-2-butene [1, 214–215]. Change suppliers to read: Aldrich (pure); Eastman (pract.).

[1, 215, before references]: In research directed toward resin acid synthesis, Ireland and Kierstead[6] found that attempted annelation of the ketone (1) with methyl vinyl ketone gave only polymeric tars. However, (1) was found to react with 1,3-dichloro-2-butene in the presence of sodium amide to give (2) in 69% yield. The vinyl chloride (2) is hydrolyzed by acid treatment to the diketone (3). This result is contrary to experiments of Prelog[7] in which he found that acid hydrolysis was accompanied by aldol condensation. Aldol condensation of (3) could be achieved by treatment with potassium t-butoxide in t-butanol, but a significant amount of the diketone (3) underwent cleavage to give (5).

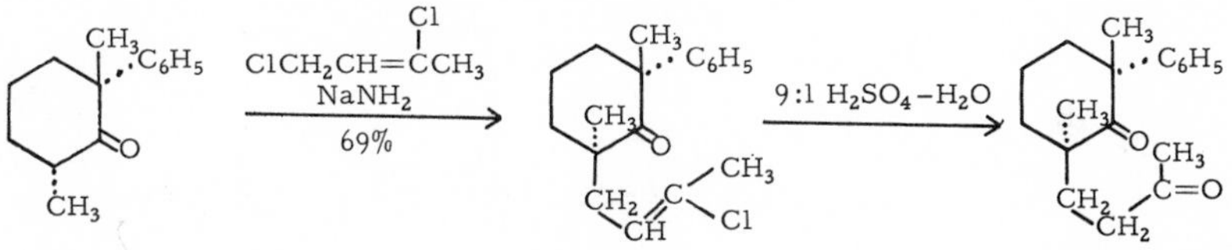

(1)   (2)   (3)

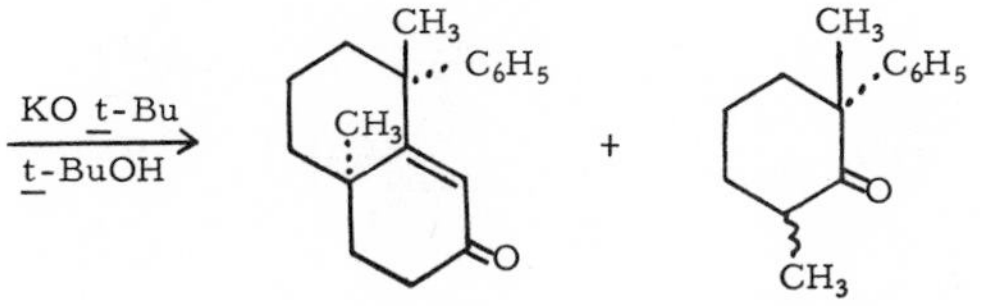

(4, 67%)   (5, 30%)

Caine and Tuller[8] found that the annelation of 2,6-dimethylcyclohexanone could be carried out in the following way. The initial condensation product (6) was dehydrohalogenated by treatment with 2 equiv. of sodium amide in liquid ammonia. Further reaction of (7) with the same reagent in toluene isomerized the triple bond

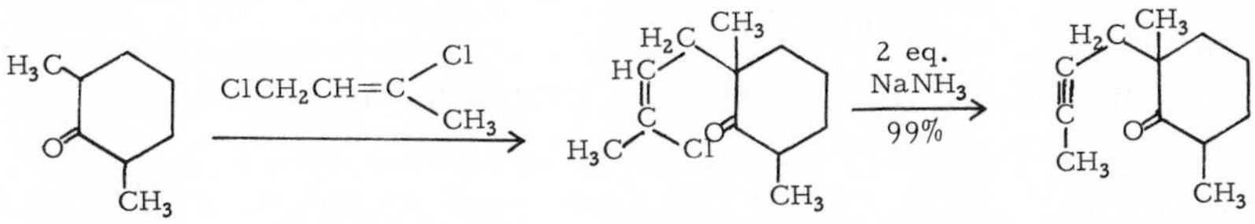

(6)   (7)

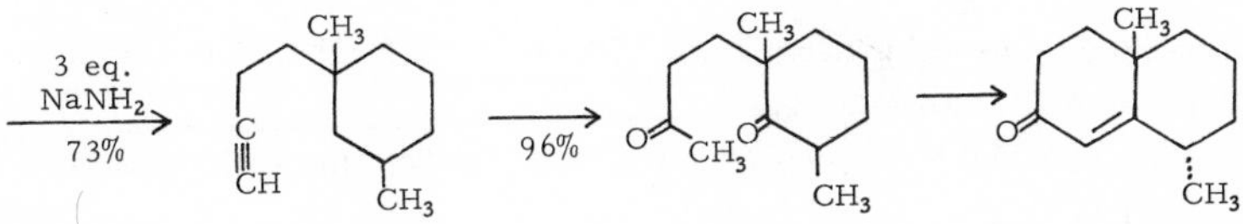

(8)   (9)   (10)

to the terminal position to give (8). This was then hydrated by the usual mercuric sulfate method to give the diketone (9), which cyclizes to *trans*-8,10-dimethyl-1(9)-octalone-2 (10) in excellent yield. This sequence broadens the scope of annelation with 1,3-dichloro-2-butene.

[6]R. E. Ireland and R. C. Kierstead, *J. Org.*, **31**, 2543 (1966)
[7]V. Prelog and M. Zimmermann, *Helv.*, **32**, 2360 (1949)
[8]D. Caine and F. N. Tuller, *J. Org.*, **34**, 222 (1969)

cis-**3,4-Dichlorocyclobutene** (5) [**1**, 215, before **2,3-Dichloro-5,6-dicyano-1,4-benzo-quinone**]. Mol. wt. 122.98, b.p. 68–69°/55 mm.

   Preparation.[1,2] Dry chlorine gas is admitted to a solution of cyclooctatetraene (1) in carbon tetrachloride maintained at $-28°$ to $-30°$ over a period of about 1 hr., until 1 mole of chlorine has been absorbed. The mixture is allowed to warm to 0°,

powdered sodium carbonate is added, and the mixture is shaken for several minutes to remove any HCl which may have been formed. The mixture containing the diene (2) is filtered into a flask containing 0.95 mole of dimethyl acetylenedicarboxylate and the solution is heated cautiously (strongly exothermal reaction) and then refluxed gently for 3 hrs. After removal of the solvent at reduced pressure, the Diels-Alder adduct (3) is pyrolyzed at a distillation temperature of 135–152°/20 mm. The crude pyrolyzate is redistilled to separate a residue consisting mainly of dimethyl phthalate, and final fractionation at 55 mm. through a 36-in. platinum spinning band column yields 47–56% of pure *cis*-3,4-dichlorocyclobutene; the forerun consists mainly of 1,4-dichlorobutadiene.

[1]M. Avram, I. Dinulescu, M. Elian, M. Fărcaşiu, E. Marica, G. Mateescu, and C. D. Nenitzescu, *Ber.*, **97**, 372 (1964)
[2]R. Pettit and J. Henery, procedure submitted to *Org. Syn.*, 1968

2,3-Dichloro-5,6-dicyano-1,4-benzoquinone (DDQ) [**1**, 215–219]. To suppliers add Koch-Light.

   The reactions of DDQ have been reviewed by D. Walker and J. D. Hiebert, *Chem. Rev.*, **67**, 153 (1967).

   Aromatization [**1**, 216, after citation of ref. 6] of the diene (4a) was affected by the reagent, if in low yield,[6a] whereas treatment with palladium charcoal in refluxing cumene resulted in concomitant hydrogenolysis to give 1,8-diphenylnaphthalene.

DDQ in C_6H_5Cl
32%

(4a)   (4b)

Dehydrogenation of carbonyl compounds [1, 217, after citation of ref. 14a]: Turner and Ringold[14b] have reported an extensive investigation of the dehydrogenation of 3-ketosteroids with DDQ. They find that the reaction is markedly catalyzed by strong acids (*p*-TsOH usually used) and that in some instances acid catalysis influences the course of the reaction. Thus Δ^4-3-ketosteroids are dehydrogenated in the uncatalyzed reaction to $\Delta^{1,4}$-3-ketones, whereas in the catalyzed reaction $\Delta^{4,6}$-3-ketones are formed exclusively.

CH$_3$ + DDQ   No catalysis

TsOH

CH$_3$

CH$_3$'

3-Keto-$\Delta^{5(10),9(11)}$-19-norsteroids are dehydrogenated to 3-keto-$\Delta^{4,9,11}$-19-norsteroids.[14c]

OH
CH$_3$

OH
CH$_3$

DDQ

(1)   (2)

Steroidal Δ^5-ene-3-ones are dehydrogenated by DDQ in refluxing benzene to $\Delta^{4,6}$-diene-3-ones in 80–85% yield. The same results are obtained with chloranil, which is much cheaper. On prolonged treatment of Δ^5-ene-3-ones with two equivalents of DDQ $\Delta^{1,4,6}$-triene-3-ones are obtained in approximately 70% yield. Actually the more available Δ^5-ene-3-ols can be used if three equivalents of quinone are employed. Yields are about 50%. Chloranil does not attack Δ^5-ene-3-ols under these conditions.[14d]

Pettit *et al.*[14e] dehydrogenated the γ,δ-unsaturated ester (1) to give the $\alpha,\beta;\gamma,\delta$-diunsaturated ester (2, 3β-acetoxyisobufalin methyl ester).

Oxidation of oxygen functions [1, 217, after citation of refs. 15–17]. One step in the total synthesis of prostaglandin E_1[17a] involved reduction of the enone (1) with zinc borohydride in dimethoxyethane. Two nitro diols epimeric at C_{15} were obtained

(1) $\xrightarrow{\text{DDQ}}$ (2)

and separated by chromatography on silica gel. The undesired 15β-epimer was then reconverted to the 15-ketone in high yield by DDQ. This recycling procedure permits channeling of the synthesis to the desired 15α-ol.

(1)   (2), both 15-epimers

[**1**, 217, after citation of ref. 19]: The dehydrogenation cited of 2-hydroxymethylene-3-ketosteroids was carried out in the 5α-series. Caspi *et al.*[19a] found that the reaction can be applied also in the 5β-series and in addition deformylated the product with tris(triphenylphosphine)chlororhodium to give 1-dehydro-3-keto-5β-steroids. This route is the most convenient and practical method for introduction of unsaturation at C_1 into 5β-3-ketosteroids.

[**1**, 218, after line 3]: Oxidation of isolapachol (3) with an equimolar quantity of DDQ results in oxidative cyclization to a mixture of two dihydrolapachones (4 and 5). An intermediate triketone is postulated. The β-form (5) is isomerized to (4), dehydro-α-lapachone, by acid, and hence (4) can be obtained readily in overall yield of 60%.[20a]

Dehydrogenation of 4,4′-dimethoxydibenzyl [**1**, 219, before references]. Findlay and Turner[24] added 103 mg. of DDQ dissolved in 1.5 ml. of dioxane to a solution of 100 mg. of 4,4′-dimethoxydibenzyl and refluxed the mixture in an oil bath at 105° for 18 hrs. The initially deep green solution became pale yellow as the hydroquinone crystallized. After cooling, the solid was removed by filtration and washed with warm benzene (1 ml.) and warm chloroform (6 ml.) and dried to give 95 mg. of pure (4). A solution of the semisolid residue in 5 ml. of ethyl acetate was passed through a column of 2 g. of neutral alumina and the column was eluted with 100 ml. of ethyl

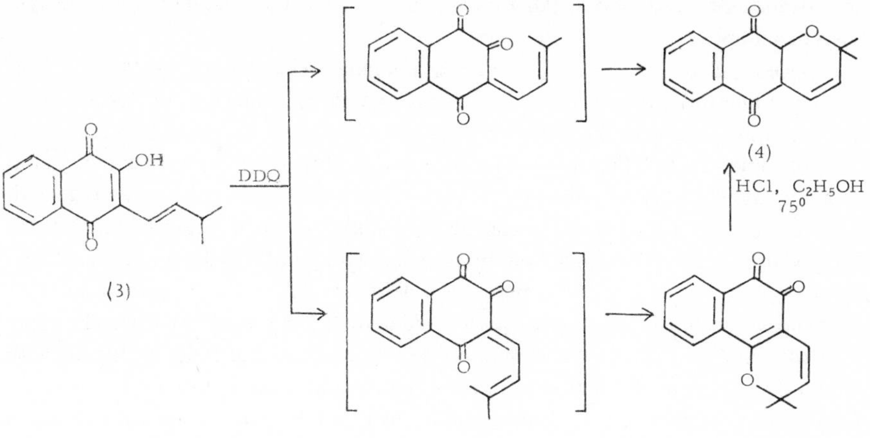

(4)

HCl, C_2H_5OH
75^0

(3)

(5)

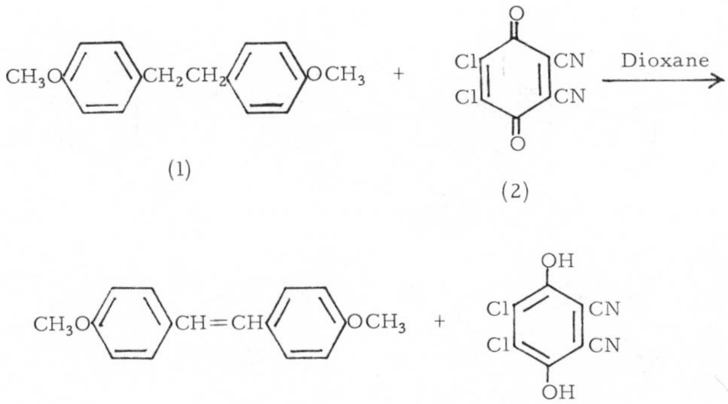

CH_3O⟨⟩CH_2CH_2⟨⟩OCH_3 + [structure with Cl, Cl, CN, CN] $\xrightarrow{\text{Dioxane}}$

(1)

(2)

CH_3O⟨⟩$CH=CH$⟨⟩OCH_3 + [structure with OH, Cl, Cl, CN, CN, OH]

(3, 83%)

(4, 91%)

acetate and the product recrystallized from ethanol to give the pure stilbene as colorless plates. DDQ is readily regenerated in 90% yield from the hydroquinone by a procedure used by Walker and Waugh (ref. 4, **1**, 219): namely, oxidation of a slurry of 5 g. of 2,3-dicyanohydroquinone in 35 ml. each of water and concd. hydrochloric acid with 9.4 g. of 70% nitric acid at 35° for 1 hr.

Cyclodehydrogenation. A British group[25] stated, without experimental details, that ethyl mycophenolate (1) was smoothly converted into ethyl mycochromenate (2) by refluxing under nitrogen with DDQ in benzene. This is apparently the first experimental *in vitro* demonstration of a hypothesis of Ollis and Sutherland[26] for

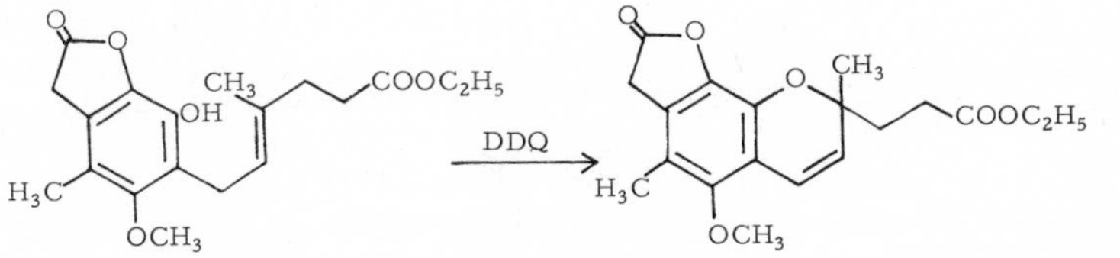

(1) $\xrightarrow{\text{DDQ}}$ (2)

the biogenesis of chromenes. An Italian group[27] has used this method for the synthesis of a number of natural chromenes.

   Preparation of 3,7-dihydroxy-2,6-anthraquinone. The highly unstable 3,7-dihydroxy-2,6-anthraquinone (8) has been prepared by oxidation of 1,4,5,8-tetrahydroxyanthracene with the high-potential quinone.[28] The 9,10-dimethyl derivative is more stable. 2,3,6,7-Tetrahydroxyanthrone was prepared from a starting material (1) readily available as described by Oliverio[29] by condensation of acetaldehyde with veratrole. Boldt[28] found that (1) can be cycloalkylated to the tetramethoxy-9,10-dimethylanthracene (2) in high yield by reaction with paraldehyde, acetic anhydride, and a catalytic amount of 60% perchloric acid. Oxidation of (2) with sodium dichromate according to Cason and Fieser[30] and demethylation with hydrogen bromide afforded 2,3,6,7-tetrahydroxyanthraquinone (3) in good overall yield. Reduction with sodium hydrosulfite to the anthrone-anthranol and acetylation gave 2,3,6,7,9-pentaacetoxyanthracene (4). Hydrogenation to (5), dehydrogenation with chloranil to (6), and deacetylation with alcoholic alkali gave 2,3,6,7-tetrahydroxyanthracene (7). Finally, oxidation of (7) with the high-potential quinone DDC gave highly un-

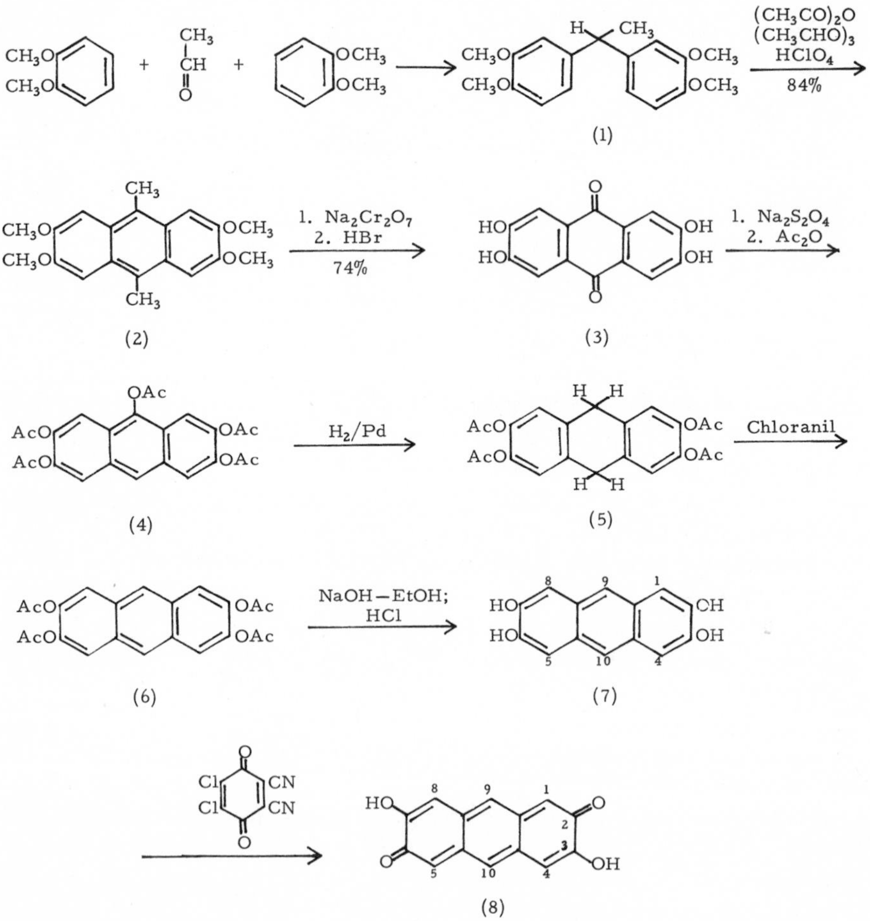

(1)

(2)   (3)

(4)   (5)

(6)   (7)

(8)

stable 3,7-dihydroxy-2,6-anthraquinone (8). The 9,10-dimethyl derivative, prepared by analogous reactions from intermediate (2), is more stable.

Of particular interest is the direct reduction of the tetrahydroxyanthraquinone (3) to the corresponding tetrahydroxyanthracene (9) by heating it with excess diborane under pressure for 4 hrs. at 50°.

Dehydrogenation of tetramethylethylene. The reagent dehydrogenates tetramethylethylene to give 2,3-dimethylbutadiene, which rapidly undergoes a Diels-Alder reaction with the quinone to give the adduct (1) in about 45% yield.[31]

[6a]H. O. House and R. W. Bashe, II, *J. Org.*, **32**, 784 (1967)

[14b]A. B. Turner and H. J. Ringold, *J. Chem. Soc.*, (C), 1720 (1967)

[14c]M. Heller, R. H. Lenhard, and S. Bernstein, *Steroids*, **10**, 211 (1967)

[14d]A. B. Turner, *J. Chem. Soc.*, (C), 2568 (1968)

[14e]T. R. Kasturi, G. R. Pettit, and K. A. Jaeggi, *Chem. Commun.*, 644 (1967)

[17a]E. J. Corey, I. Vlattas, and K. Harding, *Am. Soc.*, **91**, 535 (1969)

[19a]Y. Shimizu, H. Mitsuhashi, and E. Caspi, *Tetrahedron Letters*, 4113 (1966)

[20a]K. H. Dudley and R. W. Chiang, *J. Org.*, **34**, 120 (1969)

[24]J. W. A. Findlay and A. B. Turner, procedure submitted to *Org. Syn.*, 1968

[25]I. M. Campbell, C. H. Calzadilla, and N. J. McCorkindale, *Tetrahedron Letters*, 5107 (1966)

[26]W. D. Ollis and I. O. Sutherland, "Recent Developments in the Chemistry of Natural Phenolic Compounds," 84, Pergamon Press, Oxford 1961

[27]G. Cardillo, R. Cricchio, and L. Merlini, *Tetrahedron*, **24**, 4825 (1968)

[28]P. Boldt, *Ber.*, **100**, 1270 (1967)

[29]A. Oliverio, *Boll. Sèdute Accad. Naturali Catania*, **3**, No. 4 (1937)

[30]J. Cason and L. F. Fieser, *Am. Soc.*, **62**, 2681 (1940)

[31]A. E. Asato and E. F. Kiefer, *Chem. Commun.*, 1684 (1968)

1,1-Dichloro-2,2-difluoroethylene [**1**, 220, before reference].

A reinvestigation[2] of the cycloaddition of the reagent to butadiene indicated that a small amount of the product of 1,4-addition (2) is also formed. The amount is dependent upon the temperature, being 0.9% at 60° and 2.3% at 176°. The variation is the same as the fraction of butadiene having the cisoid configuration.

1,4-Adducts are also formed in the case of 2-alkylbutadienes; the amount increases

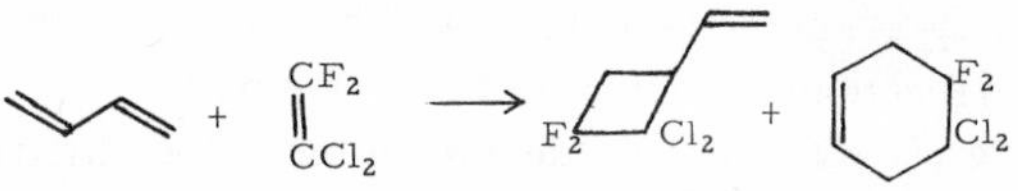

(1) (2)

as the bulk of the alkyl group is increased, reaching 45% in the case of 2-*t*-butylbutadiene.[3]

[2]J. S. Swenton and P. D. Bartlett, *Am. Soc.*, **90**, 2056 (1968)
[3]P. D. Bartlett, G. E. H. Wallbillich, A. S. Wingrove, J. S. Swenton, L. K. Montgomery, and B. D. Kramer, *ibid.*, **90**, 2049 (1968)

1,1-Dichloroethylene [**1**, 220–221]. A further paper[3] includes several procedures, for example, one for the preparation of β,β-dimethylbutyric acid:

$$\underset{\text{1 mole}}{(CH_3)_3CCl} + \underset{\text{1. 52 moles}}{CH_2{=}CCl_2} \xrightarrow[79\%]{\text{200 ml. 90\% } H_2SO_4 \text{ + 35 g. } BF_3 \text{ at } 5\text{-}15^0} CH_3\overset{CH_3}{\underset{CH_3}{C}}CH_2CO_2H$$

[1]Change to read: K. Bott, *Ber.*, **100**, 978, 2791 (1967)
[3]K. Bott and H. Hellmann, *Angew. Chem., internat. Ed.*, **5**, 870 (1966)

Dichloroketene [**1**, 221–222, before references]. Dichloroketene reacts with *cis*-cyclooctene to give *cis*-10,10-dichlorobicyclo[6.2.0]decanone-9 and with *trans*-cyclooctene to give the *trans* isomer. The reaction is thus a stereospecific cycloaddition:[4]

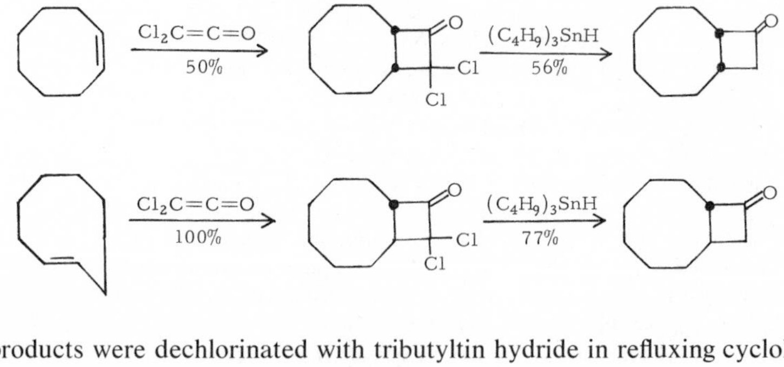

Both products were dechlorinated with tributyltin hydride in refluxing cyclohexane containing a catalytic amount of azobisisobutyronitrile.

[4]R. Montaigne and L. Ghosez, *Angew. Chem. internat. Ed.*, **7**, 221 (1968)

Dichloromethyl 2-chloroethyl ether, $HCCl_2OCH_2CH_2Cl$ [**1**, 222, before **Dichloromethylenedioxybenzene**]. Mol. wt. 163.44, b.p. 106–110°/10 mm.

Preparation by treatment of the β-chloroethyl ester of formic acid with PCl_5.[1]

Preparation of cyclopropanols.[2] When the ether is heated with methyllithium in ether solution a reactive carbenoid intermediate is formed and reacts with an olefin to form a 2-chloroethyl ether of a cyclopropanol (1).[3] The product can be converted into the cyclopropanol itself in two ways: either by splitting by an organolithium reagent (2a), or by dehydrochlorination followed by acid hydrolysis (2b):

(1) $HCCl_2OCH_2CH_2Cl$ +   [cyclohexene] $\xrightarrow[48\%]{CH_3Li}$ [bicyclic] OCH_2CH_2Cl

(2a) $\xrightarrow{94\%}$ [bicyclic] OH

(2b)   [bicyclic] OCH_2CH_2Cl $\xrightarrow{KOH}$ [bicyclic] $OCH=CH_2$ $\xrightarrow[82\%]{H_2SO_4-Glyme}$ $-CH_2=CH_2$ → [bicyclic] OH

In a review of the chemistry of the cyclopropanes, DePuy[4] describes this procedure as "one of the more versatile methods" for preparation of cyclopropanols.

[1]H. Baganz and L. Domaschke, *Ber.*, **91**, 653 (1958)
[2]C. H. DePuy, G. M. Dappen, K. L. Eilers, and R. A. Klein, *J. Org.*, **29**, 2813 (1964)
[3]U. Schöllkopf, J. Paust, A. Al-Azrak, and H. Schumacher, *Ber.*, **99**, 3391 (1966)
[4]C. H. DePuy, *Accounts Chem. Res.*, **1**, 33 (1968)

Dichloromethyllithium, Trichloromethyllithium [1, 223–224, before references].

Trichloromethyllithium reacts with hexafluoroacetone in THF at $-100°$ to yield, after acidification, complex II. On cleavage, trichloromethylbistrifluoromethyl-carbinol III is isolated in 50% yield.[5]

$(CF_3)_2C=O$ + CCl_3Li $\xrightarrow[THF]{-100°}$ $CF_3-\underset{\underset{CCl_3}{|}}{\overset{\overset{CF_3}{|}}{C}}-OH\cdots O$ [cyclopentane] $\xrightarrow{H_2SO_4}$ $CF_3-\underset{\underset{CCl_3}{|}}{\overset{\overset{CF_3}{|}}{C}}-OH$

II   III

Köbrich[6] has presented evidence that the reaction of trichloromethyllithium with olefins is stereospecific and that it probably does not proceed through prior decomposition to dichlorocarbene. He suggests a cyclic transition state in which lithium chloride is present. Tribromomethyllithium has been prepared in high yield from the reaction of tetrabromomethane and phenyllithium or *n*-butyllithium.[7]

$LiCCl_3$ + [alkene] $\longrightarrow$ [cyclic transition state] $\longrightarrow$ [cyclopropane] $+ LiCl$

[5]R. Filler and R. M. Schure, *J. Org.*, **32**, 1217 (1967)
[6]G. Köbrich *et al.*, *Angew. Chem. internat. Ed.*, **6**, 41 (1967)
[7]R. H. Fischer and G. Köbrich, *Ber.*, **101**, 3230 (1968)

Dichloromethyl methyl ether, Cl_2CHOCH_3 [**1**, 224, before **Dicobalt octacarbonyl**]. Mol. wt. 114.96, b.p. 82–85.5°. Supplier: EGA-CHEMIE KG. **Preparation**[1] by stirring a suspension of phosphorus pentachloride in phosphorus oxychloride and dropping in methyl formate. A sequence of two distillations gives satisfactory product in 77–84% yield.

$$\underset{\text{4.4 moles}}{\overset{\displaystyle O \atop \displaystyle \|}{H C O C H_3}} + \underset{\text{4 moles}}{PCl_5} \xrightarrow[POCl_3]{10-20^0} Cl_2CHOCH_3 + POCl_3$$

Aldehyde synthesis. A general method for the synthesis of aromatic aldehydes is illustrated by the reaction of mesitylene in methylene chloride and titanium tetrachloride on addition of dichloromethyl methyl ether to produce mesitylaldehyde.[2]

[1] H. Gross, A. Rieche, E. Höft, and E. Beyer, *Org. Syn.*, **47**, 47 (1967)
[2] A. Rieche, H. Gross and E. Höft, *ibid.*, **47**, 1 (1967)

2,3-Dichloropropene, $CH_2{=}CHClCH_2Cl$ [**1**, 224 before **Dicobalt octacarbonyl**]. Mol. wt. 110.97, b.p. 92.5–95°. Suppliers: E, A.

Synthesis of cyclic ketones. The reagent has been used in a general synthesis of cyclic ketones. For example, indene is converted in THF into the Grignard reagent (1) and this is added to 2,3-dichloropropene also in THF. The product (2) is cyclized to (4) by treatment with 97% formic acid.[1] The method has been extended to hetero-substituted cyclohexanones.[2]

[1] P. T. Lansbury and E. S. Nienhouse, *Am. Soc.*, **88**, 4290 (1966)
[2] P. T. Lansbury and D. J. Scharf, *ibid.*, **90**, 536 (1968)

Dichlorotris(triphenylphosphine)ruthenium, $[(C_6H_5)_3P]_3RuCl_2$ [1, 224, before **Dicobalt octacarbonyl**].

Prepared *in situ* in ether from triphenylphosphine and $RuCl_3$.

Use. The complex is an effective catalyst for homogeneous *cis*-semihydrogenation of acetylenes.[1]

[1]I. Jardine and F. J. McQuillin, *Tetrahedron Letters*, 4871 (1966)

$$\overset{O}{\overset{\|}{}}$$

N,N-Dichlorourethane (DCU), $C_2H_5OC\!-\!NCl_2$ [1, 224, before **Dicobalt octacarbonyl**].
Mol. wt. 158, yel. liq., b.p. 60°/15 mm.,$n^{20}D$ 1.4594. Supplier: A.

Preparation. This reactive pseudohalogen is prepared in 80% yield by reaction of urethane with the calculated amount of chlorine in a buffered aqueous solution. The reagent can be stored for long periods in the dark without excessive decomposition. Pure reagent can be obtained by distillation before use.[1]

Addition to alkenes. DCU adds almost quantitatively to the double bonds of styrene[1] and *trans*-stilbene[1] in an anti-Markownikoff manner to give β-chloro-N-chlorocarbamates which are reduced by aqueous sodium bisulfite or sulfite to β-chlorocarbamates. With straight-chain terminal olefins yields of β-chlorocarbamates are 60–80%. Disubstituted alkenes yield a mixture of stereoisomers. The reaction of DCU with cyclohexene gave the products indicated:

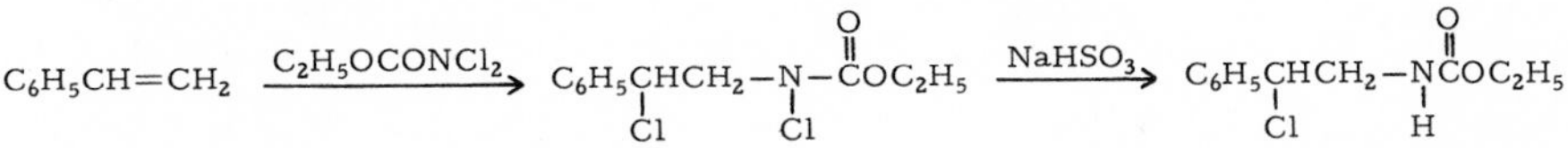

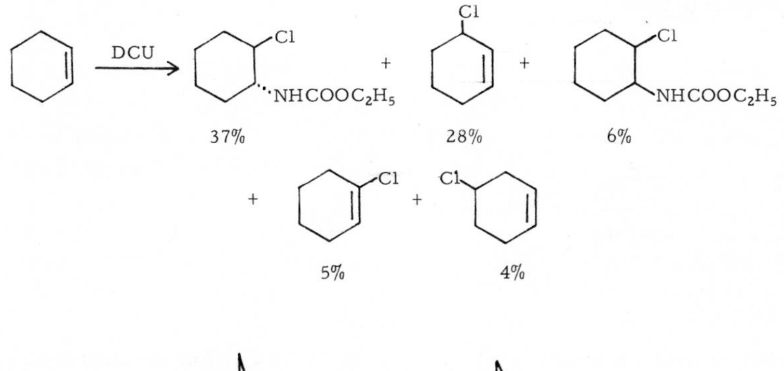

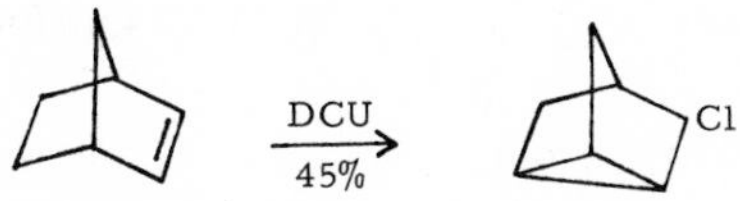

The reaction with norbornene (1) gave, in addition to chlorocarbamates of norbornene, the unexpected 3-chloronortricyclene (2) in 45% yield.

The reaction of DCU with an olefin has the usual characteristics of a free-radical chain reaction, and Foglia and Swern[1] propose the following sequence:

$$C_2H_5O\overset{O}{\overset{\|}{C}}NCl_2 \xrightarrow[-Cl\cdot]{\Delta \text{ or } h\nu} C_2H_5O\overset{O}{\overset{\|}{C}}-N\cdot \quad \overset{}{\underset{Cl}{}}C=C \quad \xrightarrow{} C_2H_5O\overset{O}{\overset{\|}{C}}-N-\overset{|}{\underset{Cl}{C}}-\overset{|}{\underset{|}{C}}\cdot$$

$$\xrightarrow{C_2H_5O\overset{O}{\overset{\|}{C}}NCl_2} C_2H_5O\overset{O}{\overset{\|}{C}}-N-\overset{|}{\underset{Cl}{C}}-\overset{|}{\underset{|}{C}}-Cl$$

Electron-withdrawing groups slow down or even prevent the addition reaction; substitution on the double bond also leads to steric retardation.[2]

On treatment with potassium hydroxide, β-chlorocarbamates, like β-iodocarbamates (*see* **Iodine isocyanate,** this volume) give aziridines in 45–75% yield. β-Chlorocarbamates from terminal olefins on pyrolysis yield 5-alkyloxazolidones in 45–80% yield.[3]

$$C_6H_5-\overset{Cl}{\underset{H}{\overset{|}{C}}}-CH_2-\overset{H}{\overset{|}{N}}\overset{O}{\overset{\|}{C}}-OC_2H_5 \xrightarrow[60\%]{KOH;\ C_2H_5OH} C_6H_5CH\overset{}{\underset{\underset{H}{N}}{\diagup\!\!\!\diagdown}}CH_2$$

$$R-\underset{O=\overset{|}{C}-OC_2H_5}{\overset{Cl}{\underset{:NH}{CH-CH_2}}} \xrightarrow{\Delta} \left[\begin{array}{c} RCH\!-\!CH_2 \\ O \diagdown \overset{+}{\underset{}{NH}} \\ C \\ O\!-\!\overset{\uparrow}{\underset{Cl^-}{C_2H_5}} \end{array} \right] \xrightarrow{-C_2H_5Cl} \underset{O}{\overset{RCH\!-\!CH_2}{O\diagdown\underset{C}{\diagup}NH}}$$

Reaction with ethers.[4] DCU reacts with di-*n*-alkyl ethers to give α-chlorobis-carbamates in good yield:

$$C_2H_5OC_2H_5 \longrightarrow ClCH_2CH(NHCO_2C_2H_5)_2$$

With mixed alkyl aromatic ethers, such as anisole, ring chlorinated products are obtained. Dibenzyl ether is converted into the biscarbonate of benzaldehyde.

[1]T. A. Foglia and D. Swern, *J. Org.,* **31,** 3625 (1966)
[2]*Idem, ibid.,* **33,** 766 (1968)
[3]*Idem, ibid.,* **32,** 75 (1967)
[4]*Idem, Tetrahedron Letters,* 3963 (1967)

Dichlorovinylene carbonate,[1] $\underset{Cl}{\overset{Cl}{}}\overset{C-O}{\underset{C-O}{\|}}C=O$ [1, 224, before **Dicobalt octacarbonyl**].

Mol. wt. 154.94, b.p. 39–40°/10 mm.

Preparation. The reagent is prepared by exhaustive chlorination of ethylene

$$\underset{H_2C}{\overset{H_2C}{}}\overset{O}{\underset{O}{\diagup\!\diagdown}}C=O \xrightarrow[hv\ (-4HCl)]{8\ Cl_2} \underset{Cl-\overset{|}{\underset{Cl}{C}}}{\overset{Cl-\overset{Cl}{\overset{|}{C}}}{}}\overset{O}{\underset{O}{\diagup\!\diagdown}}C=O \xrightarrow[DMF-Ether]{Zn(Cu)} \underset{Cl}{\overset{Cl}{}}\overset{C-O}{\underset{C-O}{\|}}C=O$$

(1)   (2)   (3)

carbonate (1, **1**, 372) followed by partial dechlorination with copper-zinc couple in the presence of a catalytic amount of DMF.

Dienophile. The reagent (3) reacts with cyclopentadiene (4) in boiling dioxane to give the *endo*-bicyclo[2.2.1]heptane derivative (5), which on treatment with either acid or alkali gives the α-dione (6):

Photocyclophile. Under irradiation in acetone (3) reacts even with ethylene at room temperature to give the cycloadduct (7).

[1]H.-D. Scharf, W. Droste, and R. Liebig, *Angew. Chem. internat. Ed.*, **7**, 215 (1968)

Di(cobalttetracarbonyl)zinc, $Zn[Co(CO)_4]_2$ [**1**, 229, before **Dicyandiamide**]. Mol. wt. 749.62. Yellow crystals prepared[1] in an autoclave charged with zinc dust, a toluene solution of dicobalt octacarbonyl under nitrogen and pressurized with carbon monoxide (3,000 p.s.i. at 20°).

Use. The oligomerization of olefins has generally been carried out with zero-valent transition metal complexes (mononuclear catalysts) and usually leads to an array of dienes (*see* **1**, 259). Schrauzer *et al.*[1] of the Shell Development Co. reasoned that a dinuclear catalyst such as $Zn[Co(CO)_4]_2$ in which the two cobalt centers are connected close to each other will lead to new transition state formation from which different products can form. As a model, they examined the dimerization of nor-bornadiene and with the new catalyst obtained in almost quantitative yield a single dimer, m.p. 65–65.6°, shown unequivocally by elemental analysis ($C_{14}H_{16}$), infra-red, nuclear magnetic resonance, and mass spectrometry to have the structure (2).

(2) Bisnor-S

The systematic name is *endo,cis,endo*-heptacyclo[5.3.1.1^{2,6}.1^{4,12}.1^{9,11}.0^{3,5}.0^{8,10}]-tetradecane, designated Bisnor-S for short. In substantiation of the working hypothesis, and assuming unrestricted rotation of the cobalt atoms in the Co-Zn-Co axis, the only transition state in which the substrate molecules would come sufficiently close for bond formation is (3), giving rise to the formation of Bisnor-S.

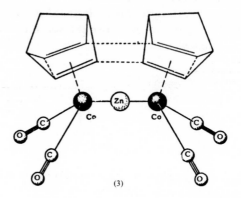

(3)

The dimerization is catalyzed markedly by boron trifluoride etherate and by aluminum chloride.

[1]G. N. Schrauzer, B. N. Bastian, and G. A. Fosselius, *Am. Soc.*, **88**, 4890 (1966)

Dicyanoacetylene [1, 230–231]. *Caution*: The reagent is toxic (handle in hood) and potentially explosive, but it is fairly stable in dilute solution in inert solvents.

Preparation [before references]. Ciganek[5] (Du Pont) has developed a preparative procedure which makes dicyanoacetylene available in large quantities for the first time. The procedure is heavily documented with warning concerning the toxicity of CS_2, NaCN, NCC≡CCN. In the first step a mixture of 2.4 l. of acetone, 100 ml. of water, and 300 ml. of CS_2 is stirred under reflux, 200 g. of sodium cyanide is added all at once, and the mixture is stirred at 50–55° for 7 hrs. The dark solution is

$$2\ CS_2\ +\ 2\ NaCN\ \xrightarrow[66-72\%]{}\ \underset{NC}{\overset{NC}{>}}C=C\underset{SNa}{\overset{SNa}{<}}\ +\ 2S$$

$$\underset{NC}{\overset{NC}{>}}C=C\underset{SNa}{\overset{SNa}{<}}\ +\ COCl_2\ \xrightarrow[53-57\%]{}\ \underset{NC}{\overset{NC}{>}}C\overset{S}{\underset{S}{<}}C=O\ +\ 2\ NaCl$$

$$\underset{NC}{\overset{NC}{>}}C\overset{S}{\underset{S}{<}}C=O\ \xrightarrow[59-76\%]{800°}\ N≡C-C≡C-C≡N\ +\ COS\ +\ CS_2\ +\ S$$

decanted and the residual solid is washed with two 100-ml. portions of hot methanol. The combined liquid is concentrated under vacuum at a temperature not exceeding 45° in a rotary evaporator equipped with a rotating trap immersed in a dry ice–acetone bath and connected through a trap cooled in dry ice–acetone to an oil pump. The residue weighs *ca.* 520 g. and the UV spectrum in methanol indicates that the yield of disodium dimercaptomaleonitrile is 250–275 g. For details of the remaining steps the original directions should be consulted.

Diels-Alder reactions with aromatic hydrocarbons. The unusual Diels-Alder addition of dicyanoacetylene to benzene provides a new synthesis of a barrellene derivative;[6] thus 2,3-dicyanobicyclo[2.2.2]octa-2,5,7-triene (1) is obtained in 14% yield

(1)

when dicyanoacetylene is heated in benzene solution at 180° for two days. The reaction is markedly catalyzed by aluminium chloride. In the presence of this Lewis acid the addition proceeds at room temperature to give (1) in 63% yield. A 1:1 complex of dicyanoacetylene and aluminum bromide can be obtained by combining cyclohexane solutions of the two components, and the complex reacts with benzene to give (1). Methylation of the ring facilitates the reaction. The reaction of hexamethylbenzene and dicyanoacetylene proceeds readily at 130° without catalysis to give the Diels-Alder adduct in 83% yield.

[2]Change to read: R. C. Cookson, J. Dance, and M. Godfrey, *Tetrahedron*, **24**, 1529 (1968)
[5]E. Ciganek, procedure submitted to *Org. Syn.*, 1968; E. Ciganek and C. G. Krespan, *J. Org.*, **33**, 541 (1968)
[6]E. Ciganek, *Tetrahedron Letters*, 3321 (1967)

Dicyanodiazomethane, $(NC)_2C=N_2$ [1, 231, before **Dicyanomethylene-2,4,7-trinitrofluorene**]. Mol. wt. 92.06, m.p. 75°, dec. *Caution*: Solid material is a potent explosive.

Preparation.[1]

$$(NC)_2CBr_2 \xrightarrow[35-40\%]{\substack{NH_2NH_2 \\ THF,\ -70°}} (NC)_2C=NNH_2 \xrightarrow[96\%]{\substack{Pb(OAc)_4 \\ CH_3CN}} (NC)_2C=N_2$$

Dicyanocarbene. Dicyanodiazomethane when heated to about 70° or irradiated with ultraviolet light loses nitrogen with formation of dicyanocarbene.[2] The most interesting reaction of this carbene is with benzene to give 7,7-dicyanonorcaradiene

(1)

(1).[3] Ordinarily norcaradienes and cycloheptatrienes exist in reversible tautomerism; however, (1) exists, as far as can be determined, in the norcaradiene form.

[1]E. Ciganek, *J. Org.*, **30**, 4198 (1965)
[2]*Idem, Am. Soc.*, **88**, 1979 (1966)
[3]*Idem, ibid.*, **89**, 1454, 1458 (1967)

Dicyclohexylcarbodiimide (DCC) [1, 231–236].

Other N-acylamines [1, 233, after citation of ref. 19]. N-Formylamino acids are readily prepared by treatment with formic acid and DCC.[19a]

Dehydration of an amide [1, 234, after citation of ref. 25]. Liberek *et al.*[25a] used this method but instead of the carbobenzoxy group they used the trityl group, which can be removed with 50% acetic acid.

Nucleotides [1, 235, lines 2–4]. *Correction*: Change to read:..., "Jacob and Khorana[27] concluded that DCC, *p*-toluenesulfonyl chloride, or mesitylenesulfonyl chloride are the most efficient." Any one of these compounds is thus effective.[27a]

Dehydration of β-hydroxy ketones [1, 235, before references]. Schmidt and Moosmüller[29] reported that the reaction of carbodiimides with primary and secondary alcohols is catalyzed by cupric chloride. Corey *et al.*,[30] in a synthesis of prostaglandins, found that the reaction of β-hydroxy ketones with DCC catalyzed by cupric chloride is a useful method for dehydration to the α,β-unsaturated ketone under mild, nonacidic, nonbasic conditions. Presumably the hydroxyl group reacts to form a carbamidate derivative which undergoes cycloelimination.

[19a]J. O. Thomas, *Tetrahedron Letters*, 335 (1967)

[25a]B. Liberek, Cz. Buczel, and Z. Grzonka, *Tetrahedron*, **22**, 2303 (1966)

[27a]Correction called to our attention by Prof. M. Smith, Univ. of British Columbia

[29]E. Schmidt and F. Moosmüller, *Ann.*, **597**, 235 (1955)

[30]E. J. Corey, N. H. Andersen, R. M. Carlson, J. Paust, E. Vedejs, I. Vlattas, and R. E. K. Winter, *Am. Soc.*, **90**, 3245 (1968)

N,N'-Dicyclohexyl-4-morpholinocarboxamidine [1, 236]. *Correction*: This tertiary amine is added to increase the solubility of the nucleotide, which then reacts with DCC to yield the 3',5'-cyclic phosphate.[2a]

[2a]Correction called to our attention by Prof. M. Smith, Univ. of British Columbia

Diels-Alder solvents [1, 236–243 ref. 6]: L. F. Fieser, *Org. Syn.*, **46**, 44 (1966).

1,1-Diethoxy-2-propyne, $HC{\equiv}CCH(OC_2H_5)_2$ [1, 244, before **Diethyl acetylenedicarboxylate**]. Mol. wt. 128.17, b.p. 138–139.5°.

Preparation. Dibromoacrolein is obtained by bromination of acrolein and then treated with triethyl orthoformate to produce 2,3-dibromo-1,1-diethoxypropane (2).[1] This is then dehydrobrominated with sodamide in liquid ammonia to the reagent (3).

Uses. The Grignard derivative (4), prepared in tetrahydrofurane, reacts with propargyl bromide and similar halides in the presence of a catalytic amount of

$$CH_2=CHCHO \xrightarrow{\text{Br}_2} BrCH_2CHBrCHO \xrightarrow[\text{79\% from (1)}]{HC(OC_2H_5)_3}$$
(1)

$$BrCH_2CHBrCH(OC_2H_5)_2 \xrightarrow[65\%]{NaNH_2, \ NH_3} HC\equiv CCH(OC_2H_5)_2$$
    (2)   (3)

$$C_2H_5MgBr \ + \ HC\equiv CCH(OC_2H_5)_2 \xrightarrow[65\%]{-C_2H_6} BrMgC\equiv CCH(OC_2H_5)_2$$
(4)

$$\xrightarrow[65\%]{HC\equiv CCH_2Br(Cu_2Cl_2)} HC\equiv CCH_2C\equiv CCH(OC_2H_5)_2$$
(5)

cuprous chloride to form 1,2-diethoxy-2,5-hexadiyne (5) in good yield.[2] Since the Grignard derivative (4) can react with itself on heating, forming 1,1,4-triethoxy-2,5-hexadiyne, it should be prepared with ice cooling.[3]

Under the conditions of the Cadiot-Chodkiewicz coupling reaction, alkylation of the reagent with 1-bromo-2-phenylacetylene can be accomplished readily.[4]

$$C_6H_5C\equiv CBr \ + \ HC\equiv CCH(OC_2H_5)_2 \longrightarrow C_6H_5C\equiv CC\equiv CCH(OC_2H_5)_2$$

[1]J. C. Sheehan and C. A. Robinson, *Am. Soc.*, **71**, 1437 (1949)
[2]J. P. Ward and D. A. van Dorp, *Rec. trav.*, **85**, 117 (1966)
[3]*Idem, ibid.*, **88**, 177 (1969)
[4]*Idem, ibid.*, **86**, 545 (1967)

Diethyl acetylenedicarboxylate [**1**, 244]. Additional suppliers: Columbia, Farchan, E. Merck.

Diethylaluminum cyanide [**1**, 244].

The preparation of the reagent has been described in detail.[1a]

Hydrocyanation [before reference].

The efficiency of diethylaluminum cyanide for conjugate addition of HCN is evident from results reported by Nagata and Yoshioka[2] for the reaction of (1) to give the nitrile (2). In benzene–toluene at 0° it took only 5 min. for the reaction to

reach an equilibrium composed of about 80% of the product (2) and 20% of the starting enone (1). Reprocessing of the recovered enone (1) gave the cyanoketone

(2) in total yield of 91.6%. The reagent is efficient also in reactions other than conjugate addition. Thus 6-methoxy-1-tetralone, hydrocyanation of which had been unsuccessful, was converted smoothly by treatment with 2.3 equivalents of diethylaluminum cyanide in benzene–toluene at $-25°$ into the cyanohydrin (4), which was dehydrated to (5) in 85% yield, with 12% recovery of (3).[3]

(3)   (4)   (5)

[1a]W. Nagata and M. Yoshioka, procedure submitted to *Org. Syn.*, 1969
[2]W. Nagata and M. Yoshioka, *Tetrahedron Letters*, 1913 (1966)
[3]W. Nagata and M. Yoshioka, procedure submitted to *Org. Syn.*, 1969

Diethyl azodicarboxylate [1, 245–247].

Diels-Alder reactions [1, 246, after citation of ref. 9]. The dienophile also reacts with tropone to give the product of 1,4-addition.[9a]

[Before references]: Aromatic hydroxylamines are oxidized in 70–90% yield on being heated with the reagent in ether.[14] Yields are lower with aliphatic hydroxylamines.

Reaction with pyrimidines.[15] Diethyl azodicarboxylate reacts in DMF or chlorobenzene with pyrimidines (1) containing an amino or hydrazine group at C_6 but

(1)   (2)

unsubstituted at C_5 to give 5-(1,2-dicarboethoxyhydrazino) derivatives (2). This convenient method for introduction of nitrogen was used in an interesting synthesis

(3)   (4)   (5)

of the antibiotic fervenulin (5). 1,3-Dimethyl-6-hydrazinouracil (3) was treated with diethyl azodicarboxylate to give (4). This was converted in a single step into the antibiotic by treatment with phosphoryl chloride in DMF (Vilsmeier conditions).

The amino compound (6) corresponding to (4) was converted into 1,3-dimethyluric acid (8) as shown.

$$\text{(6)} \qquad\qquad\qquad \text{(7)} \qquad\qquad\qquad \text{(8)}$$

Synthesis of disulfides.[16] Diethyl azodicarboxylate reacts with a mercaptan (ether, room temperature) to give a 1:1 adduct (a diethyl N-alkanesulfenylhydrazodicarboxylate, 1). The adduct reacts in refluxing benzene (5 hrs.) with another equivalent of a mercaptan to give a disulfide. The method is particularly useful for syntheses of unsymmetrical disulfides.

$$RSH \ + \ C_2H_5O_2CN{=}NCO_2C_2H_5 \longrightarrow C_2H_5O_2CNH{-}N(SR)CO_2C_2H_5 \ \xrightarrow{\ RSH\ }$$

$$\text{(1)}$$

$$RSSR \ + \ C_2H_5O_2CNHNHCO_2C_2H_5$$

Review.[17]

[9a]Y. Kitahara, I. Murata, and T. Nitta, *Tetrahedron Letters*, 3003 (1967)
[13]Definitive paper: F. Yoneda, K. Suzuki, and Y. Nitta, *J. Org.*, **32**, 727 (1967)
[14]E. C. Taylor and F. Yoneda, *Chem. Commun.*, 199 (1967)
[15]E. C. Taylor and F. Sowinski, *Am. Soc.*, **90**, 1374 (1968)
[16]T. Mukaiyama and K. Takahashi, *Tetrahedron Letters*, 5907 (1968)
[17]E. Fahr and H. Lind, *Angew. Chem., internat. Ed.*, **5**, 372 (1966)

Diethyl carbonate [**1**, 247–248, before references]. A procedure for use of the reagent for the conversion of cyclooctanone into 2-carboethoxycyclooctanone reported in *Organic Syntheses*[6] calls for first adding a dispersion of sodium hydride in mineral

oil and removing most of the oil by repeated washing with benzene. Then diethyl carbonate is added, the mixture is refluxed, and a solution of cyclooctanone in benzene is added over a period of 3–4 hrs.

This method is also useful for preparation of the 2-carbethoxycycloalkanones from cyclononanone, cyclodecanone, and cyclododecanone in yields of 85, 95, and 90%, respectively.

[6]A. P. Krapcho, J. Diamanti, C. Cayen, and R. Bingham, *Org. Syn.*, **47**, 20 (1967)

Diethyl(2-chloro-1,1,2-trifluoroethyl)amine [1, 249, before references].

N,N-Dimethyl derivatives of β-hydroxy-α-amino acids are transformed by the reagent into the corresponding β-fluoro compounds in about 60% yield.[7] The reaction fails when the amino group is free.

The reagent reacts with O-isopropylidene sugars to give chlorofluoroacetates:[8] Formation of esters was originally believed to be due to the presence of water, but in the present case esters were still obtained under strictly anhydrous conditions.

[7] A. Cohen and E. D. Bergmann, *Tetrahedron*, **22**, 3545 (1966)
[8] K. R. Wood, D. Fisher, and P. W. Kent, *J. Chem. Soc.*, (C), 1994 (1966)

Diethyl cyanomethylphosphonate [1, 250, before references].

In the first study of the reaction of this reagent with ketosteroids, Bose and Dahill[3] used sodium amide as base and THF as solvent and effected reaction with ketone groups at C_3, C_{17}, and C_{20}. Since that time Corey[4] showed that dimsyl sodium in combination with DMSO is used to advantage in Wittig reactions. Consequently Bose and Ramer[5] applied this modification to the reaction of diethyl cyanomethylphosphonate with ketosteroids and found that C_2-, C_6-, C_7- and C_{12}-, but not C_1- and C_{11}-ketosteroids react readily to give α,β-unsaturated nitriles, each apparently as a single geometrical isomer.

Piers *et al.*[6] also used dimsyl sodium in DMSO for the condensation of the cyclohexanone (1) with diethyl cyanomethylphosphonate and obtained the α,β-un-

saturated nitrile (2) in 88% yield. This reaction is the first step in a total synthesis of (±)-4-demethylaristolone (5) by the route indicated.

In a new route to cardenolides, Pettit and Yardley[7] oxidized the 3β-acetoxy-20-oxo-5α-pregnane (1) with lead tetraacetate to the 21-acetoxy derivative (2). This was then let react for 3 days at room temperature with the carbanion derived from diethyl cyanomethylphosphonate and sodium hydride in oil–tetrahydrofurane. Removal of solvent and addition of dilute hydrochloric acid yielded the imino-lactone (6), converted by boiling dilute acid into the cardenolide (7), m.p. 245°.

[4]E. J. Corey and M. Chaykovsky, *Am. Soc.*, **87**, 1345 (1965)
[5]A. K. Bose and R. M. Ramer, *Steroids*, **11**, 27 (1968)
[6]E. Piers, W. de Waal, and R. W. Britton, *Chem. Commun.*, 188 (1968)
[7]G. R. Pettit and J. P. Yardley, *Chem. Ind.*, 553 (1966); G. R. Pettit, C. L. Herald, and J. P. Yardley, *J. Org.*, in press

Diethyl β-(cyclohexylimino)ethylphosphonate (2) [1, 250, before **Diethylene glycol dimethyl ether**]. Mol. wt. 245.29, b.p. 151–152°/0.04 mm.

The reagent is prepared[1] by reaction of diethyl formylmethylphosphonate (1)[2] with an equimolecular amount of cyclohexylamine in methanol followed by distillation of the crude product in the presence of potassium carbonate.

Formylolefination.[1] In the presence of sodium hydride this phosphonate reagent reacts with aldehyde or ketones, for example cyclohexanone, in THF to give an α,β-unsaturated aldimine (3), which on hydrolysis (oxalic acid or buffered acetic acid) gives the formylolefin (4).

The reagent is useful because the Wittig reagent $(C_6H_5)_3P{=}CHCHO$ and the usual phosphonate reagent $(C_2H_5O)_2POCH_2CH(OC_2H_5)_2$ do not react with ketones. Moreover, the reaction proceeds stereoselectively to give the *trans* olefin; thus benzaldehyde affords cinnamaldehyde in 77% yield.

(2)

$$\text{(3)} \xrightarrow[86\%]{\text{H}^+} \text{(4)}$$

(3)   (4)

[1]W. Nagata and Y. Hayase, *Tetrahedron Letters*, 4359 (1968)
[2]N. D. Dawson and A. Burger, *Am. Soc.*, **74**, 5312 (1952)

Diethyl oxalate[1, 250–251].

Ethoxalyl ketones [after citation of ref. 3]. The direct monomethylation of Δ^4-cholestenone gives 4-methylcholestenone-3-one. Monomethylation at C_2 can be achieved by prior condensation at C_2 with diethyl oxalate to give the 2-ethoxy-oxalate (2).[3a] This group evidently stabilizes an enolate anion from (2) favorable for

(1) 10. 6 g.   (2)

(3)   (4) 2. 6 g.

methylation at C_2. Hydrolytic removal of the activating group under strongly alkaline conditions favors the equatorial (α) orientation of the 2-methyl group, as in (4).

[3a]Y. Mazur and F. Sondheimer, *Am. Soc.*, **80**, 5220 (1958); pertinent publications by other groups in the same period: H. J. Ringold and G. Rosenkranz, *J. Org.*, **21**, 1333 (1956); J. A. Hogg, F. H. Lincoln, R. W. Jackson, and W. P. Schneider, *Am. Soc.*, **77**, 640 (1955); M. Mousseron, F. Winternitz, and A. C. de Paulet, *Compt. rend.*, **245**, 185 (1957)

Diethyl phosphonate [1, 251–253].

Reduction of phenols [1, 252, after citation of ref. 3]. In achieving the synthesis of triptindane (11), Thompson[3a] obtained the methyl ether (8a) as an intermediate, demethylated it to (9), and effected deoxygenation to (11) by the method of Kenner and Williams[3b] consisting in reaction with diethyl phosphonate or mesyl chloride and reduction of the diethyl phosphate or the mesylate ester with sodium in liquid ammonia; yields, first procedure 58%; second procedure 36%.

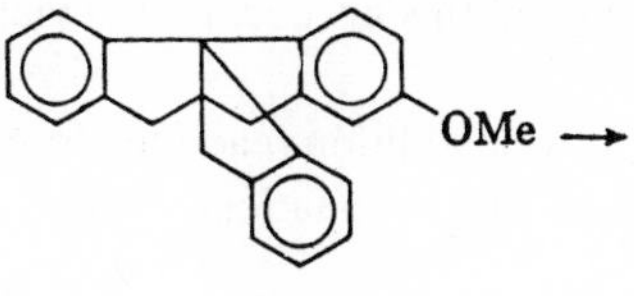

8a

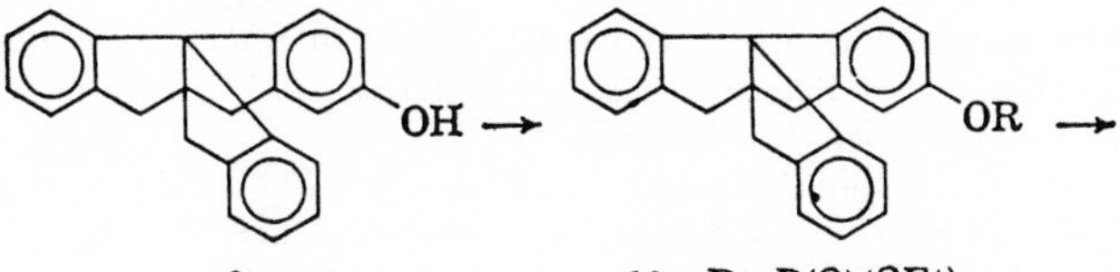

9

10a, R = P(O)(OEt)$_2$
b, R = SO$_2$Me

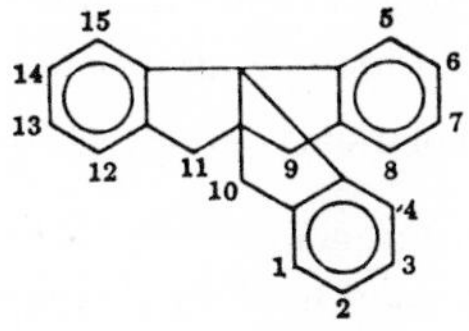

11

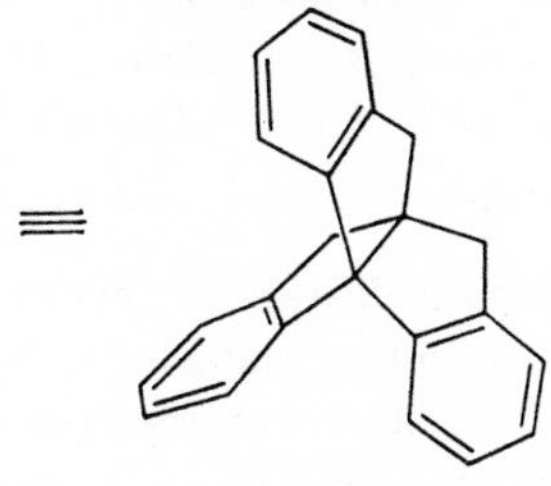

11

[3a] H. W. Thompson, *J. Org.*, **33**, 621 (1968)
[3b] G. W. Kenner and N. R. Williams, *J. Chem. Soc.*, 522 (1955)

N,N-Diethyl-1-propynylamine   (N,N-Diethylaminopropyne), $CH_3C\equiv CN(C_2H_5)_2$
[**1**, 253, before **Diethyl sulfate**]. Mol. wt. 111.19, b.p. 130–132°. Supplier: Fl. (the first commercially available alkynylamine).

Preparation.[1,2]

$$CH_3CH_2CON(C_2H_5) \xrightarrow[95\%]{COCl_2} CH_3CH_2CCl=\overset{+}{N}(C_2H_5)_2\overset{-}{Cl}$$

$$CH_3CH_2CCl=\overset{+}{N}(C_2H_5)_2\overset{-}{Cl} \xrightarrow[-2\,HCl]{LiN(C_6H_{11})_2} CH_3C\equiv CN(C_2H_5)_2$$
$$58\%$$

Uses. The reagent has a strong tendency to react with water to form an amide $[CH_3C\equiv CN(C_2H_5)_2 \xrightarrow{H_2O} CH_3CH_2CON(C_2H_5)_2]$; indeed it appears to be more reactive in this respect than DCC or ethoxyacetylene. It is useful in the formation of amides (1), of carboxylic acid anhydrides (2), and of alkyl halides from alcohols (3).[3] Like DCC, alkynylamines can be used in the synthesis of peptides.[4] According

(1) $C_6H_5COOH + H_2NC_6H_5 \xrightarrow{alkynylamine} C_6H_5CONHC_6H_5$

(2) $2\,\underline{n}\text{-}C_3H_7COOH \xrightarrow[93\text{-}96\%]{alkynylamine} (\underline{n}\text{-}C_3H_7CO)_2O$

(3) $C_6H_5CH_2OH + HF \xrightarrow[60\text{-}90\%]{alkynylamine} C_6H_5CH_2CH_2F$

to Weygand,[5] no or slight racemization occurs in this procedure and yields are in the range 40–90%.

Alkynylamines also undergo 1,2- and 1,3-cycloaddition reactions.[3,6] A preliminary communication on the acylation, alkylation, and protonation of alkynylamines has appeared.[7]

[1]H. Eilingsfeld, M. Seefelder, and H. Weidinger, *Ber.*, **96**, 2671 (1963)
[2]R. Buijle, A. Halleux, and H. G. Viehe, *Angew. Chem. internat. Ed.*, **5**, 584 (1966)
[3]H. G. Viehe, R. Fuks, and M. Reinstein, *ibid.*, **3**, 581 (1964)
[4]R. Buijle and H. G. Viehe, *ibid.*, **3**, 582 (1964)
[5]F. Weygand, W. König, R. Buijle, and H. G. Viehe, *Ber.*, **98**, 3632 (1965)
[6]R. Fuks, R. Buijle, and H. G. Viehe, *Angew. Chem. internat. Ed.*, **5**, 585 (1966)
[7]H. G. Viehe, R. Buijle, R. Fuks, R. Merényi, and J. M. F. Oth, *ibid.*, **6**, 77 (1967)

N,N-Diethyl-1,2,2-trichlorovinylamine [1, 253, before references].

The reagent has been used to convert 16-hydroxysteroids into 16-chlorosteroids, with inversion, in "high yields."[3] Thionyl chloride was unsatisfactory.

[3]G. B. Spero, J. E. Pike, F. H. Lincoln, and J. L. Thompson, *Steroids*, **11**, 769 (1968)

Diethylzinc–Methylene iodide [1, 253, before reference].

The method is particularly suitable for the reaction of vinyl ethers and other easily polymerizable olefins. Moreover, the reaction proceeds stereospecifically; thus *cis*-propenyl isobutyl ether gives *cis*-1-methyl-2-isobutoxycyclopropane and *trans*-propenyl isobutyl ether gives *trans*-1-methyl-2-isobutoxycyclopropane.[1]

Another useful feature is that the reagent generated from diethylzinc and benzal iodide shows a pronounced *syn*-stereoselectivity in the reaction with olefins. Thus the reaction of cyclohexene gives the 7-phenylnorcaranes, in which the *endo* to *exo* isomer ratio is 17 : 1.[2]

(17:1)

[1]Definitive paper: J. Furukawa, N. Kuwabata and J. Nishimura, *Tetrahedron*, **24**, 53 (1968)
[2]*Idem*, *Tetrahedron Letters*, 3495 (1968)

Difluoramine [1, 253–254].

Synthesis of diazirines [1, 254, after citation of ref. 4]. Difluoramine reacts with a substituted imine to produce a diazirine, a fluoroazo compound, or an α-fluoroalkyl-idenehydrazone in relative amounts dependent upon the nature of the alkyl groups:[4a]

$$\underset{R_2}{\overset{R_1}{>}}C{=}NR_3 \xrightarrow{\ NHF_2\ } \underset{R_2}{\overset{R_1}{>}}C{<}\underset{N}{\overset{N}{\|}} + \underset{R_2}{\overset{R_1}{>}}\underset{F}{\overset{|}{C}}{-}N{=}NR_3 + \underset{R_2}{\overset{R_1}{>}}C{=}CNNHR_3$$

[**1**, 254, before references]: Difluoramine reacts with aliphatic aldehydes and ketones to give α-difluoroaminocarbinols of varying stability.[6] Aromatic aldehydes give only slight yields of adducts, and aromatic ketones give no reaction.

$$>C{=}O \ + \ HNF_2 \ \rightleftharpoons \ >\underset{NF_2}{\overset{OH}{C<}}$$

Aldehydes and ketones react with difluoramine in concentrated (at least 92%) sulfuric acid to give *gem*-bis(difluoramino) derivatives. α,β-Unsaturated carbonyl groups undergo Michael addition.[7]

$$CH_3COCH_3 \ \xrightarrow[85\%]{\ NHF_2\ } \ CH_3\underset{NF_2}{\overset{NF_2}{\overset{|}{\underset{|}{C}}}}CH_3$$

Difluoramine reacts vigorously with acetone phenylhydrazone to give N-fluoro-dimethylketimine.[8]

$$2\,(CH_3)_2C{=}NNHC_6H_5 \ \xrightarrow{\ HNF_3\ } \ (CH_3)_2C{=}NF \ + \ N_2 \ + \ C_6H_6 \ + \ (CH_3)_2C{=}NNHC_6H_5 \cdot HF$$

Difluoramine can be alkylated by a carbonium ion generated from an alkyl halide, alcohol, olefin, or ether.[9] Ether derivatives require no catalysis; with olefins the complex with BF_3 or phosphoric acid is used.

$$(C_6H_5)_3CBr \ + \ HNF_2 \ \xrightarrow{\ SO_2(25^0)\ } \ (C_6H_5)_3CNHF_2$$

$$C_6H_5CCl_3 \ + \ HNF_2 \ + \ CF_3CO_2H \ \longrightarrow \ C_6H_5CCl_2NF_2$$

$$\text{(pyran)} \ + \ HNF_2 \ \longrightarrow \ \text{(tetrahydropyran-NF}_2\text{)}$$

[4a]W. H. Graham, *Am. Soc.*, **88**, 4677 (1966)
[6]J. P. Freeman, W. H. Graham, and C. O. Parker, *Am. Soc.*, **90**, 121 (1968)
[7]K. Baum, *ibid.*, **90**, 7083 (1968)
[8]C. L. Bumgardner and J. P. Freeman, *Tetrahedron Letters*, 5547 (1966)
[9]W. H. Graham and J. P. Freeman, *Am. Soc.*, **89**, 716 (1967)

sym-Difluorotetrachloroacetone [**1**, 254–255, before reference]. For generation of chlorofluorocarbene, *see also* R. A. Moss and R. Gerstl, *Tetrahedron*, **23**, 2549 (1967); *idem, J. Org.*, **32**, 2268 (1967).

Difluorotriphenylphosphorane $(C_6H_5)_3PF_2$ [**1**, 255, before **Diglyme**]. Mol. wt. 300.28, m.p. 134–142° (not completely pure), toxic.

Preparation. Japanese chemists[1] prepared the reagent by a procedure improved over one first described by Smith.[2] Triphenylphosphine is heated in an autoclave in benzene solution with sulfur tetrafluoride; yield 92.5%.

Preparation of alkyl fluorides.[1] The reagent reacts with primary and secondary alcohols to give the corresponding alkyl fluorides; yields are generally in the range of 50–70%.

[1]Y. Kobayashi and C. Akashi, *Chem. Pharm. Bull.*, **16**, 1009 (1968)
[2]W. C. Smith, *Am. Soc.*, **82**, 6176 (1960)

Digitonin, $C_{56}H_{72}O_{29}$ [**1**, 255, before **Diglyme**]. Mol. wt. 1229.30. Sinters at 225°, melts at 234–236°, $\alpha^{20}D - 54°$ in methanol. Solubility 25°:1 g. dissolves in 57 ml. of absolute ethanol or in 220 ml. of 95% ethanol. Very slightly soluble in water, forming a soapy suspension. Practically insoluble in chloroform or ether. Occurs in seeds of *Digitalis purpurea* and *Digitalis lanata* together with the related steroid sapogenins gitonin and tigonin and certain cardiac glycosides.

Structure. Digitonin is made up of the rare steroid sapogenin digitogenin linked through the 3β-hydroxyl group to a five-unit sugar moiety:

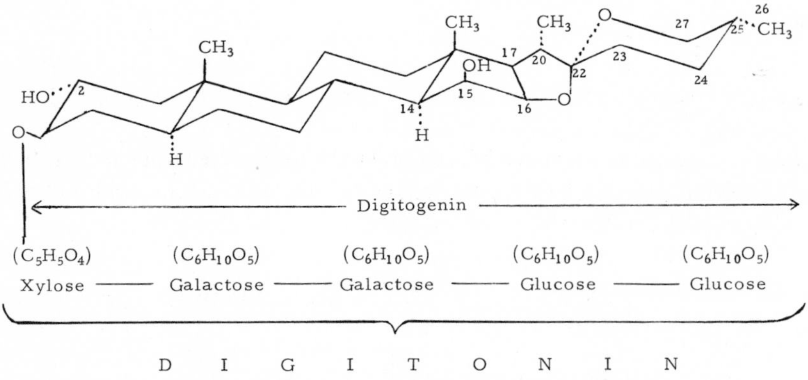

It contains two free hydroxyl groups in the aglycone portion and fifteen in the carbohydrate portion. From the results of a careful study, Tschesche and Wulff[1] concluded that the glycoside has the branched-chain structure shown in the formula:

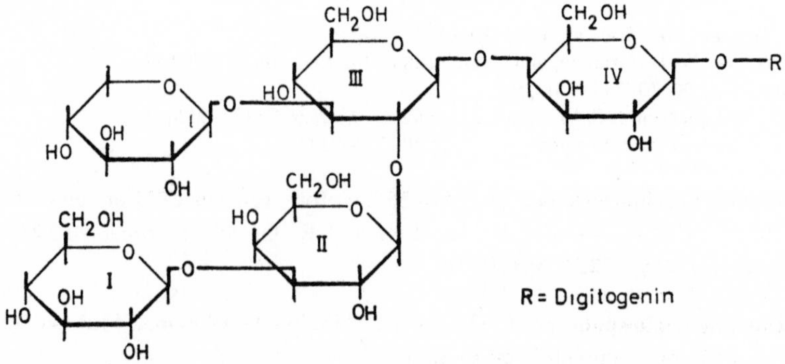

Suppliers (price range, $13–25 per 5 g.): Calbiochem., F., Fl., K.-L., E. Merck, Riedel de Haën, Sch.

Precipitation of 3β-hydroxysteroids. Recognized early as a particularly characteristic property of digitonin is its hemolytic activity, that is, its ability to effect rupture of red blood cells at high dilution. R. Ransom[2] in 1901 observed that addition of cholesterol to a solution of digitonin in 95% ethanol destroys the hemolytic activity, and Adolf Windaus[3] in 1907 discovered the reason; cholesterol combines with digitonin to form a 1:1 molecular complex, a digitonide, which is practically insoluble in 90–95% ethanol. Cholesterol occurs in body tissues in both the free

Cholesterol

form and as esters of the alcohol with higher fatty acids, and Windaus observed that the esters, unlike the free alcohol, are not precipitated by digitonin. He had procured from E. Merck-Darmstadt samples of several saponins for study and found in aqueous ethanol a common solvent for saponin and cholesterol. Of all the cholesterol complexes studied initially or subsequently, the complex of digitonin is the least soluble and hence the most satisfactory for precipitation. Tigonin, for example, differs from digitonin only in the absence of the 2α- and 15β-hydroxyl groups, and the solubility of cholesterol tigonide in 95% ethanol at 18° is 150 mg./100 ml.[4] whereas cholesterol digitonide is soluble to the extent of only 14 mg./100 ml.[5] Digitonin, with a total of 17 hydroxyl groups, which account for 24% of the molecular weight, is insoluble in ether, sparingly soluble in absolute ethanol, and more soluble in aqueous ethanol (80–95%), the solvent usually employed for precipitation of digitonides. Complex formation with cholesterol is observable at a dilution of 1:10,000. For macrodetermination of cholesterol, Windaus[6] added a solution of digitonin in hot 90% ethanol to a solution of the sample in hot 95% ethanol as long as precipitation occurred and, after several hours, collected and weighed the ether-washed digitonide. Esters of cholesterol having been shown not to complex with digitonin, a method was at hand for determination of both free and esterified cholesterol.[6] Digitonin precipitation with one portion of a tissue extract establishes the content of free cholesterol, and precipitation after saponification establishes the total amount of cholesterol present. Windaus also paved the way for microdetermination by the observation[5] that cholesterol digitonide, like cholesterol itself, gives the highly sensitive Liebermann-Burchard color reaction[7] done by adding a fresh solution of 1 drop of concentrated sulfuric acid and 1 ml. of iced acetic anhydride to a solution of the sterol in chloroform; the color is slow to develop but very intense. The test is negative with fully purified cholesterol, positive with cholesteryl acetate and Δ5-cholestene. In the methods of microdetermination subsequently developed, the cholesterol content of a digitonin precipitate is found by colorimetric determination of the intensity of the transient Liebermann-Burchard color after a suitable time lapse.

Windaus and Uibrig[8] discovered a remarkable stereospecificity in digitonin precipitation: both cholestane-3β-ol and coprostane-3β-ol are precipitated essentially quantitatively, whereas cholestane-3α-ol and coprostane-3α-ol are not precipitated. Thus for formation of a sparingly soluble digitonide the 3-hydroxyl group must be β, but can be either equatorial or axial, and C_5 can have the α- or the β-configuration, or a 5,6-double bond can be present. The precipitant proved invaluable for study of the isomerization of stanols by heating with a solution of sodium 2-methyl-2-butoxide prepared by refluxing t-amyl alcohol with sodium in benzene or xylene. Cholestanol, with an equatorial hydroxyl group, affords on equilibration only about

10% of epicholestanol (axial), but the minor component of the mixture can be isolated from the filtrate left on precipitation of the major product with digitonin. Cholestanol can be recovered from the digitonide by dissolving the complex in pyridine in which dissociation is complete, adding ether to precipitate digitonin, and working up the ethereal solution. In the case of coprostanol, the equilibrium favors the unprecipitable equatorial 3α-ol. In seeking a route from cholestanol to coprostanol, Windaus found that hydrogenation over nickel at 200° gave a mixture of cholestanol, epicholestanol, and epicoprostanol. He removed cholestanol with digitonin, equilibrated the residue with alkoxide, removed the newly formed cholesterol, and obtained a nonprecipitable residue greatly enriched in epicoprostanol. A few repetitions of the process afforded pure epicoprostanol. By repeated equilibration and digitonin precipitation, this substance was then converted into coprostanol, identical with a substance isolated as a product of bacterial reduction of cholesterol in the gut.

In view of the high cost of digitonin, we emphasize ref. 2 (**1**, 309) to the very efficient method of splitting a digitonide by dissolving it in dimethyl sulfoxide at steam bath temperature; the digitonide dissociates completely, and on cooling the sterol precipitates and can be extracted with hexane.

[1]R. Tschesche and G. Wulff, *Tetrahedron*, **19**, 621 (1963)

[2]R. Ransom, *Deut. med. Wochenshr.*, **27**, 194 (1901)

[3]A. Windaus, *Ber.*, **40**, 2637 (1907)

[4]R. Tschesche, *ibid.*, **69**, 1665 (1936)

[5]A. Windaus, *ibid.*, **42**, 238 (1909)

[6]A. Windaus, *Z. physiol.*, **65**, 110 (1910)

[7]C. Liebermann, *Ber.*, **18**, 1803 (1885); H. Burchard, Innaugural Dissertation, Rostock (1889), see *Chem. Zentr.*, **61**, I, 25 (1890)

[8]A. Windaus and C. Uibrig, *Ber.*, **47**, 2384 (1914)

Diimide [1, 257–258, before *Reviews*].

The *trans* double bond of a *cis,trans* conjugated dienoic acid is also reduced faster than the *cis* double bond by diimide (generated from hydrazine).[10a] In the case of *cis,trans* conjugated dienols (hydroxyl group α to the diene grouping), use of diimide generated from hydrazine hydrate leads to formation of a nitrogen-containing product, sometimes in considerable amount. Use of potassium azodicarboxylate as the source of diimide circumvents this difficulty.[10b]

Franzus *et al.*[10c] examined the diimide reduction of 7-oxygenated norbornadienes with the expectation of obtaining the corresponding *syn*-norbornene. Since diimide reductions proceed by *cis* addition and are subject to steric approach control, the 7-substituent should inhibit formation of the exocyclic transition state with the *syn*

anti
main

syn
minor

X = H, OCOCH$_3$, OC(CH$_3$)$_3$

double bond. Actually, the main product was the *anti* isomer and the *syn* product, if formed at all, was a minor product. A rationalization ascribed the unexpected result to strong electronic effect from coordination of the partially positive N—N bond with the oxygen atom at position 7.

[10a]K. L. Mikolajczak, M. O. Bagby, R. B. Bates, and I. A. Wolff, *J. Org.*, **30**, 2983 (1965)

[10b]R. G. Powell, C. R. Smith, Jr., and I. A. Wolff, *ibid.*, **32**, 1442 (1967)

[10c]W. C. Baird, Jr., B. Franzus, and J. H. Surridge, *Am. Soc.*, **89**, 410 (1967)

Diiron nonacarbonyl [1, 259–260].

Supplier: Alfa Inorganics. Preparation.[1a] It is formed by exposing iron pentacarbonyl to sunlight or, better, to artificial light:

$$2\,Fe(CO)_5 \xrightarrow[74\%]{h\nu} Fe_2(CO)_9 \;+\; CO$$

The reaction with acetylene is described in ref. 1, **1**, 260.

[1, 259, last line]: *Correct to read:* Structure 1 is favored by the British group.[1a]

[1, 260, before references]: When α,α'-dibromo-*o*-xylene (1) is heated with diiron nonacarbonyl, the very unstable quinonedimethane formed can be isolated as the stable π-complex with iron tricarbonyl (2).[4] On being heated to 500°, the complex

(1)   (2)   (3)

decomposes to benzocyclobutene (3). This is an example of stabilization of a highly reactive substance by formation of a complex containing a transition-state metal.

Cyclobutadiene itself has not been prepared, but the stable complex, cyclobutadieneiron tricarbonyl (3), can be prepared readily in quantities of 10 g. or more by reaction of 3,4-dichlorocyclobutene (1) with diiron nonacarbonyl (2).[5]

(1)   (2)   250 ml.   (3)

60 g.   about 275 g.

In a well-ventilated hood a 1-l. three-necked flask is immersed in an oil bath and fitted with a mechanical stirrer and condenser with a T-piece at the top with one lead connected to a nitrogen supply and the other to a gas bubbler. The flask is charged with 60 g. (0.49 mole) of *cis*-3,4-dichlorocyclobutene (this volume) in 250 ml. of benzene, and the system is flushed with nitrogen. A first 50-g. batch of diiron nonacarbonyl (2) is added and the mixture is heated at 50–55° with stirring. After about 15 min. the initial rapid evolution of carbon monoxide becomes greatly diminished and a further 25 g. of $Fe_2(CO)_9$ is added. Further 25-g. portions are added until no more carbon monoxide is liberated; a total of approximately 275 g. of $Fe_2(CO)_9$ is required and the total reaction time is about 5 hrs. The mixture is then filtered with suction through Celite and the Büchner funnel is washed thoroughly with pentane until the filtrate is colorless. Fractional distillation at reduced pressure removes benzene, then iron pentacarbonyl (b.p. 20°/30 mm.); when the $Fe(CO)_5$ has been removed, cyclobutadieneiron tricarbonyl is collected as a pale yellow oil, b.p. 47°/3 mm.

[1a]E. H. Braye and W. Hübel, *Inorg. Syn.*, **8**, 178 (1966)
[4]W. R. Roth and J. P. Meier, *Tetrahedron Letters*, 2053 (1967)
[5]R. Pettit and J. Henery, procedure submitted to *Org. Syn.*, 1968

Diisobutylaluminum hydride [1, 260–262, after (4) → (5)].

Baran[7a] reduced the δ-lactone (7a) to the lactol (7b) by stirring a mixture in toluene at −60°.

(7a)   (7b)

Other reductions [1, 262, after citation of ref. 11].

The observations of Zakharkin and Khorlina[11] of the reduction of esters to aldehydes proved useful to a Hungarian group[11a] who had attempted a new total synthesis of emetine. However, it became necessary, as a completing step, to reduce

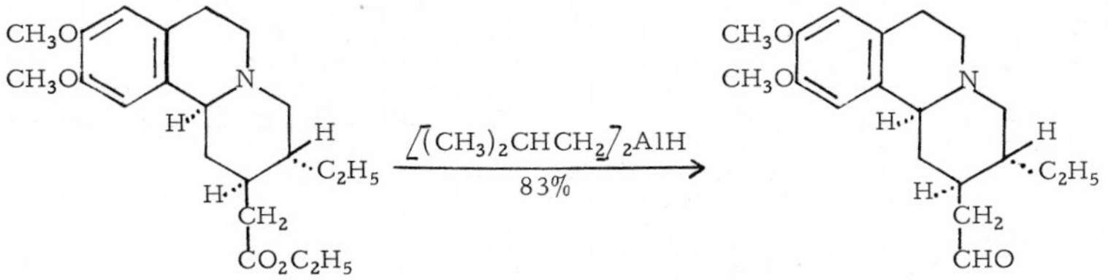

(1)   (2)

the ester (1) to the corresponding aldehyde (2), protoemitine. Various methods were tried but failed, and then the desired reduction of (1) → (2) was accomplished in very good yield by reduction of the ester (1) with diisobutylaluminum hydride in toluene at $-60°$.

Reduction of an α,β-unsaturated γ-lactone to a furane. [1, 262, before references]. The reaction was used as the terminal step in the total synthesis of the sesquiterpene (±)-lindestrene (2).[14]

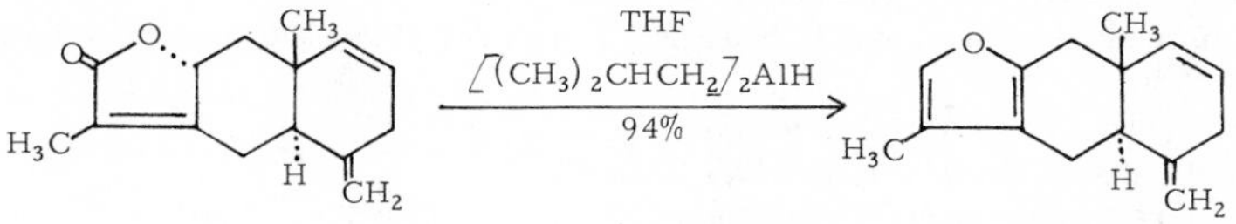

(1)   (2)

Hydroalumination of alkynes. The hydride reacts with alkynes in a hydrocarbon solvent by *cis* addition to yield a *trans*-vinylalane (1) from 1-alkynes and a *cis*-vinylalane from disubstituted alkynes. Treatment of the vinylalane with methyllithium in ether in a 1:1 ratio to give an *ate* complex (2) followed by carbonation

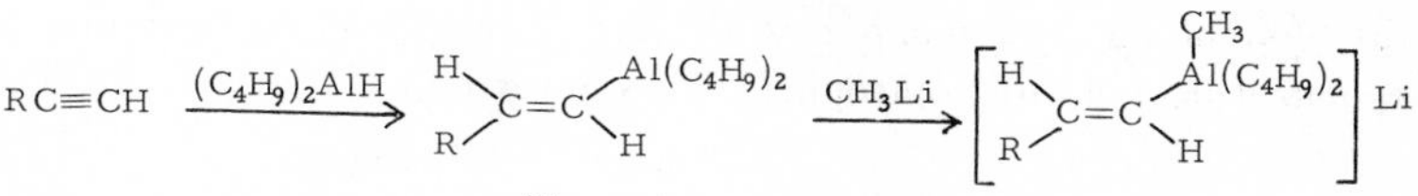

(1)   (2)

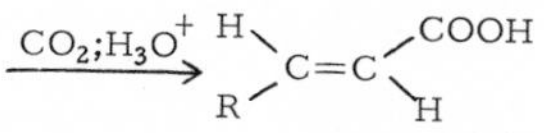

(3)

gives α,β-unsaturated acids (3) in yields of 70–80%.[15] The isobutyl moeities are converted into isobutane in the hydrolysis step. The high stereospecificity of the reaction is noteworthy.

ate-Complexes also react with cyanogen at room temperature to give sterically pure α,β-unsaturated nitriles. Thus *trans*-hept-2-enenitrile is obtained from 1-hexyne in 87% yield.[16]

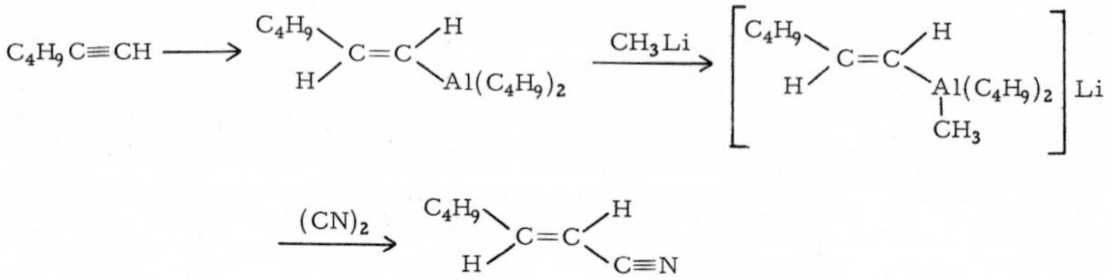

The vinylalanes react with halogens to give vinyl halides. It is not necessary to form the *ate*-complex. *trans*-Vinyl halides are obtained in the case of 1-alkynes, and *cis*-vinyl halides in the case of disubstituted alkynes.[17]

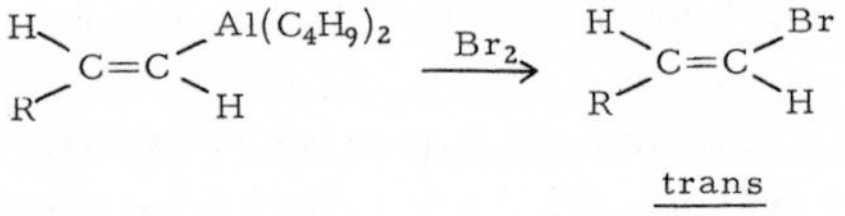

trans

[7a]J. S. Baran, *J. Org.*, **30**, 3564 (1965)
[11a]C. Szántay, L. Töke, and P. Kolonits, *J. Org.*, **31**, 1447 (1966)
[13]Correct to read: H. Minato and T. Nagasaki, *Chem. Ind.*, 899 (1965); *idem, J. Chem. Soc.*, (C), 377 (1966)
[14]H. Minato and T. Nagasaki, *J. Chem. Soc.*, (C), 621 (1968)
[15]G. Zweifel and R. B. Steele, *Am. Soc.*, **89**, 2754 (1967)
[16]G. Zweifel, J. T. Snow, and C. C. Whitney, *ibid.*, **90**, 7139 (1968)
[17]G. Zweifel and C. C. Whitney, *ibid.*, **89**, 2753 (1967)

Diisopropyl peroxydicarbonate [**1**, 263–264, ref. 2]. *Add:* For a detailed study, see M. E. Kurz and P. Kovacic, *Am. Soc.*, **89**, 4960 (1967).

3,5-Dimethoxybenzyl *p*-nitrophenyl carbonate, (1) [**1**, 267, before **1,2-Dimethoxy-ethane**]. Mol. wt. 333.29, m.p. 114–115°.

Preparation. The reagent is prepared[1] by reaction of 3,5-dimethoxybenzoic acid (Aldrich) with lithium aluminum hydride and acylation of the resulting 3,5-dimethoxybenzyl alcohol with *p*-nitrophenyl chloroformate.

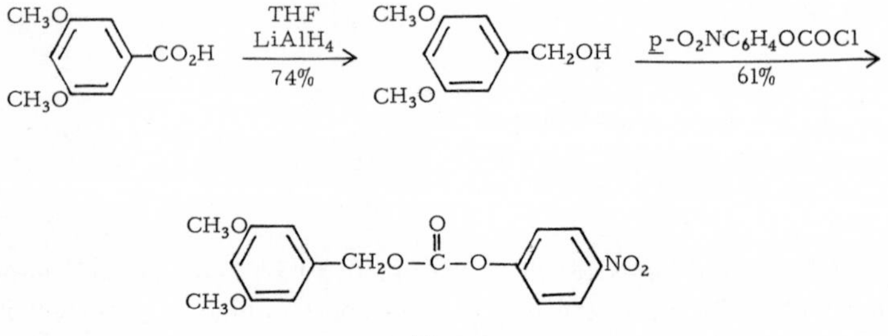

(1)

Peptide synthesis, N-protection.[1] Amino acids react with the reagent in aqueous THF in the presence of sodium hydroxide to give 3,5-dimethoxybenzyloxycarbonyl derivatives in yields of 55–75%, as illustrated for a sample of L-*serine*, $\alpha D + 13.5°$. The protective group can be cleaved in 42–85% yield without use of acid or base or

reductive cleavage by simple irradiation in aqueous dioxane with a high-pressure mercury lamp (1.5 hrs.). The method is useful because of neutral conditions. Note that under the conditions used carbobenzoxy derivatives are cleaved by irradiation in only very low yield.

[1]J. W. Chamberlin, *J. Org.*, **31**, 1658 (1966)

1,1-Dimethoxyethane [1, 267, before 1,2-Dimethoxyethane]. *See* Acetaldehyde dimethylacetal (this volume).

1,2-Dimethoxyethane (Glyme) [1, 267–268, before references].

In a systematic study of enolate anions, House[10] selected this solvent because it will provide approximately 1 M concentrations of most enolate anions, it is relatively volatile and easily removed from products, it possesses no H-atoms sufficiently acidic to exchange with enolate anions, and it enhances the reactivity of anions by solvation.

Reduction of cinnamyl alcohols by $LiAlH_4$ is faster in this solvent than in ether by a factor of 13–47.[11] THF is intermediate.

Review.[12]

[10]H. O. House, *Rec. Chem. Progress*, **28**, 99 (1967)
[11]M. J. Jorgenson and A. F. Thacher, *Chem. Commun.*, 973 (1968)
[12]C. Agami, *Bull. soc.*, 1205 (1968)

5,5-Dimethoxy-1,2,3,4-tetrachlorocyclopentadiene [1, 270, before references].

Scherer[4] effected Diels-Alder addition of this reagent to ethylene[5] in the first step of a synthesis of 4-chlorobicyclo[2.2.0]hexane-1-carboxylic acid (5). The unsaturated tetrachloride (2) on hydrogenation in ethanol in the presence of excess triethylamine gave the saturated dichloride (3) by saturation of the double bond and hydrogenolysis of two chlorine atoms. The ketal group was then hydrolyzed with 96% sulfuric acid in methylene chloride solution at room temperature, and the product (4) was treated with base to effect Favorski rearrangement to (5). The synthesis is of interest because most previous syntheses of the bicyclo[2.2.0]hexane system have been photochemical and do not give derivatives with functional groups at the bridgehead position.

(1)   (2)

(3)   (4)   (5)

Scherer[6] states that hydrogenation of (2) to (3) "seems to be tricky." Other workers have repeated the preparation satisfactorily, but one has claimed that the proper order of mixing the ingredients is: substrate, catalyst, ethanol, triethylamine. Scherer notes that the complete experimental details are given in another paper.[7] that the purity of (2) is probably a factor, and that he usually (always?) added the amine last and never had the reduction fail.

[4]K. V. Scherer, Jr., *Tetrahedron Letters*, 5685 (1966)
[5]This Diels-Alder reaction has also been effected in essentially the same yield by P. G. Gassman and J. L. Marshall, *Org. Syn.*, **48**, 68 (1968)
[6]K. V. Scherer, Jr., private communication
[7]W. G. Dauben, J. L. Chitwood, and K. V. Scherer, Jr., *Am. Soc.*, **90**, 1014 (1968)

2,5-Dimethoxytetrahydrofurane,   [**1**, 270, before **Di-methylacetamide**]. Mol. wt. 132.16, b.p. 144–146°. Suppliers: A. Columbia, E. Fl.
    Preparation by catalytic hydrogenation of 2,5-dimethoxy-2,5-dihydrofurane.[1]
    Synthesis of pyrroles. An efficient one-step synthesis of N-substituted pyrroles developed by Clauson-Kaas and Tyle[2] is illustrated by the condensation of 2,5-dimethoxytetrahydrofurane with methyl anthranilate in refluxing acetic acid to give 1-(2-methoxycarbonylphenyl)pyrrole.[3]

[1]J. Fakstorp, D. Raleigh, and L. E. Schniepp, *Am. Soc.*, **72**, 869 (1950)
[2]N. Clauson-Kaas and Z. Tyle, *Chem. Scand.*, **6**, 667, 867 (1952)
[3]A. D. Josey, *Org. Syn.*, **47**, 81 (1967)

Dimethylacetamide[**1**, 270–271, before references].
    Esterification (solvent effect). Parker,[4] in a review article on the use of aprotic solvents, cited unpublished results from his laboratory showing that "Many

carboxylic acids can be esterified using excess methyl iodide with sodium bicarbonate in dimethylacetamide at room temperature. The procedure gives cleaner products than those obtained using diazomethane or dimethyl sulfate." Alvarez and Watt[5] applied this method in a large-scale (872 g.) esterification of the bisnorcholanic acid (1); the reaction required 48 hrs. at room temperature but the yield was almost quantitative. In this

(1)

case, esterification with methanol containing 2%(w/w) of sulfuric acid gave the ester in only 53.6% yield.

[4]A. J. Parker, *Advan. Org. Chem., Methods and Results*, **5**, 37 (1965)
[5]F. S. Alvarez and A. N. Watt, *J. Org.*, **33**, 2143 (1968)

Dimethyl acetylenedicarboxylate [**1**, 272–273]. Additional suppliers: Columbia Organic Chemicals Co., Farchan Res. Labs. Fl., E. Merck, Sch.

Synthesis of heterocycles [before references]. Hendrickson *et al.*[4] developed a useful general synthesis of heterocycles in which the key step is a Michael addition of the reagent to a substrate of a variety of types having an amino, mercaptan, or hydroxyl group adjacent to an electrophilic center. An example is the reaction of α-aminopropiophenone hydrochloride, and sodium acetate to liberate the amine (1), with dimethyl acetylenedicarboxylate in refluxing methanol. Sodium chloride

separated and after 10 minutes filtration and evaporation afforded (4), easily transformed by a trace of acid into the pyrrole (5) in good yield. An advantage of the method is that the triple bond gives rise to a double bond required for aromaticity of the heterocycle.

$$(7)^5 \quad \begin{array}{c} C_6H_5C{=}O \\ | \\ C_6H_5CHNH \\ | \\ C_6H_5 \end{array} \quad + \quad \begin{array}{c} CO_2CH_3 \\ | \\ C \\ \| \\ C \\ | \\ CO_2CH_3 \end{array} \quad \xrightarrow{79\%} \quad \begin{array}{c} C_6H_5 \\ C_6H_5 \end{array}\!\!\boxed{}\!\!\begin{array}{c} CO_2CH_3 \\ CO_2CH_3 \end{array}$$

[4]J. B. Hendrickson and R. Rees, *Am. Soc.*, **83**, 1250 (1961); J. B. Hendrickson, R. Rees, and J. F. Templeton, *ibid.*, **86**, 107 (1964)
[5]D. S. James and P. E. Fanta, *J. Org.*, **27**, 3346 (1962)

p-Dimethylaminobenzaldehyde [1, 273–274, before references].

Aldehyde synthesis. The reagent reacts with an alkyl- or arylmagnesium bromide to give a *p*-dimethylaminophenylcarbinol (1). This is easily cleaved by diazonium salts (diazotized sulfanilic acid was used because 3, Ar = *p*-$HO_3SC_6H_4$-, methyl orange is easy to eliminate). The products are the aldehyde (2) and an azobenzene

$$RMgBr + \underline{p}\text{-}(CH_3)_2NC_6H_4CHO \longrightarrow R\overset{OH}{\underset{}{C}}H\!\!-\!\!\boxed{}\!\!-N(CH_3)_2 \xrightarrow[-H^+]{ArN_2^+}$$

(1)

$$RCHO + ArN{=}N\!\!-\!\!\boxed{}\!\!-N(CH_3)_2$$

(2)   (3)

(3).[5] The cleavage reaction had been known for some time, but attention had been focused on the azobenzene derivative rather than the aldehyde. Yields are in the range of 50–80%, and hence the method is useful for the conversion of RBr → RCHO.

[5]M. Stiles and A. J. Sisti, *J. Org.*, **25**, 1691 (1960)

N-(4-Dimethylamino-3,5-dinitrophenyl)maleimide (DDPM) [1, 274, before 3-Dimethyl-aminopropylamine]. Mol. wt. 306.23, m.p. 177–181°. Preparation.[1] Supplier: A.

DDPM   (2)

(3)

Reaction with thiols. The reagent reacts specifically with the thiol group of an amino acid or protein to give a derivative (2) which is colored or develops color with ninhydrin. Thus the sulfhydryl group of cysteine adds to the activated double bond to give a yellow neutral compound (2). This compound, which gives a purple color with ninhydrin, rearranges even in neutral solution to the carboxylic acid (3).[1]

Wintersberger[2] isolated from bovine pancreatic carboxypeptidase a peptide containing a thiol group involved in the binding of zinc. He first removed the zinc by exposure to a chelating agent (1,10-phenanthroline) or by denaturation, and then labeled the reactive sulfhydryl group by reaction with DDPM and determined the amino acid sequence.

Other applications for elucidation of amino acid sequences.[3]

[1]A. Witter and H. Tuppy, *Biochim. Biophysica Acta*, **45**, 429 (1960)
[2]E. Wintersberger, *Biochemistry,* **4**, 1533 (1965)
[3]A. H. Gold and H. L. Segal, *ibid.,* **3**, 778 (1964); *idem, ibid.,* **4**, 1506 (1965); T. Yamashita *et al., J. Biochem.,* **55**, 576 (1964); *idem, ibid.,* **57**, 460 (1965); K. Narita and M. Akao, *ibid.,* **58**, 507 (1965); J. N. Tsunoda and K. T. Yasunobu, *J. Biol. Chem.,* **241**, 4610 (1966); R. M. Metrione, R. B. Johnston, and R. Seng, *Arch. Biochem.,* **122**, 137 (1967)

Dimethylaminotrimethylstannane, $(CH_3)_3SnN(CH_3)_2$ [1, 274, before **N,N-Dimethylaniline**]. Mol. wt. 207.88, b.p. 126°.

Preparation.[1]

$$(CH_3)_2NLi \;+\; (CH_3)_3SnCl \xrightarrow[91\%]{(C_2H_5)_2O} (CH_3)_3SnN(CH_3)_2$$

Dehydrochlorination.[2] The reagent effects dehydrochlorination under mild conditions. Thus reaction of *n*-butyl chloride (1) gives the products shown. It was also used to effect the transformation (2). In this case even 1,5-diazabicyclo[4.3.0]-nonene-5 did not effect the reaction.

$$(1)\;\; CH_3CH_2CH_2CH_2Cl \xrightarrow[40^0,\; 4\;hrs.]{(CH_3)_3SnN(CH_3)_2} (CH_3)_3SnClHN(CH_3)_2 \;+\; \begin{cases} CH_3CH=CHCH_3 \\ \underline{cis}\; 5.2\% \\ \underline{trans}\; 88.5\% \\ CH_3CH_2CH=CH_2 \\ 6.3\% \end{cases}$$

$$(2)\;\; IrHCl_2[P(C_6H_5)_3] \xrightarrow[2\;hrs.]{80-100^0} IrCl[P(C_6H_5)_3]$$

[1]K. Jones and M. F. Lappert, *J. Chem. Soc.,* 1944 (1965)
[2]D. J. Cardin and M. F. Lappert, *Chem. Commun.,* 1034 (1967)

N,N-Dimethylaniline [1, 274–276, before references].

Reductive debromination of α-bromo- and α,α-dibromoketones.[8] α-Bromo- and α,α-dibromoketones are reductively debrominated when refluxed with N,N-dimethylaniline in an oil bath kept at 220°. Other amines, including triethylamine, N-methylaniline, and N,N-diethylaniline, fail to give appreciable amounts of dehalogenated product. Examples:

α-Bromo d-camplor   d-Camphor

α-p-Dibromopropiophenone   p-Bromopropiophenone

7-Bromo-2,2-diphenyl-   2,2-Diphenyl-
cycloheptanone   cycloheptanone

[8]A. G. Giumanini, *Chimia*, **21**, 464 (1967)

2,3-Dimethyl-2-butylborane ("Thexylborane") [**1**, 276, before reference]. Supplier: 2,3-Dimethyl-2-butene is supplied by Chemical Samples Co., Columbus, Ohio 43221.

Synthesis of ketones.[2,3] The highly hindered monoalkylborane (1) reacts with olefins in two distinct steps, first to form the thexylmonoalkylborane (2) and then to form the thexyldialkylborane (3). Two different olefins can be used. The next steps of carbonylation in diglyme solution at 100° in the presence of enough water to inhibit migration of the third alkyl group of (4) from boron to carbon to produce a

(1)   (2)

(3)   (4)   (5)

trialkylcarbinol, and hydrogen peroxide oxidation in a basic medium to give the ketone (5) proceed as described (*see* **Carbon monoxide**, this volume). Note that the success of the synthesis depends upon the fact that the thexyl group does not migrate competetively in the carbonylation reaction in the manner exhibited by other groups examined. The thexyl group appears as thexyl alcohol (2,3-dimethyl-2-butanol).

Terminal olefins or disubstituted internal olefins can be used. Yields are in the range 50–80%.

Examples.

$$CH_3C(CH_3)=CH_2 \ + \ CH_2=CHCH_2(CO_2C_2H_5) \ \xrightarrow{84\%} \ (CH_3)_2CHCH_2CCH_2CH_2CH_2CO_2C_2H_5$$

$$C_6H_5CH=CH_2 \ + \ CH_2=CH(CH_2)_8CO_2CH_3 \ \xrightarrow{73\%} \ C_6H_5CH_2CH_2C(CH_2)_{10}CO_2CH_3$$

Brown[4] has applied the synthesis to preparation of polycyclic ketones in which the carbonyl group is α- to a *trans* ring junction. Thus the reaction of the conjugated diene (1) with thexylborane (RBH$_2$) in THF at 0° gave the thexylboracyclone (2), which was carbonylated at 70 atm. and 50°. Oxidation to the cyclic ketone (3) was carried out as usual with hydrogen peroxide in the presence of sodium acetate.

One noteworthy feature of this new annelation procedure is the stereospecificity to give a *trans*-ring fusion in indanone and decalone systems. The starting dienes are made by reaction of the parent ring ketone with vinyl- or allylmagnesium halides followed by dehydration of the tertiary alcohol thus formed.

[2]H. C. Brown and E. Negishi, *Am. Soc.*, **89**, 5285 (1967)
[3]H. C. Brown and C. D. Pfaffenberger, *ibid.*, **89**, 5475 (1967)
[4]H. C. Brown and E. Negishi, *Chem. Commun.*, 594 (1968)

Dimethyl carbonate, $(CH_3O)_2C=O$ [**1**, 276, before **Dimethylchloromethylene-ammonium chloride**]. Mol. wt. 90.08, m.p. 2–4°, b.p. 90°. Suppliers: A, E.

Carbomethoxylation. In one stage of a total synthesis of *dl*-caryophyllene, Corey *et al.*[1] treated the cyclic ketone (1), 7,7-dimethylbicyclo[4.2.0]octanone-2, in dioxane with sodium hydride and dimethyl carbonate at 80–85° and obtained the β-keto ester (2) in high yield.

In a synthesis of nepetic acids, Eisenbraun *et al.*[2] found this method "ideally suited

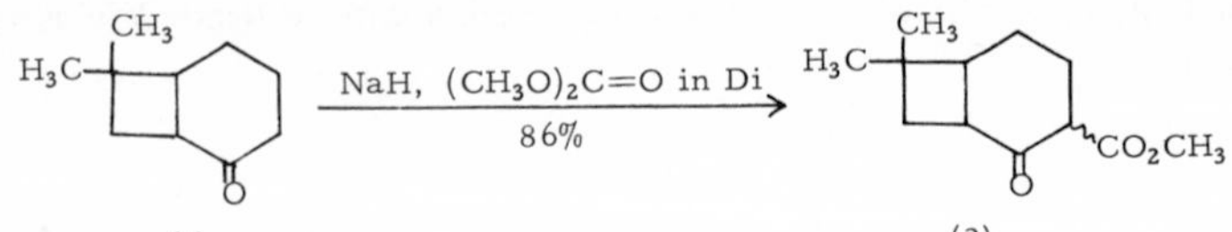

(1)   (2)

to the carbomethoxylation of 3-methylcyclohexanone." The yields in this method were better than in a two-step process involving condensation of the ketone with diethyl oxalate to give the α,γ-diketo ester followed by decarboxylation.

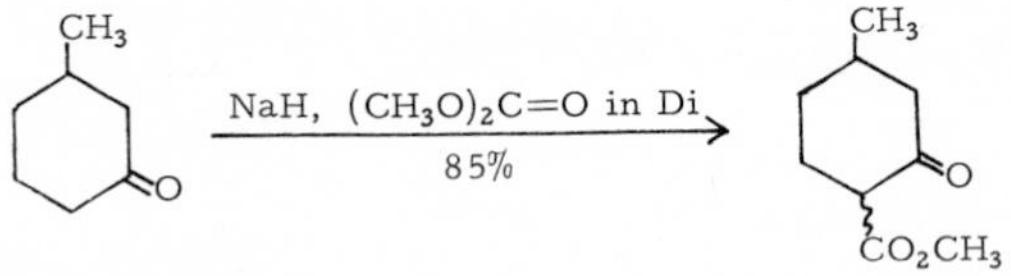

[1] E. J. Corey, R. B. Mitra, and H. Udo, *Am. Soc.*, **86**, 485 (1964)
[2] E. J. Eisenbraun, P. G. Hanel, K. S. Schorno, Sr. St. F. Dilgen, and J. Osiecki, *J. Org.*, **32**, 3010 (1967)

3,5-Dimethyl-4-chloromethylisoxazole [**1**, 276–277, before references].

A fuller account of Stork's synthesis of the unsaturated tricyclic diketone [*see* (7) on **1**, 277] is given in a communication of 1967.[3] Another communication[4] discusses the mechanism of the isoxazole annelation.

In an adaptation of the reaction to the synthesis of pyridines, a Japanese group associated with Stork[5] found that alkylation of a ketone such as acetylacetone with the reagent gives (1), which on catalytic hydrogenation in the presence of palladium

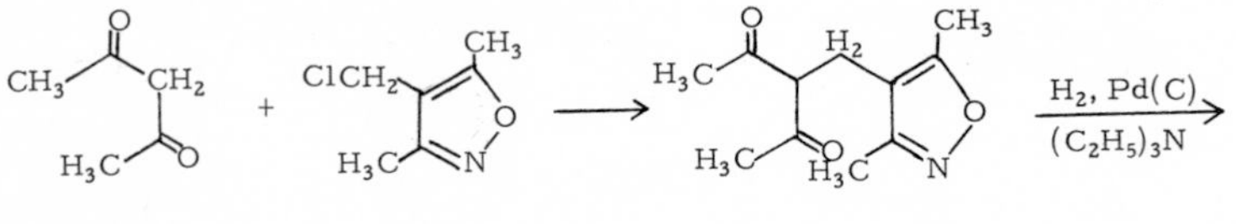

(1)

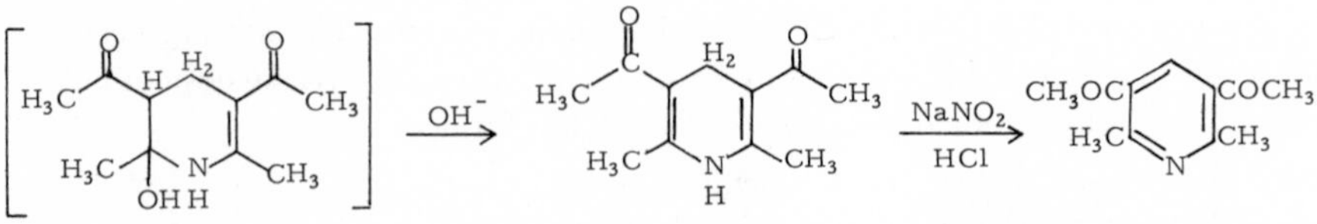

(2)   (3)   (4)

charcoal and triethylamine affords the dihydropyridine (3), which on treatment with sodium nitrite and hydrochloric acid gives the substituted pyridine (4).

The isoxazole annelation procedure has been used also in a stereospecific synthesis of *dl*-D-homotestosterone (5) and for its conversion into *dl*-progesterone.[6]

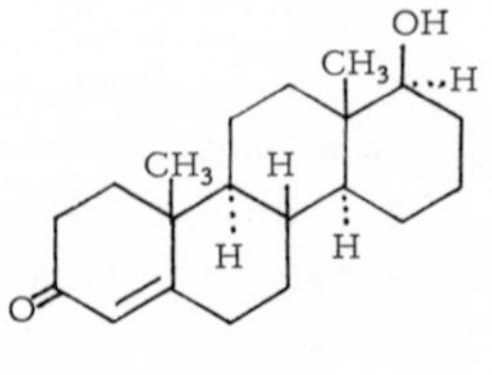

(5)

[3] G. Stork, S. Danishefsky, and M. Ohashi, *Am. Soc.*, **89**, 5459 (1967)
[4] G. Stork and J. E. McMurry, *ibid.*, **89**, 5463 (1967)
[5] M. Ohashi, H. Kamachi, H. Kakisawa, and G. Stork, *ibid.*, **89**, 5460 (1967)
[6] G. Stork and J. E. McMurry, *ibid.*, **89**, 5464 (1967).

Dimethylcopperlithium (Lithium dimethylcopper) $(CH_3)_2CuLi$ [**1**, 277, before **1,2-Dimethyl-4,5-di(mercaptomethyl)benzene**]. Mol. wt. 100.55.

Prepared[1,2] in ethereal solution from ethereal methyllithium and cuprous iodide in the molecular ratio 2:1 under nitrogen at 0°, the ether-soluble reagent "is perhaps representable as $Li^+(CH_3)_2Cu^-$ in which the anion is isoelectric with dimethylzinc."[2]

Reactions. It is an excellent reagent for the selective replacement of iodine or bromine by methyl in a wide variety of substrates, as in examples cited by Corey and Posner:[2]

The reagent adds only slowly to keto groups.[3] It has been used to effect 1,4-addition to the α,β-unsaturated ketone (1);[4] with methylmagnesium iodide catalyzed by cupric

(1)   (2)

acetate, the yield of (2) was only 16–21%. Similarly, a desired angular methyl group was introduced into the ketone (3) with the reagent to give $(+)-\Delta^{11}$-eremophilene-3-

(3)   (4)

one (4);[5] in this case the combination CH_3MgI + cupric acetate gave none of the desired eremophilene derivative. Corey[6] used the reagent to advantage in a terminal stage in the synthesis of *trans,trans*-farnesol (6).

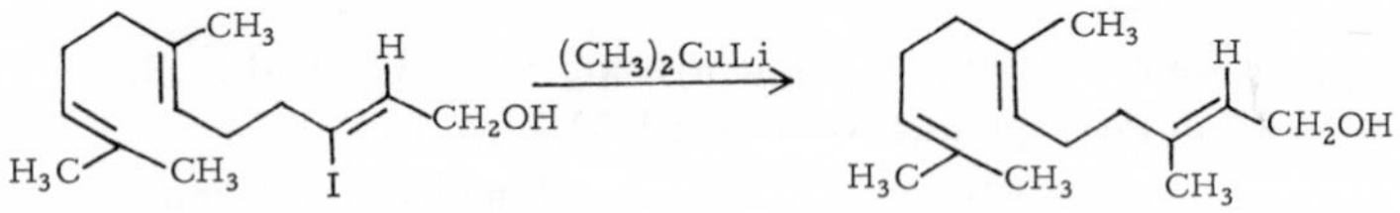

(5)   (6)

The reagent reacts with ethynylcarbinol acetates to give alkylallenes.[7] Simple acetylenes are not transformed by $(CH_3)_2CuLi$ into allenes.

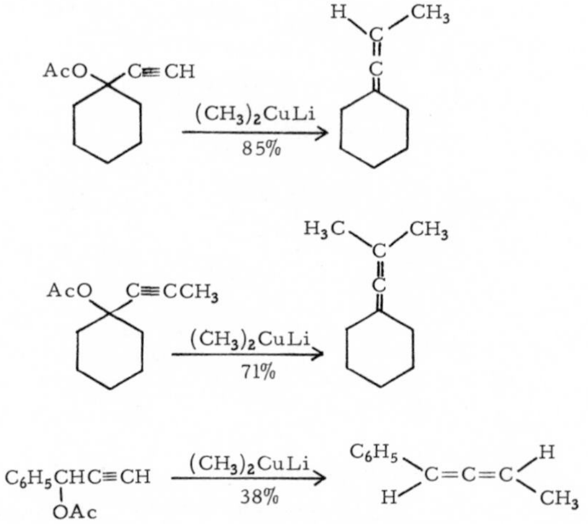

Corey and Posner[8] have prepared lithium di-*n*-butylcopper and lithium diethyl-copper and used them for cross coupling in the same way. In general they are more reactive but also less stable thermally. They also tend to induce halogen-copper exchange more than lithium dimethylcopper, but this side reaction can be reduced by addition to the reaction mixture of an excess of the alkyl halide corresponding to the *n*-alkylcopper reagent. Yields of 60–80% were obtained.

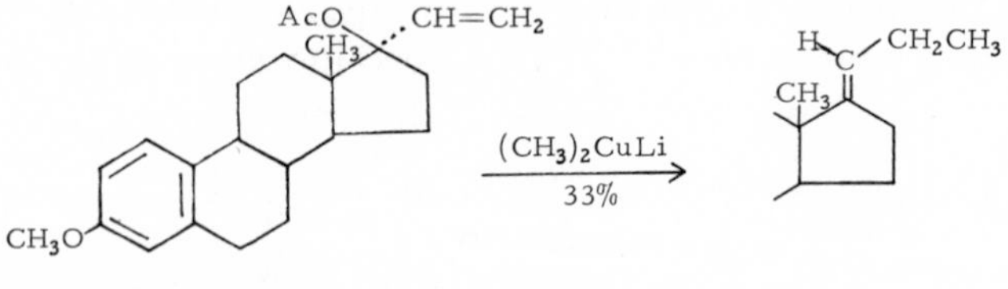

(7)   (8)

The olefin (7) reacts with the reagent (50% excess) at $-10°$ overnight to give (8) in 33% yield.[9] A similar reaction of the *gem*-difluorocyclopropene (9) gives the diene (10) in 74% yield.

(9)   (10)

[1]H. Gilman, R. G. Jones and L. A. Woods, *J. Org.*, **17**, 1630 (1952)

[2]E. J. Corey and G. H. Posner, *Am. Soc.*, **89**, 3911 (1967)

[3]J. A. Marshall and H. Roebke, *J. Org.*, **33**, 840 (1968)

[4]H. O. House, W. L. Respress, and G. M. Whitesides, *ibid.*, **31**, 3128 (1966)

[5]E. Piers and R. J. Keziere, *Canad. J. Chem.*, **47**, 137 (1969)

[6]E. J. Corey, J. A. Katzenellenbogen, and G. H. Posner, *Am. Soc.*, **89**, 4245 (1967)

[7]P. Rona and P. Crabbé, *ibid.*, **90**, 4733 (1968)

[8]E. J. Corey and G. H. Posner, *ibid.*, **90**, 5615 (1968)

[9]P. Rona, L. Tökes, J. Tremble, and P. Crabbé, *Chem. Commun.*, 43 (1969)

1,2-Dimethyl-4,5-di(mercaptomethyl)benzene   (4,5-dimethyl-*o*-xylene-α,α'-dithiol)
[**1**, 277]. Supplier: E.

Dimethylformamide [**1**, 278–281].

Purification. N. S. Moe [*Chem. Scand.*, **21** 1389 (1967)] obtained highly pure solvent for polarographic use by first drying with molecular sieves (Linde 4A) and then treatment with active alumina (Woelm, activity grade one). The final water content was shown to be about 100 p.p.m. by Karl Fischer titration.

Solvent effects [**1**, 279, after citation of ref. 14]. Phenols and carboxylic acids are converted in high yield into the methyl ethers and methyl esters, respectively, by treatment with dimethyl sulfate and potassium carbonate in DMF solution. It is possible to esterify a carbonyl group selectively in the presence of a phenolic hydroxyl group. DMF is probably not involved as a reagent since the reaction with diethyl sulfate gives only the ethyl ether or ester.[14a]

[**1**, 281, before references]: The following adaptation of the *Leuckart–Wallach reaction* appears to be the method of choice for the conversion of cyclic and unhindered acyclic ketones to tertiary amines.[24] A mixture of cyclooctanone, dimethylformamide, and formic acid is heated in an autoclave at 190°. The work-up includes

0. 79 m.   175 g.   100 g.   b. p. 63-64°/3 mm.

ether extraction of an aqueous solution of the amine hydrochloride to remove 21 g. of a 1 : 1 mixture of cyclohexanone and cyclohexanol.

Carboxylic acid N,N-dimethylamides can be obtained in one step by reaction of a carboxylic acid with DMF in the presence of 0.5 mole of phosphorus pentoxide.

Presumably the acid anhydride is an intermediate.[25] N,N-Dimethylamides were previously prepared by reaction of an acid chloride or anhydride with dimethylamine.

[14a]M. Pailer and P. Bergthaller, *Monatshefte*, **99**, 103 (1968)
[24]R. D. Bach, *J. Org.*, **33**, 1647 (1968); A. C. Cope and R. D. Bach, procedure submitted to *Org. Syn.*, 1967
[25]H. Schindlbauer, *Monatshefte*, **99**, 1799 (1968)

Dimethylformamide diethyl acetal [1, 281–282].

Condensation with active methylene compounds. One step in the total synthesis of the naturally occurring fulvene fulvoplumierin involved condensation of a mixture of the isomeric diols (1) with dimethylformamide dimethyl acetal.[1a]

(1)   (2)

[1a]G. Büchi and J. A. Carlson, *Am. Soc.*, **90**, 5336 (1968)

Dimethylformamide–Dimethyl sulfate [1, 282–283, before references]. The procedure for the preparation of 6-dimethylaminofulvene is described in detail by Hafner *et al.*[3]

[3]K. Hafner, K. H. Vöpel, G. Ploss, and C. König, *Org. Syn.*, **47**, 52 (1967)

Dimethylformamide–Phosphoryl chloride [1, 285, after second paragraph].

2-Methylamino-3-methylpyrazine (1) reacts with the preformed complex to form an immonium salt (2), which on hydrolysis gives 1-methyl-4,7-diazaindole-3-carboxaldehyde.[7a]

(1)   (2)

(3)

[7a]S. Klutchko, H. V. Hansen, and R. I. Meltzer, *J. Org.*, **30**, 3454 (1965)

N,N-Dimethylhydrazine [1, 289–290, before references].

In the procedure of Newkome and Fishel[4,4a] for the preparation of acetophenone hydrazone, a mixture of 0.1 m. of the ketone, 0.3 m. of N,N-dimethylhydrazine (MCB), 25 ml. of absolute ethanol, and 1.0 ml. of acetic acid (catalyst) is refluxed for 24 hrs., during which time the colorless solution becomes bright yellow. The

$$\text{(acetophenone)} + H_2NN(CH_3)_2 + \text{abs. } C_2H_5OH + CH_3CO_2H \xrightarrow[94\text{-}98\%]{\text{refl. 24 hrs.}}$$

0.1 m.   0.3 m.   25 ml.

$$+ \; 0.2 \text{ m. } H_2NNH_2 \text{ and 15 ml. EtOH} \xrightarrow[97\text{-}99\%]{\text{Refl.}}$$

yellow oil is distilled and a mixture of 0.05 mole of it, 0.20 mole of anhydrous hydrazine, and 15 ml. of absolute ethanol is refluxed until the reaction mixture turns colorless. The volatile materials are removed on a rotary evaporator at a flask temperature never above 20°. The colorless residual acetophenone hydrazone solidifies and is nearly pure, m.p. 24–25°.

[4a]G. R. Newkome and D. L. Fishel, procedure submitted to *Org. Syn.*, 1967

Dimethyl methylphosphonothioate, $CH_3PS(OCH_3)_2$ [**1**, 293, before **N,N-Dimethyl-p-phenylenediamine**]. Mol. wt. 140.13, b.p. 40°/4.0 mm.

Preparation.[1] First a suspension of 0.24 mole of powdered aluminum chloride in 4 moles of methylphosphonous dichloride is stirred during the addition of 4 atoms

$$AlCl_3 + CH_3PCl_2 + S \xrightarrow[91.8\%]{} CH_3PSCl_2 \xrightarrow[78\%]{2 \; NaOCH_3} CH_3PS(OCH_3)_2$$

(1)   (2)

of sulfur flowers to produce methylphosphonothioic dichloride (1). Then this is converted into the dimethoxy derivative (2) by reaction with sodium methoxide.

Synthesis of olefins.[2] The reagent (2) can be metalated by reaction with *n*-butyllithium to give the α-lithio derivative (3), which reacts with carbonyl compounds of a

$$CH_3PS(OCH_3)_2 + \underline{n}\text{-BuLi} \xrightarrow[-\underline{n}\text{-BuH}]{THF, \; N_2} LiCH_2PS(OCH_3)_2 \xrightarrow{(C_6H_5)_2C=O \; (-78°)}$$

(2)   (3)

$$\underset{\underset{OLi}{|}}{(C_6H_5)_2C}CH_2PS(OCH_3)_2 \xrightarrow[81\%]{21 \text{ hrs. at } 25°} (C_6H_5)_2C=CH_2$$

(4)   (5)

variety of types to give an adduct such as (4) which decomposes at room temperature to give an olefin (5). 1,1-Diphenylethylene is obtained by this route in 81% yield.

[1]F. W. Hoffmann, D. H. Wadsworth, and H. D. Weiss, *Am. Soc.*, **80**, 3945 (1958)
[2]E. J. Corey and G. T. Kwiatkowski, *ibid.*, **88**, 5654 (1966)

2,6-Dimethylpiperidine [**1**, 293, before **Dimethyl sulfate**]. Mol. wt. 114.19, b.p. 111–113°. Suppliers: A, B, E, F, MCB, Fl., K.-L., Sch.

Lawrence et al.[1] describe a new method for the isolation of palustric acid, one of 6 isomeric acids present in rosin. The acid represents about 10% of the acidic portion of gum resin. On thermal isomerization it yields an equilibrium mixture of abietic, neoabietic, and palustric acids.

Palustric acid

The only method previously available for the isolation of palustric acid was by partition chromatography. The new method is based upon the precipitation of the 2,6-dimethylpiperidine salt of the resin acids from an acetone solution of pine oleoresin or rosin followed by selective crystallization of the salt from 1 : 1 methanol-acetone. The yield of pure palustric acid from slash gum rosin was 4%. A 10-g. portion of the amine salt was converted into the free acid by dissolving it in 350 ml. of 95% ethanol and adding, with stirring, 100 ml. of 3 N cold H_3PO_4. Ice-water was added to the point of cloudiness and the precipitated acid was washed with water and crystallized from hot 95% ethanol.

[1]N. M. Joye, Jr., V. M. Loeblich, and R. V. Lawrence, J. Org., **30**, 654 (1965)

Dimethyl sulfide, CH_3SCH_3 [**1**, 296, before **Dimethyl sulfite**]. Mol. wt. 62.13, b.p. 37–38°, nD 1.4351. Supplied (but incorrectly named "Methyl sulfide") by A, E, F.

An olefin of type (1) is conveniently converted into an aldehyde (3) by ozonization in methanol to produce the methoxy hydroperoxide (2) and reduction of this with dimethyl sulfide.[1] This reducing agent has a number of virtues. It is highly

selective: neither nitro groups nor carbonyl functions are reduced. Any excess of dimethyl sulfide is readily removed by evaporation (b.p. 37°). Bailey et al.[2] showed that ozonization of naphthalene (1) in methanol gives a mixture of peroxidic products, (3) and (4), that this on reduction with sodium iodide and acetic acid affords phthalaldehydic acid, rather than phthaldehyde (5). This aldehyde, however, can be obtained in good yield by reduction with dimethyl sulfide.

[1]J. J. Pappas, W. P. Keaveney, E. Gancher, and M. Berger, Tetrahedron Letters, 4273 (1966)
[2]P. S. Bailey, S. S. Bath, F. Dobinson, F. J. Garcia-Sharp, and C. D. Johnson, J. Org., **29**, 697 (1964)

Dimethyl sulfone [1, 296, before references].

House and Larson[3] heated a mixture of dimethyl sulfone, dimethyl sulfoxide, sodium hydride, and dimethoxyethane to 60° to produce dimethyl sulfone anion for

reaction with the lactone (1) to produce the β-keto sulfone (2). The latter was then converted by the steps shown into the lactone (5), of interest because of the bicyclo-[3.2.1]octane system containing a bridgehead hydroxyl group. The β-keto sulfone (2) proved to be a better intermediate than a β-keto sulfoxide because it is more stable and lacks asymmetry.

[3]H. O. House and J. K. Larson, *J. Org.*, **33**, 61 (1968)

Dimethyl sulfoxide [1, 296–310]. Review.[1a] A method of purification by E. C. Steiner has been described briefly.[1b]

Solvent Effects [1, 297–301].

Displacements [1, 298, after formula (3)]. Aralkyl halides react smoothly with thiourea in DMSO to give the sulfhydryl derivatives.[12a]

Dehydrohalogenation [**1**, 299, after formulation at top]. DMSO is an effective solvent for the dehydrochlorination of the primary chloride (1). Sodium ethoxide

$$(C_6H_5)_3CCH_2CH_2Cl \ + \ DMSO \ + \ NaOC_2H_5 \ \xrightarrow[90\%]{} \ (C_6H_5)_3CCH=CH_2$$

$$(1) \hspace{7cm} (2)$$

can be used, but sodium hydroxide is almost as effective if 10% of water is added.[14a] The latter method is the more convenient and reduces the reaction time.

Double bond migration [**1**, 300, after citation of ref. 20]. Formation of the allyl ether has been used for protection of hydroxyl groups of carbohydrates. In the original procedure[20] the group was removed by isomerization with base to the *cis*-propenyl ether, which is readily cleaved by acid. A convenient modification[20a] involves treatment of the vinyl ether with mercuric chloride in the presence of mercuric oxide (to maintain a neutral medium). The method is of particular value in the case of sugars containing acid labile groups.

$$ROCH_2CH=CH_2 \ \xrightarrow[DMSO]{(CH_3)_3COK} \ ROCH=CHCH_3 \ \xrightarrow{HgCl_2 + H_2O} \ ROH \ + \ OHCCHCH_3(HgCl) \ + \ HCl$$

Benzylation of carbohydrates [**1**, 301, before *Hydrolysis*]. Carbohydrates are benzylated in good yield by benzyl chloride in DMSO in the presence of a base.[30a] The most satisfactory bases are sodium hydride, sodium amide, and sodium or potassium hydroxide.

Hydrolysis [**1**, 301]. The hydrolytic cleavage of the lactone group of zearolenone dimethyl ether (1) could not be accomplished under normal saponification conditions but proceeded in essentially quantitative yield, if with racemization, in refluxing DMSO.[31a]

$$(1) \hspace{7cm} (2)$$

In the conventional method of carrying out the **Dieckmann cyclization** of diethyl adipate to produce 2-carboethoxycyclopentanone[31b] a mixture of sodium and toluene is heated in an oil bath and agitated with a sturdy stirrer during slow addition of the ester at 60–110° (8 hrs.). Chemists[31c] of Dr. Th. Schuchardt Co., Munich, found that the process is simplified and improved by replacing the toluene by DMSO. The reaction then proceeds in homogeneous solution and requires no special stirrer.

| 5 m. | 6.3 at. | 2.5 l. | 250 ml. |

Isolation of the product is simplified, the yield is improved, and there is no limitation with respect to batch size.

Pond and Cargill[31d] found that DMSO is also superior to benzene or toluene for the **C-alkylation** of the potassium enolate of 2-carboethoxycyclopentanone. The sodium enolate gave about the same (high) yield as the potassium salt after a reaction period three times as long.

DMSO in combination with water is reported to be a superior solvent system for conversion of **olefins to bromohydrins** by NBS.[31e] It is recommended also for the **alkaline hydrolysis of hindered epoxides.**[31f]

O-Alkylation of tyrosine without protection of the amino group can be accomplished in 40–80% yield by use of DMSO as solvent.[31g] The amino acid is dissolved in DMSO and aqueous alkali and treated with an appropriate alkyl halide. The major by-product is the ether-ester resulting from dialkylation.

DMSO is an excellent solvent-catalyst for the **trimethylsilyation** of catechol amines with hexamethyldisilazane.[31h] The reaction is usually complete in 5–10 min. at 80°. The primary amino groups are then converted by reaction with various aliphatic ketones into Schiff bases suitable for gas chromatography.

Decarboxylation. 4-Pyridylacetic acid hydrochloride is decarboxylated at 30° in DMSO.[31i] Reflux temperature is required in neutral aqueous solution.[31j]

[1a]Review: D. Martin, A. Weise, and H.-J. Niclas, *Angew. Chem., internat. Ed.*, **6**, 318 (1967)
[1b]C. D. Ritchie, G. A. Skinner, and V. G. Badding, *Am. Soc.*, **89**, 2069, note 31 (1967)
[12a]H.-L. Pan and T. L. Fletcher, *Chem. Ind.*, 546 (1968)
[14a]R. O. C. Norman and C. B. Thomas, *J. Chem. Soc.*, (C), 1115 (1967)
[20]*Add*: J. Gigg and R. Gigg, *J. Chem. Soc.*, (C), 82 (1966)
[20a]R. Gigg and C. D. Warren, *Tetrahedron Letters*, 1683 (1967)
[30a]T. Iwashige and H. Saeki, *Chem. Pharm. Bull.*, **15**, 1803 (1967)
[31a]D. Taub, N. N. Girotra, R. D. Hoffsommer, C. H. Kuo, H. L. Slates, S. Weber, and N. L. Wendler, *Tetrahedron*, **24**, 2443 (1968)
[31b]P. S. Pinkney, *Org. Syn., Coll. Vol.*, **2**, 116 (1943)
[31c]Boris Zupancic and J. Trpin, procedure submitted to *Org. Syn.*, 1967
[31d]D. M. Pond and R. L. Cargill, *J. Org.*, **32**, 4064 (1967)
[31e]D. R. Dalton, J. B. Hendrickson, and D. Jones, *Chem. Commun.*, 591 (1966)
[31f]G. Barti, B. Macchia, and F. Macchia, *Tetrahedron Letters*, 3421 (1965)
[31g]S. L. Solar and R. R. Schumaker, *J. Org.*, **31**, 1996 (1966)
[31h]S. Kawai and Z. Tamura, *Chem. Pharm. Bull.*, **15**, 1493 (1967)
[31i]G. R. Jurch, Jun., and K. C. Ramey, *Chem. Commun.*, 1211 (1968)
[31j]W. von E. Doering and V. Z. Pasternak, *Am. Soc.*, **72**, 143 (1950)

Reactions [1, 301–309].

Dehydration [1, 303, after formula (5)]. 4,6-O-Benzylidene-D-glucose, a cyclic acetal, was introduced by Zervas[34a] in 1931 and has proved a valuable intermediate in a variety of carbohydrate syntheses. The compound had been prepared previously by reaction of D-glucose with benzaldehyde in suspension with fused zinc chloride in yield of only 42%.[34b] In a new procedure by Boffi[34c] the intermolecular dehydration is done in homogeneous solution in DMSO with improvement in yield and shortening of the reaction time. A solution of D-glucose in DMSO is run from a dropping

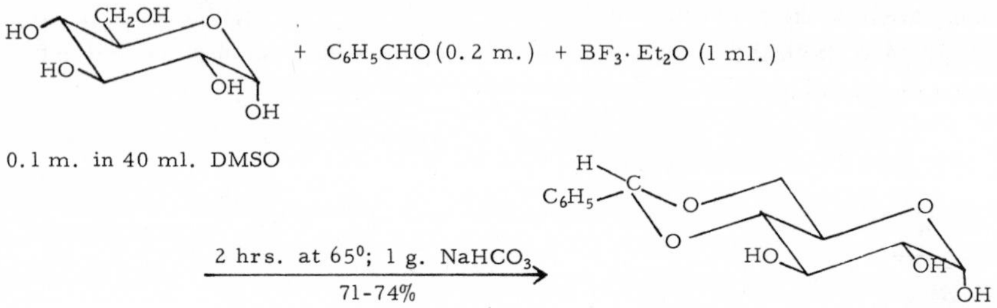

HO
CH2OH
O
HO
OH
OH
+ C6H5CHO (0.2 m.) + BF3·Et2O (1 ml.)
0.1 m. in 40 ml. DMSO
2 hrs. at 65°; 1 g. NaHCO3
71-74%
H
C
C6H5
O
O
O
HO
OH
OH

funnel in 30 min. into a stirred mixture of benzaldehyde, DMSO, and boron trifluoride etherate. After stirring at 65° for 2 hrs., the pale yellow solution is washed and neutralized with solid sodium bicarbonate. Careful evaporation at reduced pressure and crystallization from acetone–petroleum ether gives the pure acetal, m.p. 180–181°.

Oxidation [**1**, 303–308] In a search for a convenient synthesis of ninhydrin, Schipper *et al.*[35a] applied the Kornblum oxidation to 2-bromo-1,3-indanedione (1) and indeed obtained ninhydrin (2) in 36% yield. The bromo compound (1) was prepared by bromination of 1,3-indanedione with cupric bromide (**1**, 161). Subsequent-

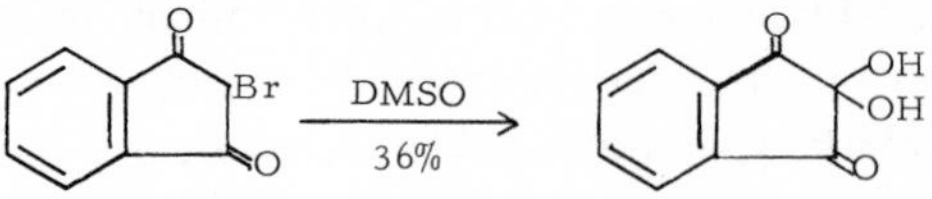

O
Br
O
DMSO
36%
O
OH
OH
O

(1) (2)

ly it was found that bromination of the dione in DMSO led directly to ninhydrin. Since bromine was not necessary in equimolar amounts it was reasoned that bromine was generated by DMSO oxidation of hydrogen bromide generated in the bromination. A procedure was then worked out in which a solution of the dione (0.20 mole), anhydrous hydrogen bromide (0.04 mole), and DMSO (0.80 mole) was heated at 70–90° until dimethyl sulfide had distilled from the reaction. Ninhydrin was obtained in 80–82% yield. The following steps are suggested:

[**1**, 303, before line 8 from below ("Although Kornblum")]: Insert: Torssell[36a] has presented evidence in support of the accepted mechanism which involves initial

$$CH_3\overset{\displaystyle O}{\overset{\|}{S}}CH_3 + 2\,HBr \longrightarrow CH_3SCH_3 + H_2O + Br_2$$

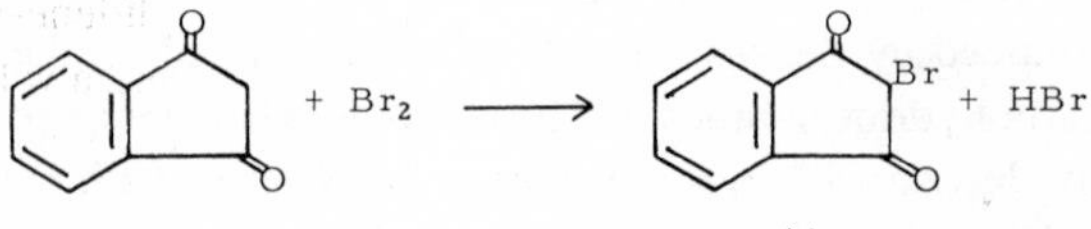

O
O
+ Br2
O
Br
O
+ HBr

(1)

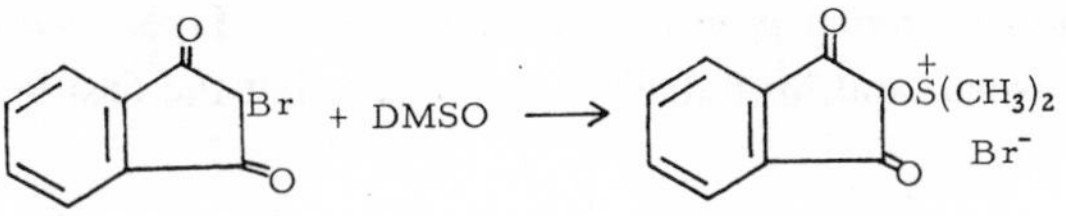

$$(3)$$

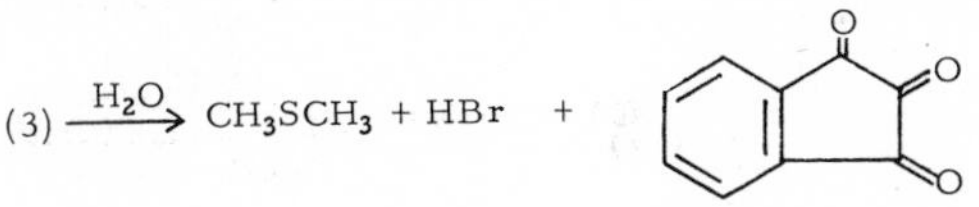

$$(3) \xrightarrow{H_2O} CH_3SCH_3 + HBr +$$

$$(4)$$

$$(4) \xrightarrow{H_2O}$$

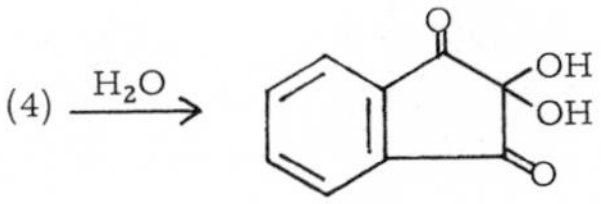

$$(2)$$

nucleophilic attack by DMSO with formation of a dimethylsulfonium salt which decomposes to the carbonyl compound:

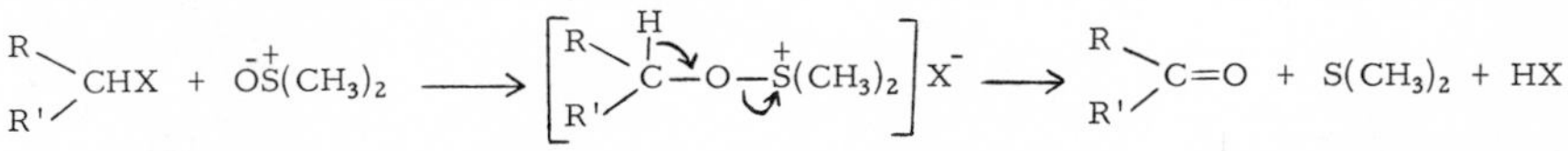

[**1**, 304, after first paragraph (". . . and the $2\beta,3\alpha$-diol")]: Cohen and Tsuji[39] found that DMSO, catalyzed by BF_3-etherate, oxidizes epoxides to α-hydroxy ketones:

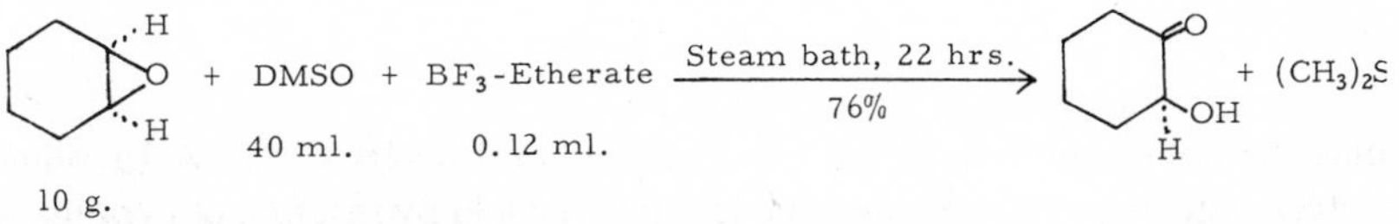

This method has been used for oxidation of methyl epoxystearate to the corresponding acyloin.[39a] In more recent work, Tsuji[39b] reports that the conversion of epoxides into α-hydroxyketones proceeds in better yield by passing air into a solution of the epoxide in DMSO (no BF_3). In this way styrene oxide gives phenacyl alcohol in 92% yield. No oxidation occurs in the absence of oxygen, but oxygen is

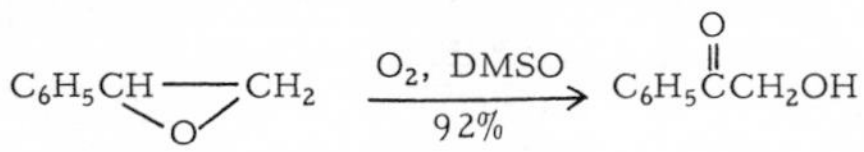

not consumed. Apparently DMSO is the oxidant. The oxidation by DMSO/BF_3 does not require oxygen.

[**1**, 305, line 10]: Change to read:

Cholane-24-ol → Cholane-24-al (85%)

[*See* J. G. Moffatt, *Org. Syn.*, **47**, 25 (1967)].

Pfitzner-Moffatt oxidation procedure [1, 305, before Dyer *et al.*[42]]. Isotopic experiments by Fenselau and Moffatt[41a] have proved that the first intermediate in the

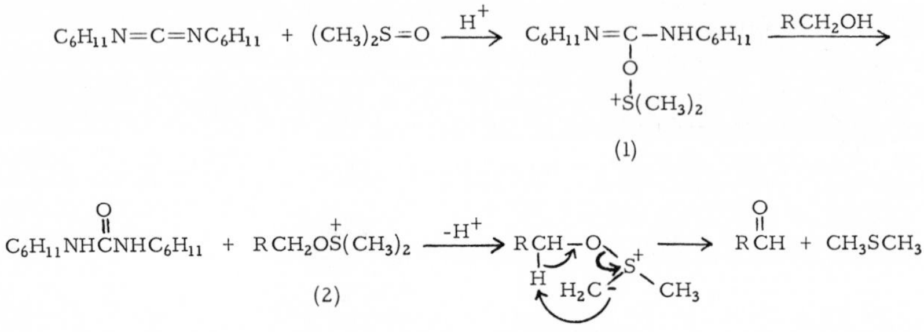

$$C_6H_{11}N=C=NC_6H_{11} + (CH_3)_2S=O \xrightarrow{H^+} C_6H_{11}N=C-NHC_6H_{11} \xrightarrow{RCH_2OH}$$

with the O and $\overset{+}{S}(CH_3)_2$ substituents below

(1)

$$C_6H_{11}\overset{O}{\overset{\|}{N}HCNHC_6H_{11}} + RCH_2O\overset{+}{S}(CH_3)_2 \xrightarrow{-H^+} RCH-O \longrightarrow R\overset{O}{\overset{\|}{C}H} + CH_3SCH_3$$

(2)

oxidation is the adduct (1). It is postulated that (1) reacts with the alcohol to form dicyclohexylurea and the alkoxysulfonium salt (2). Loss of a proton then gives dimethyl sulfide and the carbonyl compound.

The reagent reacts with compounds containing a reactive methylene group to give stable sulfonium ylides.[41b] The reaction with dimedone is typical:

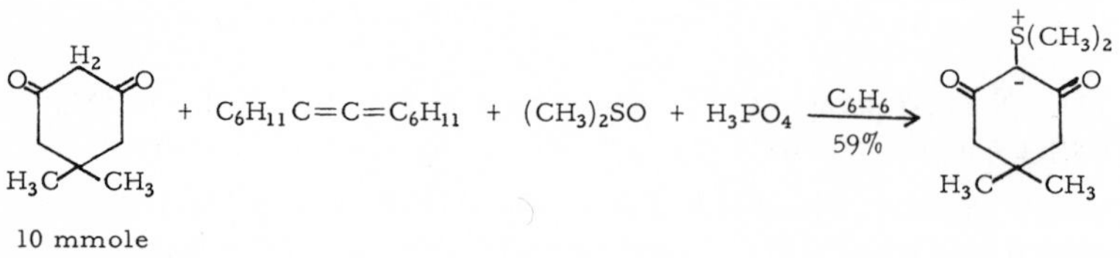

10 mmole

Jones and Wigfield[41c] used the combination: DMSO-DCC-PTFA (pyridinium trifluoroacetate, m.p. 78°, obtained in quantitiative yield by reaction of pyridine with trifluoroacetic acid in dry ether). They found the reagent useful for the oxidation of steroid Δ^5-3β-alcohols to Δ^5-3-ketones.

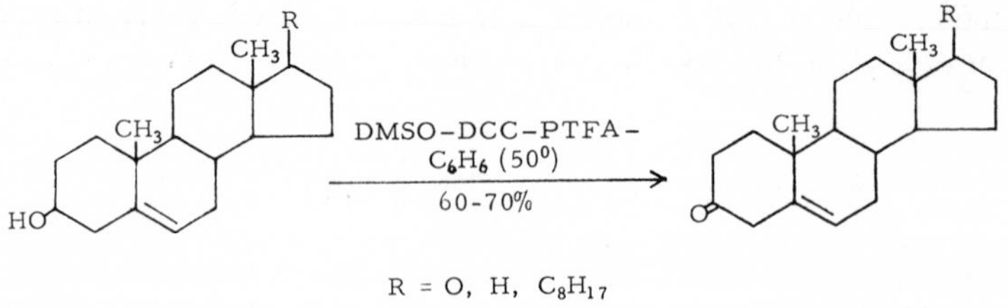

$R = O, H, C_8H_{17}$

Substitution of diethylcarbodiimide for DCC is useful since the resulting diethylurea is water soluble.[41d]

[34a]L. Zervas, *Ber.*, **64**, 2289 (1931)

[34b]H. B. Wood, H. W. Diehl, and H. G. Fletcher, *Am. Soc.*, **79**, 1986 (1957)

[34c]C. Boffi, procedure submitted to *Org. Syn.*, 1967

[35a]E. Schipper, M. Cinnamon, L. Rascher, Y. H. Chiang, and W. Oroshnik, *Tetrahedron Letters*, 6201 (1968)

[36a]K. Torssell, *Chem. Scand.*, **21**, 1(1967)

[39a]E. Brousse and D. Lefort, *Compt. rend.*, **261**, 1990 (1965)

[39b]T. Tsuji, *Tetrahedron Letters*, 2413 (1966)

[41a]A. H. Fenselau and J. G. Moffatt, *Am. Soc.*, **88**, 1762 (1966)

[41b]A. F. Cook and J. G. Moffatt, *ibid.*, **90**, 740 (1968)

[41c]J. B. Jones and D. C. Wigfield, *Canad. J. Chem.*, **44**, 2517 (1966)

[41d]Unpublished procedure of G. H. Jones and J. G. Moffatt cited by A. F. Cook and J. G. Moffatt, *Am. Soc.*, **89**, 2697 (*see* footnote 13) (1967)

Dimethyl sulfoxide–Acetic anhydride [1, 305, after citation of ref. 43]. Albright and Goldman[43a] have reported further on the oxidation of secondary alcohols to ketones with DMSO–Ac$_2$O at room temperature. In the case of yohimbine and the steroid secondary alcohols studied, oxidation apparently was faster than acetylation. The method is particularly useful for sterically hindered alcohols. The following mechanism is proposed:

The method has been applied also in the carbohydrate field.[43b] DMSO–Ac$_2$O oxidizes aromatic acyloins to α-diketones in good yield; the yield is low with aliphatic acyloins.[43c]

Reaction of cholesterol with the reagent gives as the major product the methyl thiomethyl ether.[43d] The Pfitzner-Moffatt reagent gives Δ^4-cholestenone.[43d]

Lindberg and Slessor[43e] found the reagent useful in the carbohydrate field. Condensation of the anomeric D-xylopyranosides (1 and 2) with phenylboronic acid affords the 2,4-phenylboronate esters (3 and 4), in each of which only one oxidizable hydroxyl group is exposed. However, the protective group is too sensitive for use of ordinary oxidizing agents. The combination of DMSO with acetic anhydride proved highly satisfactory and afforded the methyl α- and β-D-erythropentopyranoside-3-uloses (5) and (6) in good yield.

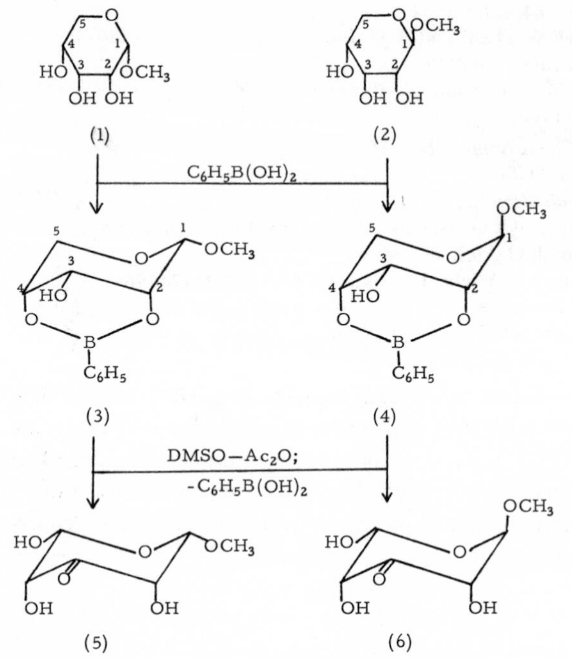

(1)   (2)

$C_6H_5B(OH)_2$

(3)   (4)

DMSO$-$Ac$_2$O;
$-C_6H_5B(OH)_2$

(5)   (6)

Various inositols are converted into pentaacetoxybenzene by the reagent; presumably a diketoinositol is an intermediate.[43f] Benzoic anhydride, P_2O_5, and PPA

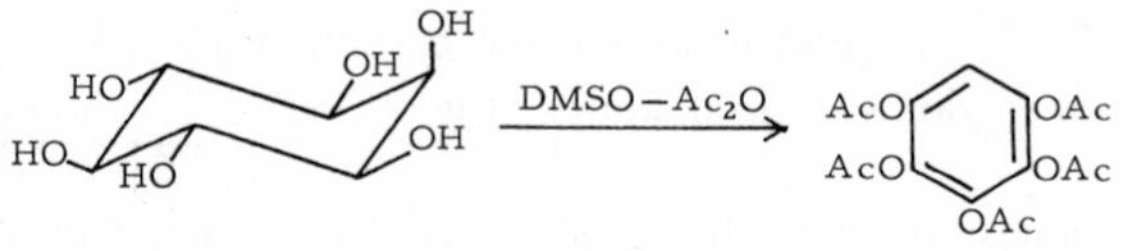

DMSO$-$Ac$_2$O

can be substituted for acetic anhydride, but yields are lower.[43g] The reagent was the only one found suitable for oxidation of (1) to the quinone (2).[43h]

DMSO$-$Ac$_2$O

(1)   (2)

Horton and Jewell[43i] examined various reagents for the oxidation to ketones of carbohydrates with isolated secondary hydroxyl groups and concluded that DMSO–Ac$_2$O is the most satisfactory. For a ketone that is water-sensitive, this oxidant has the particular advantage that all reagents can be removed by simple lyophilization.

Dimethyl sulfoxide in combination with acetic anhydride effects oxidative rearrangement of polyporic acid (3) to pulvinic acid dilactone (4), which separates from the reaction solution in high purity.[43j]

(3)   (4)

[43a] J. D. Albright and L. Goldman, *Am. Soc.*, **89**, 2416 (1967)
[43b] W. Sowa and G. H. S. Thomas, *Canad. J. Chem.*, **44**, 836 (1966)
[43c] M. VanDyke and N. D. Pritchard, *J. Org.*, **32**, 3204 (1967)
[43d] S. M. Ifzal and D. A. Wilson, *Tetrahedron Letters*, 1577 (1967)
[43e] B. Lindberg and K. N. Slessor, *Chem. Scand.*, **21**, 910 (1967); *Carbohydrate Res.*, **1**, 492 (1966)
[43f] A. J. Fatiadi, *Chem. Commun.*, 441 (1967)
[43g] J. D. Albright and L. Goldman, *Am. Soc.*, **87**, 4214 (1965)
[43h] M. S. Newman and C. C. David, *J. Org.*, **32**, 66 (1967)
[43i] D. Horton and J. S. Jewell, *Carbohydrate Res.* **2**, 251 (1966)
[43j] H. W. Moore and R. J. Wikholm, *Tetrahedron Letters*, 5049 (1968)

Dimethyl sulfoxide–Sulfur trioxide [**1**, 309, before references]. The combination of DMSO and sulfur trioxide, in the form of the pyridine complex, in the presence of trimethylamine oxidizes primary and secondary alcohols in good yield to aldehydes and ketones, respectively.[55] The reaction usually is complete within minutes and the products are isolated by acidification and precipitation with water. The reagent also oxidizes allylic alcohols to the corresponding α,β-unsaturated carbonyl compounds. One advantage over the DMSO-DCC method is that the elaborate purification required when dicyclohexylurea is a product can be dispensed with. Testosterone, with a 17β-hydroxyl group, was oxidized to Δ^4-androstene-3,17-dione very rapidly; the 17-epimer required a period of 35 min.

Isomerization of epoxides. Kenner and Stenhagen[56] mentioned briefly that epoxides

Testosterone

Epitestosterone

can be isomerized in high yield under mild conditions by methyl iodide and sodium iodide in DMF. In a more recent study of the isomerization, Kenner[57] used *n*-propyl iodide and sodium iodide in DMSO (80°, 3 hr.). Typical isomerizations were the conversion of epoxycyclohexane to cyclohexanone (90% yield) and of styrene oxide to phenylacetaldehyde (85%). Essentially no reaction occurred in sulfolane, acetonitrile, or butanone-2 and Kenner proposes that an activated derivative of dimethyl sulfoxide is involved.

[55]J. R. Parikh and W. von E. Doering, *Am. Soc.*, **89**, 5505 (1967)
[56]G. W. Kenner and E. Stenhagen, *Chem. Scand.*, **18**, 1551 (1964)
[57]D. Bethall, G. W. Kenner, and P. J. Powers, *Chem. Commun.*, 227 (1968)

Dimethyl sulfoxide-derived reagent (a). Sodium methylsulfinylmethide, now generally known as **Dimsylsodium**, [$CH_3S(O^-)=CH_2 \longleftrightarrow CH_3(S=O)-\bar{C}H_2]Na^+$ [**1**, 311, after line 8].

A procedure for conversion of a carboxylic ester containing a hydroxyl group, for example (1) into a hydroxy methylketone (2) described by Stetter and Hesse[4a] involves heating the ester with phenylsulfonylmethylmagnesium bromide to give the

$$HO(CH_2)_5CO_2C_2H_5 \ + \ C_6H_5SO_2CH_2MgBr \ \xrightarrow[-C_2H_5OMgBr]{100\%}$$

(1)

$$HO(CH_2)_5COCH_2SO_2C_6H_5 \ \xrightarrow[83\%]{AlHg} HO(CH_2)_5COCH_3$$

(2)

corresponding α-sulfonyl ketone and then reducing this with aluminum amalgam, as in the reduction of β-keto sulfoxides by Corey and Chaykovsky.

A Czech group[4b] found that dimsylsodium or dimsyllithium (by heating LiH with DMSO in THF under argon at 70–75°) reacts with 1-alkynes in DMSO or DMSO–THF to give alkali acetylides in practically quantitative yield.

$$\underset{\text{CH}_3\overset{\text{O}}{\underset{\|}{S}}\,\bar{C}H_2Na^+(Li^+)}{} + RC\equiv CH \longrightarrow \underset{\text{CH}_3\overset{\text{O}}{\underset{\|}{S}}\,CH_3}{} + RC\equiv CNa(Li)$$

The alkali acetylides so produced have been used in the following reactions:

$$RC\equiv CNa(Li) \begin{cases} \xrightarrow{R'X} RC\equiv CR' + NaX \\ \xrightarrow{R_2'SO_4} RC\equiv CR' + R'NaSO_4 \\ \xrightarrow{R'R''CO} RC\equiv C\underset{ONa(Li)}{\overset{\mid}{C}}R'R'' \end{cases}$$

Methylation. Hakomori[4c] reported that glycosides of polysaccharides can be rapidly permethylated by treatment with dimsylsodium in DMSO followed by reaction with methyl iodide:

$$ROH + CH_3CO\bar{C}H_2Na^+ \xrightarrow{N_2} R\bar{O}Na^+ + CH_3COCH_3$$

$$\downarrow CH_3I$$

$$ROCH_3 + NaI$$

Vilkas and Lederer[4d] used the procedure for the O- and N-methylation of a natural peptide glycoside and report that it is superior to the Kuhn methylation procedure. Methylation of peptides is useful in the analysis of structures by mass spectrometry.

Preparation of the reagent [**1**, 313, after citation of ref. 11]. Sodium methylsulfinylmethide prepared according to the original procedure of Corey and Chaykovsky (*loc. cit.*) decomposes slowly at 70° and rapidly at 85°. Sjöberg[11a] devised a procedure for preparing solutions of the reagent that, when solidified at 10°, can be stored for at least two months. DMSO is treated with a 50% dispersion of NaH in mineral oil and with continuous stirring treated with ultrasound (Lehfeldt apparatus). The temperature rises to 50°, a fine suspension results, and this gives way to a clear solution. The ultrasound is switched off and the solution covered with a 1-cm. layer of mineral oil. The required amount of reagent can be withdrawn from the stock solution simply by means of a pipette.

Rearrangement catalyst. The reagent effects exclusive *ortho* rearrangement of benzyltrimethylammonium iodide to 2,N,N-trimethylbenzylamine.[11b]

Decarboxylation-dehydration. Marshall and Faubl[11c] achieved the synthesis of bicyclo[3.3.1]-Δ^1-nonene (3), the most flagrant known violator of the Bredt rule, via the mesyloxy-acid (1). When this acid was treated with dimsylsodium in dimethyl

sulfoxide at 60° for 38 hrs., carbon dioxide was evolved, and chromatography afforded the lactone (2) in 30% yield and the olefin (3) in 15% yield. In a communication published alongside the one reviewed, Wiseman[11d] reported the synthesis of olefin (3) by pyrolysis of the quaternary ammonium salt (4).

Gassman and Richmond[11e] extended the scope of the Corey-Chaykovsky methyl ketone synthesis (1, 310–311) by finding that the intermediate β-ketosulfoxides can be mono- and dialkylated by using sodium hydride as base and DMSO or DMF as solvent.

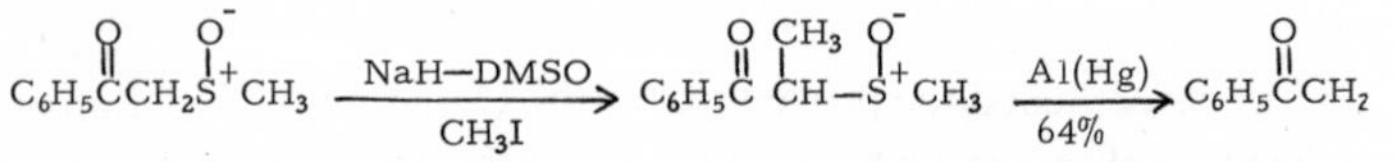

$$C_6H_5\overset{O}{\overset{\|}{C}}CH_2\overset{O^-}{\overset{\|}{S^+}}CH_3 \xrightarrow[CH_3I]{NaH-DMSO} C_6H_5\overset{O}{\overset{\|}{C}}\overset{CH_3}{\underset{}{CH}}-\overset{O^-}{\overset{\|}{S^+}}CH_3 \xrightarrow[64\%]{Al(Hg)} C_6H_5\overset{O}{\overset{\|}{C}}CH_2$$

Oku, Kakihana, and Hart[11f] describe a simple and high-yield synthesis of 1,2,3,4,5,8-hexamethylnaphthalene (5) starting with hexamethyl-2,4-cyclohexadienone (1 = 1a), readily available by oxidation of hexamethylbenzene as described (1, 826). 3,6-Dimethylbenzyne (2), generated by aprotic diazotization of 3,6-dimethylanthranilic acid, adds to the dienone (1a) to give the bridge-ring intermediate (3). Addition of dimsylsodium to the carbonyl group and gentle pyrolysis then afforded 1,2,3,4,5,8-hexamethylnaphthalene in high yield. Octamethylnaphthalene (m.p. 181°) was obtained smoothly by bischloromethylation of (5) and reduction.

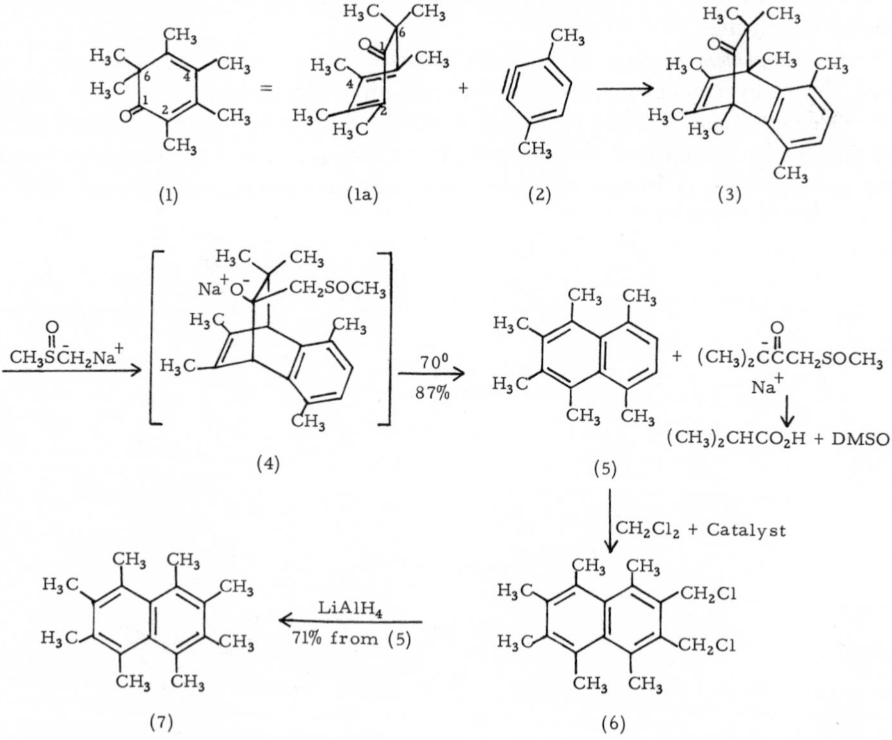

(1)   (1a)   (2)   (3)

(4)   (5)

(7)   (6)

Use of dimsylsodium in DMSO for formation of phosphonium ylides is particularly advantageous for the synthesis of volatile hydrocarbons because the high-boiling solvent facilitates isolation of lower-boiling products.[11g] Japanese workers[11h] studied the methylation of aromatic hydrocarbons with dimsylsodium. Naphthalene was not sufficiently reactive, but phenanthrene gave 9-methylphenanthrene in 86%

yield, and anthracene afforded 9-methylanthracene (77%) and 9,10-dimethylanthracene (13%).

Heathcock's synthesis of the tricyclo[4.4.0.0^{2,7}]decane system.[11i(a)] The key inter-

(1)   (2)   (3)   (4)

(5)   (6)

mediate was the Wieland-Miescher ketone (4),[11j] available in the two steps formulated.[11k] In 3 more steps this was converted into the tosyloxyketone (5), which was then cyclized to (6) by treatment with dimsylsodium "to effect tosylate elimination and establish a bond between positions 1 and 5." The yield in the cyclization step was 70%. A similar cyclization was the key step in the total synthesis of the tricyclic sesquiterpene (±)-copaene (7).[11j(b)]

(7)

Synthesis of glyoxals. Mikol and Russell[11l] have prepared dimsylpotassium by the reaction of DMSO with potassium *t*-butoxide, and used the reagent in a general

$$C_6H_5CO_2C_2H_5 + CH_3SOCH_2^-K^+ \longrightarrow [C_6H_5COCHSOCH_3]^-K^+ \xrightarrow[76-81\%]{HCl, H_2O}$$
(1)   (2)

$$\underset{(3)}{C_6H_5CO\overset{\overset{\displaystyle OH}{|}}{C}HSCH_3} \xrightarrow[\underset{\text{based on (1)}}{64-73\%}]{Cu(OAc)_2} \underset{(4)}{C_6H_5COCHO}$$

synthesis of glyoxals. The preparation of phenylglyoxal is typical of the procedure. Ethyl benzoate (1) reacts with the reagent to give (2), which on acid hydrolysis gives phenylglyoxal hemimercaptal (3). Oxidation with cupric acetate then gives phenylglyoxal (4).

Dimethyl sulfoxide-derived reagent (b). Dimethylsulfonium methylide, $(CH_3)_2S=CH_2$ [1, 314, addition].

Corey's procedure. Coxon et al.[13a] in New Zealand found that the reagent reacts with nopinone (6, numbering of the paper) to give 2β,10-epoxypinane (7) in high yield. Reduction of this epoxide with lithium aluminum hydride gave 10α-pinane-2β-ol (5).

(6)   (7)   (5)

Trost[13b] found that the reagent reacts with acenaphthylene in DMSO–THF to give 3-methylacenaphthylene (71%), 5-methylacenaphthylene (3%), and unchanged hydrocarbon (10.5%).

(1)   (2) 71%   (3) 3%

Similarly, fluoranthrene (4) gave a mixture of 24.7% of 1-methylfluoranthrene (5) and 5.3% of the 3-methyl derivative.

(4)   (5) 24. 7%   (6)

Dimethylsulfonium methylide also reacts predominantly with 3-keto-5α-steroids (dihydrotestosterone) by α-side attack.[13c] However, the isomer formed by β-attack (3) is the exclusive product when dimethyloxosulfonium methylide is used. Analogous results were obtained with cholestanone-3.

(1)   (2) Main product   (3) Minor product

The first known heterocyclic analog of bicyclobutane, 3-phenyl-1-azabicyclo-[1.1.0]butane (8), has been obtained in 60% yield by the reaction of 3-phenyl-2H-azirine (7) with dimethylsulfonium methylide in dry THF at − 10°.[13d] The reaction of

(7)   (8)

(7) with triphenylphosphonium methylide, diazomethane, or dimethyloxosulfonium methylide does not yield (8) in any detectable amount. Compound (8) is extremely sensitive to acid, but is stable to alkali and to sodium borohydride.

Dimethylsulfoxide-derived reagent (c). Dimethyloxosulfonium methylide [1, 315–318].

By careful vacuum distillation Schmidbaur and Tronich[16a] have isolated pure material and report the following physical constants: m.p. 9–10°, b.p. 41–43°/0.1 mm. [1, 318, before references]:

The reagent reacts stereospecifically with ethyl *trans*-cinnamate to give ethyl 2-

phenylcyclopropanecarboxylate, consisting to the extent of 98.9% of the *trans* isomer.[25] Yields are higher with sterically hindered esters of cinnamic acid. The reagent also reacts stereospecifically with *trans*-N,N-dimethylcinnamide.

Corey and Chaykovsky[26] give a detailed description of the preparation of the reagent from trimethyloxosulfonium iodide, dimethyl sulfoxide, and sodium hydride, and for its reaction with cyclohexanone to form the oxirane methylenecyclohexane oxide.

Landor and Punja[27] found that the reaction of the reagent with $\alpha\,\beta$-unsaturated esters gives higher yields if conducted in DMF rather than DMSO, the original solvent. The reaction is spontaneous and exothermal and is complete in a few minutes. In studying the stereochemistry of the reaction of the reagent with α,β-unsaturated ketones, Agami[28] observed two cases in which the stereochemistry of the cyclopropane ring is the same as that of the enone:

The reagent reacts with the quaternary bases (1) derived from estrone and estradiol in the presence of 2 equiv. of alkali to give annelated furane derivatives such as (2).[29]

$(CH_3)_2\overset{O}{\overset{\|}{S}}=CH_2$
NaH
70%

(1)   (2)

Dimethyloxosulfonium methylide does not react with usual Δ^4-3-ketosteroids[30] but does react with some conjugated steroid ketones, for example (3).[31]

$(CH_3)_2\overset{O}{\overset{\|}{S}}=CH_2$
DMSO
60-60%

(3)   (4)

Dimethyloxosulfonium methylide reacts with α-halo carbonyl compounds to give cyclopropanes according to the equation:[32]

$$\begin{array}{c} R-C=O \\ | \\ R'-CHX \end{array} + 3\ (CH_3)_2\overset{O}{\overset{\|}{S}}=CH_2 \longrightarrow \begin{array}{c} R-CO \\ | \quad \diagup CH_2 \\ R'-C \\ \quad \diagdown CH_2 \end{array} + 2\ (CH_3)_2SO + (CH_3)_3\overset{O}{\overset{\|}{S}}X^-$$

Yields are in the range of 15–35%.
    Examples:

—Cl
$\xrightarrow{28\%}$

$C_6H_5\overset{O}{\underset{\|}{C}}CHBrC_6H_5 \xrightarrow{35\%} C_6H_5CO-\overset{CH_2-CH_2}{\underset{}{\diagdown C\diagup}}-C_6H_5$

In the reaction of the ylide with olefins to form cyclopropanes the ylide supplies only one methylene group; in the present case the ylide supplies two methylene groups.

[4a]H. Stetter and R. Hesse, *Monatshefte*, **98**, 755 (1967)
[4b]J. Křiz, M. J. Beneš, and J. Peška, *Tetrahedron Letters*, 2881 (1965); *idem*, *Coll. Czech.*, **32**, 358 (1967)

[4c]S. Hakomori, *J. Biochemistry*, **55**, 205 (1964)

[4d]E. Vilkas and E. Lederer, *Tetrahedron Letters*, 3089 (1968)

[11a]K. Sjöberg, *Tetrahedron Letters*, 6383 (1966)

[11b]K. P. Klein and C. R. Hauser, *J. Org.*, **31**, 4276 (1966)

[11c]J. A. Marshall and H. Faubl, *Am. Soc.*, **89**, 5965 (1967)

[11d]J. R. Wiseman, *Am. Soc.*, **89**, 5966 (1967)

[11e]P. G. Gassman and G. D. Richmond, *J. Org.*, **31**, 2355 (1966)

[11f]A. Oku, T. Kakihana, and H. Hart, *Am. Soc.*, **89**, 4554 (1967)

[11g]J. G. Atkinson, M. H. Fisher, D. Horley, A. T. Morse, R. S. Stuart, and E. Synnes, *Canad. J. Chem.*, **43**, 1614 (1966)

[11h]K. Nosaki, Y. Yamamoto, and R. Noyori, *Tetrahedron Letters*, 1123 (1966)

[11i](a) C. H. Heathcock, *ibid.*, 2043 (1966); (b) *idem. Am. Soc.*, **88**, 4110 (1966)

[11j]P. Wieland and K. Miescher, *Helv.*, **33**, 2215 (1950)

[11k]S. Ramachandran and M. S. Newman, *Org. Syn.*, **41**, 38 (1961)

[11l]G. J. Mikol and G. A. Russell, *ibid.*, **48**, 109 (1968)

[13a]J. M. Coxon, E. Dansted, M. P. Hartshorn, and K. E. Richards, *Tetrahedron* **24**, 1193 (1968)

[13b]B. M. Trost, *Tetrahedron Letters*, 5761 (1966)

[13c]C. E. Cook, R. C. Corley, and M. E. Wall, *J. Org.*, **33**, 2789 (1968)

[13d]A. G. Hortman and D. A. Robertson, *Am. Soc.*, **89**, 5974 (1967)

[16a]H. Schmidbaur and W. Tronich, *Tetrahedron Letters*, 5335 (1968)

[25]C. Kaiser, B. M. Trost, G. Beson, and J. Weinstock, *J. Org.*, **30**, 3972 (1965)

[26]E. J. Corey and M. Chaykovsky, procedure submitted to *Org. Syn.*, 1967

[27]S. R. Landor and N. Punja, *J. Chem. Soc.*, (C), 2495 (1967)

[28]C. Agami, *Compt rend.*, **264** (C), 1128 (1967)

[29]H.-G. Lehmann, *Tetrahedron Letters*, 607 (1968)

[30]E. J. Corey and M. Chaykovsky, *Am. Soc.*, **87**, 1353 (1965)

[31]G. W. Krakower and H. A. Van Dine, *J. Org.*, **31**, 3467 (1966)

[32]P. Bravo, G. Gaudiano, C. Ticozzi, and A. Umani-Ronchi, *Tetrahedron Letters*, 4481 (1968)

Dimethylthiocarbamyl chloride (Dimethylthiocarbamoyl chloride), $\underset{CH_3}{\overset{CH_3}{>}}N\overset{\overset{S}{\|}}{C}Cl$

[**1**, 318, before **2,4-Dinitrobenzaldehyde**]. Mol. wt. 123.62, b.p. 90–95°/0.5 mm., m.p. 42.5–43.5°. Suppliers: A, E.

Preparation.[1,2,3] The reagent can be prepared by rapidly adding 740 g. of chlorine dissolved in 3 l. of carbon tetrachloride to a stirred, refluxing suspension of 2400 g. of tetramethylthiuram disulfide in 5 l. of carbon tetrachloride. Approximately one-half of the solvent is removed. The reaction mixture is cooled, filtered to remove precipitated sulfur, and further concentrated. Distillation then yields 1980 g. (80%) of dimethylthiocarbamyl chloride, b.p. 65–68°/0·2 mm.

$$\frac{\text{KOH} - \text{H}_2\text{O} - \text{HOCH}_2\text{CH}_2\text{OH};}{\text{HCl, ice, CHCl}_3 \text{ extract. } 81\%} \longrightarrow$$

(4)

Phenols → *thiophenols*. Newman and Hetzel[1] illustrate the general procedure by the following example. A solution of 2-naphthol and potassium hydroxide is stirred and kept at 12° during addition of dimethylthiocarbamyl chloride in THF. When the conversion to O-2-naphthyldimethylthiocarbamate is complete the mixture is made alkaline and extracted with three portions of benzene. One crystallization from methanol gives colorless product suitable for the next step, which consists in pyrolysis at 275° in a flask fitted with a gas diffusion tube (**1**, 105–106) and effects rearrangement of O-2-naphthyldimethylthiocarbamate (2) to S-2-naphthyldimethyl-thiocarbamate (3). Alkaline hydrolysis and acidification then affords 2-naphthalene-thiol (4). In some thirty cases explored[2] yields in the rearrangement step were mainly in the range 95–100%. The estrone derivative was rearranged in sulfolane solution; yield 95%.

[1]M. S. Newman, and F. W. Hetzel, procedure submitted to *Org. Syn.*, 1967
[2]M. S. Newman and H. A. Karnes, *J. Org.*, **31**, 3980 (1966)
[3]R. H. Goshorn, W. W. Levis, Jr., E. Jaul, and E. J. Ritter, *Org. Syn., Coll. Vol.*, **4**, 307 (1963)

4,4′-Dinitrodiphenylnitroxide (p-NO$_2$C$_6$H$_4$)$_2$NO· [**1**, 321, before **2,4-Dinitrofluoro-benzene**]. Mol. wt. 142.18, m.p. 109°. Preparation by treatment of 4,4′-dinitrodi-phenylhydroxylamine with NO$_2$.[1]

Oxidation of phenols to quinones. Forrester and Thompson[2] noted that potassium nitrosodisulfonate, an inorganic radical useful for the oxidation of phenols, amines,

and hydroquinones to quinones, has the limitation that it is insoluble in organic solvents. They decided to consider stable organic nitroxides as possible replace-ments, and of four such radicals tested found 4,4′-dinitrodiphenylnitroxide to be the the most useful.

[1]H. Wieland and K. Roth, *Ber.*, **53**, 210 (1920)
[2]A. R. Forrester and R. H. Thompson, *J. Chem. Soc.*, (C), 1844 (1966)

2,4-Dinitrofluorobenzene [**1**, 321–322, before references]. Further suppliers: Pierce Chem. Co.; Fl., K.-L., Sch.

[Before references]: Alditols and myoinositol react rapidly and completely to form 2,4-dinitrophenyl ethers which are crystalline and have sharp and characteristic melting points. The method of choice involves reaction at room temperature in DMF in the presence of triethylamine.[10]

2,4-Dinitrophenyl derivatives of hexosamines have been used to a limited extent for characterization and separation. Lloyd and Stacey[11] showed that the derivatives have value in synthesis of glycosides when unprotected hexosamines give poor yields in condensation reactions. The derivatives are obtained by heating the hexosamine hydrochloride with the reagent and sodium bicarbonate. The dinitrophenyl group is stable in 1 N hydrochloric acid and to methanolic ammonia, but is readily removed with the alkaline resin, Amberlite IRA-400-OH. Wolfrom *et al.* have employed this blocking group in the synthesis of anomeric 9-(2-amino-2-deoxy-D-glucopyranosyl)-adenines[12] and of 1-(2-amino-2-deoxy-β-D-glucopyranosyl)thymine.[13]

[10]M. L. Wolfrom, B. O. Juliano, M. S. Toy and A. Chaney, *Am. Soc.*, **81**, 1446 (1959)
[11]P. F. Lloyd and M. Stacey, *Tetrahedron*, **9**, 116 (1960)
[12]M. L. Wolfrom, H. G. Carg, and D. Horton, *J. Org.*, **30**, 1556 (1965)
[13]M. L. Wolfrom and H. B. Bhat, *ibid.*, **32**, 2757 (1967)

Dinitrogen tetroxide [**1**, 324–329]. *Caution*: An explosion on reaction of the reagent in the liquid phase with *n*-hexane at room temperature has been reported.[1a]

[**1**, 324, after citation of ref. 5]: In a publication subsequent to that of ref. 5, W. K. Seifert (procedure submitted to *Org. Syn.*, 1967) described a procedure in which dinitrogen tetroxide, oxygen, and cyclooctene (1) are brought into reaction in ether

solution at a temperature controlled by a cooling bath at $-20°$. The resulting mixture of adducts, (2), (3), and (4), is treated with triethylamine to effect conversion to the nitroolefin; 1-nitrocyclooctene (5) is obtained as a yellow oil in 98% yield.

Oxidation of amides (White deamination) [follows **1**, 327]. White[22a] has described the benzoylation of 2-phenylethylamine (1), the reaction of (2) with dinitrogen tetroxide to give (3), which on thermal decomposition at 77° affords 2-phenylethyl benzoate (4).

$$C_6H_5CH_2CH_2NH_2 \xrightarrow[\text{Py}]{C_6H_5COCl} C_6H_5CH_2CH_2\overset{H}{\underset{|}{N}}COC_6H_5 \xrightarrow{N_2O_4}$$

(1)   (2)

$$C_6H_5CH_2CH_2\overset{NO}{\underset{|}{N}}COC_6H_5 \xrightarrow{\Delta} C_6H_5CH_2CH_2OCOC_6H_5 \ + \ N_2$$

(3)   (4)

Furoxanes [1, 328, before references]. Peterson[29] found that dinitrogen tetroxide reacts with excess acetone at 0–5° to form a highly unstable intermediate (1) which when heated to 50° decomposes with evolution of nitrogen oxides to give diacetyl-furoxane (2) in high yield. The oxide (2) can be reduced to diacetylfurazane (3) with trimethyl phosphite. The reaction has been applied successfully to acetophenone.

$$CH_3COCH_3 \ + \ N_2O_4 \longrightarrow \text{Product} \xrightarrow[93\%]{50^0}$$

(1)

(2)

(3)

[1a]T. Urbański and J. Falecki, *Chem. Ind.*, 1424 (1967)

[22a]E. H. White, *Org. Syn.*, **47**, 44 (1967)

[29]L. I. Peterson, *Tetrahedron Letters*, 1727 (1966)

2,4-Dinitrophenylhydrazine [1, 330–331].

Carbonyl compounds [after ref. 5]. McMurry[5a] desired to selectively reduce an olefinic double bond with diborane in the presence of a keto group. This was success-fully achieved by conversion to the dinitrophenylhydrazone, hydroboration and re-moval of the protective group by ozonolysis in ethyl acetate at −78°. Oximes and oxime acetates are reduced by BH_3. Attempted protection by ketalization in this case was unsuccessful because of simultaneous migration of the double bond.

[5a]J. E. McMurry, *Chem. Commun.*, 433 (1968); *idem, Am. Soc.*, **90**, 6821 (1968)

Di-*p*-nitrophenyl sulfite, $(p\text{-}NO_2C_6H_4\text{—}O)_2S\text{=}O$ [1, 333, before **Dioxane**]. Mol. wt., 226.33, m.p. 104–106°.

Preparation.[1] The reagent is obtained by the reaction of *p*-nitrophenol in ether at 0° in the presence of triethylamine with freshly distilled thionyl chloride.

$$O_2N\text{—}\bigcirc\text{—}OH \ + \ Cl\text{—}\overset{O}{\underset{||}{S}}\text{—}Cl \ + \ HO\text{—}\bigcirc\text{—}NO_2 \xrightarrow[50\text{-}60\%]{\text{Ether } (0^0); \ 2 \text{ crystallizations}}$$

Peptide synthesis.[2] The reagent reacts with an N-protected amino acid to give an active *p*-nitrophenyl ester for use in coupling with another unit. Trouble sometimes experienced from partial racemization of a dipeptide can be eliminated by use of leucine[3] or proline[4] as the terminal group. Of course, glycine can also be used as the terminal group. The reagent has been used for synthesis of cyclic peptides when the DCC method was unsuccessful.[5]

[1] B. Iselin and R. Schwyzer, *Helv.*, **43**, 1760 (1960)
[2] B. Iselin, W. Rittel, P. Sieber, and R. Schwyzer, *ibid.*, **40**, 373 (1957)
[3] R. O. Studer and W. Lergier, *ibid.*, **48**, 460 (1965)
[4] M. Ohno and N. Izumiya *Bull. Chem. Soc. Japan*, **38**, 1831 (1965)
[5] M. Ohno, T. Kato, S. Makisumi, and N. Izumiya, *ibid.*, **39**, 1738, 1747 (1966)

Dioxane dibromide [**1**, 333–334, before references]. Treatment of guanosine (1) with dioxane dibromide gives the 8-bromo derivative (2) in 65% yield.[4,5] The hydrobromic acid liberated in the reaction can be used directly as catalyst for acetonide

(1) Guanosine   (2)   (3)

formation. Thus, on addition of acetone and dimethoxypropane to the reaction mixture, guanosine is converted directly into the 8-bromo-2',3'-acetonide (3) in 60% yield.

[4] M. Ikehara, H. Tada, and K. Muneyama, *Chem. Pharm. Bull.*, **13**, 639 (1965)
[5] M. Ikehara and K. Muneyama, *J. Org.*, **32**, 3039 (1967)

Diphenylcarbamoyl chloride [**1**, 337]. Wilshire[2] is enthusiastic about use of this reagent for Friedel-Crafts acylation and eventual introduction of a carboxyl group.

$$(C_6H_5)_2NCOCl + HAr \xrightarrow{AlCl_3} (C_6H_5)_2N\overset{\overset{O}{\|}}{C}Ar \xrightarrow{Hydrol.} ArCO_2H$$

[2]J. F. K. Wilshire, *Australian J. Chem.*, **20**, 575 (1967)

Diphenylcarbodiimide [**1**, 337–338, after first formulation]. Diphenylcarbodiimide has been prepared also by cycloaddition of benzonitrile oxide (1) with N-sulfinyl-aniline (2) and pyrolysis of the resulting 4,5-diphenyl-1-keto-1,2,3,4-thiaoxadiazole (3).[2]

(1)   (2)   (3)

[2]P. Rajagopalan and B. G. Advani, *J. Org.*, **30**, 3369 (1965); P. Rajagopalan, B. G. Advani, and C. N. Talaty, procedure submitted to *Org. Syn.*, 1967

Diphenyldiazomethane [**1**, 338–339].

Peptide synthesis [before references]. Zervas and his group[9] have found benz-hydryl esters useful in peptide synthesis. They prepared the esters either by the reac-tion of the silver salt of an N-protected amino acid with diphenylmethyl chloride or by reaction of diphenyldiazomethane with the N-protected amino acid. Cleavage of the protective group was accomplished by treatment with 0.2 N hydrogen chloride in nitromethane. They prepared both the α- and γ-benzhydryl esters of L-glutamic acid.[10]

[9]G. C. Stelakatos, A. Paganou, and L. Zervas, *J. Chem. Soc.*, (C), 1191 (1966)
[10]J. Taylor-Papadimitriou, C. Yovanidis, A. Paganou, and L. Zervas, *ibid.*, 1830 (1967)

1,1-Diphenylhydrazine [**1**, 340, after citation of refs. 1 and 2].

A newer procedure reported by Koga and Anselme[2a] involves the following steps; the overall yield of pure product is 70%.

$$(C_6H_5)_2NCOCl \xrightarrow{NaN_3} (C_6H_5)_2NCON_2 \xrightarrow{t-BuOH} (C_2H_5)_2NNHCOOC(CH_3)_3 \xrightarrow{H_2O} (C_6H_5)_2NNH_2$$

[2a]N. Koga and J.-P. Anselme, *J. Org.*, **33**, 3963 (1968)

Diphenyliodonium chloride [**1**, 341–342]. Supplier: A.

[Before references]: The preparation of 1-phenyl-2,4-pentanedione (5) has been described in detail.[3a] The overall yield was 85–91%, calculated on the assumption that only one of the phenyl groups of the reagent is available for phenylation.

[3a]K. G. Hampton, T. M. Harris, and C. R. Hauser, procedure submitted to *Org. Syn.*, 1968

1,3-Diphenylisobenzofurane [**1**, 342–343].

Trapping agent [before references]. Wittig and Fritze[10] used the reagent to trap the allene 1,2-cyclohexadiene (2), formed from 1-bromocyclohexene (1) by dehydro-halogenation with potassium *t*-butoxide in DMSO.

[10]G. Wittig and P. Fritze, *Angew, Chem., internat. Ed.*, **5**, 846 (1966); *idem., Ann.*, **711**, 82 (1968)

[2-(*p*-Diphenyl)isopropyl]phenyl carbonate (1) [**1**, 343, before **Diphenylketene**]. Mol. wt. 332.4, m.p. 114.115°.

This mixed carbonate is prepared from (*p*-diphenyl)dimethylcarbinol and the phenyl ester of chlorocarbonic acid.[1] It is recommended for the N-protection of α-

amino acids. The advantage is that the protecting group is very easily cleaved by dilute acetic acid under conditions to which other acid-sensitive protective groups are stable.[2]

The corresponding azide (2, mol. wt. 270.3, m.p. 109–110°) can be used equally well.

[1]P. Sieber and B. Iselin, *Helv.*, **51**, 622 (1968)
[2]*Idem, ibid.*, **51**, 614 (1968)

Diphenylphosphide, lithium salt [**1**, 345, ref. 2]. Definitive paper: F. G. Mann and M. J. Pragnell, *J. Chem. Soc.*, 4120 (1965).

***p*-Diphenylphosphinobenzoic acid,** $(C_6H_5)_2PC_6H_4COOH(p)$ [**1**, 345, before **Diphenylphosphorochloridate**]. Mol. wt. 306.29, m.p. 156°.

Preparation.[1]

Use in Wittig synthesis. Schiemenz and Thobe[2] have used this reagent in place of triphenylphosphine in Wittig reactions; it has the advantage that the resulting oxide, *p*-diphenylphosphinylbenzoic acid, $(C_6H_5)_2P(O)—C_6H_4COOH(p)$, can be removed from the product by aqueous sodium bicarbonate. The oxide can be reconverted to the reagent by trichlorosilane.[3]

[1]H. Gilman and G. E. Brown, *Am. Soc.*, **67**, 824 (1945)
[2]G. P. Schiemenz and J. Thobe, *Ber.*, **99**, 2663 (1966)
[3]Method of H. Fritzsche, U. Hasserodt, and F. Korti, *ibid.*, **98**, 171 (1965)

Diphenylphosphorochloridate [1, 345–346].

[Top of 1, 346, end of first paragraph]: The reagent has been used to block the amino group in the synthesis of methyl 2-amino-2-desoxy-β-D-glucopyranosides.[4a] The blocking group is either removed by high-pressure hydrogenation (PtO_2) or replaced by a benzyl group to afford a derivative removable by hydrogenation at a much lower temperature. Wolfrom[4b] made use of this blocking group in amino sugar and nucleoside synthesis. See also review.[4c]

[4a]L. Zervas and S. Konstas, *Ber.*, **93**, 435 (1960)
[4b]M. L. Wolfrom, P. J. Conigliaro, and E. J. Soltes, *J. Org.*, **32**, 653 (1967)
[4c]R. L. Whistler and M. L. Wolfrom, *Methods Carbohydrate Chem.* **2**, 270, 272, 277, 282 (1963)

Diphenylsulfonium isopropylide, $(C_6H_5)_2S\overset{...}{\cdots}C(CH_3)_2$ (4) [1, 348, before **Diphenyl-sulfoxide**]. Unstable above $-20°$ to air and moisture.

Generation in situ. Corey[1] has generated this highly reactive sulfonium ylide by two methods; the preferred method is from diphenylethylsulfonium fluoroborate (2), prepared from diphenyl sulfide (1) and triethyloxonium fluoroborate. This is then heated with 1.1 equiv. of lithium diisopropylamide and 1 equiv. of methylene

chloride (this combination is equivalent to dichloromethyllithium, Cl_2CHLi) to give a precipitate of the unstable diphenylisopropylsulfonium iodide (3). Treatment of (3) with 1.1 equiv. of lithium diisopropylamide at $-70°$ gives a turbid orange solution of the reagent (4). The sterically hindered lithium diisopropylamide was found to be the most satisfactory base; it is freshly prepared from *n*-butyllithium in hexane and diisopropylamine in dimethoxyethane at $-70°$.

Dimethoxyethane was found to be superior to THF as solvent, particularly for the conversion of (3) into (4).

Reaction with carbonyl compounds. The reagent reacts with saturated aldehydes and ketones to give an oxirane in 74–82% yield. The reaction requires about 1–2 hrs. at temperatures of $-70°$ to $-30°$ and can be followed by the fading of the orange color of the ylide.[1]

In the reaction with α,β-unsaturated carbonyl compounds[2] the reagent is an iso-propylidene transfer reagent and gives *gem*-dimethylcyclopropanes as shown by the reaction of 2-cyclohexenone and of methyl acrylate:

Note that this reagent has a greater tendency to form a cyclopropane derivative than dimethylsulfonium methylide, which reacts with 2-cyclohexenone to give only the oxirane.

The new reagent was used in a simple, stereospecific synthesis of the natural insecticide chrysanthemic acid (6) from methyl 5-methyl-*trans*-2,4-hexadienoate

$$CH_3CCH_2Cl + HC\equiv CH + CH_3OH \xrightarrow[CH_3O^-]{Ni(CO)_4} (CH_3)_2C=CHCH\overset{t}{=}CHCOOCH_3$$

with CH_2 under the first carbon.

(5)

$$\xrightarrow[72.5\%]{(4)} (CH_3)_2C=CH\cdots \overset{H}{\underset{\underset{H_3C}{\overset{\displaystyle C}{\diagdown}}CH_3}{C}}-\overset{H}{\underset{}{C}}-COOCH_3$$

(6)

(5). The starting ester has been prepared[3] by the reaction of methallyl chloride, acetylene, and methanol in the presence of nickel carbonyl followed by treatment with base. Reaction with (4) gives the methyl ester of (±)-*trans*-chrysanthemic acid in 72.5% yield.

[1] E. J. Corey, M. Jautelat, and W. Oppolzer, *Tetrahedron Letters*, 2325 (1967)
[2] E. J. Corey and M. Jautelat, *Am. Soc.*, **89**, 3912 (1967)
[3] G. P. Chiusoli and L. Cassar, *Angew. Chem., internat. Ed.*, **6**, 124 (1967)

Diphenyl triphenylphosphoranylidenemethylphosphonate, $(C_6H_5)_3\overset{+}{P}\overset{-}{C}H\overset{O}{\overset{\|}{P}}(OC_6H_5)_2$
[**1**, 349, before **Diphenylzinc**]. Mol. wt. 508.47, m.p. 149–150°.

This stable ylide can be prepared on a large scale by quaternization of triphenylphosphine with diphenyl chloromethylphosphonate (175°, 4 hrs., 77% yield).[1]

The reagent reacts with aromatic and aliphatic aldehydes at 100–110° to give the

$$\underline{p}\text{-}C_6H_4CHO + (C_6H_5)_3\overset{+}{P}\overset{-}{C}H\overset{O}{\overset{\|}{P}}(OC_6H_5)_2 \longrightarrow \underline{p}\text{-}C_6H_4CH\overset{t}{=}CH\overset{O}{\overset{\|}{P}}(OC_6H_5)_2$$

trans isomers of diphenyl vinylphosphonates. The reaction is more rapid in DMSO than in toluene. The reaction has been applied to suitably protected nucleosides and sugar aldehydes as a useful alternative to the phosphonate method. Hydrolysis of the phenyl esters makes possible the synthesis of phosphonic acids.

[1] G. H. Jones, E. K. Hamamura, and J. G. Moffatt, *Tetrahedron Letters*, 5731 (1968)

Dipotassium platinum tetrachloride, K_2PtCl_4 [**1**, 350, before **Dipotassium tetramethyl osmate**]. Supplier: Alfa Inorganics.

Preliminary communications from Australia state that this catalyst can be used in acetic acid for the labeling of synthetic organic compounds by homogeneous deuteration or tritiation.[1]

[1]J. L. Garnett and R. J. Hodges, *Am. Soc.*, **89**, 4546 (1967); J. L. Garnett, J. H. O'Keefe and P. J. Claringbold, *Tetrahedron Letters*, 2687 (1968)

Disodium acetylide [**1**, 350, before **Disodium phenanthrene**]. A mixture of mono- and disodium acetylide reacts with an α,ω-dibromide (1) to give a nonconjugated linear polyacetylene (2) and a cyclic polyacetylene (3).[1] The method has been improved by carrying out the reaction in an autoclave at room temperature.[2]

$$Br(CH_2)_nBr \ + \ \begin{matrix} NaC\equiv CH \\ NaC\equiv CNa \end{matrix} \longrightarrow HC\equiv C(CH_2\,_nC\equiv CH)_xH \ + \ (CH_2)_n \begin{matrix} C\equiv C \\ C\equiv C \end{matrix} (CH_2)_n \Bigg]_x$$

(1)   (2)   (3)

[1]J. H. Wotiz, R. F. Adams, and C. G. Parsons, *Am. Soc.*, **83**, 373 (1961)
[2]A. J. Hubert and J. Dale, *Chem. Ind.*, 1224 (1961); A. J. Hubert, *J. Chem. Soc.*, (C), 2149 (1967)

Disodium phenanthrene ($C_{14}H_{10}Na_2$) [**1**, 350–351, before reference].

The *vic*-dichloride (1), the adduct of benzyne and *cis*-3,4-dichlorocyclobutene, was successfully dechlorinated by disodium phenanthrene to give (2) in 27% yield.[2] Other reagents give mixtures of tetralin and 1,4-dihydronaphthalene. The product (2) is correctly named as benzobicyclo[2.2.0]hexa-2,5-diene, but can be called "hemi Dewar naphthalene." Similar dehalogenations of *vic*-dihalides to give substituted cyclobutene derivatives have been carried out using naphthalene-sodium.[3]

(1)   (2)

[2]R. N. McDonald and D. G. Frickey, *Am. Soc.*, **90**, 5315 (1968)
[3]C. G. Scouten, F. E. Barton, Jr., J. R. Burgess, P. R. Story, and J. F. Garst, *Chem. Commun.*, 78 (1969)

1,3-Dithiane, [**1**, 351, before **5,5′-Dithiobis(2-nitrobenzoic acid)**]. Mol. wt. 120.23, m.p. 53–54°.

Preparation.[1] The reagent is prepared in 77–84% yield by the addition of an equimolar solution of 1,3-propanedithiol (Aldrich, Fluka) and methylal to a solution of boron trifluoride etherate in refluxing chloroform solution.

C—C Bond formation. 1,3-Dithiane is readily converted in THF into the carbanion salt (2) on treatment with *n*-butyllithium at $-30°$ under nitrogen.[2] The clear, colorless solution is stable under N_2 at $-20°$ for at least three weeks. The carbanion

$$HS(CH_2)_3SH + H_2C(OCH_3)_2 \xrightarrow[\text{Refl. CHCl}_3]{BF_3 \cdot (C_2H_5)_2O} \quad \left[\begin{array}{c} \text{S} \quad \text{S} \end{array}\right] + 2\ CH_3OH$$

(1)

is very reactive to a wide variety of alkyl halides (particularly iodides), and yields of products are 70–90%. A second alkyl group can also be introduced efficiently as shown in the preparation of 2,2-diisopropyl-1,3-dithiane (5). 1,3-Dithianes of type (5) can be split to the corresponding carbonyl compound (6) by mercuric chloride

(see **1**, 654) or by bromine in aqueous acetic acid.[3] Cleavage of 1,3-dithianes of type (3) gives aldehydes.

Carbanions of type (2) or type (4) also react readily with 1,2-oxides to form 1,3-dithiane derivatives of β-hydroxyaldehydes (from type 2) or β-hydroxyketones (from type 4). For example, the carbanion (7) reacts with styrene oxide to give (8) in 70% yield: on hydrolysis and dehydration (8) is converted into benzylideneacetone (9).

Carbanions of type (2) or (4) react readily with ketones to give mercaptals of α-hydroxy aldehydes and α-hydroxy ketones, respectively:

Anions of type (4), for example (7), react with carbon dioxide at $-70°$ to give 1,3-dithianes of α-keto carboxylic acids (11) in 70–75% yield. The reaction of carboxylic acid derivatives is more complex, but the reaction with nitriles to give 1,3-dithianes of 1,2-diketones such as (12) usually proceeds without complication.[4]

$$\text{(7)} \xrightarrow[\text{70-75\%}]{\text{CO}_2,\ \text{H}_2\text{O}} \text{(11)} + \text{LiOH}$$

82% $\Big\downarrow$ C$_6$H$_5$C≡CN, H$_2$O

(12)   + LiOH

Both Corey[5] and Brook[6] found that carbanions of type (2) or (4) react with chlorotrimethylsilane or related compounds to give 1,3-dithianes of α-silyl ketones or aldehydes:

$$\text{(2)} + (\text{CH}_3)_3\text{SiCl} \xrightarrow[\text{70.6\%}]{-\text{LiCl}} \text{(13)} \longrightarrow \text{(14)}$$

For the hydrolysis step, for example (13) → (14), Corey used mercuric chloride–mercuric oxide in aqueous methanol, while Brook used a modification of Wolfrom's procedure (1, 654, ref. 14), using acetone–benzene–water as solvent. For volatile ketones, Brook prefers DMSO–water as the solvent system.

Corey and Crouse[7] have shown that the lithio derivatives of 1,3-dithianes can be used to carry out various modifications of 2-cyclohexenone. Thus (7) reacts with cyclohexenone by 1,2-addition to give (15). On treatment with aqueous 1% sulfuric acid in dioxane, (15) rearranges in high yield to the allylic isomer (16). The secondary hydroxyl group of (16) is readily oxidized without attack of the dithiane system by activated manganese dioxide to give (18). Selective hydrolysis of (16) was carried out to give (17) by using mercuric chloride in aqueous acetonitrile in the presence of cadmium carbonate. The conversion of (18) into (19) was carried out by oxidative hydrolysis with N-chlorosuccinimide–silver nitrate in aqueous acetonitrile. The enedione (19) was readily reduced to the saturated 1,4-diketone (20). The synthesis of (17), (19), and (20) illustrates that bisthiocarbanions can be used for synthesis of 1,4-dioxygenated structures at various oxidation levels.

2-Lithio-1,3-dithiane has also been used for the synthesis of cyclic mono- and diketones.[8] Thus (2) reacts with an α,ω-dichloroalkane to give in high yield a 2-(ω-chloroalkyl)-1,3-dithiane (21), which undergoes ring closure when treated with 1 equivalent of n-butyllithium under nitrogen at a low temperature. Yields are about

(2)   (21)

(22)   (23)

80% when $n = 2-6$, but the yield in the formation of an eight-membered ring is very low. Hydrolysis of the trimethylenethioketals was carried out in ethylene glycol with mercuric chloride (trace of acid).

The preparation of the bisthioketal of cyclohexane-1,3-dione (25) illustrates the use of 2-lithio-1,3-dithiane for synthesis of cyclic diketones. The lithio derivative (2) is transformed as above into the bisdithiane (24), which is then heated successively with n-butyllithium, 1-iodo-3-chloropropane, and finally n-butyllithium.[8]

(2)   (24)   (25)

Seebach and Beck[9] have described a detailed procedure for the preparation of cyclobutanone.

Chemists[10] at the Stanford Research Institute used Corey's procedure for the synthesis of (5 below) and (7 below), two of the three principal components of the sex attractant of the bark beetle, *Ips confusus*. The former was synthesized by reaction of 2-isobutyl-1,3-dithiane (2) with 2-bromomethylbutadiene (1) followed by deblocking with mercuric chloride and cadmium carbonate to give methyl-6-

methylene-7-octene-4-one (4). Sodium borohydride reduction gave the natural product (5).

The second attractant (7) was prepared by the same procedure by the condensation of (1) with 2-isobutenyl-1,3-dithiane (6).

The dithiane route was useful in these syntheses because (1) could not be converted into the Grignard reagent or the lithium reagent.

The dithiane group can be converted into the dioxolane group by exchange with dry ethylene glycol–THF–mercuric chloride.[11]

Synthesis of cyclophanes. Boekelheide[12] has extended Corey's use of 1,3-

dithianes to a new synthesis of cyclophanes, previously available in modest yield, mainly by Wurtz dimerization. For example, isophthalaldehyde was treated with 1,3-propanedithiol (*p*-TsOH) to give (1), isophthalaldehyde bis(1,3-propanedithiol-acetal). This was converted into the dianion by treatment with *n*-butyllithium and then the [2.2]metacyclophane derivative (2) was obtained by reaction with *m*-xylylene dibromide (28% yield). This was converted into the diketone (3) by hydrolysis with mercuric chloride in methanol–THF in a sealed tube (42% yield). The dithiane (2) on treatment with Raney nickel gives [2.2]metacyclophane itself in 68% yield.

(1)   (2)

(3)

Similar reactions were carried out with *p*-xylylene dibromide to give an unsymmetrical cyclophane.

This procedure has the advantage over the Wurtz reaction in that functional groups can be obtained in the bridges.

[1] E. J. Corey and D. Seebach, procedure submitted to *Org. Syn.*, 1966

[2] *Idem, Angew Chem., internat. Ed.*, **4**, 1075 (1965)

[3] F. Weygand and H. J. Bestmann, *Ber.*, **90**, 1230 (1950)

[4] E. J. Corey and D. Seebach, *Angew. Chem., internat. Ed.*, **4**, 1077 (1965)

[5] E. J. Corey, D. Seebach, and R. Freedman, *Am. Soc.*, **89**, 434 (1967)

[6] A. G. Brook, J. M. Duff, P. F. Jones, and N. R. Davis, *ibid.*, **89**, 431 (1967)

[7] E. J. Corey and D. Crouse, *J. Org.*, **33**, 298 (1968)

[8] D. Seebach, N. R. Jones, and E. J. Corey, *ibid.*, **33**, 300 (1968)

[9] D. Seebach and A. Beck, procedure submitted to *Org. Syn.*, 1968

[10] C. A. Reece, J. O. Rodin, R. G. Brownlee, W. G. Duncan, and R. M. Silverstein, *Tetrahedron*, **24**, 4249 (1968)

[11] E. J. Corey *et al., Am. Soc.*, **90**, 3245 (1968)

[12] T. Hylton and V. Boekelheide, *ibid.*, **90**, 6887 (1968)

Di-(2,2,2-trichloroethyl)phosphorochloridate, $(Cl_3CCH_2O)_2POCl$ [**1**, 352, before **Divinylmercury**]. Mol. wt. 379.24, m.p. 37–42°.

The reagent is prepared[1] by the reaction of 2,2,2-trichloroethanol with phosphoryl chloride.

The reagent reacts with protected nucleosides to give the 5′-di-(2,2,2-trichloroethyl)phosphate, which on treatment with zinc dust in pyridine–water (9:1) is cleaved to the nucleoside 5′-phosphate.[2]

$$HOCH_2 \underset{HO \quad R}{\overset{O}{\diagup}} Base + (Cl_3CCH_2O)_2POCl \xrightarrow[40-70\%]{} (Cl_3CCH_2O)_2\overset{\overset{O}{\|}}{P}OCH_2 \underset{HO \quad R}{\overset{O}{\diagup}} Base$$

$$\xrightarrow[90-95\%]{Zn} (HO)_2\overset{\overset{O}{\|}}{P}OCH_2 \underset{HO \quad R}{\overset{O}{\diagup}} Base$$

[1]By analogy with di-(2,2,2-trifluoroethyl)phosphorochloridate described in Houben-Weyl, "Organische Phosphoroverbindungen," Part 2, p. 276, Verlag Thieme, Stuttgart, 1964

[2]F. Eckstein and K.-H. Scheit, *Angew. Chem., internat. Ed.*, **6**, 362 (1967); A. Franke, K.-H. Scheit, and F. Eckstein, *Ber.*, **101**, 2998 (1968)

"dri-Na" [**1**, 353, before **Drying agents**]. *See* **Sodium-lead alloy** (this volume).

E

Ethanedithiol [1, 356–357, before references].

The method of protecting a keto group by conversion to the ethylenethioketal (2) initially suffered from lack of method for easy removal of the protective group, since ethylenethioketals are stable to base and hydrolyzed only imperfectly by acid.

Daum and Clarke[6] report that ethylenethioketals can be oxidized smoothly with excess perphthalic acid to disulfones (3) and that the ketone function can be regenerated by decomposition under alkaline conditions in the presence of oxygen. This new protecting group is useful in cases where an acid-sensitive moiety has been introduced after protection of the ketone. Unfortunately the yields in the last step reported for two test cases were only 39% and 40%.

[6]S. J. Daum and R. L. Clarke, *Tetrahedron Letters*, 165 (1967)

Ethanolamine [1, 357]. *Correction:* Mol. wt. 61.09, m.p. 9–10°.

New use [before references]. Rosin, a glassy brown solid obtained from the exudate of pine trees, consists chiefly of a mixture of crystalline dienic acids of the formula $C_{20}H_{30}O_2$, namely (1)–(4) and (6)–(7). On mild dehydrogenation, acids (1)–(4) all yield an identical product, dehydroabietic acid (8), which has one aromatic ring. In an improved procedure for the preparation of (8)[3] a mixture of 500 g. of gum rosin with 1 g. of 5% palladium on carbon is stirred mechanically under a blanket of nitrogen, and the temperature is raised to 280° and held there with stirring under a slow stream of nitrogen for 1 hr. A solution of 100 g. of the resulting disproportionated rosin in 250 ml. of 95% ethanol is filtered by suction through a pad of filter aid, warmed to 70°, and 18 g. of 2-ethanolamine is added. The solution is diluted with 250 ml. of 80–85° water and extracted with three 75-ml. portions of isooctane (heat to 60° between extractions). Crystallization of the amine salt commences at about 50° and is let continue overnight. The crystalline product is slurried with cold 50% ethanol and recrystallized, and then a solution in hot ethanol

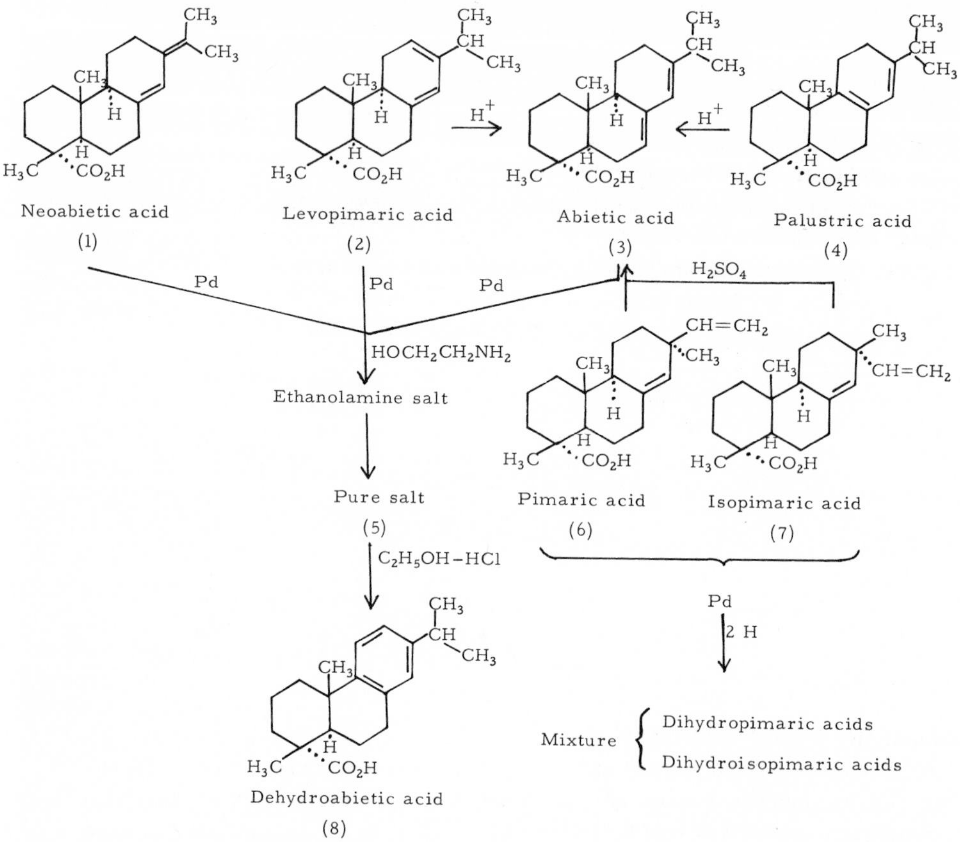

Neoabietic acid
(1)

Levopimaric acid
(2)

Abietic acid
(3)

Palustric acid
(4)

Pure salt
(5)

Pimaric acid
(6)

Isopimaric acid
(7)

Dehydroabietic acid
(8)

Mixture $\left\{\begin{array}{l}\text{Dihydropimaric acids}\\\text{Dihydroisopimaric acids}\end{array}\right.$

is acidified with hydrochloric acid for liberation of pure dehydroabietic acid, m.p. 171.5–172.5°, $\alpha_D + 62°$ (2% in EtOH); yield 30–36 g. (51–61%).

Pimaric acid (6) and isopimaric acid (7) differ in carbon skeleton from abietic acid, and the amounts initially present in rosin are lost in the process described for the preparation of dehydroabietic acid. In the step of dehydrogenation with palladium the two acids act as hydrogen acceptors and are converted into a mixture of dihydropimaric and dihydroisopimaric acids. Note that pimaric acid and isopimaric acid have been shown to be rearranged to abietic acid by concentrated sulfuric acid.

[3]N. J. Halbrook and R. V. Lawrence, *J. Org.*, **31**, 4246 (1966); procedure submitted to *Org. Syn.*, 1967

Ethoxyacetylene [1, 357–360]. Add to suppliers: Humphrey Chemical Co., North Haven, Conn.; Fl.

Peptide synthesis [1, 359, after citation of ref. 14]. When phthalic acid is allowed to react with ethoxyacetylene in the presence of an amino acid ester, the phthaloyl derivative is obtained in good yield.[14a]

[14a]G. R. Banks, D. Cohen, and G. E. Pattenden and J. A. G. Thomas, *J. Chem. Soc.*, (C), 126 (1967)

Ethoxycarbonylhydrazine [1, 360]. Supplier: E.

N-Ethoxycarbonyl-2-ethoxy-1,3-dihydroquinoline (EEDQ) [1, 360, before **Ethoxycarbonylhydrazine]**. Mol. wt. 247.29, m.p. 63.5–65°. Supplier: A.

Preparation. This interesting pseudo base first described by Belleau *et al.*[1] is now readily available by the following simplified procedure.[2]

A solution of 92 ml. (2 m.) of absolute ethanol and 155 ml. (1.07 m.) of triethylamine was added dropwise to a stirred and well-cooled (− 5°) mixture of 97 ml. of ethyl chloroformate and 130 g. (1 mole) of quinoline in 300 ml. of benzene. After stirring for 1 hr. more, the mixture was washed with water and the aqueous layer was extracted with chloroform. The combined organic solution was evaporated to dryness under vacuum. On addition of a small amount of ether (20 ml.) to the residue a white solid separated and after standing it was collected and washed thoroughly with cold ether; yield 140 g., m.p. 63.5–65°. The mother liquor after standing in the cold overnight afforded an additional 25 g. of product; the total yield was 66%.

The reagent promotes the coupling in high yields of acylamino acids with amino acid esters in benzene, ethanol, or THF at room temperature. No racemization was detected in the supersensitive Young test, and Bz–Leu–Gly–OEt, αD − 33.5°, was synthesized in 95% yield. Activation of the carboxyl group involves the transient formation of a mixed carbonic anhydride.[3]

[1]B. Belleau, R. Martel, G. Lacasse, M. Ménard, N. L. Weinberg, and Y. G. Perron, *Am. Soc.*, **90**, 823 (1968)
[2]B. Belleau, personal communication
[3]B. Belleau and G. Malek, *Am. Soc.*, **90**, 1651 (1968)

Ethyl azidoformate [1, 363, after citation of ref. 3].

Brown and Edwards[3a] irradiated a mixture of dihydropyran and ethyl azidoformate and obtained in good yield a highly reactive product (not purified) shown to be the aziridine (6) by reaction with water to give the urethane (7).

The reagent also undergoes photolytic reaction with enol acetates such as isopropenyl acetate or 1-acetoxycyclohexene.[3b] Again the N-carboethoxyaziridine is obtained as an unstable oil. Products derived from C—H insertion of the postulated carboethoxynitrene are formed to a lesser extent.

[3a]I. Brown and O. E. Edwards, *Canad. J. Chem.*, **43**, 1266 (1965)
[3b]J. F. W. Keana, S. B. Keana, and D. Beetham, *J. Org.*, **32**, 3057 (1967)

N-Ethylbenzisoxazolium fluoroborate [**1**, 364, before references].

Two derivatives of this reagent have been shown to be useful for preparation of activated esters: N-ethyl-5,7-dichlorobenzisoxazolium fluoroborate (1)[3] and N-ethyl-7-hydroxybenzisoxazolium fluoroborate (2).[4]

(1)   (2)

[3]S. Rajappa and A. S. Akerbar, *Chem. Commun.*, 826 (1966)
[4]D. S. Kemp and S. W. Chien, *Am. Soc.*, **89**, 2743 (1967)

Ethyl bromoacetate, $BrCH_2CO_2C_2H_5$ [**1**, 364, before **Ethyl carbamate**]. Mol. wt. 167.02, b.p. 57–59°/15 mm. Suppliers: E, A.

Conversion of olefins into esters. Brown[1] has extended the one-carbon homologation of olefins with carbon monoxide and the three-carbon homologation of olefins with acrolein to a two-carbon homologation with ethyl bromoacetate. The olefin is converted into the trialkylborane in THF at 0° by addition of the calculated quantity of diborane in THF. An equimolecular quantity of ethyl bromoacetate is added, followed by an equimolecular quantity of potassium *t*-butoxide in *t*-butanol. The reaction is apparently complete immediately. Ethyl chloroacetate can also be used, but the reaction is somewhat slower and gives slightly lower yields.

Examples.

$$CH_3CH_2CH{=}CH_2 \xrightarrow[93\%]{} CH_3(CH_2)_4CO_2C_2H_5$$

$$(CH_3)_2C{=}CH_2 \xrightarrow[98\%]{} (CH_3)_2CHCH_2CH_2CO_2C_2H_5$$

Brown suggests that the reaction involves (a) formation of the carbanion of the ester, (b) coordination of the carbanion with the trialkylborane, (c) rearrangement, and (d) protonolysis.

(a) $\underline{t}\text{-BuO}^-\text{K}^+ + \text{BrCH}_2\text{COOC}_2\text{H}_5 \longrightarrow \text{K}^+\text{C}^-\text{HBrCO}_2\text{C}_2\text{H}_5 + \underline{t}\text{-BuOH}$

(b) $\text{R}_3\text{B} + \text{K}^+\text{C}^-\text{HBrCO}_2\text{C}_2\text{H}_5 \longrightarrow \text{K}^+[\text{R}_3\text{BCHBrCO}_2\text{C}_2\text{H}_5]^-$

(c) $\text{K}^+[\text{R}_3\text{BCHBrCO}_2\text{C}_2\text{H}_5]^- \longrightarrow \text{K}^+[\text{R}_2\text{BrBCHRCO}_2\text{C}_2\text{H}_5]^-$

$$\downarrow$$

$$\text{KBr} + \text{R}_2\text{BCHRCO}_2\text{C}_2\text{H}_5$$

(d) $\text{R}_2\text{BCHRCO}_2\text{C}_2\text{H}_5 + \underline{t}\text{-BuOH} \longrightarrow \text{RCH}_2\text{CO}_2\text{C}_2\text{H}_5 + \underline{t}\text{-BuOBR}_2$

[1]H. C. Brown, M. M. Rogić, M. W. Rathke, and G. W. Kabalka, *Am. Soc.*, **90**, 818 (1968)

Ethyl chloroformate [1, 364–367].

Mixed anhydride synthesis [1, 366, after citation of ref. 6]. Wieland[6a] used the reagent for a one-step cyclization of peptides. Thus L-Try-Gly-L-Leu-L-Ala-D-Thr (1) was treated with 5 equiv. of pyridine hydrochloride in DMF–THF at 15°. The mixed anhydride (2) is formed but not isolated, and addition of triethylamine leads to cyclization to (3) in 30% yield. The yield is significantly lower (8%) in the absence of pyridine hydrochloride. The one-step synthesis with bis-(2,4-dinitrophenyl)-carbonate in place of ethyl chloroformate proceeds in only 13% yield.

[6a]Th. Wieland, J. Faesel, and H. Faulstich, *Ann.*, **713**, 201 (1968)

Ethyl diazoacetate [1, 367–370, before references].

Furane synthesis. 1,4-Addition of carbenoids to conjugated dienes is extremely rare; however, a Syntex group[11] found that difluorocarbene (generated from sodium chlorodifluoroacetate) undergoes 1,4-addition to 17β-acetoxy-2-methoxymethylene-5α-androstane-3-one (1) to give the two epimers (2) in a total yield of 70%. Storm and Spencer[12] extended this reaction to a useful synthesis of furanes. Instead of difluorocarbene they used carboethoxycarbene generated from ethyl diazoacetate in the presence of copper sulfate. Reaction with 2-methoxymethylenecholestanone (1, with appropriate changes in ring D) proceeded in the same way but with spontan-

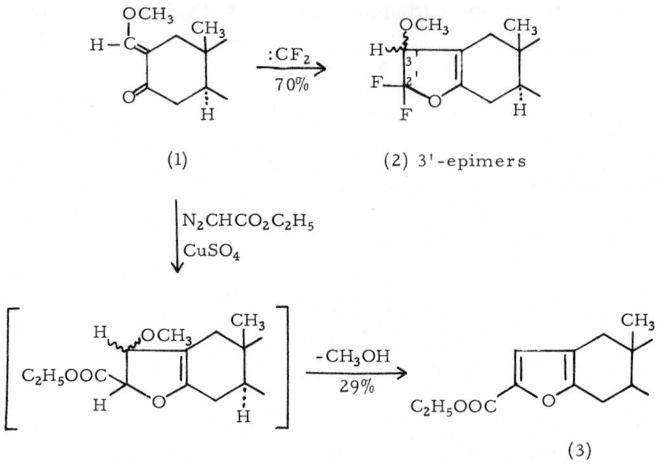
:CF_2
70%
(1)
(2) 3'-epimers
$N_2CHCO_2C_2H_5$
$CuSO_4$
$-CH_3OH$
29%
(3)

eous loss of methanol to give the furanecarboxylic acid ester (3). This product was converted into the parent furane in quantitative yield by hydrolysis to the acid and decarboxylation at the melting point in the presence of copper powder.

Spencer *et al.*[13] used this reaction as a key step in the synthesis of racemic methyl vinhaticoate (6), a tetracyclic furanoid diterpene. Thus treatment of the α-methoxymethylene ketone (4) with ethyl diazoacetate in the presence of copper sulfate

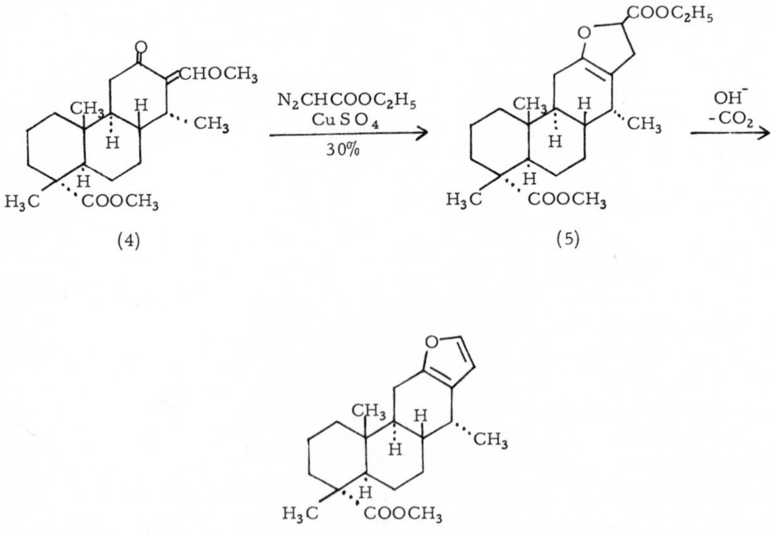
$N_2CHCOOC_2H_5$
$CuSO_4$
30%
OH^-
$-CO_2$
(4)
(5)

(6)

at 160° gave the furoic ester (5) in about 30% yield. This was selectively hydrolyzed and decarboxylated to give racemic methyl vinhaticoate (6).

Reaction with trialkylboranes.[14] Ethyl diazoacetate reacts with trialkylboranes with loss of nitrogen to give, after hydrolysis, the homologated ethyl ester:

$$R_3B \ + \ N_2CHCOOC_2H_5 \ \xrightarrow[\text{2) } H_2O]{\text{1) } -N_2} \ RCH_2COOC_2H_5$$

The yield of ethyl octanoate from 1-hexene is 83%.

Diazoacetonitrile[15] reacts in the same way to give homologated nitriles:

$$R_3B \ + \ N_2CHCN \ \xrightarrow[\text{2) } H_2O]{\text{1) } -N_2} \ RCH_2CN$$

[11]P. Hodge, J. A. Edwards, and J. H. Fried, *Tetrahedron Letters*, 5175 (1966)

[12]D. L. Storm and T. A. Spencer, *ibid.*, 1865 (1967)

[13]T. A. Spencer, R. M. Villarica, D. L. Storm, T. D. Weaver, R. J. Friary, J. Posler, and P. R. Shafer, *Am. Soc.*, **89**, 5498 (1967)

[14]J. Hooz and S. Linke, *Am. Soc.*, **90**, 6891 (1968)

[15]T. Curtius, *Ber.*, **31**, 2489 (1898); *caution!* The isolation of this diazo compound is occasionally fraught with explosions.

Ethyl dibromoacetate, $Br_2CHCOOC_2H_5$ [**1**, 370, before **Ethyldicyclohexylamine**]. Mol. wt. 245.91, b.p. 194°. Supplier: E.

Reaction with organoboranes.[1] Brown has extended the reaction of ethyl bromoacetate with trialkylboranes to ethyl dibromoacetate. If one equivalent of potassium *t*-butoxide is used, an α-halocarboxylic acid is obtained; dialkylation is achieved by use of two equivalents of the base. Since the first reaction occurs readily at 0°, whereas the second requires a higher temperature (50°), two different alkyl groups

$$CH_2{=}CH_2 \ \longrightarrow \ (C_2H_5)_3B \ \xrightarrow[\text{t-BuOK}]{Br_2CHCOOC_2H_5} \ C_2H_5CHBrCOOC_2H_5$$
$$97\%$$

$$2 \ \underline{t}\text{-BuOK} \ \bigg\downarrow Br_2CHCOOC_2H_5$$

$$(C_2H_5)_2CHCOOC_2H_5$$
$$69\%$$

can be introduced. Ethyl dichloroacetate can also be used but yields are somewhat lower, particularly in the case of hindered trialkylboranes.

[1]H. C. Brown, M. M. Rogić, M. W. Rathke, and G. W. Kabalka, *Am. Soc.*, **90**, 1911 (1968)

Ethyldicyclohexylamine [**1**, 370, before references].

The last step in the first total synthesis of the tetracycline antibiotic terramycin (1) by Muxfeldt and co-workers[5] involved dialkylation of a primary amine group at C_4.

(1)

This was accomplished in 33% yield using dimethyl sulfate and ethyldicyclohexyl-amine in THF.

[5]H. Muxfeldt, G. Hardtmann, F. Kathawala, E. Vedejs, and J. B. Mooberry, *Am. Soc.*, **90**, 6534 (1968)

1-Ethyl-3-(3′-dimethylaminopropyl)carbodiimide hydrochloride [1, 371].

Preparation.[1a] A slightly modified procedure has been described in detail.

[1a]J. C. Sheehan and P. A. Cruickshank, *Org. Syn.*, **48**, 83 (1968)

Ethyl (dimethylsulfuranylidine)acetate (EDSA) [1, 372, before Ethylene carbonate].

Mol. wt. 148.23, liq., n^{25}D 1.5253–1.5263.

Preparation.[1] This ylide is prepared in two steps as shown.

$$BrCH_2COOC_2H_5 + (CH_3)_2S \xrightarrow[90\%]{} (CH_3)_2\overset{+}{S}\overset{Br^-}{}CH_2CO_2C_2H_5 \xrightarrow[95°]{K_2CO_3-NaOH}$$

$$(CH_3)_2S=CHCOOC_2H_5$$

$$(1)\ \ EDSA$$

Reactions. In a reaction reminiscent of methylene transfer with dimethyloxo-sulfonium methylide, EDSA reacts with α,β-unsaturated aldehydes and ketones in aprotic solvents to give cyclopropanes in 65–90% yield.[1] EDSA reacts with α,β-unsaturated esters to give esters of acyclic polybasic acids.[2]

$$CH_2=CHCOCH_3 + (1) \xrightarrow[87\%]{\substack{45°,\ 2\ 1/2\ hrs. \\ CH_2Cl_2}} H_2C\overset{\overset{HCCOCH_3}{\diagup\diagdown}}{} CHCOOC_2H_5 + (CH_3)_2S$$

$$CH_3CH=CHCHO + (1) \xrightarrow[50\%]{\substack{60° \\ acetone}} H_3C-\underset{H}{\overset{\overset{HCCHO}{\diagup\diagdown}}{C}} CHCOOC_2H_5 + (CH_3)_2S$$

EDSA reacts with anhydrides (also acid chlorides, acetylenic esters and ketones) to give stable sulfur ylides and with α-diketones to give epoxy esters.[3]

$$(1) + (C_6H_5CO)_2O \xrightarrow[72\%]{} C_2H_5O_2C\overset{O}{\overset{\|}{C}}\underset{\overset{\|}{S(CH_3)_2}}{C}C_6H_5$$

$$(1) + C_6H_5COCOC_6H_5 \xrightarrow[92\%]{} C_6H_5C\overset{O}{\overset{\|}{C}}\underset{C_6H_5}{\overset{\overset{O}{\diagup\diagdown}}{}}CHCOOC_2H_5$$

[1]G. B. Payne, *J. Org.*, **32**, 3351 (1967); *idem, ibid.*, **33**, 1285 (1968)
[2]*Idem, ibid.*, **33**, 1284 (1968)
[3]*Idem, ibid.*, **33**, 3517 (1968)

Ethylene oxide [1, 377–378]. Suppliers: E, Fl.

Generation of dihalocarbenes [before reference]. A German group[2] has generated dihalocarbenes by heating a mixture of a haloform, ethylene oxide, and tetraethyl-ammonium bromide (used for solubility reasons) in the presence of an olefin in a sealed tube at 150° for about five hours. It is postulated that bromide anion attacks the oxide with generation of the strongly basic alkoxide anion, which removes a proton from the haloform to generate a trihalomethide anion, which is then converted

into the dihalocarbene. The method is satisfactory for generation of dichlorocarbene, but rather low yields are obtained in the case of fluorochlorocarbene and of difluoro-carbene.

Wittig reactions. Ethylene oxide can be used as the base for generation of Wittig reagents from phosphonium salts. It is often not necessary to prepare the salts; thus a mixture of ethylene oxide, triphenylphosphine, and ethyl bromoacetate reacts with benzaldehyde at 25° to give ethyl cinnamate (91% yield, *trans:cis* = 93:7).[3]

[2] P. Weyerstahl, D. Klamann, C. Finger, F. Nerdel, and J. Buddrus, *Ber.*, **100**, 1858 (1967)
[3] J. Buddrus, *Angew. Chem., internat. Ed.*, 7, 536 (1968)

Ethyl formate [1, 380–383].

Formylation of ketones [before references]. Alkylation at the α'-methylene or α'-methinyl group of α-formyl cyclic ketones has been effected in good yield.[11] The reaction as applied to 2-methylcyclohexanone[12] proceeds as indicated.

[11] S. Boatman, T. M. Harris, and C. R. Hauser, *Am. Soc.*, **87**, 82 (1965)
[12] *Idem, Org. Syn.*, **48**, 40 (1968)

N-Ethyl-5-phenylisoxazolium-3'-sulfonate [1, 384–385, before references].

A definitive paper[5] includes references to uses of the reagent in peptide synthesis. Pettit[6] recommends the reagent for the synthesis of steroidal peptides.

[5]R. B. Woodward, R. A. Olofson, and H. Mayer, *Tetrahedron*, **22**, *Suppl.*, **8**, 321 (1966)
[6]G. R. Pettit, R. L. Smith, and H. Klinger, *J. Med. Chem.*, **10**, 145 (1967)

Ethyl vinyl ether [1, 386–388, ref. 7]. *Add:* J. Smrt and S. Chládek, *Coll. Czech.*, **31**, 2978 (1966).

F

Ferric chloride [1, 390–392].

   Oxidation [1, 391, after citation of ref. 9a]. Ferric chloride (1 *N*) in a 1:1 two-phase system with chloroform oxidizes (1), the trifluoroacetate of methoxy-O-methylnorbelladine, to the dienone (2) in 12% yield. The product (2) on hydrolysis with 2 *N* Na₂CO₃–CHCl₃ undergoes a second intramolecular condensation to give the ring system of the crinine alkaloids, (3).[9b]

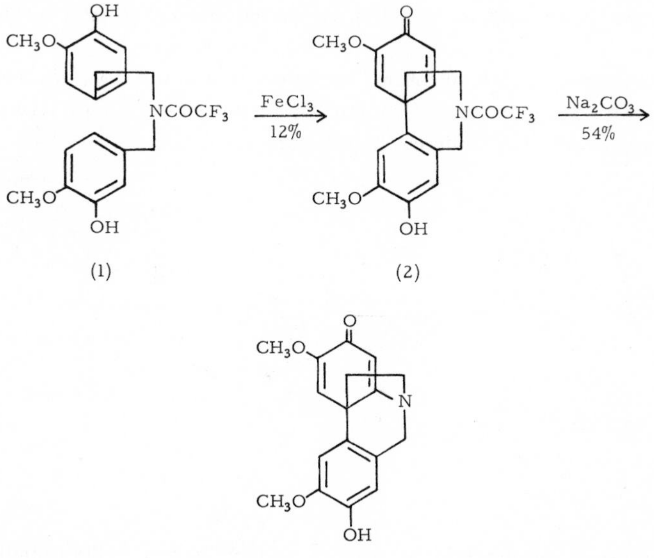

(1)   (2)

(3)

[9b]B. Frank and H. J. Lubs, *Angew. Chem., internat. Ed.*, **7**, 223 (1968)

Fluorosulfuric acid, formerly known as **Fluorosulfonic acid** [1, 396–397]. FSO₂OH. Mol. wt. 100.08, b.p. 165.5°. Supplier: Allied Chem. Corp.

   Stable carbonium ions. Olah *et al.*[5] have reported direct observation (NMR) of a phenonium ion intermediate, first postulated by Cram.[6] 1-*p*-Anisyl-2-chloroethane (1) on being ionized with FSO₂OH–SbCl₅ in SO₂ at −70° gave the bridged ion of structure (2) determined by NMR.

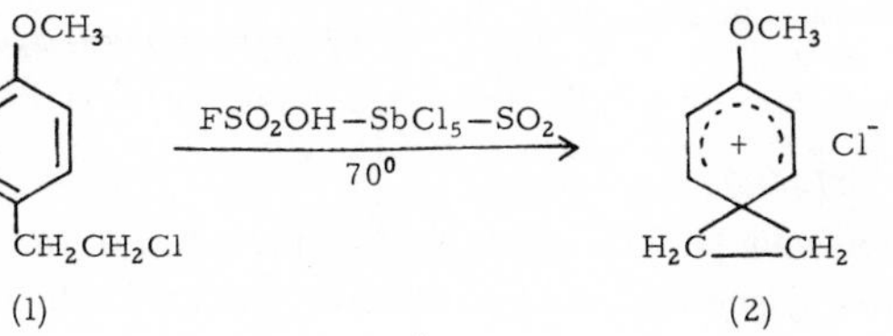

(1)   (2)

Olah[7] has prepared an extensive summary of his work on stable, long-lived carbonium ions; references to subsequent papers are listed below.[8]

Review.[9]

[5]G. A. Olah, M. B. Comisarow, E. Namanworth, and B. Ramsey, *Am. Soc.*, **89**, 5259 (1967)
[6]D. J. Cram, *ibid.*, **71**, 3863 (1949); *idem, ibid.*, **74**, 2129 (1952)
[7]G. A. Olah, *Chem. Eng. News*, **45**, 78, March 27 (1967)
[8]G. A. Olah *et al.*, *Am. Soc.*, **89**, 156, 711, 1027, 1268, 1725, 2227, 2692, 2694, 2993, 2996, 3576, 3582, 3586, 3591, 4736, 4739, 4744, 4752, 4756, 5687, 5692, 5694 (1967); *idem, ibid.*, **90**, 401, 405, 927, 933, 938, 943, 947, 1884, 2583, 2587, 2726, 4323, 4666, 4672, 6085, 6087, 6461, 6964, 6988 (1968)
[9]R. J. Gillespie, *Accounts of Chemical Research*, **1**, 202 (1968)

Fluoroxytrifluoromethane CF_3OF [**1**, 397, before **Formaldehyde**]. Mol. wt. 88.01, a gas.

Preparation[1] by treating methanol or carbon monoxide with silver difluoride and fluorine.

Uses. Preliminary communications state first[2] that fluoroxytrifluoromethane reacts cleanly with the vinyl ester (1a) and the enamine (1b) in $CFCl_3$ as solvent at $-75°$ to afford in each case 2α-fluorocholestanone (2).

(1a) R = OAc

(1b) R = —N⟨

(2)

A second use is exemplified by the reaction of fluoroxytrifluoromethane with estrone methyl ether (3) to give 10β-fluoro-19-norandrosta-1,4-diene-3,17-dione (4).[3]

(3)   (4)

[1]K. G. Kellogg and G. H. Cady, *Am. Soc.*, **70**, 3986 (1948)
[2]D. H. R. Barton, L. S. Godinho, R. H. Hesse, and M. M. Pechet, *Chem. Commun.*, 804 (1968)
[3]D. H. R. Barton, A. K. Ganguly, R. H. Hesse, S. N. Loo, and M. M. Pechet, *ibid.*, 806 (1968)

Formaldehyde [**1**, 397–402].

Reductive methylation [**1**, 397, after citation of ref. 3]. For the preparation of ethyl *p*-dimethylaminophenylacetate, Romanelli and Becker[3a] placed 41.8 g. of ethyl *p*-nitrophenylacetate, 40 ml. of 40% aqueous formaldehyde, 200 ml. of 95% ethanol, and 2 g. of 10% palladium on charcoal in the bottle of a Parr hydrogenation apparatus. After repeated evacuation and filling with hydrogen, hydrogenation was carried out at 55 p.s.i. (about 2–4 hrs.).

Steroid BMD derivatives [1, 401, before references]. A Syntex Research group[23] cleaved BMD derivatives of various difluoromethylene steroids with 40% aqueous hydrofluoric acid "in high yield," and cite a patent[24] for this procedure.

[3a]M. G. Romanelli and E. I. Becker, *Org. Syn.*, **47**, 69 (1967)
[23]I. T. Harrison, C. Beard, L. Kirkham, I. M. Jamieson, W. Rooks, and J. H. Fried, *J. Med. Chem.*, **11**, 868 (1968)
[24]F. Alvarez, J. B. Siddall, and A. Ruiz, U.S. Pat. 3,338,930 (1967)

Formamide [1, 402–403, before references].

Synthesis of ω-cyano acids. Wasserman and Druckrey[8,9] developed a novel method for the preparation of ω-cyano acids (IV), involving in the first step condensation of a cyclic acyloin (I, $x = 4, 5, 6,$ and 10) with formamide in an acidic

medium to produce a fused-ring oxazole (II). In a typical case, for example when $x = 4$, a solution of 4 g. of the oxazole in 1 l. of CH_2Cl_2 containing methylene blue as sensitizer was irradiated with a 275-W sunlamp for 12–14 hrs. while dry oxygen was bubbled through the stirred solution to generate singlet oxygen (·O—O·). Evaporation of the solvent at room temperature gave a crude product of IR showing sharp nitrile (2250 cm^{-1}) and anhydride absorption (1785, 1765 cm^{-1}); the NMR spectrum exhibits a sharp singlet at τ 0.9 characteristic of a formyl hydrogen. The anhydride (III) readily liberated CO during workup to yield the nitrile acid IV. Yields in the conversions II → IV ($x = 4, 5, 6, 10$) were 80–90%. As illustrated for the case of oxazole V from cyclopentadecanone, the reaction appears to proceed through an intermediate transannular peroxide VI, which then undergoes rearrangement to the cyano anhydride III, $x = 10$. Loss of CO from the mixed anhydride of formic acid leads to VII, the observed product.

V $\xrightarrow{O_2^{\bullet}}$ **VI** $\rightarrow$

III, x = 10 $\xrightarrow{-CO}$ **VII**

Reaction with esters.[10] In the presence of methoxide ion as catalyst, esters react with formamide or N-methylformamide to give amides.

$$RCOOCH_3 + HCONH_2 \xrightarrow[50-74\%]{(Na^+O^-CH_3),\ 94-96^0,\ 23-72\ hrs.} RCONH_2 + HCO_2CH_3 + CH_3OH$$

[8]H. H. Wasserman and E. Druckrey, *Am. Soc.*, **90**, 2440 (1968)
[9]Ref. 1 of this paper[1] should be to *Tetrahedron Suppl.*, **7**, 441 (1966)
[10]E. L. Allred and M. D. Hurwitz, *J. Org.*, **30**, 2376 (1965)

Formamidine acetate [**1**, 403–404]. Change ref. 2 to: E. C. Taylor, W. H. Ehrhart, and M. Kawanisi, *Org. Syn.*, **46**, 39 (1966).

Formic acid [**1**, 404–407, before references].

Isomerization of ethynylcarbinols. Rupe[12] first observed that ethynylcarbinols when refluxed in formic acid (90%) are isomerized to unsaturated carbonyl compounds, which he considered to be aldehydes. Chanley[13] later investigated the reaction in detail and found that the predominant product is an α,β-unsaturated ketone. Thus 1-ethynyl-1-cyclohexanol (1) is converted mainly into 1-acetyl-1-cyclohexene (2), with only traces of (3) being formed.

(1) $\xrightarrow[\text{Refl. 45 min.}]{\text{HCOOH}}$ (2) 50%   +   (3) 0.8%

Other examples:

(4)[14]   cis or trans $\xrightarrow{95\%}$

(5)[15] $\xrightarrow{81\%}$

Removal of blocking groups. Regeneration of aldehydes from their acetals can be accomplished by refluxing in formic acid for 10–60 min.[17] The reaction is applicable to sensitive aldehydes, such as α-acetylenic aldehydes.

$$RCH(OR')_2 \;+\; 2\,HCO_2H \longrightarrow RCHO \;+\; 2\,HCO_2R' \;+\; H_2O$$

Halpern and Nitecki[18] experienced difficulty in removal of the *t*-butyloxycarbonyl group (*t*-BOC) of *t*-BOC-L-threonyl-ϵ-carbobenzoyllysine benzyl ester by conventional methods (CF_3CO_2H or CH_3OH–HCl) but found that the blocking group is easily removed by treatment with 98% formic acid at room temperature for 1–3 hrs. Carbobenzoxy and O-benzyl ether protecting groups are completely stable. The acid-labile blocking groups (N-trityl, N-*o*-nitrophenylsulfonyl, and O-*t*-butyl ether and ester functions) are also smoothly cleaved.

[12]H. Rupe *et al.*, *Helv.*, **9**, 672 (1926); *idem, ibid.*, **11**, 449, 656, 965 (1928)
[13]J. D. Chanley, *Am. Soc.*, **70**, 244 (1948)
[14]M. S. Newman and P. H. Goble, *ibid.*, **82**, 4098 (1960).
[15]W. S. Johnson, S. L. Gray, J. K. Crandall, and D. M. Bailey, *ibid.*, **86**, 1966 (1964)
[16]S. W. Pelletier and S. Prabhakar, *ibid.*, **90**, 5318 (1968)
[17]A. Gorgues, *Compt. rend.*, **265** (C), 1130 (1967)
[18]B. Halpern and D. E. Nitecki, *Tetrahedron Letters*, 3031 (1967)

G

Gases, inert and reagent [Gases, **1**, 409, after **Galvinoxyl**]. Produced for Merck and Co., Inc., Rahway, N.J. by the Matheson Co., Inc., East Rutherford, N.J.

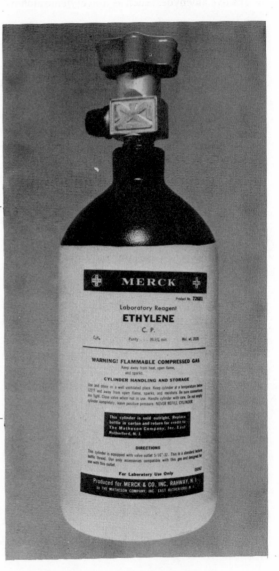

	Purity (min.)
Ammonia	99.99%
Argon	99.998%
Carbon dioxide	99.8%
Carbon monoxide	99.5%
Chlorine	99.5%
Ethylene	99.5%
Helium	99.995%
Hydrogen	99.95%
Hydrogen bromide	99.8%
Hydrogen chloride	99.0%
Hydrogen sulfide	99.6%
Methane	99.0%
Nitrogen	99.99%
Oxygen	99.6%
Sulfur dioxide	99.98%

Fig. G. Cylinder shown half size.

Offered in unique bench type cylinders (Fig. G) that stand up alone without support, take little space, and are easy to handle.

Grignard reagents [1, 415–424].

[1, 415, after Metal and Thermit reagents]: Foote Mineral Co. offers the following reagents for organic synthesis and as potential catalysts for anionic polymerization:

Cyclopentyllithium as a 20% by wt. solution in cyclohexane, 1 mole per bottle, $15.00.

Cyclohexyllithium as a 5% by wt. solution in toluene, 1/3 mole per bottle, $10.00.

Peninsular ChemResearch offers vinylmagnesium chloride in cases containing 1 mole of reagent dissolved in about 500 ml. of THF.

MCB offers: 2 M Ethylmagnesium bromide

2 M Phenylmagnesium bromide

2 M Cyclohexylmagnesium bromide

2 M t-Butylmagnesium bromide

2 M Isopropylmagnesium bromide

E. C. Ashby [*Quart. Rev.*, **21**, 259 (1967)] has reviewed papers on the composition of Grignard reagents and the mechanism of Grignard reactions.

Activated magnesium[7a] [1, 417, after citation of ref. 7]. A batch of magnesium turnings (Mallinckrodt) or chips (Metal and Thermit Corp.) is stirred vigorously under nitrogen for one day. The magnesium becomes finely divided and grey to grey-black in color. This form has been used to convert p-(dimethylamino)bromo-benzene into the Grignard reagent. Previously the Grignard derivative had been obtained only by the entrainment method or with an initiator such as iodine or ethyl iodide.

[7a]A. Mendel, *J. Organometallic Chem.*, **6**, 97 (1966)

H

Hexachlorocyclopentadiene [1, 425, after formulation].

Chemists at Hyman Laboratories[1] found that naphthalene forms a diadduct with hexachlorocyclopentadiene (25–35% yield). The reaction is of interest because the

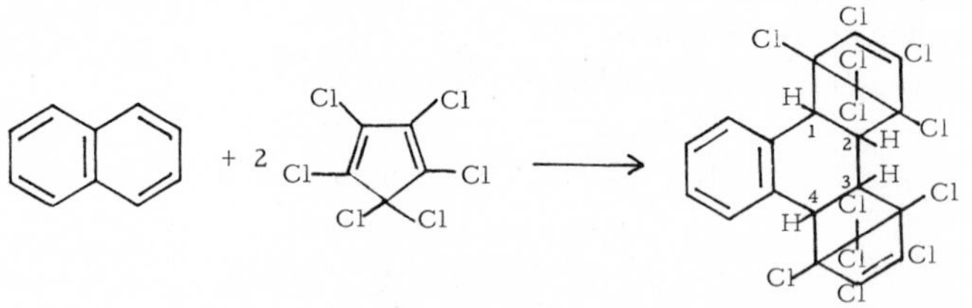

adduct undergoes substitution in the aromatic ring at the β-position, and thus β-substituted naphthalenes can be obtained by reversal of the Diels-Alder addition. The orientations of the hydrogen atoms at the 1-, 2-, 3-, and 4-positions are not known.

Review.[2]

[1] A. A. Danish, M. Silverman, and Y. A. Tajima, *Am. Soc.*, **76**, 6144 (1954); J. G. E. Fenyes, *J. Org.*, **27**, 2614 (1962); M. Look, procedure submitted to *Org. Syn.*, 1966
[2] W. E. Ungnade and E. T. McBee, *Chem. Rev.*, **58**, 249 (1958)

Hexachlorocyclotriphosphazatriene (Phosphonitrilic chloride) (1) [1, 425, before Hexaethylphosphorous triamide]. Mol. wt. 346.99, m.p. 113–115°. Supplier: Albright and Wilson, Birmingham, England.

Reviews.[1]

Preparation. The reagent was first obtained by Liebig[2] by the reaction of phosphorus pentachloride and ammonia. At the present time it is prepared from phosphorus pentachloride and ammonium chloride in *s*-tetrachloroethane.[3]

Reactions. The reagent reacts with sodium benzoate at high temperatures to give benzonitrile and benzoic anhydride.[4]

Amides and hydrazides can be prepared in good yields by reaction of the sodium salt of a carboxylic acid with the reagent in THF, benzene, or cyclohexane at room temperature followed by addition of an amine or hydrazine.[5]

The reaction presumably proceeds as follows:

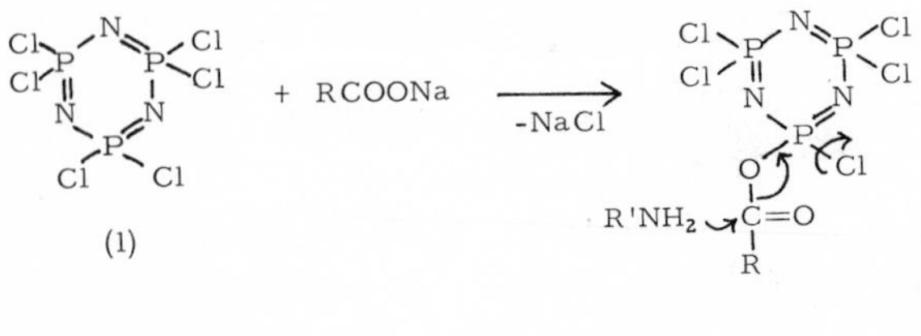

[1]R. A. Shaw, B. W. Fitzsimmons, and B. C. Smith, *Chem. Rev.*, **62**, 247 (1962); N. L. Paddock, *Quart. Rev.*, **18**, 168 (1964); R. A. Shaw, *Chem. Ind.*, 1737 (1967)
[2]J. Liebig, *Ann.*, **11**, 139 (1834)
[3]M. L. Nielsen and G. Cranford, *Inorg. Syn.*, **6**, 94 (1960)
[4]I. I. Bezman and W. R. Reed, *Am. Soc.*, **82**, 2167 (1960)
[5]L. Caglioti, M. Poloni, and G. Rosini, *J. Org.*, **33**, 2979 (1968)

Hexaethylphosphorous triamide [Tris(diethylamino)phosphine, $(C_2H_5)_2N_3P$] [1, 425, before references].

Partial desulfurization. Disulfides (cyclic, benzylic, aralkyl, and dialkyl) are converted into sulfides by reaction with the reagent at 25–80°.[3] For example, when dibenzyl disulfide is treated with a 10% excess of the phosphine in refluxing benzene

$$RSSR' + [(C_2H_5)_2N]_3P \longrightarrow RSR' + [(C_2H_5)_2N]_3P=S$$

(1.5 hrs.), dibenzyl sulfide is obtained in 80% yield. An interesting reaction is the conversion of (1) into (2) in quantitative yield.

(1)   (2)

[3]D. N. Harpp, J. C. Gleason, and J. P. Snyder, *Am. Soc.*, **90**, 4181 (1968)

Hexafluoro-2-butyne [1, 425–426, before references].

Paquette[4] considered that this reactive dienophile might undergo reaction with 2(1H)-pyridone (1), a cisoid diene which has so far failed to undergo a Diels-Alder reaction, but the product (2) results from 1,2-addition of the amide proton to the triple bond. The N-methyl derivative of (1), which cannot undergo this type of reaction, gives rise only to black tars.

(1)   (2)

[4]L. A. Paquette, *J. Org.*, **30**, 2107 (1965)

Hexamethyldisilazane [1, 427]. Other suppliers: Fl., K.-L., Sch.

Derivatives of alcohols [before references]. In a study of the preparation of O-trimethylsilyl ethers of carbohydrates, Sweeley *et al.*[4] found that practically no reaction occurred with hexamethyldisilazane alone, but that maximum yields are obtained by a combination of hexamethyldisilazane and trimethylchlorosilane, $(CH_3)_3SiCl$. The following proportions are recommended: 0.2 ml. of hexamethyl-disilazane, 0.1 ml. of trimethylchlorosilane, and 1 ml. of pyridine. Carter[5] has prepared the reagent in pyridine from 2.5 ml. of hexamethyldisilazane and 1.6 ml. of trimethylchlorosilane. A clear colorless solution is obtained by centrifugation and can be stored in the dark for several weeks. A mixture of the two reagents suitable for trimethylsilylation is sold by Pierce Chemical Co. under the name TRT-SIL.

(1)

Trimethylsilyl ethers are much more volatile than usual ethers and hence well suited for gas-liquid chromatography. Thus Meinwald[6] was unable to effect direct purification of an allenic sesquiterpenoid (1), the defensive substance of the grasshopper *Romalea microptera*; however, the bistrimethylsilyl derivative was purified without difficulty by gas-liquid chromatography.

Djerassi[7] has reported extensive studies on the mass spectral fragmentation of trimethylsilyl ethers.

[5]H. E. Carter and R. C. Gaver, *J. Lipid Res.*, **8**, 391 (1967)

[6]J. Meinwald, K. Erickson, M. Hartshorn, Y. C. Meinwald, and T. Eisner, *Tetrahedron Letters*, 2959 (1968)

[7]J. Diekman and C. Djerassi, *J. Org.*, **32**, 1005 (1967); J. Diekman, J. B. Thomson, and C. Djerassi, *ibid.*, **32**, 3904 (1967)

Hexamethylenetetramine [1, 427–430].

Sommelet reaction [1, 428–430, after citation of ref. 11]. Ackerman and Surrey[11a] report a procedure in which α,α'-diamino-*m*-xylene (1) (supplied by California

(1)

Chemical Co. and Aldrich Chemical Co.) is treated with hexamethylenetetramine, hydrochloric acid, and aqueous acetic acid at the reflux temperature. The yield of isophthalaldehyde was about 60%.

[11a]J. H. Ackerman and A. R. Surrey, *Org. Syn.*, **47**, 76 (1967)

Hexamethylphosphoric triamide, HMPT [(CH₃)₂N]₃PO [1, 430–431 (numbers of new refs. start with 7)].

Reviews.[7] Ducom[8] reports that the m.p. of scrupulously purified material is 7.2°.

Reduction. α,β-Unsaturated ketones are reduced to the corresponding saturated ketones by lithium (or potassium) in hexamethylphosphoric triamide. Use of ether as a cosolvent improves the yield, for in its absence some of the unsaturated ketone escapes reduction.[9] Yields are comparable to those obtained in liquid ammonia.

Displacements. Ordinarily displacement reactions of neopentyl-type bromides is difficult. However, Lewis *et al.*[10] achieved displacement of the bromide ion from (1) by lithium acetylide–ethylenediamine rapidly in HMPT or DMSO. Under these conditions the initial yne-terminal product (2) is isomerized to the internal isomer (3). Liquid ammonia and DMF proved unsatisfactory.

Paquette and Philips[11] likewise report that HMPT is an excellent medium for a displacement reaction of a neopentyl-type bromide. They used this solvent for con-

(1)   (2)   (3)

version of the dimesylate (4) into the diiodide (5) and for cyclization of (5) to the sulfide (7).

(4)   (5)   (6)

(7)

The reagent has been characterized as an excellent amidation reagent.[12] When a carboxylic acid is heated with HMPT for 30–60 min. at 180–200°, the corresponding N,N-dimethylamide is formed in yield of 50–90%. Caubère,[13] using the combination HMPT-THF in the presence of an excess of sodamide, showed that a halobenzene (reacting through benzyne as intermediate) can undergo various nucleophilic substitutions.

Solvent effects in a displacement. Cavé, Goutarel, *et al.*[14] examined the reaction of several 3β-tosyloxysteroids with sodium azide in DMSO, N-methylpyrrolidone, and HMPT, and obtained the highest yields of 3α-azidosteroids in the last solvent (S_N2 reaction). The same result was noted with 20α- and 20β-tosyloxysteroids, which are converted into 20β- and 20α-azidosteroids, respectively. When a protonic solvent is used, the major products are those formed by elimination.

Dehydrohalogenation. α-Bromoketones when heated at 120–140° in HMPT give the α,β-unsaturated ketones in high yield without rearrangement. The product is isolated simply by dilution with water; yields are at least as good, usually better, than with $Li_2CO_3/LiBr/DMF$.[15]

[7]H. Normant, *Bull. soc.*, 791 (1968), review with 187 references; *idem, Angew. Chem., internat. Ed.*, **6**, 1046 (1967)

[8]J. Ducom, *Compt. rend.*, **264** (C), 722 (1967)

[9]P. Angibeaud, M. Larchevêque, H. Normant, and B. Tchoubar, *Bull. soc.*, 595 (1968)

[10]R. G. Lewis, D. H. Gustafson, and W. F. Erman, *Tetrahedron Letters*, 401 (1967)

[11]L. A. Paquette and J. C. Philips, *ibid.*, 4645 (1967)

[12]J. Kopecký and J. Šmejkal, *Chem. Ind.*, 1529 (1966)

[13]P. Caubère, *Bull. soc.*, 3446, 3451 (1967)

[14]A. Cavé, F.-X. Jarreau, Q. Khuong-Huu, M. Leboeuf, N. Serban, and R. Goutarel, *ibid.*, 701 (1967); M. Leboeuf, A. Cavé, and R. Goutarel, *Compt. rend.*, **264**, 1090 (1967)

[15]R. Hanna, *Tetrahedron Letters*, 2105 (1968)

Hexamethylphosphorous triamide, $[(CH_3)_2N]_3P$ **[1,** 431–432]. Suppliers: A. Fl., K.-L., Sch.

Wittig reaction [**1,** 432, before references]. Oediger and Eiter[7] have used the reagent instead of triphenylphosphine in the Wittig reaction. It is useful because the nonolefinic product, hexamethylphosphoric triamide, is water-soluble.

Reduction of hydroperoxides. In a synthesis of ecdysone from ergosterol, one step involved ozonization of (1) to the aldehyde (2) without isomerization.[8] Reduction of the intermediate hydroperoxide was accomplished under very mild conditions with

hexamethylphosphorous triamide, which is converted into hexamethylphosphoric triamide; this product can be readily removed from the aldehyde by washing with dilute aqueous hydrochloric acid.

[7]H. Oediger and K. Eiter, *Ann.*, **682**, 58 (1965)
[8]A. Furlenmeier, A. Fürst, A. Langemann, G. Waldvogel, P. Hocks, U. Kerb, and R. Wiechert, *Helv.*, **50**, 2387 (1967)

Hydrazine [1, 434–445].

Wolff-Kishner reduction [1, 435, after citation of ref. 7]. A later review[7a] discusses the mechanism of Wolff-Kishner reduction.

Synthesis of phenylcyclopropane [1, 441, before line 2 from bottom]. A preferred procedure for the preparation of phenylcyclopropane (5) described by Petersen and

Skell[46a] involves heating a mixture of ethanol and hydrazine hydrate under reflux and adding cinnamaldehyde dropwise at a controlled rate. For a time, the mixture turns orange because of the formation of cinnamalazine (4). After some 3 hrs., phenyl-cyclopropane begins to codistil with the last of the hydrazine hydrate. The yield of phenylcyclopropane is 45–56%.

For a synthesis of pyrazoles, *see* **Phenyl(trihaloromethyl)mercury**, this volume.

[7a]H. H. Szmant, *Angew. Chem., internat. Ed.*, **7**, 120 (1968)
[46a]R. J. Petersen and P. S. Skell, *Org. Syn.*, **47**, 98 (1967)

Hydrazoic acid [1, 446–448].

Schmidt reaction [1, 446–447]. In the course of studies of the odoriferous constituents of musk from the perfume gland of the musk deer, in addition to mus-

(III) Muscone, $C_{16}H_{30}O$ (IV) Muscopyridine ($C_{16}H_{25}N$)

cone (III), Schinz, Ruzicka, Geyer, and Prelog[4a] isolated an optically active base $C_{16}H_{25}N$, $\alpha D + 17.4°$, λ_{max} 267 mμ, log ϵ 3.7, which was named muscopyridine. This base is attacked only slowly by potassium permanganate but on prolonged oxidation gives pyridine-2,6-dicarboxylic acid (II). The observation established the presence of a 2,6-dialkylpyridine group (I) and also suggested that the natural base does not contain any nonaromatic double bonds. Biemann, Büchi, and Walker[4b] made the reasonable assumption that the similarity in composition between the two C_{16} musk constituents, muscone ($C_{16}H_{30}O$) and muscopyridine ($C_{16}H_{25}N$), is not fortuitous but due to a biogenetic relationship, and proposed for muscopyridine the structure IV; the ring system corresponds to that of muscone, and a methyl group at the same position as that in muscone accounts for the optical activity.

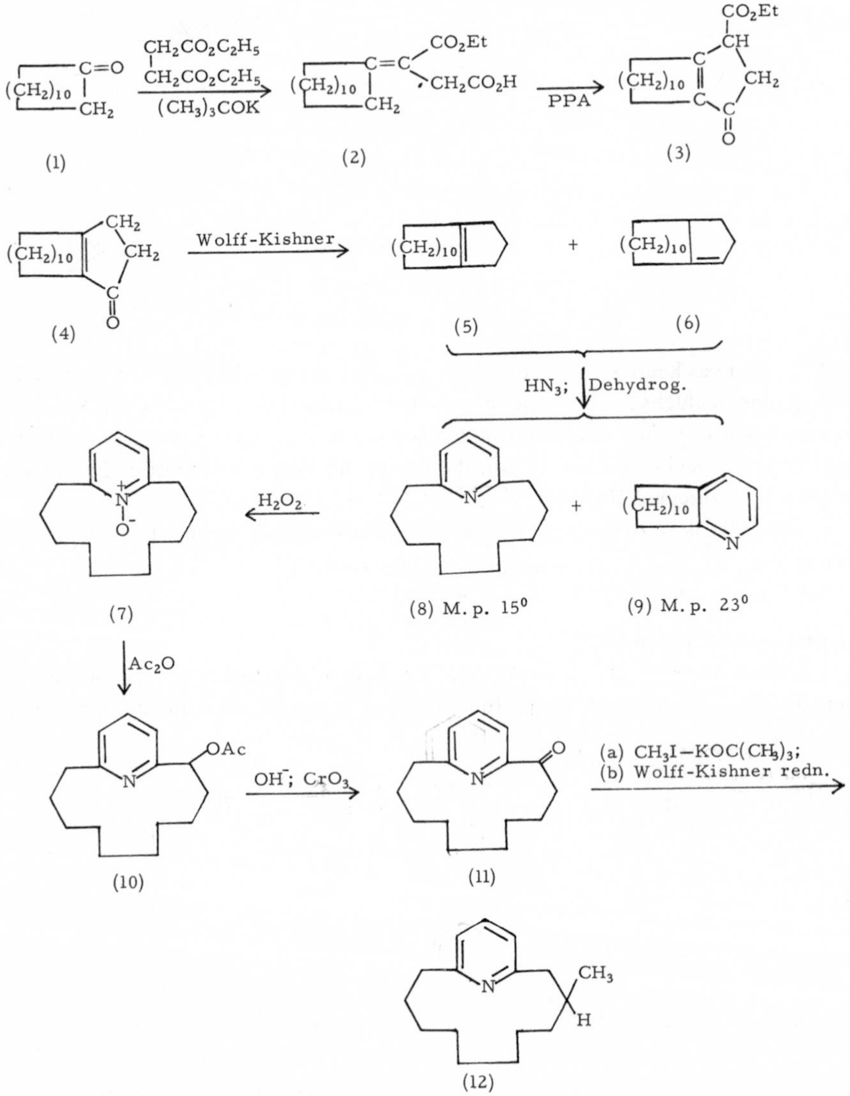

CH2CO2C2H5
CH2CO2C2H5
(CH3)3COK
PPA
CO2Et
CH2CO2H
(1)
(2)
(3)
Wolff-Kishner
(4)
(5)
(6)
HN3; Dehydrog.
H2O2
(7)
(8) M. p. 15°
(9) M. p. 23°
Ac2O
OAc
OH⁻; CrO3
(10)
(11)
(a) CH3I–KOC(CH3)3;
(b) Wolff-Kishner redn.
CH3
H
(12)

In a total synthesis of muscopyridine, the key step involved a Schmidt reaction of an olefin with hydrazoic acid to give an unsaturated amine. The starting material was cyclododecanone (1) which was transformed into (2) by Stobbe condensation with diethyl succinate. Refluxing polyphosphoric acid effected cyclization and decarboxylation to (4). Wolff-Kishner reduction of (4) is accompanied by a double-bond migration to give a mixture of the olefins (5) and (6). The mixture on treatment with hydrazoic acid gave a mixture of sensitive tetrahydropyridines, which were directly aromatized by dehydrogenation with palladium catalyst in 1-methylnaphthalene solution (dehydrogenation in *p*-cymene was slow). This afforded a mixture of iso-meric pyridinophanes (8) and (9), which were crystalline, if low melting, and easily separated by chromatography. The desired isomer (8) was then converted into the N-oxide (7) which, on reaction with acetic anhydride afforded the C-acetoxy deriva-tive (10). Hydrolysis and oxidation gave the ketone (11), and methylation with methyl iodide and potassium *t*-butoxide introduced a methyl group adjacent to the carbonyl function. Wolff-Kishner reduction gave an oily substance forming a picro-lonate, m.p. 163–166°, not lowered on admixture of the picrolonate of natural (+)-muscopyridine (Eastman supplies picrolonic acid). Finally, the racemic base was resolved by means of di-*p*-toluoyl-L-tartrate (**1**, 351) to a product characterized by a picrolonate that did not depress the m.p. of muscopyridine picrolonate.

Reaction with quinones [**1**, 447–448, at end]. Structure (5) assigned by Misiti, Moore, and Folkers[8] to the product of the reaction of hydrazoic acid in sulfuric acid with trimethyl-*p*-benzoquinone has been shown to be incorrect by independent groups at the University of Manchester[8a] and the I.C.I. laboratories.[8b] The structure now regarded by both groups as correct is that shown in formula (6).

(6)

[4a]H. Schinz, L. Ruzicka, U. Geyer, and V. Prelog, *Helv.*, **29**, 1524 (1946)
[4b]K. Biemann, G. Büchi, and B. H. Walker, *Am. Soc.*, **79**, 5558 (1957)
[8]Definitive paper: D. Misiti, H. W. Moore, and K. Folkers, *Tetrahedron*, **22**, 1201 (1966)
[8a]R. W. Rickards and R. M. Smith, *Tetrahedron Letters*, 2361 (1966)
[8b]G. R. Bedford, G. Jones, and B. R. Webster, *ibid.*, 2367 (1966)

Hydriodic acid [**1**, 449–450].

Reduction [after citation of ref. 5]. An Australian group[5a] found that the procedure of Wolfrom and Brown[5] was the most satisfactory route to *p*-diacetylbenzene. Terephthalic acid was converted into the bis acid chloride by thionyl chloride and then to the bisdiazoketone (excess diazomethane). This was reduced with 47% hydriodic acid in chloroform to give *p*-diacetylbenzene in 68% overall yield. Substitution of potassium iodide and phosphoric acid reduced the yield to about 60%.

[5a]P. M. Pojer, E. Ritchie, and W. C. Taylor, *Australian J. Chem.*, **21**, 1375 (1968)

Hydrobromic acid (48%) [**1**, 450–452, before references].

Aromatic cyclodehydration. Bradsher[17] introduced this name for reactions in which intramolecular condensation is accompanied by dehydration to give an aromatic system. In an extensive investigation of such reactions he has used almost consistently hydrobromic acid in refluxing acetic acid as the acid catalyst. Only a few typical examples are cited.

(1)[18]

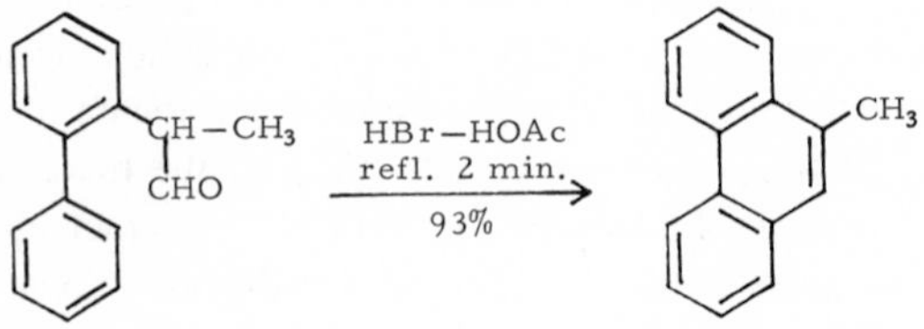
CH—CH3
CHO
HBr—HOAc
refl. 2 min.
93%
CH3

(2)[19]

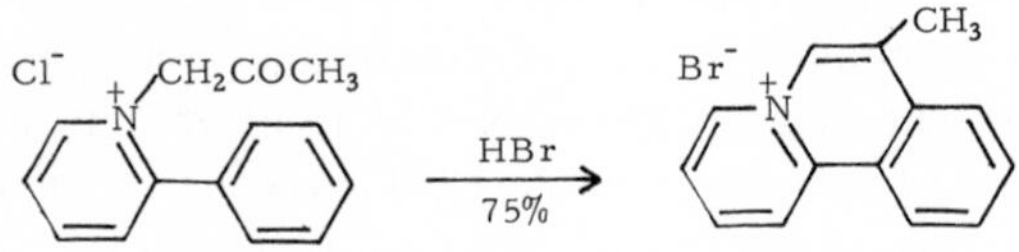
Cl⁻
CH2COCH3
HBr
75%
Br⁻
CH3

(3)[20]

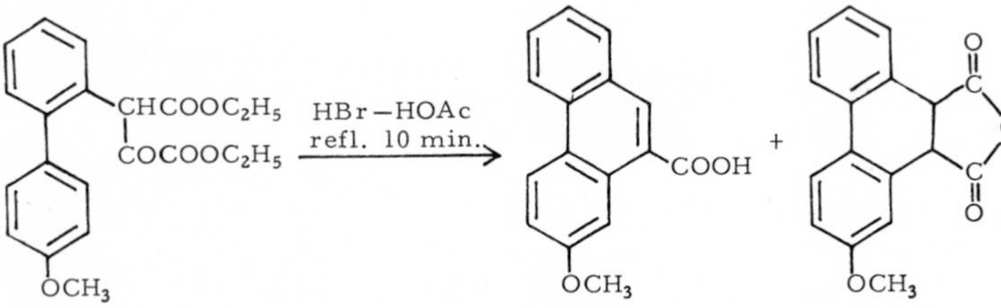
CHCOOC2H5
COCOOC2H5
OCH3
HBr—HOAc
refl. 10 min.
COOH
OCH3
+
O
OCH3

2.9 g. 0.9 g. 0.4 g.

Bradsher's reagent was found to be superior to PPA or a mixture of sulfuric acid–phosphoric acid for cyclodehydration of β-hydroxy ketones of the type (4).[21]

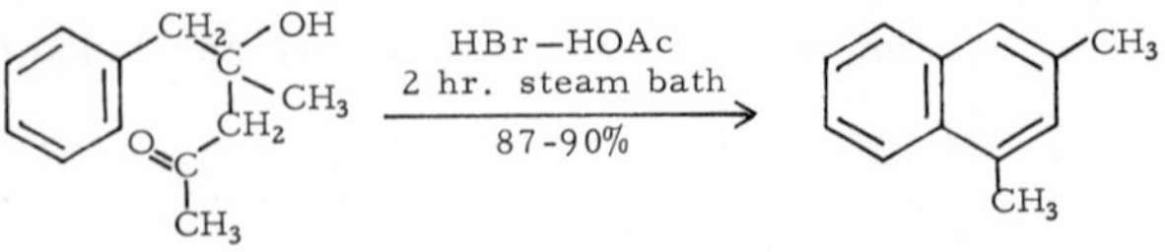
CH2 OH
C
CH3
CH2
C
CH3
HBr—HOAc
2 hr. steam bath
87-90%
CH3
CH3

(4) (5)

Hydrogenation. Palladium-catalyzed hydrogenation of Δ^4-3-ketosteroids in acetic acid solution containing hydrobromic acid gives a high $5\beta:5\alpha$ ratio of 3-

5α   5β

ketones.[22] This acid is much more effective than hydrochloric or sulfuric acid, which have been used to increase the ratio of 5β-ketones.

[17]C. K. Bradsher, *Chem. Revs.*, **38**, 447 (1946)
[18]C. K. Bradsher and W. J. Jackson, Jr., *Am. Soc.*, **76**, 734 (1954)
[19]C. K. Bradsher and L. E. Beavers, *ibid.*, **77**, 453 (1955)
[20]C. K. Bradsher, F. C. Brown, and P. H. Leake, *ibid.*, **79**, 1471 (1957)
[21]P. Canonne, P. Holm, and L. C. Leitch, *Canad. J. Chem.*, **45**, 2151 (1967)
[22]S. Nishimura, M. Shimahara, and M. Shiota, *Chem. Ind.*, 1796 (1966)

Hydrogen chloride, anhydrous, HCl [1, 454, before **Hydrogen cyanide**]. Mol. wt. 36.46. Supplied in cylinders; *see* **Gases inert and reagent**, this volume.

C. A. Brown and his father H. C. Brown[1] developed an efficient apparatus for the automatic generation of hydrogen from $NaBH_4$ and hydrochloric acid as required for the hydrogenation of unsaturated compounds.[2] The elder Brown with Rei[3] later adopted the apparatus to the conversion of reactive alcohols (tertiary) to the chlorides and to hydrochlorination of certain olefins. Hydrogen chloride is generated automatically as required, and generation ceases when the reaction is complete. It is possible to follow the rate of utilization of hydrogen chloride and to convert the alcohol or olefin essentially quantitatively into product without excessive contact with the hydrochlorination reagent.

[1]C. A. Brown and H. C. Brown, *Am. Soc.*, **84**, 2829 (1962)
[2]Apparatus available from Delmar Scientific Laboratories, Inc., Maywood, Ill. 60154
[3]H. C. Brown and Min-Hon Rei, *J. Org.*, **30**, 1091 (1966)

Hydrogen fluoride, anhydrous [1, 455–456, before references].

In the von Pechmann coumarin synthesis[5] from a phenol and a β-keto ester, the classical condensing agent and solvent is sulfuric acid. Koo[6] reported higher yields of 4-methyl-7-hydroxycoumarin by use of polyphosphoric acid, but Wall *et al.*[7] tried application of the reagent to α-aryl-β-keto esters such as (2) with discouraging results. They then found that liquid hydrogen fluoride gives excellent results. Equivalent quantities of resorcinol and the β-keto ester (2) were dissolved in liquid H_2F_2

(1)   (2)   (3)

and the mixture was stirred overnight, during which time nearly all of the hydrogen fluoride had evaporated. That remaining was removed in a stream of nitrogen and the residual oil solidified when washed with water.

Peptide synthesis, cleavage of blocking groups. Sakakibara and Shimonishi[8] showed that treatment of a synthetic fully blocked derivative of oxytocin, an octapeptide hormone of the posterior pituitary gland, with anhydrous hydrogen fluoride removes the N-carbobenzoxy, S-benzyl, and S-*p*-methoxybenzyl protecting groups from the peptide. Anisole is added to prevent polymerization of benzyl fluorides. Lenard and Robinson[9] used the reagent to remove the completed peptide from the resin in a Merrifield solid-phase synthesis of bradykinin.

[5]H. von Pechmann and C. Duisberg, *Ber.*, **16**, 2119 (1883)
[6]J. Koo, *Chem. Ind.*, 445 (1955)
[7]C. E. Cook, R. C. Corley, and M. E. Wall, *J. Org.*, **30**, 4114 (1965)
[8]S. Sakakibara and Y. Shimonishi, *Bull. Chem. Soc. Japan*, **38**, 1412 (1965)
[9]J. Lenard and A. B. Robinson, *Am. Soc.*, **89**, 181 (1967)

Hydrogen fluoride–Antimony pentafluoride [1, 456, before **Hydrogen peroxide**].

Saturated aliphatic hydrocarbons are readily carbonylated by CO in liquid HF in the presence of SbF_5. The final product is a carboxylic acid, or ester, or a simple ketone, depending on whether the reaction mixture is solvolyzed with water, ROH, or a hydrocarbon.[1] A carbonium hexafluoroantimonate is probably the initial product.

Isopentane is transformed into a mixture of five acids:

[1]R. Paatz and G. Weisgerber, *Ber.*, **100**, 984 (1967)

Hydrogen peroxide [1, 456–457]. 90% Hydrogen peroxide is supplied by Becco Chemical Division, FMC Co., Buffalo 7, N.Y.

Hydrogen peroxide, basic [1, 466–470].

Dakin reaction [1, 467, after citation of ref. 11]. G. H. Stout has pointed out that the discussion misleadingly implies that the Dakin reaction is specific to carbonyl compounds bearing an *ortho* hydroxyl group. Since Dakin[11a] showed that vanillin can be oxidized in good yield to methoxyhydroquinone it is evident that a *p*-hydroxyl group is equally effective.

[11a]H. D. Dakin, *Am. Chem. J.*, **42**, 477 (1909)

Hydrogen peroxide, neutral [**1**, 471–472, before references].

Hydrogen peroxide oxidizes the N,N-dimethylhydrazones of benzaldehyde and cinnamaldehyde to the corresponding nitriles in good yield.[6]

[6]R. F. Smith, J. A. Albright, and A. M. Waring, *J. Org.*, **31**, 4100 (1966)

Hydroxylamine hydrochloride [**1**, 478–481, before references].

Aldehydes, particularly aromatic aldehydes, when refluxed in formic acid with a slight excess of hydroxylamine hydrochloride and sodium formate are converted into nitriles.[15] Probably the oxime formate (2) is an intermediate and in the presence

of base in the work-up loses formaldehyde (as formic acid) to give the nitrile (3).

Aliphatic aldehydes, their trimers, or bisulfite addition compounds, when refluxed in 95% ethanol with hydroxylamine hydrochloride and a few drops of hydrochloric acid for 6 hrs., give the corresponding nitriles in practically quantitative yield.[16]

[15]T. van Es, *J. Chem. Soc.*, 1564 (1965)
[16]J. A. Findlay and C. S. Tang, *Canad. J. Chem.*, **45**, 1014 (1967)

Hydroxylamine-O-sulfonic acid [**1**, 481–484].

[**1**, 481]: A simplified preparation from hydroxylamine sulfate and 60% oleum is described by Schmitz *et al.*[1a]

Generation of nitrene [**1**, 482]. Appel and Büchner[4a] reasoned that treatment of the reagent with base might liberate NH (nitrene, imene); and so they examined the reaction of the reagent with 1,4-butadiene in methanol in the presence of sodium methoxide. 3-Pyrroline was formed, but in very low yield.

Fragmentation [1, 482]. A process described as the fragmentation of an α,β-epoxyketoxime to an acetylenic ketone [4b] probably involves the steps:

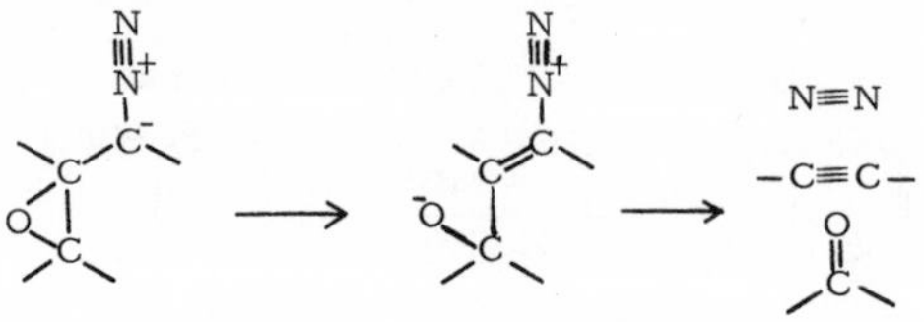

One application is to the steroid α,β-epoxyketoxime (1) in which the dihydroxyacetone side chain is protected as the BMD (bismethylenedioxy) derivative. Treatment of (1) with 3 equivalents of hydroxylamine-O-sulfonic acid and 7 equivalents

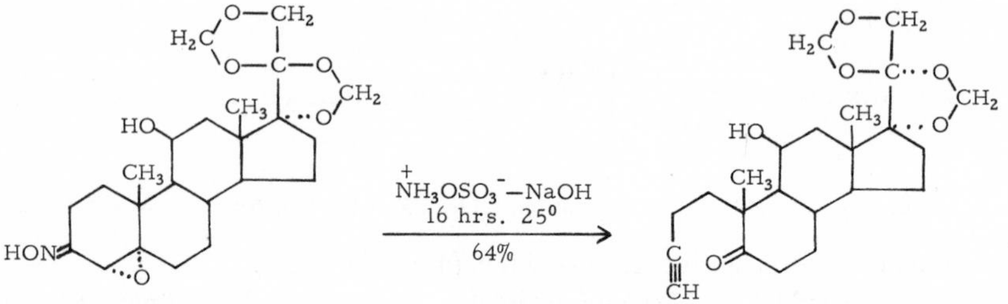

(1)   (2)

of NaOH in ethanol at room temperature gives the acetylenic ketone in fairly good yield. Another example is the fragmentation of the spirostane derivative (3).

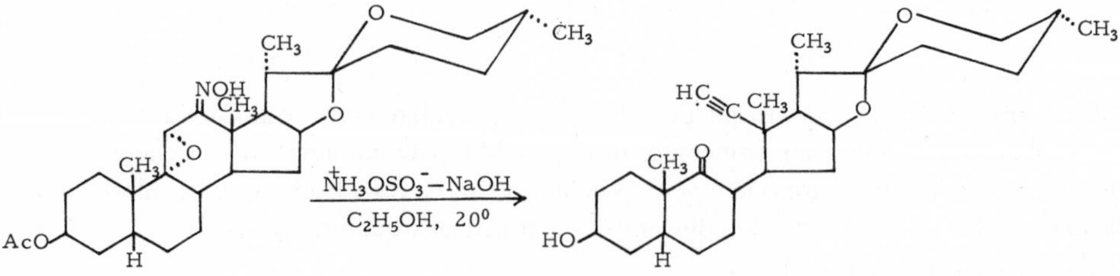

(3)   (4)

Diaziridines and diazirines [1, 483]. A Lederle group[13] investigated the reaction of hydroxylamine-O-sulfonic acid with steroid ketones and found that only nonconjugated 2(5α)-ketones and 3(5α or 5β)-ketones react. Δ^4-3-Ketosteroids, 17-ketosteroids, and 20-ketosteroids were found unreactive. A solution of 502 mg. of 17α-methyl-5α-androstane-17β-ol-3-one (1) in methanol was saturated with ammonia at 2° and treated with 236 mg. of hydroxylamine-O-sulfonic acid, added in small portions. The diaziridine (2) was oxidized with silver oxide in ether in practically quantitative yield to the diazirine (3).

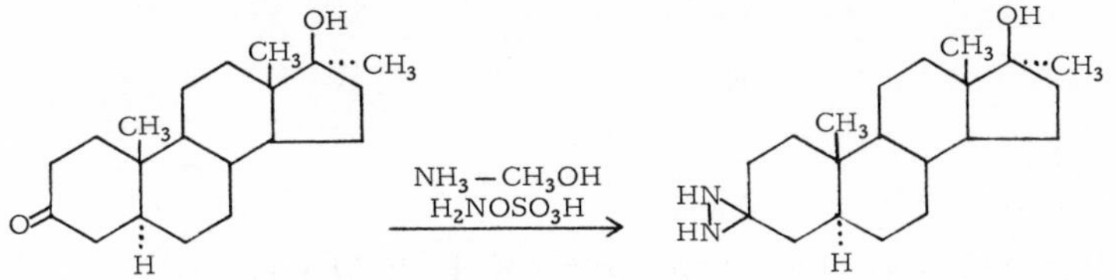

(1)   (2)

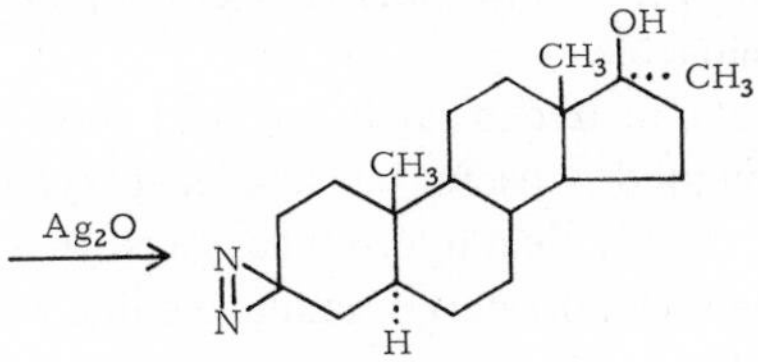

(3)

[1a]E. Schmitz, R. Ohme, and S. Schramm, *Ann.*, **702**, 131 (1967)
[4a]R. Appel and O. Büchner, *Angew. Chem., internat. Ed.*, **1**, 332 (1962)
[4b]P. Wieland, H. Kaufmann and A. Eschenmoser, *Helv.*, **50**, 2108 (1967)
[13]R. F. R. Church, A. S. Kende, and M. J. Weiss, *Am. Soc.*, **87**, 2665 (1965)

N-Hydroxysuccinimide trifluoroacetate [**1**, 487, before **Hyprobromous acid**]. Mol. wt. 197.09, oil.

Preparation. A solution of N-hydroxysuccinimide and a slight excess of trifluoroacetic anhydride in benzene is refluxed for 5 hrs.[1]

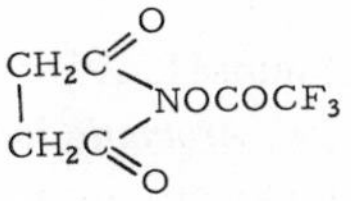

Use in peptide synthesis.[1] The reagent reacts with N-protected amino acids by ester interchange to give active esters of use in synthesis. Only very slight racemization is observed.[2] Use of *p*-nitrophenyltrifluoroacetate or of 2,4,5-trichlorophenyl trifluoroacetate leads to complete racemization.

(1)

[1]S. Sakakibara and N. Inukai, *Bull. Chem. Soc. Japan*, **38**, 1979 (1965)
[2]*Idem, ibid.*, **39**, 1567 (1966)

I

Imidazole [1, 492–494]. Other suppliers: Fl., K.-L., E. Merck.

[Before references]: Stewart[13] found that depsipeptide ester bonds can be formed using imidazole as catalyst in the *p*-nitrophenyl ester coupling. No reaction was observed in the absence of imidazole.

Imidazole has been found effective in catalyzing the hydrolysis of acetoxyflavones in 60% methanol.[14] The method is useful because acetoxyflavones are purified by crystallization much more readily than hydroxyflavones. In a typical procedure the acetoxyflavone is suspended with 0.1 part of imidazole in 60% aqueous ethanol, and the mixture is refluxed for 24–50 hrs.

[10]*Add: See also* W. J. McGahren and M. Goodman, *Tetrahedron*, **23**, 2017 (1967)
[13]F. H. C. Stewart, *Chem. Ind.*, 1960 (1967)
[14]J. H. Looker, M. J. Holm, J. L. Minor, and S. A. Kagal, *J. Heterocyclic Chem.*, **1**, 253 (1964)

Iodine [1, 495–500].

Aromatic iodination [1, 497, after citation of ref. 12]. Polyalkylbenzenes having bulky groups are not reactive toward iodine alone but may react in the presence of an oxidizing agent. In a detailed study of agents used in this connection (silver perchlorate, mercuric oxide, iodic acid, potassium persulfate, etc.) Japanese investigators[12a] found the combination of iodine with periodic acid dihydrate to be the most satisfactory.

Oxidation [1, 497–498, at end]. Propylene reacts with iodine and peracetic acid in acetic acid to give 1-iodo-2-acetoxypropane in 63–72% yield.[21a] The reaction is

considered to involve attack by peracetic acid on an olefin-iodine π-complex. The reaction is applicable to other olefins.

β-Ketosulfoxides (1) can be converted in high yield into α-ketoacetals (2) by reaction with iodine in methanol. The iodine is believed to function in two ways: it removes methyl mercaptan from the equilibrium and is a source of HI, which is

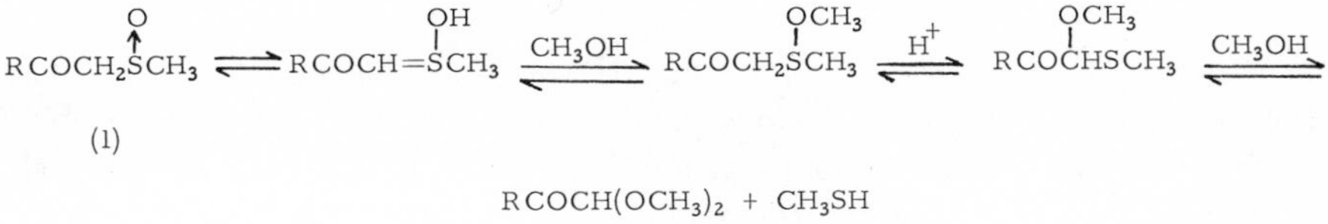

$$\underset{(1)}{RCOCH_2\overset{\overset{O}{\uparrow}}{S}CH_3} \rightleftharpoons RCOCH{=}\overset{\overset{OH}{|}}{S}CH_3 \xrightarrow{CH_3OH} RCOCH_2\overset{\overset{OCH_3}{|}}{S}CH_3 \overset{H^+}{\rightleftharpoons} RCO\overset{\overset{OCH_3}{|}}{C}HSCH_3 \xrightarrow{CH_3OH}$$

$$RCOCH(OCH_3)_2 + CH_3SH$$

$$(2)$$

$$2\ CH_3SH \xrightarrow{I_2} CH_3SSCH_3 + HI$$

necessary for catalysis of the Pummerer rearrangement. Bromine is also effective but has no advantage.[21b]

Oxidation of an aldehyde or ketone hydrazone (3) with iodine in a neutral medium gives the corresponding azine (6);[21c] the reaction is interpreted as proceeding through

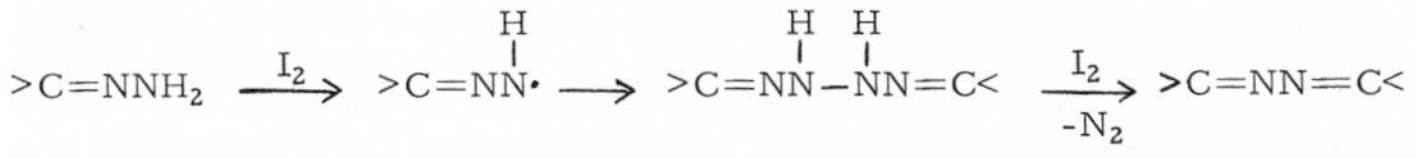

$$\underset{(3)}{>C{=}NNH_2} \xrightarrow{I_2} \underset{(4)}{>C{=}N\overset{\overset{H}{|}}{N}\cdot} \longrightarrow \underset{(5)}{>C{=}N\overset{\overset{H}{|}}{N}{-}\overset{\overset{H}{|}}{N}N{=}C<} \underset{-N_2}{\xrightarrow{I_2}} \underset{(6)}{>C{=}NN{=}C<}$$

a radical (4) which then dimerizes (5). Further oxidation with loss of nitrogen affords the azine (6).

Catalyst for dehydration [1, 499]. *Correction* contributed by H. H. Hatt, Monash University, Victoria, Australia:

"When describing the uses of iodine as a dehydrating agent you instance its effectiveness (which is undoubted) in the rearrangement of benzopinacol. The following comments show, I think, that it is not the most desirable of agents and that its mode of action is unlikely to be that given [on 1, 498]. A point not mentioned by users is that in the rearrangement of benzopinacol the color of the iodine vanishes shortly after reaction commences. Beale and I[25a] showed that hydriodic acid in like amount was just as effective as iodine. Furthermore, if sodium acetate was added sufficient to neutralize any hydriodic acid formed, benzopinacol could be boiled unrearranged in an acetic acid solution strongly colored with iodine. The above evidence is pretty well conclusive that hydriodic acid is the rearranging agent. Use of iodine has the serious disadvantage that it forms hydriodic acid by oxidizing some benzopinacol to benzophenone. Especially this is so when the rearrangement is used to measure migratory aptitudes. Stephenson and I[25b] found that it could lead to quite erroneous migratory aptitudes when the pinacol carried *ortho* substituents and rearranged slowly. We found that perchloric acid in acetic acid did not cause such oxidation and was a more powerful agent. It was the only reagent found effective for the rearrangement of 2,2'-diphenylbenzopinacol:"

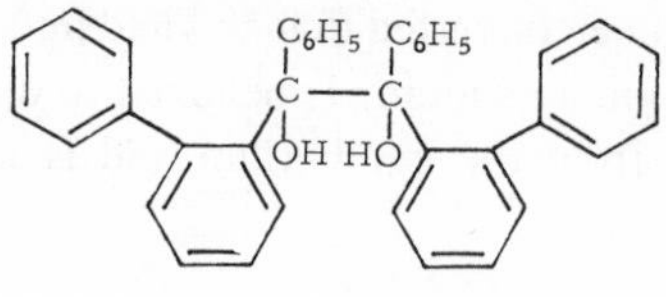

Catalysis [1, 499, after citation of ref. 32]. Canadian chemists[32a] observed that triphenylcarbinol was converted into the methyl ether in 90% yield by treatment with iodine in methanol. The reaction is general for arylmethyl alkyl ethers. Although iodine functions as a catalyst, highest yields are obtained when it it used in an

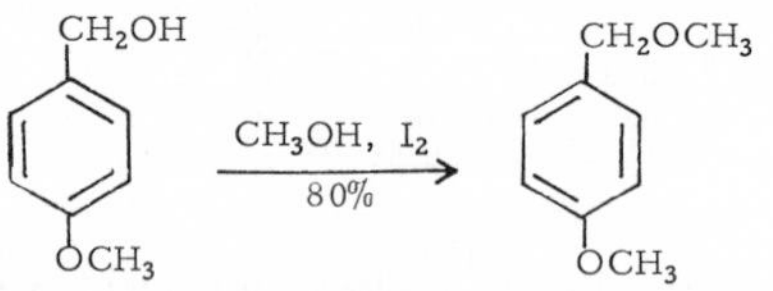

approximately equimolar amount. Furthermore the following Friedel-Crafts reaction was realized with iodine as catalyst:

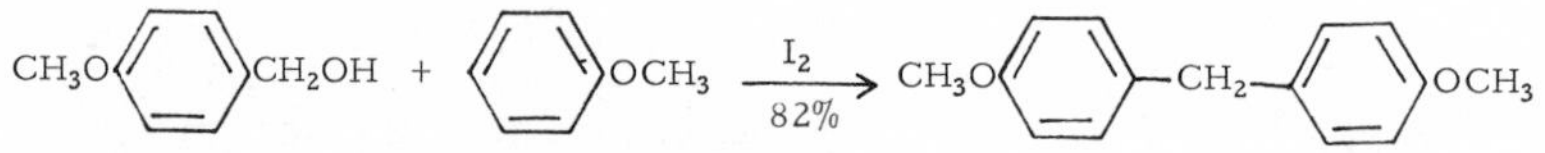

[12a]H. Suzuki, K. Nakamura, and R. Goto, *Bull. Chem. Soc. Japan*, **39**, 129 (1966)
[21a]Y. Ogata and K. Aoki, *J. Org.*, **31**, 1625 (1966); procedure submitted to *Org. Syn.*, 1966
[21b]T. L. Moore, *J. Org.*, **32**, 2786 (1967)
[21c]D. H. R. Barton, R. E. O'Brien, and S. Sternhell, *J. Chem. Soc.* 470 (1962)
[25a]C. H. Beale and H. H. Hatt, *Am. Soc.*, **54**, 2405 (1932)
[25b]H. H. Hatt, A. Pilgrim, and E. F. M. Stephenson, *J. Chem. Soc.*, 478 (1941)
[32a]R. G. Rutherford, O. A. Mamer, J. M. Prokipcak, and R. A. Jobin, *Canad. J. Chem.*, **44**, 2337 (1966)

Iodine azide [1, 500–501, before references].

Fowler, Hassner, and Levy[4] showed that iodine azide generated *in situ* by reaction of sodium azide with iodine monochloride reacts with straight-chain *cis*- and *trans*-olefins to give, respectively, the *threo* and *erythro* adducts. Terminal olefins form adducts where the azido function is at the 2-position; conjugated olefins such as 1,2-dihydronaphthalene lead to products with the azido function occupying the allylic position. The Colorado investigators were successful in adding IN_3 to diphenylacetylene in moderate yield to give the unstable yellow crystalline monoiodo

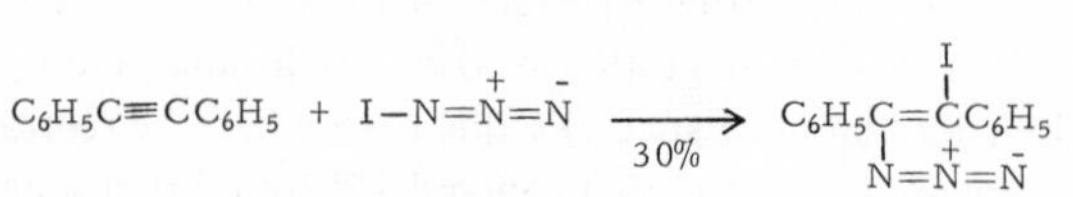

azide adduct (2), expected to have *trans* stereochemistry. The pale yellow product (m.p. 76°) decomposes extensively.

Hassner and Fowler[5] have found that the addition of iodine azide to olefins provides a general synthesis of 2H-azirines:

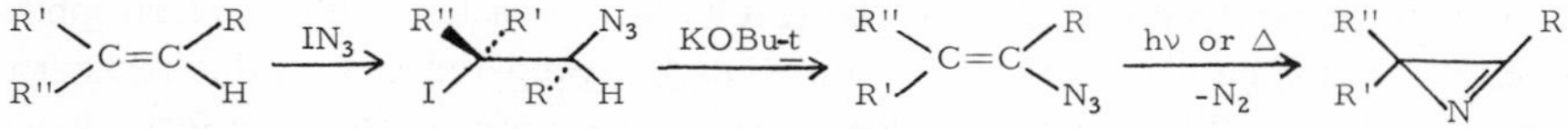

The iodo azide undergoes stereospecific *trans* dehydrohalogenation to give a vinyl azide, which on photolysis or pyrolysis gives the 2H-azirine. Reduction of the 2H-azirine with lithium aluminium hydride gives the *cis*-aziridine in good yield.

[4]F. W. Fowler, A. Hassner, and L. A. Levy, *Am. Soc.*, **89**, 2077 (1967)
[5]A. Hassner and F. W. Fowler, *Tetrahedron Letters*, 1545 (1967); *idem*, *J. Org.*, **33**, 2686 (1968)

Iodine isocyanate [1, 501, before references].

Hassner *et al.*[5] have discussed in detail the procedure and scope of the addition to olefins. Lithium or sodium methoxide is recommended as catalyst for conversion of the iodo isocyanate to the carbonate. If the end product desired is the aziridine it is usually advantageous to convert the iodo isocyanate into the sodium bisulfite adduct which is convertible by base into the aziridine.

Iodine isocyanate has been used in one step of a stereospecific synthesis of *trans*-1,2-diaminocyclohexane.[6] Iodine isocyanate is added to cyclohexene and the crude

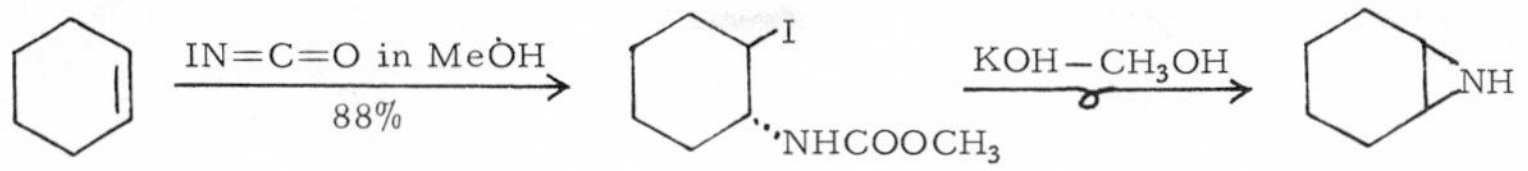

trans-iodo isocyanate is converted into the carbamate (2). Reaction with methanolic potassium hydroxide converted (2) with inversion into the aziridine (3). Treatment with sodium azide in ethanol, followed by catalytic hydrogenation and treatment with hydrochloric acid, afforded *trans*-1,2-diaminocyclohexane dihydrochloride (4).

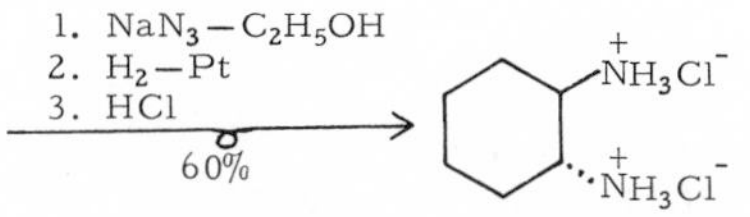

Paquette and Kuhla[7] used iodine isocyanate in the synthesis of 1-carbomethoxy-2-

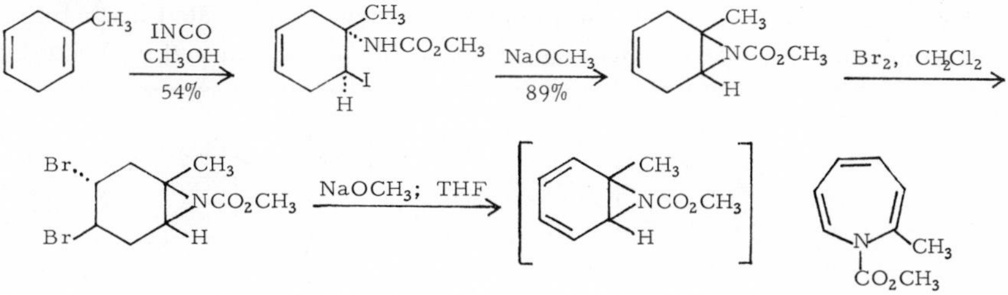

methylazepine from 2,5-dihydrotoluene. The reaction provides a new general route to 1H-azepines.

Swern[8] has determined the relative rates of reaction of iodine isocyanate with a variety of unsaturated compounds; the results are consistent with an electrophilic reaction. Although it is convenient to use reagent prepared *in situ*, this reagent is unsatisfactory in the case of acetylenes, which react preferentially to form diiodo compounds.[9] In this case it is preferable to use a preformed solution of the reagent, prepared as follows.[10] An excess of silver cyanate is treated with iodine in ether, THF, or glyme at $-30°$ in the dark. Such material reacts at least 10 times faster with olefins than the reagent prepared *in situ*.

[3]*Add*: Procedure submitted to *Org. Syn.*
[5]A. Hassner, M. E. Lorber, and C. Heathcock, *J. Org.*, **32**, 540 (1967)
[6]G. Swift and D. Swern, *ibid.*, **32**, 511 (1967)
[7]L. A. Paquette and D. E. Kuhla, *Tetrahedron Letters*, 4517 (1967)
[8]C. G. Gebelein and D. Swern, *J. Org.*, **33**, 2758 (1968)
[9]B. E. Grimwood and D. Swern, *ibid.*, **32**, 3665 (1967)
[10]S. Rosen and D. Swern, *Anal. Chem.*, **38**, 1392 (1966)

Iodine monobromide [**1**, 501–502, after citation of ref. 1]. The reagent effects mono-bromination of steroid aldehydes in high yield.[2] The diastereoisomeric product in

which the bromine acquires the β-orientation is favored. The reaction has been used for the stepwise degradation of the bile acid side chain.[3]

[2]Y. Yanuka, R. Katz, and S. Sarel, *Chem. Commun.*, 849 (1968)
[3]*Idem, ibid.*, 851 (1968)

Iodine nitrate, INO_3 [**1**, 503, before **Iodine pentafluoride**]. Mol. wt. 188.92.

The reagent is generated *in situ* from silver nitrate and iodine:[1]

$$AgNO_3 + I_2 \longrightarrow AgI + INO_3$$

It reacts with a solution of Δ^2-cholestene in acetonitrile to give 3α-iodo-2β-hydroxy-cholestane nitrate ester (2). When dinitrogen tetroxide was treated in chloroform with iodine and Δ^2-cholestene was added, the same 3α-iodo-2β-hydroxycholestane

(1)   (2)

nitrate ester (2) was obtained (60%). However, if the order of addition is changed, and a solution of dinitrogen tetroxide is added to a solution of iodine and Δ^2-cholestene, 2β-iodo-3α-nitrocholestane (3) is obtained as the sole product (60%).

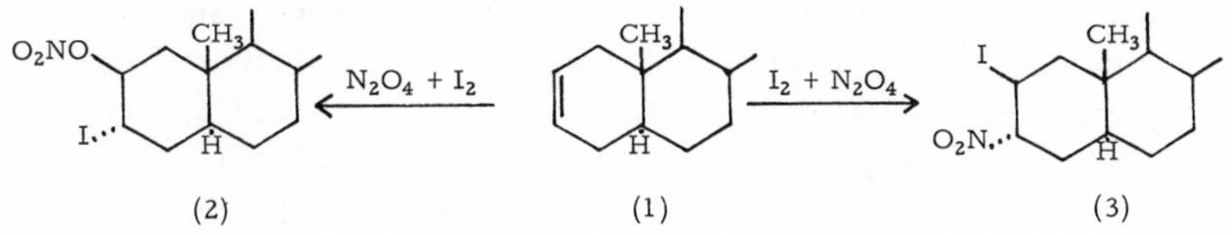

(2)   (1)   (3)

[1]J. E. Kropp, A. Hassner, and G. J. Kent, *Chem. Commun.*, 906 (1968)

Iodobenzene dichloride [1, 505–506, before references]
    Note, however, that Cristol *et al.*[5] chlorinated acenaphthylene (1) with iodobenzene dichloride in chloroform containing 1,3,5-trinitrobenzene as radical-inhibitor

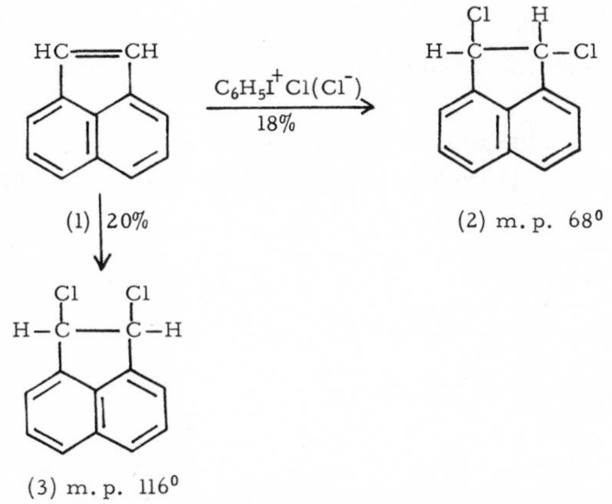

(1) | 20%

(2) m. p. 68°

(3) m. p. 116°

and isolated *trans*-1,2-dichloroacenaphthene (2) in low yield; with chlorine they obtained the higher melting *cis* isomer (3), also in low yield. The configurations were established unequivocally by partial resolution experiments which distinguish between *cis-meso* and *dl-trans* forms.

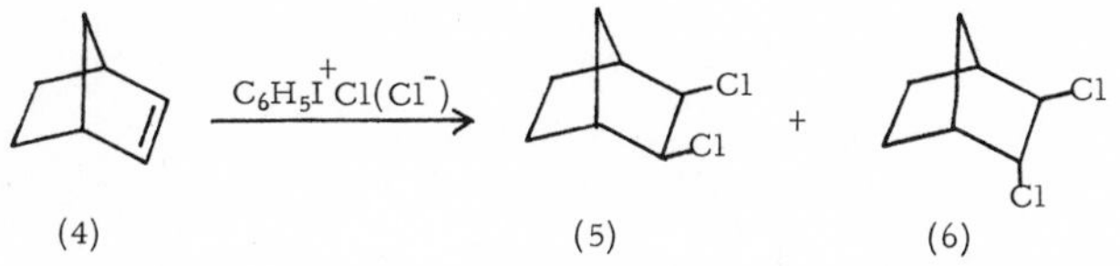

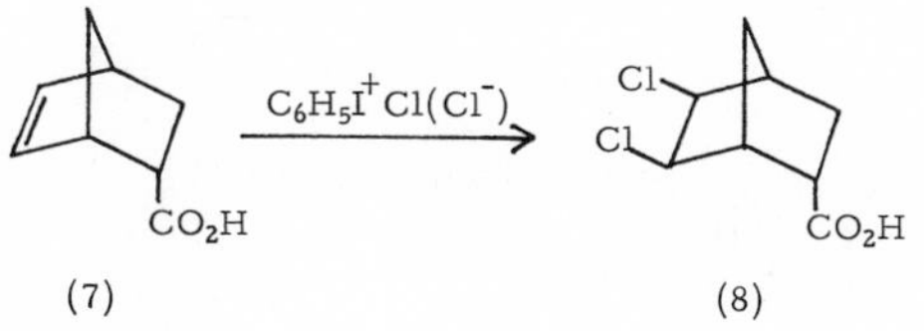

(4)   (5)   (6)

(7)   (8)

The reaction of cyclohexene with iodobenzene dichloride likewise gives exclusively the *trans*-dichloride.[6] Reaction with chlorine in sulfuryl chloride also gives predominantly the *trans*-dichloride.[7] Similarly, the reagent reacts with *p*-dioxene and with 1,4-dihydronaphthalene to give *trans*-dichlorides.[8] Norbornene (4) reacts with the reagent to give a mixture of *exo-cis*-2,3-dichloronorbornane and *trans*-2,3-dichloronorbornane (in unspecified yield).[9] Reaction of the norbornenecarboxylic acid (7) gives as the main product the *exo-cis*-dihalide (8).[10] Thus it appears that the stereochemistry of the reaction is influenced strongly by steric factors.

[5]S. J. Cristol, F. R. Stermitz, and P. S. Ramey, *Am. Soc.*, **78**, 4939 (1956)
[6]J. R. Campbell, J. K. N. Jones, and S. Wolfe, *Canad. J. Chem.*, **44**, 2339 (1966)
[7]K. K. Summerbell and H. E. Lunk, *Am. Soc.*, **79**, 4802 (1957)
[8]M. Mousseron, R. Jacquier, R. Henry, and M. Mousseron-Canet, *Bull. soc.*, **20**, 628 (1953)
[9]M. L. Poutsma, *Am. Soc.*, **87**, 4293 (1965)
[10]S. Masson and A. Thuillier, *Compt. rend.*, **264** (C), 1189 (1967)

1-Iodoheptafluoropropane, $CF_3CF_2CF_2I$ [**1**, 506, before **Iodomethylmercuric iodide**]. Mol. wt. 295.94, b.p. 41.2°, sp. gr. 2.1306, $n^{0.5}D$ 1.3391.

Preparation. Examples: by reaction of iodotrifluoromethane with tetrafluoroethylene;[1] by treatment of heptafluorobutyryl iodide and iodine in a platinum tube at 550–602°.[2]

Suppliers. Koch-Light Labs.; K and K Labs.

Uses. (a) Preparation of Grignard reagents.[3,4,5] (b) Addition to multiple bonds:

Norbornene[6]

$HC{\equiv}CH$ [7] $\xrightarrow{CF_3CF_2CF_2I}$ $IHC{=}CHC_3F_7$

(c) Iodinating agent:[8]

[1]R. N. Haszeldine, *J. Chem. Soc.*, 2856 (1949); 3761 (1953)
[2]R. N. Haszeldine, *ibid.*, 584 (1951)
[3]Brit. pat. 75,7893 [*C.A.*, **51**, 2126 (1957)]

[4]R. N. Haszeldine, *J. Chem. Soc.*, 3423 (1952)
[5]O. R. Pierce, A. F. Meiners, and E. T. McBee, *Am. Soc.*, **75**, 2516 (1953)
[6]N. O. Brace, *ibid.*, **86**, 523 (1964)
[7]R. N. Haszeldine, *J. Chem. Soc.*, 2789 (1950)
[8]C. Burgess, G. Cooley, P. Feather, and V. Petrow, *Tetrahedron*, **23**, 4111 (1967)

Ion-exchange resins [**1**, 511–519].

Acidic resins [**1**, 514, after citation of ref. 17]. The biogenetically patterned cyclization of polyenes by Lewis acid catalysts can also be effected by cation-exchange resins (Amberlite IR-20 and XE-100).[17a] Thus methyl *trans,trans*-farnesate (1) is cyclized by XE-100 in acetic acid to (2), (3), and (4), separable by gas chroma-

tography. When the cyclization is effected at 60°, the bicyclic (3) becomes the predominant product in yield of 42%.

Solid-phase peptide synthesis [**1**, 516–517, after last line]. The chloromethyl-copolystyrene-2% divinylbenzene copolymer is now available commercially.[34a] The solid-phase peptide synthesis of glycyl-L-aspartyl-L-serylglycine has been reported in detail.[34b]

Peptide benzyl esters can be transesterified at room temperature with methanol or ethanol in the presence of a strong anion-exchange resin (Bio-Rad AGl-X8, OH⁻ form). The reaction is convenient for the cleavage of peptides from the resin support in the Merrifield solid-phase peptide synthesis.[34c]

Beyerman[34d] recommends transesterification catalyzed by tertiary amines (triethylamine, N-methylpiperidine) for cleavage of peptide-polymers to peptide esters. The experimental conditions are mild (4–15 hrs. room temperature).

Anion-exchange celluloses [**1**, 518, before references]. DEAE-cellulose is available from Calbiochem. and from Brown Co., Berlin, N.H. 03570 (Selectacel). Tener *et al.*[38a] used the following treatment before separation of polynucleotides. The resin is washed with 0.1 *N* sodium hydroxide and then 0.1 *N* hydrochloric acid. The cycle is repeated twice and the exchanger (in the chloride form) is washed free of acid with distilled water. Fines are removed by decantation twice.

[17a]H. Moriyama, Y. Sugihara, and K. Nakanishi, *Tetrahedron Letters*, 2851 (1968)
[35a]BioRad Laboratories, 32nd and Griffin Ave., Richmond, Calif., 94804; Cyclo Chemical Co., 1922 East 64th St., Los Angeles, Calif. 90022, and Calbiochem., 3625 Medford St., Los Angeles, Calif., 90063

[34b]R. B. Merrifield and M. A. Corigliano, *Biochem. Preparations*, **12**, 98 (1968)

[34c]B. Halpern, L. Chew, V. Close, and W. Patton, *Tetrahedron Letters*, 5163 (1968)

[34d]H. C. Beyerman, H. Hindriks, and E. W. B. de Leer, *Chem. Commun.*, 1668 (1968)

[38a]G. M. Tener, H. G. Khorana, R. Markham, and E. H. Pol, *Am. Soc.*, **80**, 6223 (1958)

Iridium on barium sulfate or calcium carbonate [**1**, 519, before **Iron**]. The most stereoselective reduction of the methylene compound (1) to the 16β-methyl compound (2) was accomplished by use of iridium deposited on barium sulfate or calcium carbonate; less than 2% of the 16α-methyl isomer was formed. Platinum catalysts were less stereoselective.[1]

(1)   (2)

[1]G. I. Gregory, J. S. Hunt, P. J. May, F. A. Nice, and G. H. Phillipps, *J. Chem. Soc.*, (C), 2201 (1966)

Iridium catalyst [**1**, 519, before **Iron**]. An iridium catalyst prepared by the method of R. Adams is useful for the reduction of aromatic nitro compounds to arylhydroxyl-amines.[1]

[1]K. Taya, *Chem. Commun.*, 464 (1966)

Iridium tetrachloride, IrCl$_4$ [**1**, 519, before **Iron**]. Mol. wt. 334.03, brownish black hygroscopic mass. Supplier: Platinum Chemicals, Box 565, Asbury Park, N.J. 07712.

As noted (**1**, 132), an early procedure of Eliel and Doyle for the reduction of 4-*t*-butylcyclohexanone to *cis*-4-*t*-butylcyclohexanol used iridium trichloride supplied by Fisher. This reagent is no longer available and, in a newer procedure,[1] iridium tetrachloride is used as catalyst in combination with trimethyl phosphite, which undergoes hydrolysis to phosphorous acid; the actual reducing agent is probably

an iridium species containing one or more phosphate groups as ligands. To a solution of iridium tetrachloride (0.012 mole) in 4.5 ml. of concd. hydrochloric acid is added 50 ml. of trimethyl phosphite, and this solution is added to a solution of 0.2 mole of 4-t-butylcyclohexanone (Dow Chem. Co.) in 635 ml. of isopropanol in a 2-l. flask equipped with a reflux condenser. The solution is refluxed for 48 hrs., the isopropanol is removed on a rotary evaporator at reduced pressure, and the residue is diluted with 250 ml. of water and extracted with four 150-ml. portions of ether. Concentration of the dried extract then affords the cis-alcohol as a white solid, and recrystallization from 60% aqueous ethanol affords greater than 99% pure cis-alcohol, m.p. 82–83.5°.

[1]E. L. Eliel, T. W. Doyle, R. O. Hutchins, and E. C. Gilbert, procedure submitted to *Org. Syn.*, 1968; the procedure was first described by Y. M. H. Haddad, H. B. Henbest, J. Husbands, and T. R. B. Mitchell, *Proc. Chem. Soc.*, 361 (1964)

Iron [1, 519].

Effect of traces of iron [after citation of ref. 3]. A group at Merck, Sharp and Dohme[3a] has been unable to confirm the effect of iron on the bromination of estrone.

Ketones from carboxylic acids. In a procedure[4] for the preparation of 4-heptanone, a mixture of 4 moles of n-butyric acid and 2.2 moles of iron powder (Fisher) is refluxed for 5 hrs. under nitrogen, and then distilled.

$$2\ CH_3CH_2CH_2CO_2H\ +\ Fe\ \longrightarrow (CH_3CH_2CH_2COO)_2Fe\ +\ H_2$$

$$(CH_3CH_2CH_2COO)_2Fe\ \xrightarrow[69-75\%]{\Delta}\ (CH_3CH_2CH_2)_2CO$$

Friedel-Crafts catalyst. Iron serves as a satisfactory catalyst for the reaction of phenolic ethers with t-butyl chloride.[5]

[3a]T. Utne, R. B. Jobson, and F. W. Landgraf, *J. Org.*, **33**, 1654 (1968)
[4]R. Davis, C. Granito, and H. P. Schultz, *Org. Syn.*, **47**, 75 (1967)
[5]F. Krausz, *Bull. soc.*, 1740 (1960)

Iron pentacarbonyl [1, 519–520, before references].

Carbonyl compounds can be regenerated from their oximes by refluxing in di-n-butyl ether with an equivalent amount of iron pentacarbonyl and a catalytic amount of boron trifluoride etherate.[6]

Steroidal $\Delta^{2,4}$- and $\Delta^{5,7}$-dienes form tricarbonyliron complexes in 30–70% yield when treated with iron pentacarbonyl. Transoid $\Delta^{3,5}$- and $\Delta^{4,6}$-dienes under the same conditions give the complex of $\Delta^{2,4}$-dienes. The cisoid $\Delta^{2,4}$-diene can be recovered by treatment with ferric chloride. It is thus possible to convert heteroannular steroidal dienes into the less stable homoannular isomer.[7]

[6]H. Alper and J. T. Edward, *J. Org.*, **32**, 2938 (1967)
[7]H. Alper and J. T. Edward, *J. Organometallic Chem.*, **14**, 411 (1968)

Isopropenyl methyl ether, $CH_2{=}C(CH_3)OCH_3$ [**1,** 526, before **Isopropylidene malonate**]. Mol. wt. 72.10, b.p. 36°.

Preparation.[1]

Isopropenyl acetate is converted into the dimethylketal of acetone (2,2-dimethoxy-propane) by treatment with mercuric acetate and boron trifluoride etherate.[2] Elimination of the elements of methanol by reaction with acetic anhydride and pyridine give isopropenyl methyl ether.

Synthesis of β-ketoallenes and α,β-unsaturated ketones.[1] Isopropenyl methyl ether, under acid catalysis (*p*-toluenesulfonic acid or phosphoric acid particularly), reacts with a tertiary acetylenic carbinol to give a β-ketoallene in high yield, as exemplified by the reaction with 3-methylbutyne-1-ol-3 (1). The β-ketoallene (2) is

isomerized in high yield by treatment with 1% methanolic sodium hydroxide to the conjugated dienone (3), obtained as a *cis-trans* mixture in which the *trans* isomer predominates (86%:14%).

The reaction provides a useful synthesis of pseudoionone (6) from dehydrolinalool (4).

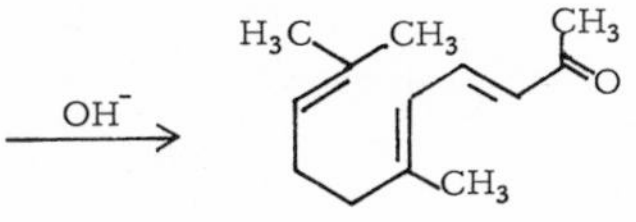

$$\xrightarrow{\text{OH}^-}$$

(6)

Synthesis of γ,δ-unsaturated ketones.[3] Isopropenyl methyl ether reacts with tertiary vinylcarbinols to give γ,δ-unsaturated ketones. Phosphoric acid is used as

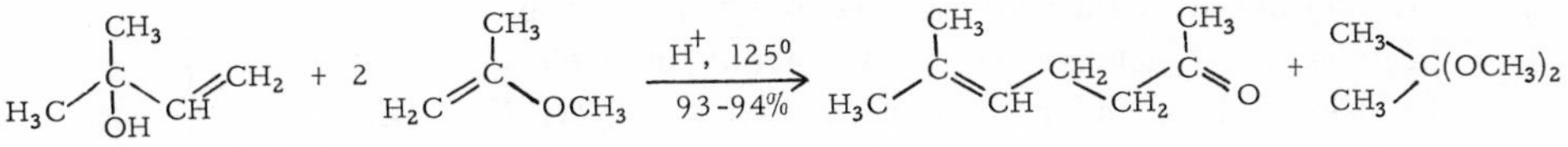

$$\underset{(1)}{\text{(1)}} \quad + \quad 2 \quad \xrightarrow[\text{93-94\%}]{\text{H}^+, \ 125^0} \quad \underset{(2)}{\text{(2)}} \quad +$$

catalyst, and the reaction is carried out in heptane or ligroin in a pressure vessel at 125° for 15 hrs. The reaction is believed to proceed through an allyl enol ether (a) which undergoes a thermal Claisen rearrangement to give (2).

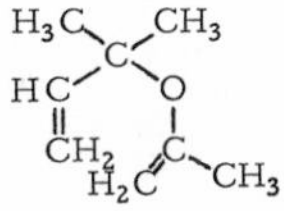

(a)

[1]G. Saucy and R. Marbet, *Helv.*, **50**, 1158 (1967)
[2]W. J. Croxall, F. J. Glavis, and W. T. Neher, *Am. Soc.*, **70**, 2805 (1948)
[3]G. Saucy and R. Marbet, *Helv.*, **50**, 2091 (1967)

K

Ketene [**1**, 528–531, before references].

A Schering group was interested in acetylation of the tertiary hydroxylic steroid (1). The usual acidic catalysts could not be used since they would lead to dehydration with formation of the $\Delta^{14,16}$-diene. The acetylation was achieved (but only in about 20% yield) by using ketene and potassium *t*-butoxide in THF. The strength of the base required is roughly parallel to the degree of hindrance of the hydroxyl group.

(1)

[18]J. N. Gardner, T. L. Popper, F. E. Carlon, O. Gnoj, and H. L. Herzog, *J. Org.*, **33**, 3695 (1968)

L

Lead [**1**, 532, before **Lead acetate**]. At. wt. 207.21.

The Hungarian chemist Mézáros[1] states that pyrophoric lead can be prepared by reaction of lead oxide with furfural vapors at 290°. It can be purified by washing with benzene and aqueous alcohol. It is described as a new reagent for Wurtz-like reactions, for example:

$$2 \ CH_3CH_2CH_2CH_2Br \xrightarrow[44\%]{Pb} CH_3CH_2CH_2CH_2CH_2CH_2CH_2CH_3$$

$$2 \ C_6H_5COCl \xrightarrow[53\%]{Pb} C_6H_5\overset{O}{\overset{\|}{C}} \ \overset{O}{\overset{\|}{C}}C_6H_5$$

Azoo and Grimshaw[2] prepared a finely divided form of lead by reaction of lead tetraacetate with aqueous sodium borohydride. This form converted benzyl chloride in benzene (reflux) into dibenzyl in 70% yield. However, a commercial lead powder ("100 mesh to dust") was equally effective. Both forms of lead were also effective for reduction of aromatic nitro compounds to azoxy compounds; yields are generally in the range 40–70%. Only the *trans* isomer is formed.

[1]L. Mézáros, *Tetrahedron Letters*, 4951 (1967)
[2]J. A. Azoo and J. Grimshaw, *J. Chem. Soc.*, (C). 2403 (1968)

Lead acetate trihydrate [**1**, 532–533, before references].

Lead acetate was used[4] for preferential replacement of bromine by an acetoxy group:

$$(CH_2)_5 \overset{\overset{CCl}{\|}}{\underset{CHBr}{CH}} \xrightarrow[80-90\%]{Pb(OAc)_2} (CH_2)_5 \overset{\overset{CCl}{\|}}{\underset{CHOCOCH_3}{CH}}$$

Lead acetate proved to be superior to silver acetate, which had been used previously for such a displacement. The example cited is one step in a method for conversion of cyclic ketones into cyclic β-diketones.

[4]K. Schank, B. Eistert, and J. H. Felzmann, *Ber.*, **99**, 1414 (1966)

Lead dioxide [**1**, 533–536].

Hydroquinones → quinones [**1**, 533–534, at end]. The most convenient synthesis of 4,5-dimethoxy-*o*-benzoquinone (8) involves oxidation of catchol (7) with lead dioxide (Riedel-deHaën) in the presence of sodium methoxide.[7a]

(7)   (8)

Oxidative decarboxylation [1, 535, after formulas (1) → (2). Eisenbraun[10a] has found that the oxidative decarboxylation of nepetonic acid (1) is not an isolated case but is applicable to γ-keto acids in general. Commercially available lead dioxide (Merck Reagent Grade, Baker's Analyzed Chemically Pure, and Frank W. Kerr Co. Reagent Grade) are about as satisfactory as the especially prepared lead dioxide of Doering and Finkelstein.[9] Yields are in the range 30–40% for the γ-keto acids having no alkyl or aryl substituents in the α- or β-position, but γ-keto acids substituted in the α- or β-position give pure α,β-unsaturated ketones in yields as high as 92%. In the most satisfactory procedure, an intimate mixture of lead dioxide, the γ-keto acid, and powdered soft glass is placed in a sublimation tube, which is then evacuated and inserted part way into a preheated (250°) sublimation apparatus. The α,β-unsaturated ketone distills and condenses in a cooled portion of the tube. The entire operation requires about 10 min.

Caution: The reactants should be well mixed and air should be excluded from the hot residue of the decarboxylation reaction.

[1, 536, before references]: Barrelle and Glenat[15] examined the oxidation of alcohols of type (1) to the ketones (2) with a commercial lead dioxide (Prolabo). When

$$RCHOHC{\equiv}CH \quad \xrightarrow{\text{PbO}_2} \quad RCC{\equiv}CH$$
$$\overset{\|}{\underset{O}{}}$$

(1)   (2)

R was an alkyl or a cyclohexyl group, yields were in the range 25–40%. When the hydroxyl group was α to an aryl group or a double bond, yields of 60–80% were realized.

[7a]H.-W. Wanzlick and U. Jahnke, *Ber.*, **101**, 3744 (1968)
[10a]D. V. Hertzler, J. M. Berdahl, and E. J. Eisenbraun, *J. Org.*, **33**, 2008 (1968)
[15]M. Barrelle and R. Glenat, *Bull. soc.*, 453 (1967)

Lead tetraacetate [1, 537–563].

α-Acetoxylation of carbonyl compounds [1, 539–542; end of first paragraph on 541]. Pettit[10a] also found that 21-acetoxylation of 20-ketosteroids is advantageously conducted by lead tetraacetate oxidation catalyzed by boron trifluoride ether. The yield of Δ[5]-3β,21-diacetoxy-20-ketopregnene from pregnenolone was 69%.

[1, 542, formulation at top of page]: *Correction*: The second and third formulas are incorrect and should be changed to read as follows.[18a]

Hypoiodite reaction [1, 552, end of page]. Cedrene (1) is oxidized to cendranoxide (2) in 50% yield by lead tetraacetate in combination with iodine.[56a] The oxide is obtained only in traces when lead tetraacetate is used alone.

Oxidative decarboxylation [**1**, 554–557; after citation of ref. 70a]. A simplified procedure for oxidative decarboxylation of disubstituted malonic acids has been described by Tufariello and Kissel.[70b] The malonic acid is oxidized by lead tetraacetate in refluxing benzene containing 2 equivalents of pyridine. Carbon dioxide is evolved and a *gem*-diacetate is formed. This is readily hydrolyzed by either acid or base to the ketone. Yields are satisfactory (45–70%).

Kochi[70c] found that oxidative decarboxylation by lead tetraacetate is catalyzed not only by pyridine but even more markedly by cupric acetate, $Cu(OAc)_2$, and other copper salts. Since the reaction is inhibited by oxygen, a free-radical reaction apparently is involved. The method is useful in synthesis. Thus Jensen and W. S. Johnson[70d] converted the tetrahydroabietic acid (1) into the diene mixture (2) in

76% yield. The procedure was used also in a three-step synthesis of fichtelite (6) from abietic acid (3).

Herz *et al.*[70e] used this catalytic method for the conversion of (7) into (8), ($\pm$)-methyl trachylobanate, a member of a new class of pentacyclic triterpenes discovered by Ourisson *et al.*[70f]

(7)   (8)

The oxidation decarboxylation of monocarboxylic acids is retarded by oxygen,[70e] but oxygen increases the yield of olefins in oxidative bisdecarboxylation of (9) $\rightarrow$ (10).[70g]

Atmosph.	Yield of(10)
N_2	38.4%
Air	43%
O_2	52%

(9)   (10)

In a joint publication three groups report that oxidative decarboxylation of 1,2-dicarboxylic acids generally proceeds in higher yields upon electrolysis than with lead tetraacetate [P. C. Radlick *et al.*, J. J. Sims, and E. E. van Tamelen and T. Whitesides, *Tetrahedron Letters*, 5117 (1968)]. A similar conclusion was reported independently and simultaneously by H. H. Westberg and H. J. Dauben, Jr. [*ibid.*, 5123 (1968)].

Cholanic acid is converted into Δ^{22}-24-norcholene in 60% yield by oxidation with lead tetraacetate catalyzed by cupric acetate [A. S. Vaidya, S. M. Dixit, and A. S. Rao, *Tetrahedron Letters*, 5173 (1968)].

In the case of certain unsaturated carboxylic acids treatment with $Pb(OAc)_4$ leads to the formation of an acetoxylactone, for example (12).[70h]

(11)   (12)

Lead tetraacetate reacts slowly with pyridine to give a red solution slowly changing to yellow. From an aged solution of lead tetraacetate and pyridine in benzene. Partch[70i] isolated lead tetraacetate pyridinate as a yellow solid.

Primary amides are converted by treatment with lead tetraacetate in acetic acid into arylamines: [70j] an acyl nitrene is suggested as the intermediate.

$$R\overset{O}{\overset{\|}{C}}-NH_2 \xrightarrow{Pb(OAc)_4} [R\overset{O}{\overset{\|}{C}}-\ddot{N}:] \longrightarrow R-N=C=O \xrightarrow{AcOH} R-\overset{H}{\underset{OAc}{\overset{|}{N}}}-\underset{|}{C}=O \longrightarrow R-\overset{H}{\overset{|}{N}}COCH_3$$

Butler[70k] has discussed reactions of lead tetraacetate with substituted hydrazones as a route to novel heterocyclic ring systems.

In a new route to α-keto esters, Zbiral and Werner[70l] acetylated methoxymethyl-enetriphenylphosphorane and oxidized the product with lead tetraacetate.

$$(C_6H_5)_3P=CHOCH_3 \xrightarrow[-HCl]{RCOCl} (C_6H_5)_3P=\overset{OCH_3}{\overset{|}{C}}COR \xrightarrow[-(C_6H_5)_3PO]{Pb(OAc)_4} O=\overset{OCH_3}{\overset{|}{C}}-\underset{\underset{O}{\|}}{C}R$$

Miscellaneous Oxidations [1, 559–561; 560, after citation of ref. 88]. de Groot and Wynberg[88a] used lead tetraacetate in pyridine (Partch[88] conditions) for selective oxidation of the α-hydroxy keto function of I without oxidation of the sulfur.

I   II

Oximes react with lead tetraacetate (one-half equivalent) in acetic acid at 70° (1 hr.) to give the corresponding carbonyl compound in 60-90% yield. The reaction can even be applied to unsaturated oximes if an equivalent amount of anhydrous

$$2 \overset{R}{\underset{R}{>}}C=NOH + Pb(OAc)_4 \longrightarrow 2 \overset{R}{\underset{R}{>}}C=O + N_2 + Pb(OAc)_2 + 2 HOAc$$

sodium acetate is present; for example, citral is obtained from the oxime in 80% yield. The oxidation of acetophenone oxime was examined with nine reagents; lead tetraacetate was by far superior (95% yield).[88b]

$$(CH_3)_2C=CH(CH_2)_2\overset{CH_3}{\overset{|}{C}}=CHCH=NOH \xrightarrow[80\%]{Pb(OAc)_4-NaOAc} (CH_3)_2C=CH(CH_2)_2\overset{CH_3}{\overset{|}{C}}=CHCH=O$$

[10a]G. R. Pettit, C. L. Herald, and J. P. Yardley, *J. Org.*, in press
[18a]This correction was kindly reported by Dr. Jerry W. Ellis

[56a]K. H. Baggaley, T. Norin, and S. Sundin, *Chem. Scand.*, **22**, 1709 (1968)

[70b]J. J. Tufariello and W. J. Kissel, *Tetrahedron Letters*, 6145 (1966)

[70c]J. K. Kochi, *Am. Soc.*, **87**, 1811 (1965)

[70d]N. P. Jensen and W. S. Johnson, *J. Org.*, **32**, 2045 (1967)

[70e]W. Herz, R. N. Mirrington, and H. Young, *Tetrahedron Letters*, 405 (1968)

[70f]G. Hugel, L. Lods, J. M. Mellor, D. W. Theobold, and G. Ourisson, *Bull. soc.*, 1974 (1963); *ibid.*, 2882, 2888 (1965); G. Hugel, L. Lods, J. M. Mellor, and G. Ourisson, *ibid.*, 2894 (1965)

[70g]C. M. Cimarusti and J. Wolinsky, *Am. Soc.*, **90**, 113 (1968)

[70h]R. M. Moriarty, H. G. Walsh, and H. Gopal, *Tetrahedron Letters*, 4363, 4369 (1966)

[70i]R. E. Partch and J. Monthony, *Tetrahedron Letters*, 4427 (1967)

[70j]B. Acott and A. L. J. Beckwith, *Chem. Commun.*, 161 (1965)

[70k]R. N. Butler, *Chem. Ind.*, 437 (1968)

[70l]E. Zbiral and E. Werner, *Tetrahedron Letters*, 2001 (1966)

[72]*Add: See also* B. Acott, A. L. J. Beckwith, A. Hassanali, and J. W. Redmond, *Tetrahedron Letters*, 4039 (1965)

[88a]Ae. de Groot and H. Wynberg, *J. Org.*, **31**, 3954 (1966)

[88b]Y. Yukawa, M. Sakai, and S. Suzuki, *Bull. Chem. Soc. Japan*, **39**, 2266 (1966)

Lead tetraacetate–N-Bromosuccinimide [1, 563, before **Lead tetrabenzoate**].

Barton, Lier, and McGhie[1] used the combination of lead tetraacetate and N-bromosuccinimide in refluxing benzene to effect allylic acetoxylation and suggest that the mechanism and scope of this new reaction deserve further investigation. Thus β-amyrene, Δ^{12}-oleanene (1), was converted into Δ^{12}-11α-acetoxyoleanene;

(1) 5 g.   (2) 2.5 g.

after hydrolysis the corresponding alcohol was isolated in about 50% yield.

[1]D. H. R. Barton, E. F. Lier, and J. F. McGhie, *J. Chem. Soc.*, (C), 1031 (1968)

Lead tetra(trifluoroacetate), $Pb(OCOCF_3)_4$ [1, 564, before **Lemieux-Johnson oxidation**].

Mol. wt. 659.13, too hygroscopic for m.p. determination. Supplier: Peninsular ChemResearch Inc.

Preparation. The white crystalline reagent, which is very sensitive to moisture, was first prepared and used as a polymerization catalyst for olefins by a du Pont chemist.[1] A mixture of Pb_3O_4(7.5 g.), $(CF_3CO)_2O$ (15 g.), and CF_3CO_2H (26 g.) is stirred at room temperature until colorless.

Oxidation.[2] The reagent reacts with nonactivated hydrocarbons such as benzene and *n*-heptane, as well as toluene, to give trifluoroacetoxy derivatives which are readily hydrolyzed to the corresponding phenols or alcohols. Yields are in the range of 45 ± 10%.

$$C_6H_6 \longrightarrow C_6H_5O\overset{\overset{O}{\|}}{C}CF_3 \xrightarrow{H_2O} \cdot C_6H_5OH$$

$$\underline{n}\text{-}C_7H_{16} \longrightarrow \underline{n}\text{-}C_7H_{15}O\overset{\overset{O}{\|}}{C}CF_3 \xrightarrow{H_2O} \underline{n}\text{-}C_7H_{15}OH$$

$$C_6H_5CH_3 \longrightarrow C_6H_5CH_2O\overset{\overset{O}{\|}}{C}CF_3 \xrightarrow{H_2O} C_6H_5CH_2OH$$

[1] J. R. Convery, German patent 1,094,462 (1958) [*C.A.*, **56**, 1603 (1962)]
[2] R. E. Partch, *Am. Soc.*, **89**, 3662 (1967)

Levulinic acid [1, 564–566, before references]. Ponder and Walker[10] reported that addition of nitrosyl chloride to an olefin followed by hydrolysis of the adduct with levulinic acid made 0.1 N in HCl is a convenient general method for the conversion of an olefin into the corresponding chloroketone. Yields (based on the olefin) are

$$>C=C< \xrightarrow{NOX} \overset{\underset{NO}{|}}{-}\overset{\overset{X}{|}}{C}-\overset{|}{C}- \rightleftharpoons \left(\overset{\underset{NO}{|}}{-}\overset{\overset{X}{|}}{C}-\overset{|}{C}-\right)_2 \xrightarrow{H^+} -\overset{\overset{}{\|}}{\underset{O}{C}}-\overset{\overset{X}{|}}{C}-$$

in the range 60–90%. The reaction fails, however, with *cis*- and *trans*-stilbene. The hydrocarbons form adducts, but on attempted hydrolysis these lose NOCl and revert to the starting olefins.

[10] B. W. Ponder and D. R. Walker, *J. Org.*, **32**, 4136 (1967)

N-Lithioethylenediamine [1, 567–570, after formula (17)]. The Poona group (ref. 2) extended their studies on reactions of the reagent to medium-size ring sesquiterpenes and diterpenes.[2a]

[Before references]: The reagent, in excess, isomerizes the olefin (1) to (2) in

(1)   (2) not orthodene   (3) β-Pinene

92% yield.[6] Structure (2) was originally assigned to a bicyclic hydrocarbon named "orthodene" but since identified as β-pinene (3).

[2a] B. N. Joshi, K. K. Chakravarti, and S. C. Bhattacharyya, *Tetrahedron*, **23**, 1251 (1967)
[6] A. W. Burgstahler and R. E. Sticker, *ibid.*, **24**, 2435 (1968)

3-Lithio-1-trimethylsilylpropyne, $[\overset{3}{C}H_2C\equiv\overset{1}{C}Si(CH_3)_3]Li$ **[1, 570, before Lithium].**
Preparation in solution.

$$(CH_3)_3SiCl + CH_3C\equiv CLi \xrightarrow[\text{30 hrs.}]{\text{Ether}} CH_3C\equiv CSi(CH_3)_3 \xrightarrow[\text{-BuH}]{\text{n-BuLi (Argon)}} [CH_2C\equiv CSi(CH_3)_3]Li$$

(1)   (2)   (3)   (4)

Corey and Kirst[1] prepared this reagent (4) by refluxing trimethylchlorosilane (1) in ether with propynyllithium (2) for 30 hrs. to produce 1-trimethylsilylpropyne (3) and adding an equivalent amount of *n*-butyllithium to effect metalation to (4) in the presence of tetramethylethylenediamine as complexing agent.

Synthesis of acetylenes.[1] The reagent reacts with a primary halide in ether (0°, 12 hrs.) to give almost exclusively an acetylene, rather than an allene. Removal of the

$$CH_3(CH_2)_5I \ + \ [CH_2C{\equiv}CCSi(CH_3)_3]Li \ \longrightarrow \ CH_3(CH_2)_6C{\equiv}CSi(CH_3)_3 \ + \ CH_3(CH_2)_6{=}C{=}CSi(CH_3)_3$$

55%   (trace)

$\big\downarrow$ Ag$^+$, followed by CN$^-$

$$CH_3(CH_2)_6C{\equiv}CH$$

protective trimethylsilyl group by treatment with ethanolic silver nitrate followed by sodium cyanide affords a terminal alkyne.

Synthesis of 1,5-dienes and 1-ene-5-ynes.[1] The Corey synthesis is particularly interesting because it can be used to generate the 1,5-diene system characteristic of acyclic isoprenoids. Thus *trans,trans*-farnesol has been synthesized as follows, starting with geranyl bromide (5). Propynylation with (4) proceeds stereospecifically to give (6), and treatment with ethanolic silver nitrate at 25° followed by sodium cyanide afforded the acetylene (7). The next step, hydroxymethylation to (9), was carried out by a procedure introduced by Sondheimer[2] involving reaction with

ethylmagnesium bromide to form the Grignard derivative (8), reaction of this with gaseous formaldehyde under nitrogen, and acidification. The next two steps were as described previously by Corey, Katzenellenbogen, and Posner,[3] who had found that a mixture of lithium aluminum hydride and sodium methoxide refluxed in THF followed by iodination affords the γ-iodoalcohol (10). Alkylation with dimethylcopperlithium (2, 151) then gave an alcohol identical with natural *trans,trans*-farnesol (11).

[1] E. J. Corey and H. A. Kirst, *Tetrahedron Letters*, 5041 (1968)
[2] F. Sondheimer, *Am. Soc.*, **74**, 4040 (1952)
[3] E. J. Corey, J. A. Katzenellenbogen, and G. A. Posner, *ibid.*, **89**, 4245 (1967)

Lithium acetylide, [1, 573–574, before references].

Lithium acetylide can be prepared by heating LiH with excess dimethyl sulfoxide under argon at 70–75° to form the lithium salt of DMSO.[5] A small amount of triphenylmethane is added and then acetylene is introduced until the red salt of triphenylmethyllithium disappears. Lithium acetylide is preferred to sodium acetylide in alkylation reactions with readily enolizable ketones.

Lithium acetylide can be prepared in quantitative yield by passing acetylene slowly through a solution of naphthalene–lithium in THF.[6] α,β-Unsaturated ketones added to this solution are ethynylated in good yield.

Another route to lithium acetylide involves heating lithium with graphite in a bomb or tube above 850° to form dilithium acetylide, a yellow to light grey refracting material which can be ground to a fine powder.[7] Dilithium acetylide reacts with acetylene in liquid ammonia rapidly to give a clear solution of lithium acetylide.

$$LiC\equiv CLi + HC\equiv CH \longrightarrow 2\ LiC\equiv CH$$

Preparation of the reagent in this way sometimes improves the yield in an ethynylation over that obtained with reagent prepared from lithium and acetylene.[8]

[5] J. Křiž, M. J. Beneš, and J. Peška, *Tetrahedron Letters*, 2881 (1965)
[6] K. Suga, S. Watanabe, and K. Takahashi, *Chem. Ind.*, 1748 (1967); K. Suga, S. Watanabe, and T. Suzuki, *Canad. J. Chem.* **46**, 3041 (1968)
[7] A. Hérold, *Bull. soc.*, **22**, 999 (1955)
[8] K. R. Martin, C. W. Kamienski, M. H. Dellinger, and R. O. Bach, *J. Org.*, **33**, 778 (1968)

Lithium–Alkylamine reduction [1, 574–581].

[1, 576, after citation of ref. 6]. The method of reducing naphthalene with lithium

(1)   (2)   (3)

85%   86%

(H$_2$O)

83% | Pb(OAc)$_4$

(4)

and a mixture of ethylamine and dimethylamine to a mixture of $\Delta^{9,10}$-octalin (82%) and $\Delta^{1,9}$-octalin and removal of the minor component by selective hydroboration with bis-3-methyl-2-butylborane and peroxide oxidation reported by Benkeser and Kaiser[6] is described also in an *Org. Syn.* procedure.[6a]

[**1**, 581, before references]: Borowitz *et al.*[19] found that in the lithium-amine reduction of chromane (1) to 5,6,7,8-tetrahydrochromane (2) a combination of ethylamine and dimethylamine in 1:1 ratio (by volume) gave a higher yield and a purer product than ethylamine alone or other amine combinations. The product was converted into 6-ketononanolide (4) as shown.

[6a]E. M. Kaiser and R. A. Benkeser, procedure submitted to *Org. Syn.*, 1968
[19]I. J. Borowitz, G. Gonis, R. Kelsey, R. Rapp, and G. J. Williams, *J. Org.*, **31**, 3032 (1966)

Lithium aluminum hydride [**1**, 581–595].

[**1**, 582, line 6 from bottom]: *Delete* "or $Li^+AlH_4^-$."

Aziridine syntheses [**1**, 594, before references]. The preparation cited for synthesis of *cis*-2-benzyl-3-phenylaziridine is general for ketoximes having an aromatic ring attached to the carbon atom α or β to the oximino function and to aldoximes having an aromatic ring attached to the carbon atom β to the oximino function.[36]

Other examples:

Homogeneous hydrogenation catalyst. Acetylenes can be reduced stereospecifically to *trans*-olefins by the reagent in THF or diglyme. In one experiment conducted in toluene, *cis*-addition was observed.[37]

Slaugh[38] found that $LiAlH_4$ can function as a hydrogenation catalyst for reduction of acetylenes and conjugated dienes to enes in THF solution; an autoclave pressurized with hydrogen was employed. The reduction of acetylenes proceeds stereospecifically to give the *trans*-olefins. Tracer studies showed that $LiAlH_4$ adds to the triple bond or the conjugated diene system to form a metal alkyl, which then undergoes hydrogenolysis.

$$CH_2=CHCH=CHCH_3 \ + \ LiAlH_4 \ \longrightarrow \underline{n}\text{-}(C_5H_9)LiAlH_3 \ \xrightarrow{H_2} \ \underline{n}\text{-}C_5H_{10} \ + \ LiAlH_4$$

[32]*Change to:* M. J. Jorgenson and A. F. Thacher, *Org. Syn.*, **48**, 75 (1968)
[36]K. Kotera and K. Kitahonoki, *ibid.*, **48**, 20 (1968)
[37]E. F. Magoon and L. H. Slaugh, *Tetrahedron*, **23**, 4509 (1967)
[38]L. H. Slaugh, *ibid.*, **22**, 1741 (1966)

Lithium aluminum hydride–Aluminum chloride [1, 595–599].

Reduction of ketones [1, 597–598, at end]. In a convenient preparation of 5α-androstane-16-one (4), Jones *et al.*[13a] condensed 5α-androstane-17-one (1) with benzaldehyde to give the conjugated ketone (2). Then the 17-keto group was eliminated by reduction with LiAlH$_4$–AlCl$_3$ and the product ozonized. Use of the hydride alone gave the 16-benzylidene-17β-alcohol. This method has been applied also to the

(1) $\xrightarrow[96\%]{C_6H_5CHO}$ (2) $\xrightarrow[90\%]{LiAlH_4-AlCl_3}$ (3)

$\xrightarrow[95\%]{O_3}$ (4)

preparation of 5α- and 5β-2-ketosteroids from 5α- and 5β-3-ketosteroids.[13b]

Asby and Prather[13c] studied the composition of mixed hydride reagents in ether solution and concluded that the reaction of LiAlH$_4$ and AlCl$_3$ in the ratios 3:1, 1:1, 1:3, and 1:4 produces AlH$_3$, H$_2$AlCl, HAlCl$_2$, and HAlCl$_2$ + AlCl$_3$, respectively.

[9]*Change to read:* R. A. Daignault and E. L. Eliel, *Org. Syn.*, **47**, 37 (1967)
[13]*Change to read:* E. L. Eliel, R. J. L. Martin, and D. Nasipuri, *ibid.*, **47**, 16 (1967)
[13a]J. E. Bridgeman, E. R. H. Jones, G. D. Meakins, and J. Wicha, *Chem. Commun.*, 898 (1967)
[13b]M. Fetizon, J.-C. Gramain, and I. Hanna, *Compt. Rend. (C)*, 929 (1967)
[13c]E. C. Ashby and J. Prather, *Am. Soc.*, **88**, 729 (1966)

Lithium aluminum hydride–3-O-Benzyl-1,2-O-cyclohexylidene-α-D-glucofuranose complex[1] [1, 599, before Lithium aluminum hydride–Boron trifluoride etherate].

(1)

The carbohydrate portion of the complex is formulated in (1). The complex is prepared by adding the modified sugar to a stirred suspension of LiAlH$_4$ in dry ether. After hydrogen evolution has subsided, the solution is refluxed for 2 hrs. The complex has been shown to effect asymmetric reduction of ketones; optically active alcohols of up to 40% optical purity have been obtained and they all have the (S)-configuration. On the other hand, if increasing quantities of ethanol are added to the lithium aluminum hydride complex, the configuration of the secondary alcohol formed changes from (S) to (R). Thus the stereoselectivity increases to a maximum and then decreases as more ethanol is added. Furthermore, maximum selectivities are substantially increased by initially employing larger quantities of standardized solutions of lithium aluminum hydride.

Formulation of the complex from $LiAlH_4$ and 3-O-benzyl-1,2-O-cyclohexylidene-α-ᴅ-glucofuranose (1) as (2) clarifies the issue. Two active metal hydride atoms are available, but one (a) is so highly shielded by the benzyl group that the other (b) opens the carbonyl group of the ketone (3) in a single direction and gives the S-

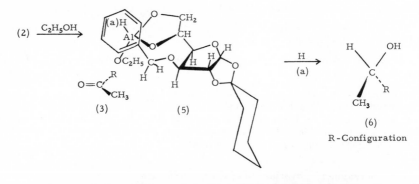

alcohol (4). Treatment of the complex (2) with small amounts of ethanol replaces the more reactive hydrogen (b) by ethoxyl, and the resulting product (5) utilizes hydrogen atom (a) and gives the R-alcohol (6).

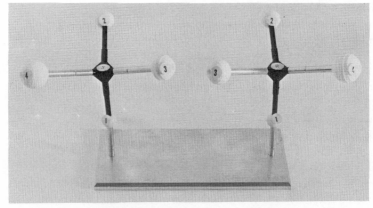

Figure L-1a   R and S configurations.

The R or S specification of configuration is summarized nicely by models in which group priorities based on atomic numbers follow the order of decreasing size of ball: 4, 3, 2, 1 (Fig. L-1a).

[1]S. R. Landor, B. J. Miller, and A. R. Tatchell, *J. Chem. Soc.*, (C), 1822, 2280 (1966); *idem*, *ibid.*, 197 (1967)

Lithium–Ammonia [1, 601–603, before references].

Estradiol methyl ether has been reduced satisfactorily by lithium and gaseous ammonia.[8] The yield is not so high as that obtainable with liquid ammonia, but the operation is considerably simplified.

Unexpectedly the enedione (1) is converted into the cyclopropanol (2) on reduction with lithium in ammonia and ether.[9]

(1)   (2)

[8]J. F. Fisher and L. L. Smith, *Steroids*, **9**, 97 (1967)
[9]P. S. Venkataramani and W. Reusch, *Tetrahedron Letters*, 5283 (1968)

Lithium bromide [1, 604, before references].

This halide markedly promotes the reaction of an organocadmium compound with acyl chlorides (but not with ketones). The effect was used to advantage in the synthesis of α-oxo esters.[3]

$$(CH_3)_2Cd + ClCOCO_2C_2H_5 \xrightarrow[51\%]{LiBr,\ THF,\ -70°} CH_3COCO_2C_2H_5$$

[3]J. Kollonitsch, *J. Chem. Soc.*, (A), 453, 456 (1966)

Lithium carbonate–Lithium bromide [1, 606–608, before references].

6-Methoxy-1-tetralone (7) is converted into 6-methoxy-1-naphthol (8) in 80% yield by bromination followed by dehydrohalogenation.[8] The bromination was

(7, 7 g.)   10.1 g.   (8, 4.95 g.)

carried out in ether containing a trace of hydrogen chloride; dehydrobromination was effected in refluxing DMF with lithium carbonate–lithium bromide. Calcium carbonate was less satisfactory. Dehydrogenation of (7) (palladium, quinones) was unsuccessful.

[8]T. R. Kasturi and T. Arunachalam, *Canad. J. Chem.*, **46**, 3625 (1968)

Lithium chloride [1, 609, before references].

The usual conversion of benzosuberanone (1) into benzo[2,3]tropone (3) involves two bromination and dehydrobromination sequences with moderate yield. Collinton

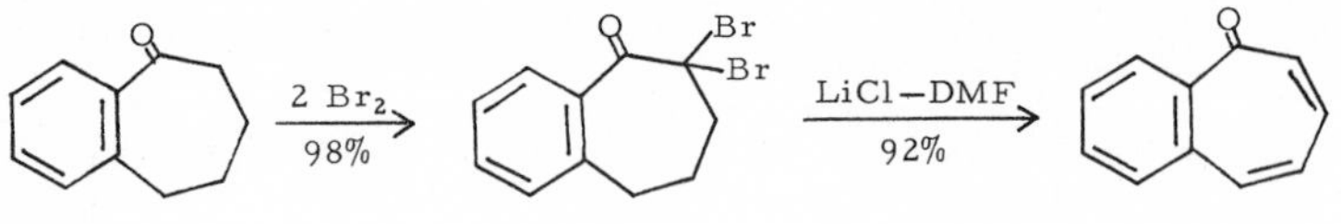

(1)   (2)   (3)

and Jones[5] found that improved yields are obtained if (1) is dibrominated to the α,α-bromoketone (2) and this then dehydrobrominated by lithium chloride in DMF. They suggest the following scheme for the elimination reaction.

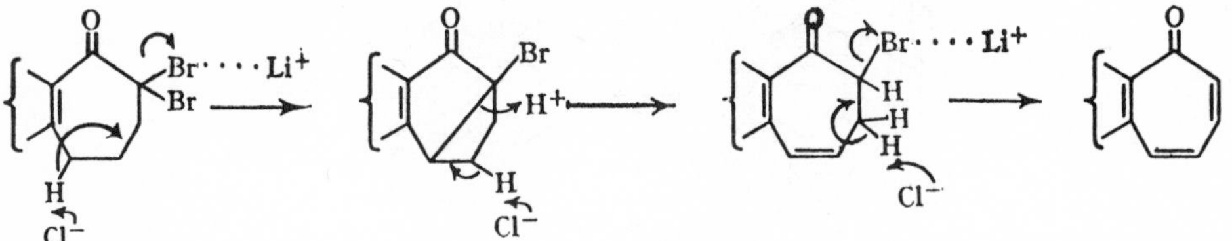

SCHEME

[5]E. W. Collinton and G. Jones, *Chem. Commun.*, 958 (1968)

Lithium dicyclohexylamide [1, 610, before Lithium diethoxyaluminum hydride].

A convenient new synthesis of *cis*- and *trans*-cyclodecene by Traynham *et al.*[1] utilizes as starting material cyclodecane, now available from Columbian Carbon Co., Lake Charles, La. 70601. Chlorination, with irradiation from a 150-w. light bulb, affords 1-chlorocyclodecane. One portion of the product was dehydrohalogenated as

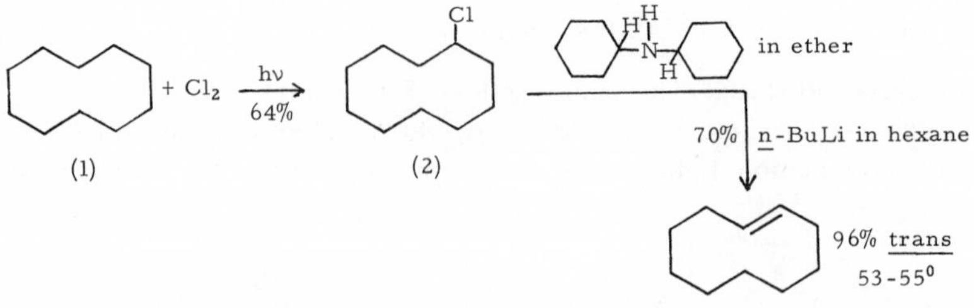

follows. A solution of *n*-butyllithium in hexane was added to a solution of dicyclohexylamine in ether under nitrogen in a flask provided with a magnetic stirrer and a condenser, and the mixture was added to a solution of chlorocyclodecane in hexane. After refluxing for 24 hrs., work-up afforded *trans*-cyclodecene (b.p. 53–55°, 96% *trans* by gas chromatography). The *cis* isomer can be prepared in 80% yield by dehydrohalogenation of (2) with potassium *t*-butoxide (*which see*, this volume).

[1] J. G. Traynham, D. B. Stone, and J. L. Couvillion, *J. Org.*, **32**, 510 (1967)

Lithium diethylamide [1, 610–611].

Reaction with epoxides [1, 611, after line 2]. The reaction of epoxides of medium-size rings with lithium diethylamide is complicated. Thus *cis*-cyclooctene oxide (1) gives mainly the bicyclic alcohol (2), and *trans*-cyclooctene oxide (5) gives mainly the epimeric bicyclic alcohol (6).[3a] Using deuterium tracer studies, Cope showed that the bicyclic alcohols (2) and (6) arise by loss of a hydrogen atom from an α-

(1)   (2) 70%   (3) 16%   (4) 2%

(5)   (6) 55–60%   (3) 10–15%   (7) 32%

carbon atom of the epoxide (α-elimination) and carbenoid insertion into a trans-annular C—H bond.

In contrast both *cis*- and *trans*-cyclododecene oxide (8, 9) on treatment with base give as the major product the allylic alcohol, *trans*-2-cyclododecenol (10).[3b] This reaction evidently involves elimination of a hydrogen β to the oxide ring.

(8, 9) <u>cis</u> and <u>trans</u>   (10)

From an extensive study of the isomerization of cyclic oxides with lithium diethyl-amide, Crandall[3c] suggests that β-elimination to give allylic alcohols is the preferred path where a favorable *trans*, coplanar transition state is possible, and that when this is not attainable α-elimination and carbenoid insertion are observed.

Gunstone[3d] rearranged methyl vernolate (11) to methyl cariolate (12) by treatment with lithium diethylamide in ether for 1 hr. at 0°. He suggested that natural products

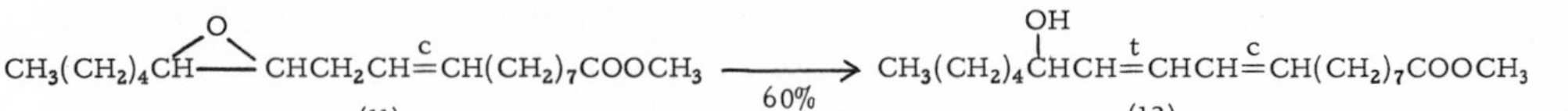

$$CH_3(CH_2)_4CH \overset{O}{-\!\!\!\triangle\!\!\!-} CHCH_2CH \overset{c}{=\!\!=} CH(CH_2)_7COOCH_3 \xrightarrow[60\%]{} CH_3(CH_2)_4\overset{OH}{\underset{|}{C}}HCH \overset{t}{=\!\!=} CHCH \overset{c}{=\!\!=} CH(CH_2)_7COOCH_3$$

$$(11) \qquad\qquad\qquad\qquad\qquad\qquad\qquad\qquad\qquad (12)$$

containing the grouping —CHOHCH$\overset{t}{=}$CH— may be formed from a *cis*-oelfin, —CH$\overset{c}{=}$CHCH$_2$—, by epoxide rearrangement.

   Ziegler ring closure [1, 611 before references]. This base was used for the Ziegler ring closure of dinitriles,[10] for example:

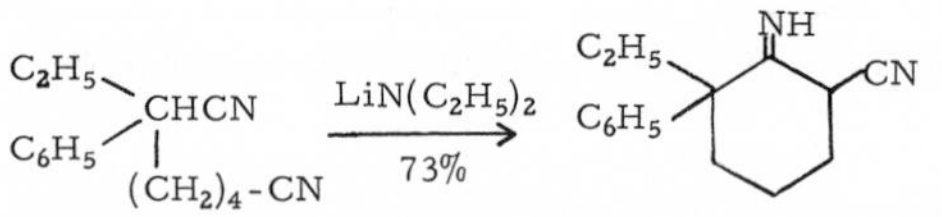

   Intramolecular alkylation of acetylenic halides.[11] Some acetylenic halides when treated with this base in THF at − 10° for 1–3 hrs. undergo intramolecular alkylation:

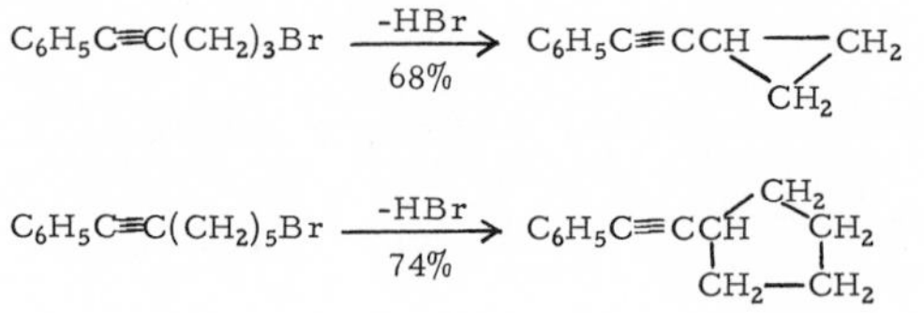

The usual ring-size dependence for cyclization was noted. Dehydrohalogenation to the terminal olefin was observed in attempted preparation of cyclobutanes. The allene isomer in favorable cases also undergoes intramolecular cyclization:

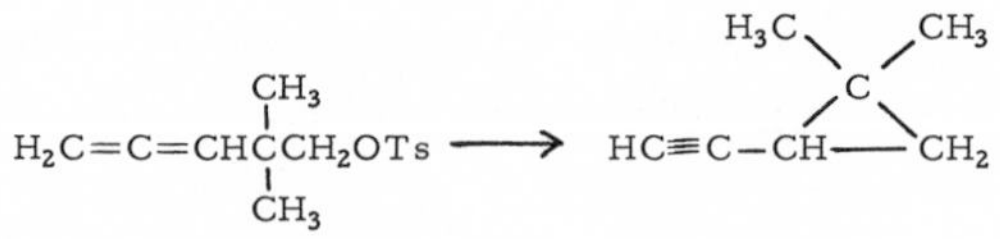

[3a]For a review with references, *see* A. C. Cope, M. M. Martin, and M. A. McKervey, *Quart. Rev.*, **20**, 143–145 (1966)

[3b]H. Nozaki, T. Mori, and R. Noyori, *Tetrahedron*, **22**, 1207 (1966)

[3c]J. K. Crandall and L.-H. C. Lin, *J. Org.*, **33**, 2375 (1968), and earlier references cited therein

[3d]H. B. S. Conacher and F. D. Gunstone, *Chem. Commun.*, 281 (1968)

[10]S. S. Kulp, *Canad. J. Chem.*, **45**, 1981 (1967)

[11]J. K. Crandall and D. J. Keyton, *Chem. Commun.*, 1069 (1968)

Lithium diisobutylmethylaluminum hydride [**1**, 611, before **Lithium dimethylaminosulfonylmethide**]. Mol. wt. 164.19.

   Zweifel and Steele[1] prepared the reagent (3) by adding 0.1 m. of methyllithium in ether to 0.1 m. of diisobutylaluminum hydride in glyme while maintaining the temperature below 25°. Whereas diisobutylaluminum hydride reduces alkynes by

$$CH_3Li + [(CH_3)_2CHCH_2]_2AlH \longrightarrow [(CH_3)_2CHCH_2]_2Al^-HCH_3(Li^+)$$

(1)   (2)   (3)

cis-addition, the new reagent reacts by trans-addition. Carbonation of the adduct (4) and acidification yields the cis-α,β-unsaturated acid (5) in good yield.

$$[(CH_3)_2CHCH_2]_2Al^-HCH_3(Li^+) + RC\equiv CR \longrightarrow \left[\begin{array}{c} H \\ R \end{array} C=C \begin{array}{c} R \\ AlR_2 \\ | \\ CH_3 \end{array} \right] Li \xrightarrow[2) H^+]{1) CO_2} \begin{array}{c} H \\ R \end{array} C=C \begin{array}{c} R \\ CO_2H \end{array}$$

(3)   (4)   (5)

[1]G. Zweifel and R. B. Steele, Am. Soc., 89, 5085 (1967)

Lithium diisopropylamide, $HC \begin{array}{c} CH_3 \\ | \\ CH_3 \end{array} -N \begin{array}{c} Li \\ | \end{array} -CH \begin{array}{c} CH_3 \\ | \\ CH_3 \end{array}$ [1, 611, before **Lithium dimethylaminosul-**

fonylmethide]. Mol. wt. 107.12. Diisopropylamine, mol. wt. 101.19, b.p. 82–84°, suppliers, A, E, F, Sch.

Directed aldol condensation. Aldol condensation between an aldehyde and a ketone usually is not successful because self-addition of the aldehyde is the preferred reaction. Wittig and Reiff,[1] however, showed that, if the aldehyde is first converted into a Schiff base (cyclohexylamine was used) and then metalated with lithium diisopropylamide (chosen for obvious steric reasons), aldol condensation can be achieved, usually in good yield.[2] In the case of ketones, this route is superior to olefination via a phosphorylide.

$$CH_3CHO \xrightarrow{C_6H_{11}NH_2} CH_3CH=NC_6H_{11} \xrightarrow[\text{Ether, } 0^0]{LiN(i-C_3H_7)_2} LiCH_2CH=NC_6H_{11}$$

(1)   (2)   (3)

$$\xrightarrow[-70^0]{(C_6H_5)_2C=O} \begin{array}{c} C_6H_5 \\ C_6H_5 \end{array} C \begin{array}{c} CH_2CH \\ \diagdown NC_6H_{11} \\ O-Li \end{array} \xrightarrow[-LiOH]{H_2O} \begin{array}{c} C_6H_5 \\ C_6H_5 \end{array} C \begin{array}{c} CH_2CH \\ \diagdown NC_6H_{11} \\ O-H \end{array}$$

(4)   (5) 92%

$$\xrightarrow[85\%]{\begin{array}{c} CO_2H \\ | \\ CO_2H \end{array} \text{ Steam }} \begin{array}{c} C_6H_5 \\ C_6H_5 \end{array} C=CHCHO + C_6H_{11}NH_2$$

(6)

[1]G. Wittig and H. Reiff, Angew. Chem., internat. Ed., 7, 7 (1968); G. Wittig, Record Chem. Progr., 28, 45 (1967)
[2]G. Wittig and H. Hesse, Procedure submitted to Org. Syn., 1968

Lithium–Diphenyl [1, 612, before references].

If the reaction of $\Delta^{1,4}$-3-ketosteroids with lithium and diphenyl in THF described in ref. 2 is carried out at −60° to −40°, Δ^4-3-ketosteroids can be obtained.[3] The reaction is useful because introduction of a Δ^4-double bond into 5β-3-ketosteroids proceeds in low yield.

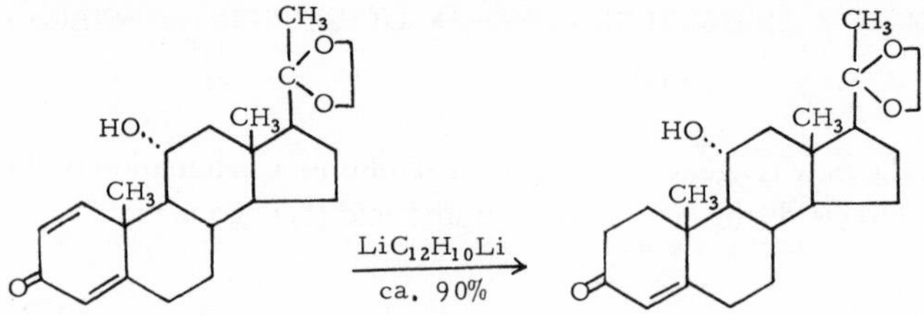

[3]P. Wieland and G. Anner, *Helv.*, **51**, 1698 (1968)

Lithium–Ethylenediamine [**1**, 614–615, before references].

This combination reduces 1,4-di-*t*-butylbenzene in fair yield to 1,4-di-*t*-butyl-cyclohexene.[3]

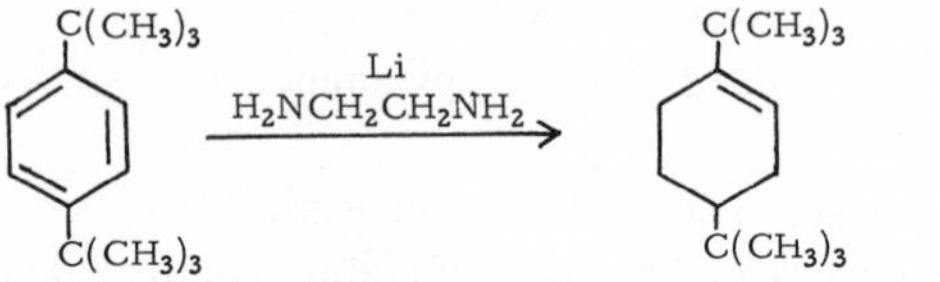

M. p. 54-54. 5°

Totaryl methyl ether (1) is not reduced by lithium in liquid ammonia, but it reacts with this more powerful system to give a mixture of four products. The chief of these is totarol (2), the product of demethylation, not reduction. Three minor products (3, 4, 5) have lost the oxygen function.[4]

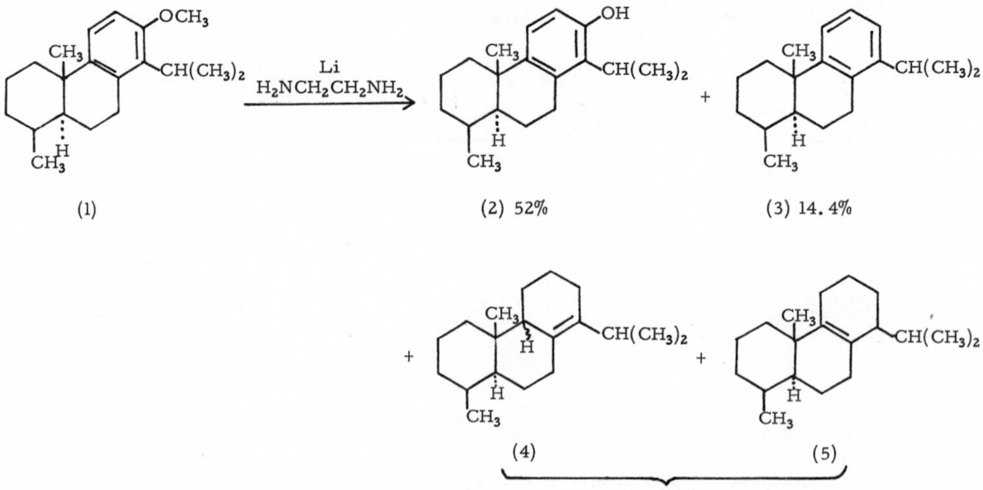

(1)   (2) 52%   (3) 14. 4%

(4)   (5)

3. 7%

[3]R. D. Stolow and J. A. Ward, *J. Org.*, **31**, 965 (1966)
[4]C. R. Bennett and R. C. Cambie, *Tetrahedron*, **22**, 2845 (1966)

Lithium hydride, LiH [**1**, 615, before **Lithium iodide**]. Mol. wt. 7.95. Suppliers: Alfa Inorganics, Fl., K.-L., Sch.

Use. See **Methyllithium** (in this volume).

Lithium nitride [**1**, 618, before references]

Reaction with acid chlorides.[3] The reagent reacts with benzoyl chloride in diglyme at room temperature to give tribenzamide in fairly good yield.

$$3 \ C_6H_5COCl \ + \ Li_3N \ \xrightarrow[61\%]{\text{Diglyme}} \ C_6H_5\overset{\overset{O}{\|}}{C}-N(\overset{\overset{O}{\|}}{C}C_6H_5)_2 \ + \ 3 \ LiCl$$

M. p. 206-207°

[3]F. P. Baldwin, E. J. Blanchard, and P. E. Koenig, *J. Org.*, **30**, 671 (1965)

Lithium tri-*t*-butoxyaluminum hydride [**1**, 620-625].

[**1**, 620, after citation of ref. 2]: Siggins *et al.*[2a] worked out a detailed procedure for reduction of 3,5-dinitrobenzoyl chloride to the corresponding aldehyde.

[**1**, 624, before references]: Surprisingly the tricyclic diketone (1), an intermediate in a synthesis of estrone, is reduced stereoselectively to the 17α-ketol (2).[19]

3,4,5-Trimethoxybenzoyl chloride was reduced to 3,4,5,-trimethoxybenzaldehyde by the complex hydride more conveniently than by Rosenmund reduction (74%).[20]

α-Fluoroacylfluorides are reduced to the fluoroaldehydes satisfactorily by the reagent.[21] Reduction by usual methods is often accompanied by hydrogenolysis of the C—F bond.

Saturated and unsaturated fatty aldehydes have been prepared in good yield by reduction of the acid chlorides with the reagent.[22]

In the course of a total synthesis of the macrolide zearalenone (1), a Merck group (D. Taub *et al.*[23]) found that the reagent reduces exclusively the less hindered car-

(1)

(2) 4.16 g.   (3) 670 mg.   (4)   (5)

bonyl group of 3,5-dimethoxyphthalic anhydride (2) but that 5,7-dimethoxyphthalide (4, over-reduction) and 3,5-dimethoxyphthalic acid (5, hydrolysis) are formed as well.

The combination of lithium tri-*t*-butoxyaluminum hydride (or di-*t*-butoxyaluminum hydride) with salts of transition metals, particularly cobalt, furnishes highly active homogeneous hydrogenation catalysts.[24]

[2a]J. E. Siggins, A. A. Larsen, J. H. Ackerman, and C. D. Carabateas, procedure submitted to *Org. Syn.*, 1968
[19]C. H. Kuo, D. Taub, and N. L. Wendler, *J. Org.*, **33**, 3126 (1968)
[20]D. C. Ayers, B. G. Carpenter, and R. C. Denney, *J. Chem. Soc.*, 3578 (1965)
[21]E. D. Bergmann and A. Cohen, *Tetrahedron Letters*, 1151 (1965)
[22]P. Vankata Rao, S. Ramachandran, and D. G. Cornwell, *J. Lipid Res.*, **8**, 380 (1967)
[23]D. Taub, N. N. Girotra, R. D. Hoffsommer, C. H. Kuo, H. L. Slates, S. Weber, and N. L. Wendler, *Tetrahedron*, **24**, 2443 (1968)
[24]R. Stern and L. Sajus, *Tetrahedron Letters*, 6313 (1968)

Lithium triethoxyaluminum hydride [**1**, 625, before references].

McQuillin and Yeats[3] found that the terpene lactone (1) could be reduced by the reagent to the lactol (2). Use of sodium borohydride gave the diol.

(1)   (2)

[3]P. J. McQuillin and R. B. Yeats, *J. Chem. Soc.*, 4273 (1965)

Lithium trimethoxyaluminum hydride [**1**, 625, before references]. The reagent greatly enhances the reaction of carbon monoxide with organoboranes.[4] The reaction can be carried out at atmospheric pressure at 0–25° and exhibits the 1 : 1 : 1 stoichiometry indicated in the formulation of a typical example:

$$3 \ CH_3(CH_2)_3CH{=}CH_2 \xrightarrow[\text{THF}]{B_2H_6} [CH_3(CH_2)_5]_3B$$

$$[CH_3(CH_2)_5]_3B \ + \ CO \ + \ LiAlH(OCH_3)_3 \longrightarrow [X] \xrightarrow[\text{Buffer}]{H_2O_2} CH_3(CH_2)_5CHO \ + \ 2 \ CH_3(CH_2)_5CH_2OH$$

Yields of aldehydes, as indicated by the yields of alcohols obtained on reduction, were 87–98% in five cases. One disadvantage is that only one of the three alkyl groups of the organoborane is converted into the aldehyde.

[4]H. C. Brown, R. A. Coleman, and M. W. Rathke, *Am. Soc.*, **90**, 500 (1968)

M

Magnesium [**1**, 627–629, ref. 4]. *Change second part to read:* D. Bryce-Smith and B. J. Wakefield, *Org. Syn.*, **47**, 103 (1967).

Magnesium bromide, anhydrous, $MgBr_2$ [**1**, 629, before **Magnesium bromide etherate**]. Mol. wt. 184.15. Supplier: A. D. MacKay, Inc.

The reagent can be prepared by the reaction of magnesium with bromine in anhydrous ether.[1]

Procedures applicable to the preparation of saturated alkyl bromides are not suitable for the synthesis of corresponding unsaturated bromides, as they lead to excessive alteration of double bonds. Methanesulfonates of unsaturated long-chain alcohols are conveniently obtained in good purity and high yield[2] and can be converted quantitatively into the corresponding alkenyl bromides by reaction with anhydrous magnesium bromide in ether.[3] Both reactions proceed without *cis-trans* isomerization or other alteration of double bonds.

In a procedure for the preparation of *cis*-9-octadecenyl bromide,[4] a solution of 26.8 g. (0.1 mole) of pure *cis*-9-octadecenol (available from the Lipids Preparation Laboratory of the Hormel Institute, Austin, Minn. 55912) in 90 ml. of pyridine is stirred in an ice bath under a stream of purified nitrogen and 17.2 g. (0.15 mole) of

$$CH_3(CH_2)_7CH \overset{c}{=} CH(CH_2)_7CH_2OH \ + \ CH_3SO_2Cl \ \xrightarrow[-HCl]{Py} \ CH_3(CH_2)_7CH \overset{c}{=} CH(CH_2)_7CH_2OSO_2CH_3$$

$$\xrightarrow[-MgBr(OSO_2CH_3)]{MgBr_2-Ether} \ CH_3(CH_2)_7CH \overset{c}{=} CH(CH_2)_7CH_2Br$$

methanesulfonyl chloride is added dropwise during 1 hr. Stirring is continued for another 5 hrs. at room temperature and the reaction product is worked up by ether extraction and then crystallized from absolute ethanol at −30° to give long needles of *cis*-9-octadecenylmethanesulfonate which is dried by a stream of dry nitrogen and then under high vacuum; the yield of pure product, m.p. 9–10°, is 79.5–80%. A second crop raises the yield to 87–88%.

In the last step a 0.05-mole portion (17.4 g) of the methanesulfonate and 650 ml. of absolute ether are placed in a 1-l. three-necked flask fitted with a condenser, inlet and outlet tubes for *dry* nitrogen, and a mechanical stirrer. A three-fold excess of anhydrous magnesium bromide (0.15 mole) is added while stirring vigorously to ensure complete reaction of the heterogeneous mixture. Stirring is continued for 24 hrs. at room temperature. Work-up includes distribution between ether and air-free water, filtration of a solution in hexane, removal of solvent in a stream of pure nitrogen, and drying under high vacuum.

[1] H. H. Rowley, *Am. Soc.*, **72**, 3305 (1950)
[2] W. J. Baumann and H. K. Mangold, *J. Org.*, **29**, 3055 (1964)
[3] *Idem, J. Lipid Res.*, **7**, 568 (1966)
[4] W. J. Baumann, R. D. Gee, and H. K. Mangold, procedure submitted to *Org. Syn.*, 1967

Magnesium–Mercuric chloride [1, 631, before Magnesium methyl carbonate]. A French group[1] found the combination of magnesium shavings in dry pyridine to be very satisfactory for the reductive dimerization of indanones, tetralones, and benzosuberones. Powdered magnesium reacted too violently. Lithium in dry ether was almost as satisfactory. Aluminum amalgam was less satisfactory; photochemical reduction was unsatisfactory, and electrolytic reduction gave low yields.

[1]G. Majerus, É. Yax, and G. Ourisson, *Bull. soc.*, 4143 (1967)

Magnesium methoxide, $Mg(OCH_3)_2$ [1, 631, before Magnesium methyl carbonate]. Mol. wt. 86.39. Supplier: Stauffer Chemical Co., Anderson Chemical Division, 3940 Summit St., Weston, Mich. 49289.

Preparation.[1] One liter of dry methanol (distilled from magnesium methoxide) is measured into a 2-l. flask fitted with a drying tube, the flask is cooled in an ice bath, and three 3-g. portions of magnesium are added and allowed to react completely. The flask is then removed from the cooling bath and fitted with a condenser, and the solution is allowed to react with eight 1.5-g. batches of magnesium. On cooling in a freezer, considerable magnesium methoxide crystallizes; residual solution is decanted and replaced by dry methanol.

For preparation of a solution of magnesium methoxide, 1.2 l. of dry methanol (distilled from magnesium methoxide) is cooled with ice in a 2-l. flask fitted with a drying tube and four 3-g. batches of magnesium are allowed to react completely.

Condensation catalyst. Muxfeldt et al.[2] found this reagent a suitable basic catalyst for the condensation of benzaldehyde (1) with 2,2-dimethoxy-3-butanone (2) to produce the intermediates (3) and (4) and finally 4-phenylcyclopentane-1,2-dione (5).

It is postulated that the ionic magnesium complex (4) holds the open-chain progenitor (3) in the proper conformation for intramolecular Michael condensation. Trials with other basic catalysts were unsuccessful. The product of condensation of the ketal (2) with dimethyl oxalate similarly could be cyclized to give 2,5-dihydroxy-1,4-benzoquinone (7).

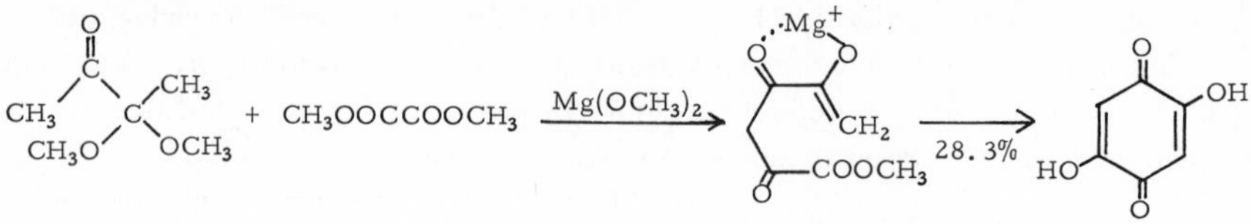

(2)   (6)   (7)

The natural pyrone yangonin (10) was synthesized by condensation of triacetic acid lactone methyl ether (8) with *p*-methoxybenzaldehyde (9) in the presence of magnesium methoxide (prepared from 200 mg. magnesium and 10 ml. CH_3OH).[3]

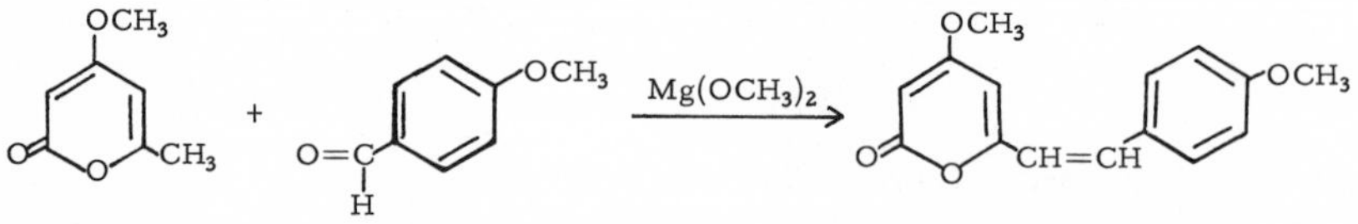

(8) 580 mg.   (9)   (10) 160 mg.

[1]H. Muxfeldt, private communication
[2]H. Muxfeldt, M. Weigele, and V. Van Rheenen, *J. Org.*, **30**, 3573 (1965)
[3]J. B. Bu'Lock and H. G. Smith, *J. Chem. Soc.*, 502 (1960); see also L. J. Douglas and T. Money, *Tetrahedron*, **23**, 3545 (1967). The latter paper states that condensation of triacetic acid lactone with benzaldehyde in the presence of piperidine and acetic acid leads to a product identified as (11)

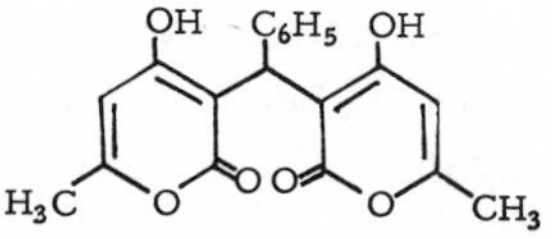

(11)

Magnesium methyl carbonate [**1**, 631–633, ref. 7]. The definitive paper: H. L. Finkbeiner, *J. Org.*, **30**, 3414 (1965).

Magnesium oxide [**1**, 633–634, before references].

The combination of magnesium oxide in DMF was used for dehydrobromination of the bromo ketone (2) to give (3).[5]

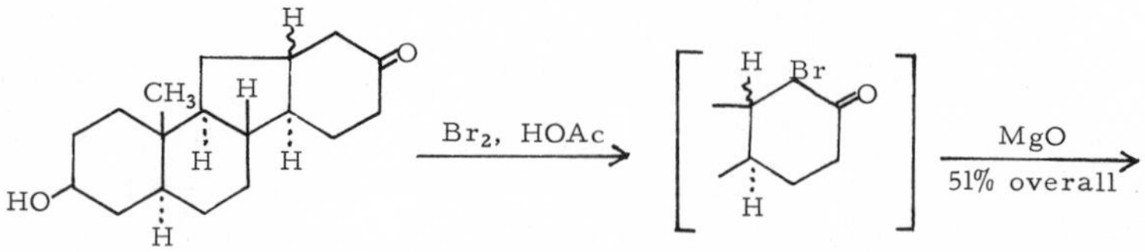

(1)   (2)

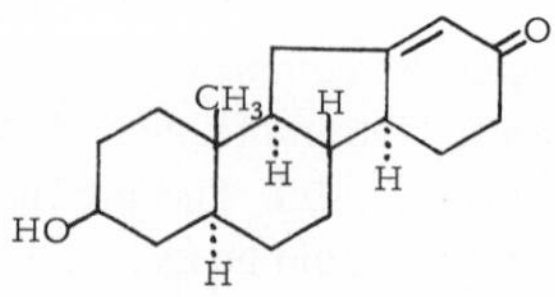

(3)

[5]J. P. Kutney, J. Cable, W. A. F. Gladstone, H. W. Hanssen, E. J. Torupka, and W. D. C. Warnock, *Am. Soc.*, **90**, 5332 (1968)

Malonic dialdehyde tetraethyl acetal, $\begin{array}{c} C_2H_5O \\ C_2H_5O \end{array}$ CHCH$_2$CH $\begin{array}{c} OC_2H_5 \\ OC_2H_5 \end{array}$ [1, 636,

before **Manganese dioxide**]. Mol. wt. 164.20, $n^{20°}D$ 1.4081. Supplier: A.

Use.[1] The reagent (1) is split by hydrochloric acid to give malondialdehyde (2), which condenses specifically with arginyl residues (3) of proteins to give δ-N-(2-

pyrimidinyl)-L-ornithine (4); because of the strong acid required, some side reactions occur. The peptide bond adjacent to the modified arginyl residue is resistant to trypsin hydrolysis. The reagent is thus of use in the sequence analysis of proteins.

[1]T. P. King, *Biochemistry*, **5**, 3454 (1966)

Manganese dioxide, (b) active [1, 637–643]. Additional supplier: Winthrop Laboratories, 90 Park Ave., New York, N.Y. 10016.

Preparation [1, 637–638, after citation of ref. 7]. Belew and Tek-Ling[7a] have prepared an active form of manganese dioxide by ozonization of an aqueous solution of manganese (II) nitrate containing perchloric acid. This material oxidizes benzyl alcohol to benzaldehyde in 82% yield.

Goldman[7b] has prepared precipitated manganese dioxide by the Attenburrow procedure as modified by Pratt and Suskind[7c]; this material can be stored in a closed bottle and is activated, as needed, by azeotropic distillation of the excess water with benzene for about one hour. The activated reagent can be stored under benzene for more than one year.

Oxidation of nitrogen compounds [bottom of 1, 640]. Bhatnagar and George[20a] found that chalcone phenylhydrazones are oxidized to pyrazoles in good yield by active manganese dioxide prepared according to Pratt and McGovern.[19] Benzalacetophenone hydrazone (1), for example, gave 1,3,5-triphenylpyrazole (4) in 73% yield. Radical intermediates (2) and (3) are suggested. *o*-Phenylenediamine and *p*-phenylenediamine are oxidized by manganese dioxide to the corresponding diaminoazo compounds in about 25% yield.[20b]

[**1**, 642, after citation of ref. 29]: The reagent converts imidazolines into imidazoles in high yield. Thus (1) is converted into (2) in 72% yield by stirring a chloroform solution of (1) with a fourfold excess of finely powdered Attenburrow reagent.[29a]

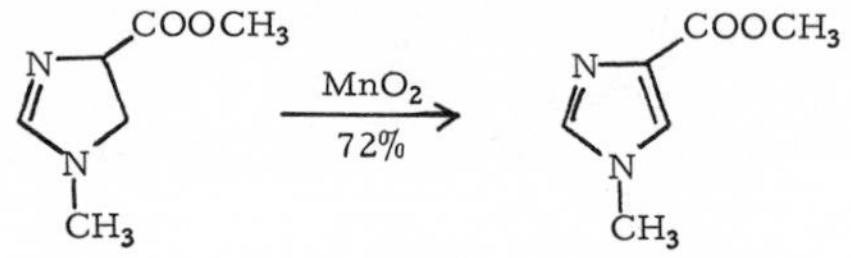

(1)   (2)

Review.[32]

[**1**, 642, before references]: Oxidative ring closure of reticuline (1) to the morphinane derivative isosalutaridine (2) has been effected with active MnO_2 utilizing a heterogeneous dilution principle in order to keep the concentration of (1) on the MnO_2 surface low and the distance between molecules large.[33] The MnO_2 was mixed

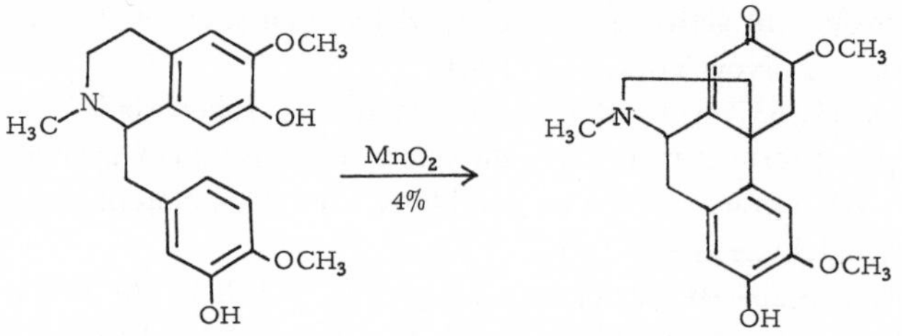

(1)   (2)

with three times its weight of silica gel (E. Merck, particle size <0.08 mm.). The reaction is of interest because it appears to be involved in the biosynthesis of morphine alkaloids.[34]

Oxidative rearrangements. Hall and Story,[35] using active MnO_2 prepared by the

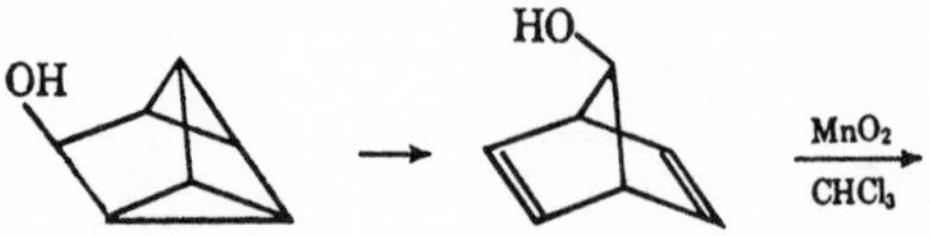

1   2

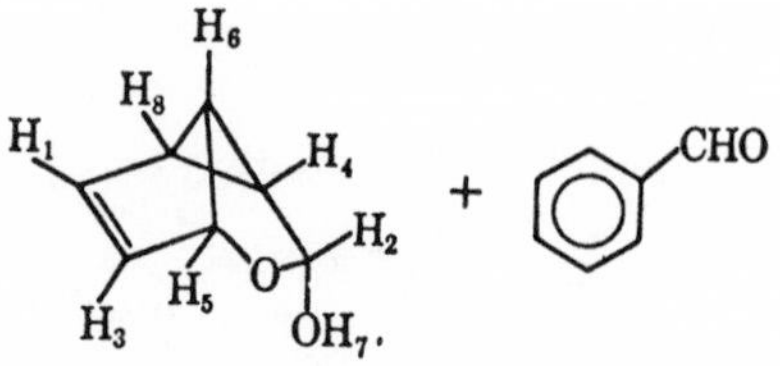

3

method of Mancera, Rosenkranz, and Sondheimer [Ref. 5: *J. Chem. Soc.*, 2189 (1953)], found that quadricyclanol (1) in chloroform solution is rapidly rearranged by the metal oxide into norbornadienol (2), which is then oxidized at 45° to the tricyclic oxide (3) and benzaldehyde. Yields are variable (5–70%); other forms of MnO_2 were ineffective. In formula 3 the protons are numbered (H_1 to H_8) to facilitate analysis of the NMR spectrum, which was consistent only with structure 3. Hall and Story suggest a mechanism in which the first step is formation of a manganese cation (2a), followed by isomerization to the cyclic structure (3).

A rearrangement may be involved in the oxidation of the inositol derivative (4) to the hemiacetal lactone (5),[36] a key step in the conversion of cyclitols to hexoses.

However, the preferred route is oxidation of (4) by the Pfitzner-Moffatt reagent followed by Baeyer-Villiger reaction.

Oxidation to fuchsones.[37] Attenburrow MnO$_2$ was used for oxidation of 3,5-disubstituted-4-hydroxytriphenylmethanes to 3,5-disubstituted fuchsones in high yield. Nickel peroxide and lead dioxide were equally satisfactory. The 3,5-disubstitution appears to be a requisite for smooth oxidation.

Oxidation of allylic or benzylic alcohols. Manganese dioxide prepared by ozonization of manganese (II) nitrate is an effective agent for oxidation of allylic and benzylic alcohols.[38]

Weedon *et al.*[39] examined the oxidation of geraniol and nerol with seven samples of active MnO$_2$ and obtained the highest yields (80%) with a commercial sample prepared according to Ball, Goodwin, and Morton (ref. 1, **1**, 642), dried over P$_2$O$_5$ and used in methylene chloride suspension, and with alkaline MnO$_2$ prepared according

Geraniol   Nerol

to Attenburrow *et al.*[4] and used in petroleum ether. Yields with acidic MnO$_2$ (Mancera *et al.*[5]) were appreciably lower.

Wiley and Irick[40] prepared active MnO$_2$ by addition of saturated aqueous potassium permanganate to a hot solution of manganese sulfate monohydrate in 300 ml. of water until the purple color just persisted. The precipitated MnO$_2$ was collected and dried, and used in the oxidation of pyridoxine hydrochloride to pyridoxal hydrochloride.

(6) Pyridoxine hydrochloride   (7) Pyridoxal hydrochloride

MnO$_2$ in dimethyl sulfoxide at 100° was the best reagent found for oxidation of 5-hydroxyuracil (8) to uracil-5-aldehyde (9). The ratio of substrate to reagent was 1 : 5. The yield dropped to 40–60% with water as the medium.[41] No difference was noted between Attenburrow, Wiley and Irick, or commercial reagent.

(8) 5-Hydroxyuracil   (9) Uracil-5-aldehyde

Corey *et al.*[42] were interested in developing a simple procedure for oxidation of allylic alcohols to carboxylic acids without *cis-trans* isomerization of the α,β-unsaturated linkage. They reasoned that in the presence of hydrogen cyanide and cyanide ion the α,β-unsaturated aldehyde would be converted into the cyanohydrin which would be oxidized by MnO_2 to an acyl cyanide, which in the presence of an alcohol would be converted into an ester:

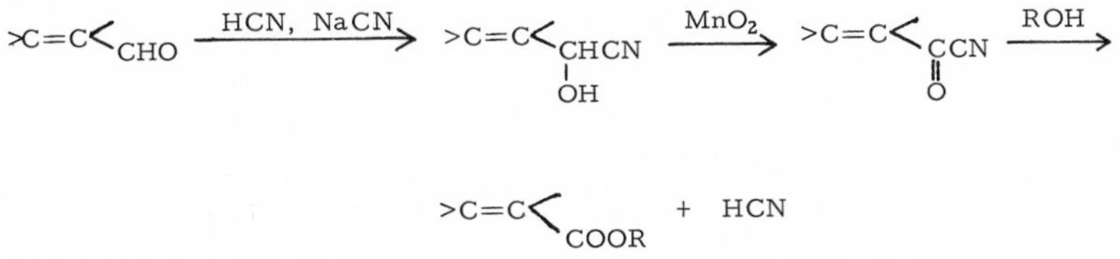

The reaction as applied to geraniol is typical. The alcohol (50 mg.) was oxidized by active MnO_2 in hexane to geranial, isolated by filtration and removal of solvent (48 mg.). The aldehyde was then stirred with sodium cyanide, acetic acid (to generate HCN), methanol, and MnO_2 for 12 hrs. at 20–25°. The methanol was removed, and methyl geranate (51 mg.) isolated by ether extraction. The yields in general are high and no isomerization occurs.

Nonconjugated aldehydes are not converted into esters by this procedure.

The method was developed particularly for one step in the synthesis of the C_{18}-Cecropia juvenile hormone.[43] Thus the alcohol (10) was transformed into the methyl ester (11) in 70% yield.

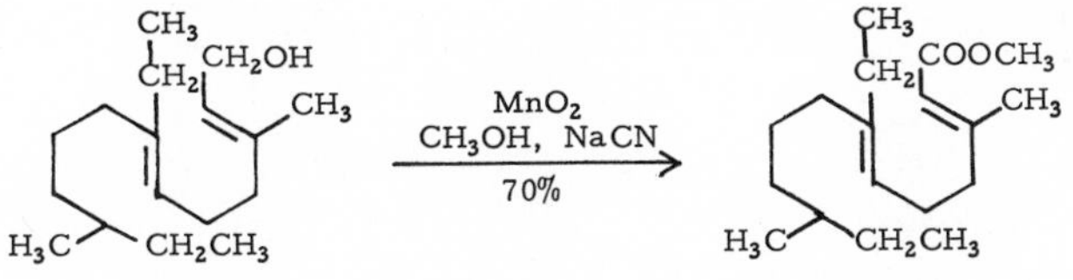

(10)   (11)

For oxidation of aldehydes to acids (rather than esters), *see* **Silver (II) oxide**, this volume.

Oxidation of alkamines. Observations of the Henbest group[24,25] have been extended.[44-46] For example:[46]

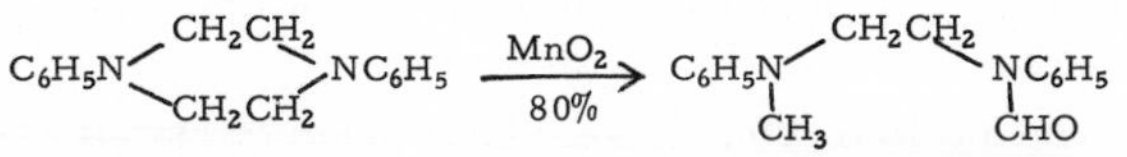

Oxidation of dihydrobenzenes. Ethyl 2,4-pentadienoate (2) reacts with Δ^1-pyrrolidinocyclohexene (1) to give the 1:1 adduct of 1,4-cycloaddition (3), which undergoes reverse Michael addition and tautomerism to give (4). This is conveniently oxidized to the aromatic system (5) by Attenburrow manganese dioxide.[47]

(1)   (2)   (3)

(4)   (5)

Degradative oxidation. In studying the oxidation of dipotassium rhodizonate (1) to croconic acid trihydrate (2) with loss of carbon dioxide, Burgstahler and Bark-hurst[48] found commercial manganese dioxide to be unsatisfactory but found that suitable material can be prepared by heating manganese carbonate at 295–310° for 12–18 hrs. followed by treatment with 2 M nitric acid for 30 min. to remove residual carbonate and then washing with water and drying at 150–160° for 18–24 hrs.[49] Then 56 g. (0.65 mole) of this active dioxide and 24.6 g. (0.10 mole) of dipotassium rhodi-zonate (Aldrich, Eastman) are added with stirring to a solution of 40 g. (0.10 mole) of

(1)   (2)

sodium hydroxide in 1 l. of water and the mixture is stirred at 20–25° for 10 min. and then refluxed for 1 hr. While still hot, it is filtered by suction and the brown residue (mostly manganese dioxide) is washed with 800 ml. of hot water. The combined fil-trate and washings are neutralized with 210 ml. of concd. hydrochloric acid and then mixed with a hot solution of 50 g. (0.2 mole) of barium chloride dihydrate in 150 ml. of water. The resulting solution is heated to 90° and allowed to cool slowly to room temperature and the bright yellow precipitate of barium croconate monohydrate is collected by suction filtration, washed with 100 ml. of water, and dried in air. The yield is 20–25 g. (68–85%).

For liberation of the free acid, 15.0 g. (0.051 mole) of barium croconate mono-hydrate is added, with stirring, to 50 ml. of an aqueous solution of 3.0 ml. (0.055 mole) of concd. sulfuric acid heated to 55°. Stirring is continued for 1 hr. and the bar-ium sulfate is removed by filtration, washed with 10 ml. of hot water, and discarded. The filtrate and washings are evaporated to dryness in a rotary evaporator on the steam bath until crystallization occurs. The deep yellow crystals are filtered by suction from the cooled solution and washed with 5 ml. of absolute ethanol. Further concentration of the filtrate and washings gives a total of 5.8–8.5 g. (68–87%) of croconic acid trihydrate, dec. about 155°.

[7a]J. S. Belew and C. Tek-Ling, *Chem. Ind.*, 1958 (1967)

[7b]I. M. Goldman, *J. Org.*, **34**, 1979 (1969)

[7c]E. F. Pratt and S. P. Suskind, *ibid.*, **28**, 638 (1963)

[20a]I. Bhatnagar and M. V. George, *Tetrahedron*, **24**, 1293 (1968)

[20b]*Idem, J. Org.*, **33**, 2407 (1968)

[29a]P. K. Martin, H. R. Matthews, H. Rapoport, and G. Thyagarajan, *J. Org.*, **33**, 3758 (1968)

[32]R. M. Evans, *Quart. Rev.*, **13**, 61 (1959)

[33]B. Frank, Z. Dunkelmann, and H. J. Lubs, *Angew. Chem., internat. Ed.*, **6**, 1075 (1967)

[34]D. H. R. Barton, G. W. Kirby, W. Steglich, G. M. Thomas, A. R. Battersby, T. A. Dobson, and H. Ramuz, *J. Chem. Soc.*, 2423 (1965)

[35]T. K. Hall and P. R. Story, *Am. Soc.*, **89**, 6759 (1967)

[36]H. Fukami, H.-S. Koh, T. Sakata, and M. Nakajima, *Tetrahedron Letters*, 4771 (1967)

[37]H.-D. Becker, *J. Org.*, **32**, 2943 (1967)

[38]J. S. Belew and C. Tek-Ling, *Chem. Ind.*, 1958 (1967)

[39]J. W. K. Burrell, R. F. Garwood, L. M. Jackman, E. Oskay, and B. C. L. Weedon, *J. Chem. Soc.*, 2144 (1966)

[40]R. H. Wiley and G. Irick, *J. Med. Chem.*, **5**, 49 (1962)

[41]R. Brossmer and D. Ziegler, *Tetrahedron Letters*, 5253 (1966)

[42]E. J. Corey, N. W. Gilman, B. E. Ganem, *Am. Soc.*, **90**, 5616 (1968)

[43]E. J. Corey, J. A. Katzenellenbogen, N. W. Gilman, S. A. Roman, and B. W. Erickson, *ibid.*, **90**, 5618 (1968)

[44]H. B. Henbest and R. Patton, *J. Chem. Soc.*, 3557 (1960)

[45]E. F. Curragh, H. B. Henbest, and A. Thomas, *J. Chem. Soc.*, 3559 (1960)

[46]H. B. Henbest and M. J. W. Stratford (replaces preliminary paper[25]), *J. Chem. Soc.*, (C), 995 (1966)

[47]S. Danishefsky and R. Cunningham, *J. Org.*, **30**, 3676 (1965)

[48]A. W. Burgstahler and R. C. Barkhurst, Univ. of Kansas, private communication

[49]Procedure of A. S. Fatiadi, H. S. Isbell, and W. F. Sager, *J. Res. Nat. Bur. Std.*, **67A**, 153 (1963)

Manganic acetate, $Mn(OAc)_3 \cdot 2H_2O$ [**1**, 643, before β-**Mercaptoethanol**]. Mol. wt., 268.09.

Preparation.[1] The reagent is prepared by heating a mixture of 500 ml. of acetic and 48 g. of manganese(ous) acetate, $Mn(OAc)_2 \cdot 4H_2O$ (Fisher) to reflux for 20 min., then slowly adding 8.0 g. of $KMnO_4$. After refluxing for an additional 30 min., the mixture is cooled to room temperature and 85 ml. of water is added. After 16 hrs. the manganese (III) acetate is filtered off, washed with acetic acid, and air dried. The most reactive form is obtained by adding acetic anhydride equivalent to the water of hydration of $Mn(OAc)_2 \cdot 4H_2O$.

Oxidation of olefins. Two groups[1,2] simultaneously reported that, in the presence of acetic acid, the reagent oxidizes olefins to γ-lactones. Acetic anhydride enhances the rate of reaction and also improves the yield. Recommended conditions employ

(1)   (2)

0.1 mole of olefin, 50 ml. of acetic acid, 0.05 mole of $Mn(OAc)_3 \cdot 2H_2O$, and a reflux period of 30–60 min. An example is the oxidation of α-methylstyrene (1) to γ-methyl-γ-phenyl butyrolactone (2).[1]

Other examples:[2]

$$C_6H_5CH{=}CHC_6H_5 \xrightarrow{16\%}$$

Oxidation of aromatic hydrocarbons. Oxidation of toluene by manganic acetate in refluxing acetic acid gives a tolylacetic acid, isomeric methylbenzyl acetates (mainly *ortho*), and benzyl acetate. The reaction involves two competing mechanisms, the more important being a free-radical pathway involving $\cdot CH_2COOH$ generated by thermolysis of manganic acetate.

[1] J. B. Bush, Jr., and H. Finkbeiner, *Am. Soc.*, **90**, 5903 (1968)
[2] E. I. Heiba, R. M. Dessau, and W. J. Koehl, Jr., *ibid.*, **90**, 5905 (1968)
[3] *Idem, ibid.*, **91**, 138 (1969)

Manganic tris(acetylacetonate) (MTA), $Mn(C_5H_7O_2)_3$ [**1**, 643, before β-**Mercaptoethanol**]. Mol. wt. 352.25. Supplier: Alfa Inorganics.

Oxidative coupling of phenols.[1] Dewar found this reagent the most useful of various manganic derivatives for oxidative coupling of phenols. For example, β-naphthol (1) is converted into 2,2'-dehydroxy-1,1'-binaphthyl (2) in 69% yield (acetonitrile or carbon disulfide, 5 hrs.). The reagent is soluble in organic solvents,

and does not oxidize the biphenol further to a quinone as potassium ferricyanide does. However, oxygen must be excluded. The reaction evidently involves oxidation of the phenol by electron transfer to give an aryloxy radical which then dimerizes.

[1] M. J. S. Dewar and T. Nakaya, *Am. Soc.*, **90**, 7134 (1968)

Mercuric acetate [**1**, 644–652].

Addition to olefins [**1**, 651, after citation of ref. 36]. Oxymercuration has been reviewed by Kitching.[36a]

Oxidative cyclizations [1, 652, before references] have been realized by Julia, Colomer, and Julia[38] by treatment of certain phenyl-substituted olefins with mercuric acetate. 4-Phenyl-1-butene (1) on treatment with mercuric acetate in acetic acid, followed by treatment with perchloric acid, gives a mixture from which the three products formulated were isolated in the low yields indicated (some metallic mercury is deposited).

Markownikov hydration of olefins. H. C. Brown and Geoghegan[39] report that Markownikov hydration of olefins can be achieved very simply by oxymercuration with mercuric acetate followed by demercuration with sodium borohydride.

For example, a mixture of 10.0 mmoles of mercuric acetate, 10 ml. of water, and 10 ml. of tetrahydrofurane is stirred mechanically in a small flask, 10 mmoles of 1-hexene is added and the mixture is stirred for 10 min. at 25° to complete the oxymercuration stage. Then 10 ml. of 3 M sodium hydroxide is added, followed by 10 ml. of a solution of 0.5 M sodium borohydride in 3 M sodium hydroxide. Reduction of the oxymercurial is almost instantaneous. The mercury is allowed to settle, and sodium chloride is added to saturate the water layer. The upper layer of THF is separated and contains 2-hexanol in essentially quantitative yield.

The two-step reaction is useful for the hydration of cyclic and bicyclic olefins because it gives predominantly alcohols epimeric with those obtained by addition of a Grignard reagent to the corresponding ketones.[40] Therefore hydration of the intermediate mercurial occurs predominantly from the less hindered side.

Compare

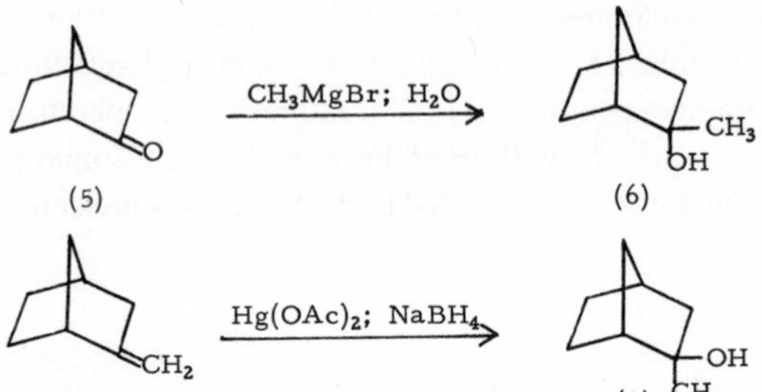
CH3MgBr; H2O
CH3
OH
Hg(OAc)2; NaBH4
CH2
OH
CH3

(5) (6) (7) (8)

A further advantage is that the reaction appears to be free from rearrangements involving carbonium ion intermediates.[41] Thus norbornene (9) is converted in close to quantitative yield into *exo*-norborneol (10) of >99.8% purity.

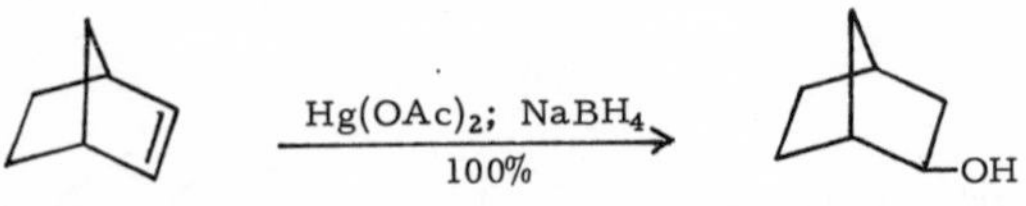
Hg(OAc)2; NaBH4
100%
OH

(9) (10)

The reaction with *syn*- and *anti*-substituted norbornenes is stereoselective. Thus *syn*-hydroxynorbornene (11) gives *exo,syn*-2,7-dihydroxynorbornane (12) in 83% yield and *anti*-hydroxynorbornene (13) gives *exo,anti*-2,7-dihydroxynorbornane (14) in 96% yield.[42]

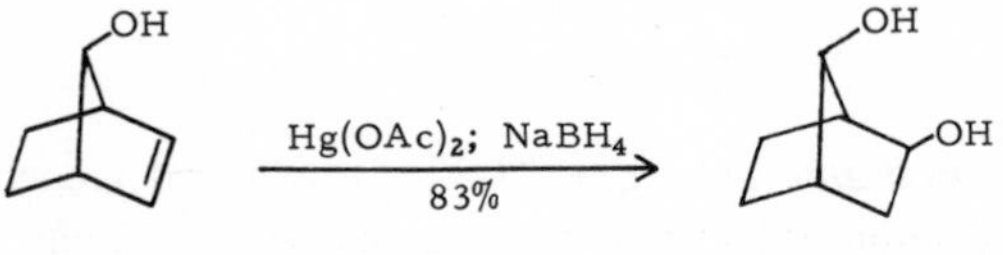
OH
Hg(OAc)2; NaBH4
83%
OH
OH

(11) (12)

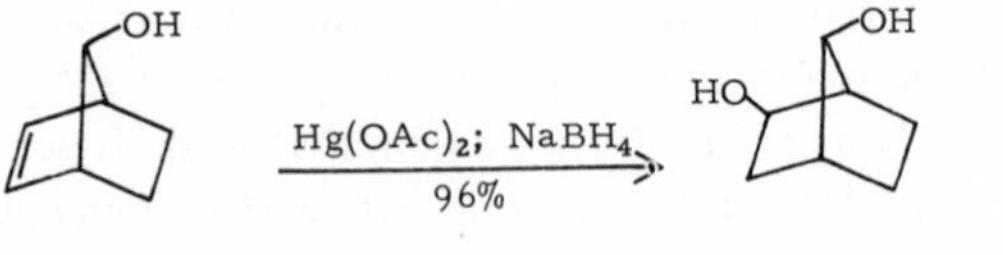
OH
Hg(OAc)2; NaBH4
96%
HO
OH

(13) (14)

A New Zealand group[43] used the Brown reaction to convert α-terpineol (15) into 1,8-cineol (16 = 16a) in about 90% yield. This transformation had been accomplished

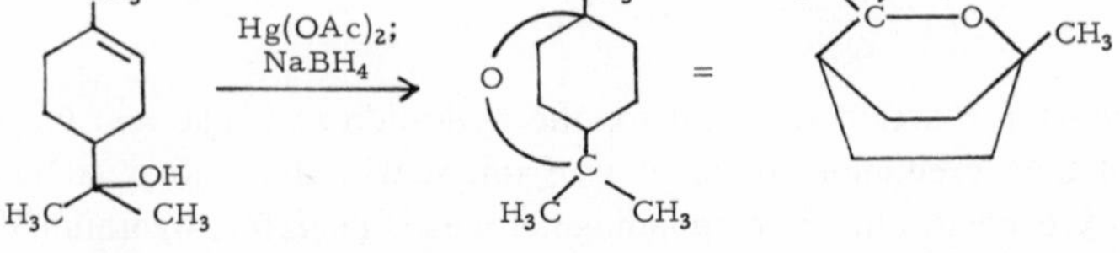
CH3
Hg(OAc)2;
NaBH4
OH
H3C
CH3
CH3
O
C
H3C
CH3
=
H3C
CH3
C
O
CH3

(15) (16) (16a)

originally with sulfuric acid in less than 5% yield, later improved to 19% by reaction with mercuric acetate and subsequent demercuration with hydrazine.

cis → trans Isomerization. The bicyclic diterpenoid alcohol abienol (1) is a component of many *abies* oleoresins, and the structure was uncertain only with regard to the configuration of the Δ^{12}-double bond, although comparison of the NMR spectrum with that of the *cis*- and *trans*-communic acids and of α- or β-ocimenes favored

(1) cis-Abienol   (2) trans-Abienol

the *cis* assignment. Mills[44] noted by chance that the alcohol when treated in acetic acid with mercuric acetate followed by zinc dust gave a compound of somewhat longer retention time on g.l.c. characterized as *trans*-abienol, m.p. 51–52.5°, αD +25°, λ^{EtOH} 232 mμ (22,500). Discovery of the *trans* isomer confirmed the *cis* assignment to the natural alcohol.

Acetoacetylation. Mercuric salts, particularly mercuric acetate, are effective catalysts for the acetoacetylation of weakly nucleophilic compounds (e.g., urea, diphenylamine, *p*-nitroaniline, phenol) with diketene at room temperature.[45]

[36a]W. Kitching, *Organometallic Chem. Rev.*, **3** A, 61 (1968)

[38]M. Julia, E. Colomer, and S. Julia, *Bull. soc.*, 2397 (1966)

[39]H. C. Brown and P. Geoghegan, Jr., *Am. Soc.*, **89**, 1522 (1967)

[40]H. C. Brown and W. J. Hammar, *ibid.*, **89**, 1524 (1967)

[41]H. C. Brown, J. H. Kawakami, and S. Ikegami, *ibid.*, **89**, 1525 (1967)

[42]W. C. Baird, Jr., and M. Buza, *J. Org.*, **33**, 4105 (1968)

[43]J. M. Coxon, M. P. Hartshorn, J. W. Mitchell and K. E. Richards, *Chem. Ind.*, 652 (1968)

[44]J. S. Mills, *J. Chem. Soc.*, (C), 2514 (1967)

[45]S. I. Zavialov, V. I. Gunar, I. A. Mikhailopulo, and L. F. Ovechkina, *Tetrahedron*, **22**, 2003 (1966)

Mercuric oxide, yellow [**1**, 655–658, before references].

Oxidation of the 1,1-disubstituted hydrazine, 3-amino-2-oxazolidinone (1), with bromine water, with potassium iodate–HNO_3, or with potassium bromate in 6 N HCl affords a compound melting at 299° and now recognized as the *trans*-3,3'-azobis(2-oxazolidinone) of formula (2). Forgione *et al.*[15] explored oxidation with yellow mercuric oxide in dioxane or THF at 25° and obtained an isomeric product, m.p. 171°, in 50% yield along with a little of the *trans* isomer (2). Infrared, UV,

Raman, and NMR spectra as well as mass spectrometric fragmentation behavior were all as expected. Convincing evidence of the *cis-trans* nature of the two compounds was obtained by the UV light catalyzed transformation of (3) to (2) in the crystal state. The isomerization proceeded to about 40% conversion in 8 hrs. It is suggested that the mercuric oxide, which is polymeric, is able to form a highly ordered stereospecific intermediate chelate.

[15]P. S. Forgione, G. S. Sprague, and H. J. Troffkin, *Am. Soc.*, **88**, 1079 (1966)

Mercurous trifluoroacetate, $Hg_2(OCOCF_3)_2$ [1, 660, before **Mercury p-toluenesulfonamide**]. Mol. wt. 627.26.

The reagent is prepared by the reaction of mercurous carbonate with trifluoroacetic acid (used in excess) or of sodium trifluoroacetate with mercurous nitrate (67.7% yield).[1]

Synthesis of phenylacetylenes.[2] The salt oxidizes the hydrazones of substituted benzyl ketones to phenylacetylenes in ether or dioxane at 40–50°. Oxygenated solvents are necessary since they form complexes with trifluoroacetic acid, which would otherwise add to the acetylenes. Strictly anhydrous conditions are required.

$$C_6H_5CH_2\overset{\overset{\displaystyle NNH_2}{\|}}{C}-C_6H_5 \xrightarrow{2\,Hg_2(OCOCF_3)_2} C_6H_5-C\equiv C-C_6H_5 + 4[\,CF_3COOH\cdot(C_2H_5)_2O\,] + 4\,Hg + N_2$$

43%

[1]F. Swarts, *Bull. Soc. Chim. Belges*, **48**, 179 (1939)
[2]R. J. Theis and R. D. Dessy, *J. Org.*, **31**, 624 (1966)

Mesyl chloride [1, 662–664]. *Caution*: The reagent is a lachrymator and skin irritant.

For deoxygenation of a phenol by conversion into the mesylate or diethyl phosphate and reduction with sodium and ammonia, *see* **Diethyl phosphonate** (both volumes).

Reaction with methyl D-glycopyranosides[11] [1, 664, before references]. Mesyl chloride (2 equiv.) reacts with methyl α-D-glucopyranoside in DMF with selective replacement of the primary alcoholic group by chlorine to give a 6-chloro-6-desoxy-hexopyranoside. The 6-O-mesyl derivative is not an intermediate. In the case of methyl α-D-xylopyranoside (no primary hydroxyl group), 99% of unchanged glycoside was recovered from the reaction.

$$
\begin{bmatrix}
\text{CHOH} \\
\text{H}\overset{|}{\text{C}}\text{OH} \\
\text{HO}\overset{|}{\text{C}}\text{H} \\
\text{H}\overset{|}{\text{C}}\text{OH} \\
\text{H}\overset{|}{\text{C}}\text{---} \\
\text{CH}_2\text{OH}
\end{bmatrix}\text{O}
\quad\xrightarrow[\text{65}^0 \ \text{97\%}]{\text{CH}_3\text{SO}_2\text{Cl}-\text{DMF}}\quad
\begin{bmatrix}
\text{CHOH} \\
\text{H}\overset{|}{\text{C}}\text{OH} \\
\text{HO}\overset{|}{\text{C}}\text{H} \\
\text{H}\overset{|}{\text{C}}\text{OH} \\
\text{H}\overset{|}{\text{C}}\text{---} \\
\text{CH}_2\text{Cl}
\end{bmatrix}\text{O}
$$

[11]M. E. Evans, L. Long, Jr., F. W. Parrish, *J. Org.*, **33**, 1074 (1968)

N-Methanesulfinyl-*p*-toluidine, $CH_3SONHC_6H_4CH_3$-*p* [1, 666, before **Methanesulfonic acid**]. Mol. wt. 169.25, m.p. 115–116°.

Prepared[1] from *p*-toluidine and methinesulfinyl chloride.[2]

Olefin synthesis. On treatment with 2 equiv. of *n*-butyllithium, the reagent forms the dilithio derivative (2) which reacts with a ketone, for example benzophenone, to

$$
\underset{\text{(1)}}{CH_3SONHC_6H_4CH_3\text{-}\underline{p}} \ + \ 2\,\underline{n}\text{-BuLi} \xrightarrow[\text{THF}]{-78^0} \underset{\text{(2)}}{\overset{\text{Li}}{\underset{|}{LiCH_2SON}}C_6H_4CH_3\text{-}\underline{p}} \xrightarrow[97\%]{\begin{array}{l}1)\ (C_6H_5)_2CO\\2)\ H_2O\end{array}}
$$

$$
\underset{\text{(3)}}{\overset{C_6H_5}{\underset{C_6H_5}{>}}\overset{\text{OH}}{\underset{|}{C}}\text{-}CH_2SONHC_6H_4CH_3\text{-}\underline{p}} \xrightarrow[96\%]{\Delta} \underset{\text{(4)}}{\overset{C_6H_5}{\underset{C_6H_5}{>}}C=CH_2} \ + \ SO_2 \ + \ \underline{p}\text{-}CH_3C_6H_4NH_2
$$

give a β-hydroxysulfinamide (3). Heating this adduct to the melting point (137–139°) effects elimination of *p*-toluidine and sulfur dioxide to give 1,1-diphenylethylene in high yield.

The reaction of (2) with an ester affords, after hydrolysis, a methyl ketone in good yield. Thus the reaction with ethyl benzoate affords acetophenone:

$$
C_6H_5COOC_2H_5 \ + \ \underset{\overset{|}{\text{Li}}\ \overset{|}{\text{Li}}}{CH_2SONC_6H_4CH_3\text{-}\underline{p}} \xrightarrow[\text{2) H}_2\text{O}]{\text{1) THF (0}^0)} C_6H_5COCH_3
$$

The decomposition of β-hydroxylsulfinamides occurs stereospecifically by *cis* elimination.[3] Thus the *trans-β*-hydroxysulfinanilide (5) affords *trans*-cyclododecene

(6) in more than 95% yield. Further evidence is that *trans-2*-hydroxycyclohexylsulfinanilide (7) is thermally stable. In this case *cis* elimination would necessitate the formation of the extremely unstable *trans*-cyclohexene.

[1]E. J. Corey and T. Durst, *Am. Soc.*, **88**, 5656 (1966); *idem, ibid.*, **90**, 5548 (1968)
[2]The acid chloride was obtained according to I. B. Douglass, B. S. Farah, and E. G. Thomas, *J. Org.*, **26**, 1996 (1961)
[3]E. J. Corey and T. Durst, *Am. Soc.*, **90**, 5553 (1968)

Methanesulfonic acid [**1**, 666–667]. The reagent is no longer available from Standard Oil Co. of Indiana. Pennsalt Manufacturing Co. supplies 90% reagent and Fluka supplies > 99% reagent.

Protection of carboxamides and sulfonamides[4] [**1**, 667, before references]. The benzyl group is a convenient protective group for carboxamides and sulfonamides; it is easily removed by treatment with methanesulfonic acid, which proved to be superior to sulfuric acid.[4]

Cyclization reaction. The reagent, 90% acid provided by Pennsalt Manufacturing Co., was used to effect condensation of *o*-acetylbenzoic acid (1) with 1,2-dimethoxy-

naphthalene (2) to give 3-methyl-3-(3,4-dimethoxy-1-naphthyl)phthalide (3).[5] As cyclizing agent, methanesulfonic acid proved to be markedly superior to concentrated sulfuric acid as no oxidation or sulfonation of the dimethoxynaphthalene occurred.

[4]B. Loev, M. A. Haas, and F. Dowalo, *Chem. Ind.*, 973 (1968)
[5]M. S. Newman and C. C. Davis, *J. Org.*, **32**, 66 (1967)

Methoxyacetylene [**1**, 668, before references].

Edman and Simmons[5] found this method (ethoxyacetylene was used rather than methoxyacetylene) the most satisfactory for dehydration of norbornadiene-2,3-dicarboxylic acid (5). All other anhydride syntheses tried, including the DCC method, gave poor yields.

[5]J. R. Edman and H. E. Simmons, *J. Org.*, **33**, 3808 (1968)

4-Methoxy-5,6-dihydro-2H-pyrane (3) [**1**, 669, before **α-Methoxyethylenetriphenyl-phosphorane**]. Mol. wt. 114.14, b.p. 156–157°.

Preparation.[1] 4,4-Dimethoxytetrahydropyrane (2) is distilled with 0.1% of mesitylenesulfonic acid to form the enol methyl ether (3).

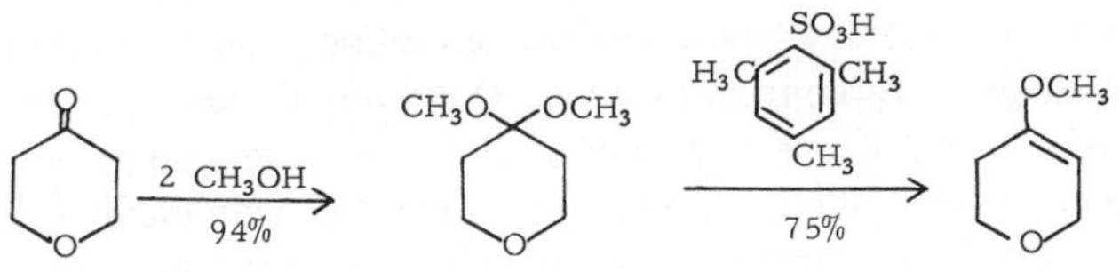

(1)   (2)   (3)

Protection of a hydroxyl group.[1] Like dihydropyrane, the reagent adds an alcohol under catalysis by *p*-toluenesulfonic acid to give a ketal (4), but it has the advantage that a new asymmetric center is not introduced. The ketal system is very labile to dilute acid. The reagent has been used for hydroxyl group protection in oligoribo-nucleotide synthesis.

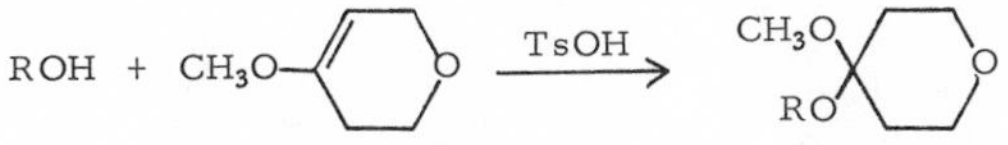

(4)

[1]C. B. Reese, R. Saffhill, and J. E. Sulston, *Am. Soc.*, **89**, 3366 (1967)

α-Methoxymethylenetriphenylphosphorane [**1**, 669–670, before reference].

In model studies of the reaction of 20-ketosteroids with the reagent, Pettit *et al.*[2] found it desirable to protect hydroxyl groups as the tetrahydropyranyl ethers and to carry out the reaction in refluxing diethylene glycol dimethyl ether (7 hrs.). Thus they obtained the vinyl ether (2) from the tetrahydropyranyl ether of pregnenolone in 83% yield. The vinyl ether was converted into the corresponding aldehyde by 70% perchloric acid–diethyl ether (the protective group is also hydrolyzed).

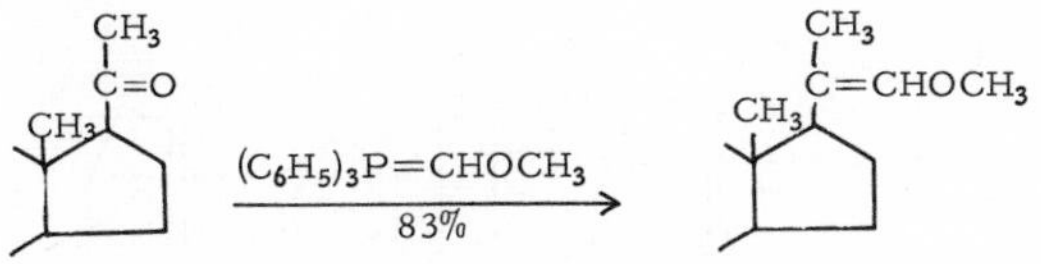

(1)   (2)

[2]G. R. Pettit, B. Green, G. L. Dunn, and P. Sunder-Plassmann, *J. Org.*, in press

Methylal [**1**, 671–672, ref. 3].

Definitive paper, U. Schöllkopf, H. Küppers, H.-J. Traenckner, and W. Pitteroff, *Ann.*, **704**, 120 (1967).

***d-* and *l-α*-Methylbenzylamine,** $C_6H_5CH(NH_2)CH_3$ [**1**, 673, before **Methyl borate**].

Mol. wt. 121.18, m.p. 184–185°, $\alpha_D \pm 39.5°$. **Preparation** of *dl*.[1] Supplier of *dl*: Eastman. **Resolution.**[2]

Use for resolution of cycloalkenes. *trans*-Cycloalkenes of intermediate size (C_8–C_{10}) should be capable of existing in enantiomeric forms because of the inability of the *trans* double bond to rotate with respect to the remainder of the molecule. But in the absence of salt-forming groups, resolution cannot be accomplished by the usual methods of forming derivatives. However, Cope *et al.*[3] found that the strong tendency of an alkene to complex with a platinum compound provides an effective method of resolution. The complex of ethylene with platinous chloride and (+) or (−)-α-methylbenzylamine exists in only one form since ethylene is symmetrical. But addition of the base to a solution of the platinum complex of *trans*-cyclooctene opens the way for formation of the diastereoisomeric complexes derived from the R- and S-forms of the base. Fractional crystallization at −20° (liquid at 25°) effected separation. Liberation of the (−)-hydrocarbon from the complex with potassium cyanide gave a product of $\alpha_D - 411°$.

Diastereoisomeric complexes

Similar resolutions are reported for *cis-trans*-1,5-cyclooctadiene (3,4),[4,5] *trans*-6, 7,10,11-tetrahydro-5H-benzocyclononene (5, 6),[6] and *trans*-bicyclo[8.2.2]tetradeca-5,10,12,13-tetraene (7).[7]

[1]A. W. Ingersoll, *Org. Syn., Coll. Vol.*, **2**, 503 (1943)

[2]*Idem, ibid.*, **2**, 506 (1943)

[3]A. C. Cope, C. R. Ganellin, H. W. Johnson, Jr., T. V. Van Auken, and H. J. S. Winkler, *Am. Soc.*, **85**, 3276 (1963)

[4]A. C. Cope, J. K. Hecht, H. W. Johnson, Jr., H. Keller, and H. J. S. Winkler, *ibid.*, **88**, 761 (1966)

[5]Construction of a model of this isomer cannot be accomplished without gross distortion.

[6]A. C. Cope and M. W. Fordice, *Am. Soc.*, **89**, 6187 (1967)

[7]A. C. Cope and B. A. Pawson, *ibid.*, **90**, 636 (1968)

Methyl dichlorofluoroacetate, $CCl_2FCO_2CH_3$ [1, 676, before **Methylene chloride**]. Mol. wt. 160.96, b.p. 114.5–115.5°/732 mm.

Preparation.[1] A mixture of 1 mole of dichlorofluoroacetic acid (supplier[1a]), 1.5 moles of methanol, and 50 ml. of concd. sulfuric acid was refluxed for 5 hrs., let stand at 25° for 17 hrs., and the ester was distilled from the reaction mixture, washed neutral, dried, and distilled from P_2O_5; yield 145 g. (90%).

Generation of chlorofluorocarbene. Experiments conducted by Moore and Levine[1] to demonstrate the formation of chlorofluorocarbene are less impressive than the results of a Japanese group.[2] Methanol (0.6 mole) was added gradually to a mixture of 0.75 mole of cyclohexene, 0.6 mole of sodium hydride, and 0.6 mole of methyl dichlorofluoroacetate at room temperature. The yield of 7-chloro-7-fluoro-norcarane of 60% is the highest ever reported in the literature.

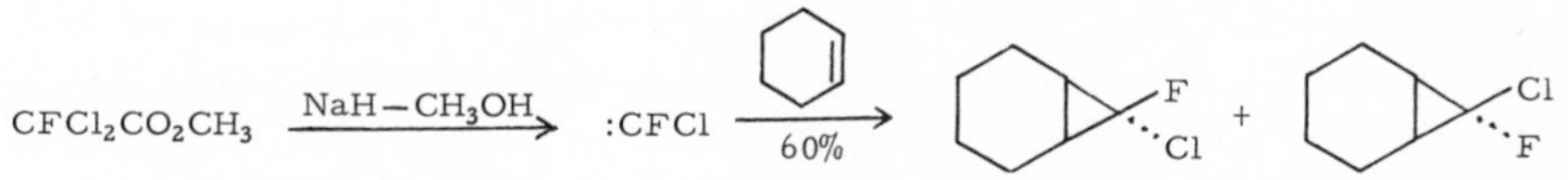

[1]R. A. Moore and R. Levine, *J. Org.*, **29**, 1883 (1964)

[1a]General Chemical Division, Allied Chemical Corp., Morristown, N.J. 07960

[2]T. Ando, H. Yamanaka, S. Terabe, A. Horike, and W. Funasaka, *Tetrahedron Letters*, 1123 (1967)

Methylene chloride [1, 676–677]. *Correction*:[1a] Carruthers[1] used an older numbering system rather than that of the more modern Ring Index system shown here. Actually he obtained 6-, 2-, and 3-acetylchrysene by acetylation of chrysene in nitrobenzene or carbon disulfide and the 6-isomer alone by use of methylene chloride.

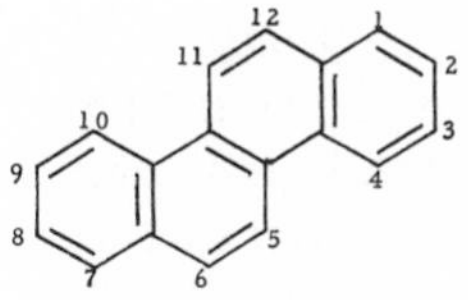

Chrysene

[1a]Correction called to our attention by Prof. R. G. Harvey, Univ. of Chicago

Methylenemagnesium bromide (iodide), $CH_2(MgX)_2$ [1, 678, before **Methylenetriphenylphosphorane**]. Prepared[1] by reaction of magnesium amalgam with one of the following halides: methylene bromide, CH_2Br_2, mol. wt. 173.86, b.p. 98.2°; methylene iodide, CH_2I_2, mol. wt. 267.85, b.p. 180°. Supplier of both: Eastman. Both reagents react with carbon dioxide to give malonic acid:

$$CH_2I_2 \;+\; 2\,Mg \;\longrightarrow\; CH_2(MgI)_2 \;\xrightarrow{CO_2;\; H^+}\; CH_2(CO_2H)_2$$

But the most interesting reaction is with carbonyl compounds, discovered by Cainelli *et al.*,[1] which affords an alternative to the Wittig reaction:

$$CH_2(MgI_2)_2 \; + \; O{=}C{<} \; \longrightarrow \; \underset{\underset{MgI}{|}}{CH_2{-}\overset{|}{C}{-}OMgI} \; \xrightarrow{H_2O} \; CH_2{=}C{<}$$

Yields are in the range 30–80%. In a typical procedure a solution of the ketone and methylene bromide (iodide) is added by drops to a stirred suspension of magnesium amalgam (argon). α,β-Unsaturated ketones react by either (or both) 1,2- and 1,4-addition. A hydroxyl group may be present if an additional mole of reagent is employed.

Note. Fidler *et al.*[2] had attempted to prepare methylenemagnesium bromide and iodide by reaction of the halides with magnesium but found the assumed products to have slight activity towards benzaldehyde. The later Italian workers achieved success by use of the evidently more reactive magnesium amalgam.

[1]G. Cainelli, F. Berlini, P. Grasselli, and G. Zubiani, *Tetrahedron Letters*, 5153 (1967)
[2]D. A. Fidler, J. R. Jones, S. L. Clark, and H. Stange, *Am. Soc.*, 77, 6634 (1955)

Methyl iodide [1, 682–685].

Methylation of carotenoid alcohols [1, 685]. Müller and Karrer[20] used Kuhn's conditions (CH_3I–DMSO–DMF–BaO) for methylation of hydroxycartenoids.[20a]

Methylation of carbohydrates. Anderson and Cree[21] used the combination methyl iodide–sodium hydride—DMSO and achieved complete methylation of mono-saccharides and acidic disaccharides in one step, but acidic polysaccharides were methylated only partially. Stacey *et al.*[22] used methyl bromide, sodium hydride, and DMF or N-methyl-2-pyrrolidone for methylation of glucopyranosides.

Desulfurization. Helmkamp and Pettitt[23] found that *cis*-2,3-dimethylthirane can be desulfurized by refluxing with methyl iodide in acetone; the products are *cis*-2-butene and trimethylsulfonium iodide. Later, Pettitt and Helmkamp[24] used the method to effect desulfurization of cyclooctene sulfide.

[20a]See also D. F. Schneider and B. C. L. Weedon, *J. Chem. Soc.*, (C), 1686 (1967)
[21]D. M. W. Anderson and G. M. Cree, *Carbohydrate Res.*, 2, 162 (1967)
[22]J. S. Brimacombe, B. D. Jones, M. Stacey, and J. J. Willard, *ibid.*, 2, 167 (1966)
[23]G. K. Helmkamp and D. J. Pettitt, *J. Org.*, 25, 1754 (1960)
[24]D. J. Pettitt and G. K. Helmkamp, *ibid.*, 28, 2932 (1963); *idem, ibid.*, 29, 2702 (1964)

Methyllithium [1, 686–689]. To suppliers add: Foote Mineral Co., Sch.

Allene synthesis [1, 686–688; p. 688 after line 4]. Sharma *et al.*,[7a] of the Indian

Institute of Technology, used the method of Untch *et al.*[7] to convert *cis,cis*-1,5-cyclo-nonadiene (1) into the ene-allene 1,2,6-cyclodecatriene (2) and reduced the allene group of (2) with sodium in liquid ammonia to afford a diene shown by gas chromatography to be a single substance. IR and NMR spectroscopy, and conversion to a hydrocarbon identified as cyclodecane, established that the substance is *cis,cis*-1,6-cyclodecadiene (3).

$$\text{(1)} \qquad \xrightarrow[\text{60\%}]{\text{CBr}_4 \; + \; \text{CH}_3\text{Li} \; (-65^0)} \qquad \text{(2)} \qquad \xrightarrow[\text{76\%}]{\text{Na}-\text{NH}_3} \qquad \text{(3)}$$

[**1**, 688, after citation of ref. 8]: A few cases have been reported in which a non-allenic product has been isolated. Thus the reaction of 7,7-dibromonorcarane (1) with methyllithium in diethyl ether gives, in 20% yield, a product (3) which evidently is derived by an insertion reaction of the intermediate carbene (2):[8a]

$$\text{(1)} \qquad \xrightarrow{\text{CH}_3\text{Li}} \qquad \text{(2)} \qquad \xrightarrow{(\text{C}_2\text{H}_5)_2\text{O}} \qquad \text{(3)}$$

Of greater interest is the reaction of (1) with methyllithium in ether at $-80°$ found by Moore[8a] to give a hydrocarbon fraction, 40% of which consists essentially of the highly strained hydrocarbon (4).

$$\text{(1)} \qquad \xrightarrow[\text{40\%}]{\text{CH}_3\text{Li}-\text{Ether} \; (-80^0)} \qquad \text{(4)}$$

Skattebøl[8b, 8c] investigated the action of methyllithium on the unsaturated *gem*-dibromocyclopropane with an unsaturated side chain (6) and isolated two products in about equal amounts. The allene (6) predominates when the reaction is carried

$$\text{(5)} \qquad \xrightarrow[-78^0]{\text{CH}_3\text{Li}} \qquad \text{(6)} \; 52\% \quad + \quad \text{(7)} \; 48\%$$

out at 0°. The interesting, strained tricyclic hydrocarbon (7) probably results from an intramolecular addition of a complexed carbenoid intermediate.

Δ^9-Octalin (10) is readily prepared according to R. A. Benkeser (1955) by reduction of naphthalene with lithium and ethylamine and isomerization of small amounts of the $\Delta^{1(9)}$-isomer. An Indian group[8d] converted this hydrocarbon into the

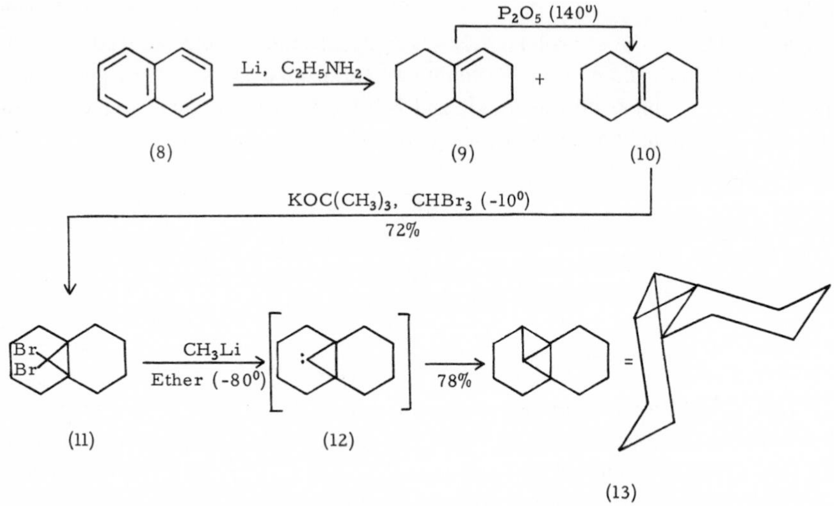

(8)   (9)   (10)

(11)   (12)   (13)

gem-dibromocyclopropane derivative (11) and investigated the reaction of this at a low temperature in ether with methyllithium. The highly strained polycyclic hydrocarbon (13) was formed in good yield, probably through the carbene (12).

Untch *et al.*[8e] have described a convenient one-step olefin-to-allene conversion which combines two steps in one as follows:

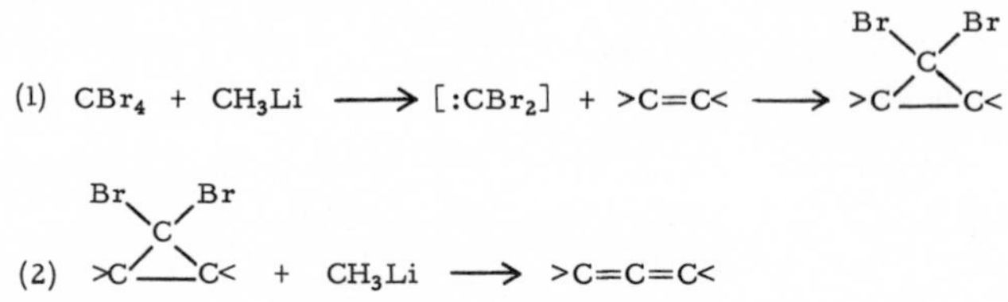

Thus 0.5 mole of 1,5-cyclooctadiene was treated in a nitrogen atmosphere at $-65°$ with carbon tetrabromide and then methyllithium in ether. After a suitable reaction period, work-up afforded $\Delta^{1,2,6}$-cyclononatriene in 70% yield (based upon CBr_4). Yields were markedly lower when *n*-butyllithium was used.

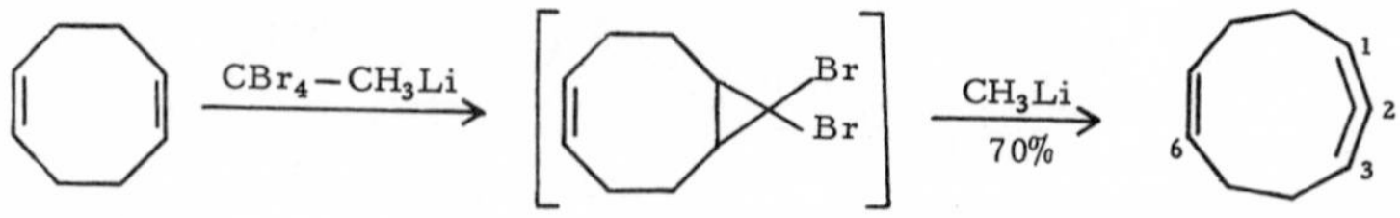

Moore and Ozretich[8f] synthesized $\Delta^{1,2,3}$-cyclodecatriene (3), a cyclic cumulene, by treating $\Delta^{1,2}$-cyclononadiene (1) with one equivalent of phenyl(tribromomethyl)-mercury in refluxing benzene, followed by removal of phenylmercuric bromide and the solvent, and obtained 10,10-dibromobicyclo[7.1.0]decene-1,2 (2), which on reaction with methyllithium afforded the cumulene (3).

Methyl ketones from acids [1, 688]. In the series of diterpene acids, Bory *et al.*[10a]

found that an axial methyl ester (1) reacts smoothly with methyllithium to give the corresponding methyl ketone (2) but that an equatorial ester (3) gives a mixture of the methyl ketone (4) and the alcohol (5).

Another example is a procedure by Bare and House[10b] for the synthesis of methyl cyclohexyl ketone from cyclohexanecarboxylic acid. A suspension of lithium hydride in 1,2-dimethoxyethane (freshly distilled from $LiAlH_4$) is stirred during dropwise addition of a solution of cyclohexanecarboxylic acid in 1,2-dimethoxy-ethane, and the mixture is refluxed with stirring to complete the formation of lithium

cyclohexanecarboxylate and evolution of hydrogen. The mixture is then cooled and an ethereal solution of methyllithium is added dropwise over a 30-min. period. Acidification, work-up, and distillation then afford methyl cyclohexyl ketone (4) as a colorless liquid. In another publication, House and Bare[10c] explain their postulation that the reaction involves the di-lithium derivative (3).

Enolate anions [1, 688, before references]. House and Trost[12] developed a method for the preparation of a specific enolate anion by treatment of an enol acetate with methyllithium.

Standardization.[13] Methyllithium can be standardized by reaction with dimethyl-phenylchlorosilane (Dow-Corning Co., Midland, Mich.) and subsequent gas chromatographic analysis.

$$CH_3Li \ + \ C_6H_5-\underset{\underset{CH_3}{|}}{\overset{\overset{CH_3}{|}}{Si}}-Cl \ \xrightarrow[-NaCl]{} \ C_6H_5-\underset{\underset{CH_3}{|}}{\overset{\overset{CH_3}{|}}{Si}}-CH_3$$

[7a]S. N. Sharma, R. K. Srivastava, and D. Devaprabhakara, *Canad. J. Chem.*, **46**, 84 (1968)
[8a]W. R. Moore, H. R. Ward, and R. F. Merritt, *Am. Soc.*, **83**, 2019 (1961)
[8b]L. Skattebøl, *Chem. Ind.*, 2146 (1962)
[8c]L. Skattebøl, *J. Org.*, **31**, 2789 (1966)
[8d]R. Vaidyanthaswamy and D. Devaprabhakara, *Chem. Ind.*, 515 (1968)
[8e]K. G. Untch, D. J. Martin, and N. T. Castelluci, *J. Org.*, **30**, 3572 (1965)
[8f]W. R. Moore and T. M. Ozretich, *Tetrahedron Letters*, 3205 (1967)
[10a]S. Bory, M. Fétizon, and J. Rens, *Bull. soc.*, 2011 (1966)
[10b]T. M. Bare and H. O. House, procedure submitted to *Org. Syn.*, 1968
[10c]H. O. House and T. M. Bare, *J. Org.*, **33**, 943 (1968)
[12]H. O. House and B. M. Trost, *J. Org.*, **30**, 2502 (1965)
[13]H. O. House and W. L. Respess, *J. Organometallic Chem.*, **4**, 95 (1965)

Methylmagnesium iodide [1, 689–690, before reference].

Israeli chemists[2] used methylmagnesium iodide (neat at 155–165°, 15 min.) for cleavage of the dimethyl ether (1) of *dl*-cannabidiol (2) in 80% yield. The demethylation reaction had been brought to their attention by G. Ourisson, in whose laboratory dimethoxyresorcinol derivatives had been demethylated in this way.

(1)   (2)

[2]R. Mechoulam and Y. Gaoni, *Am. Soc.*, **87**, 3273 (1965)

N-Methylmorpholine [1, 690].

In the mixed anhydride synthesis of peptides, N-methylmorpholine was found to give little or no racemization in cases where triethylamine, the commonly used base, caused extensive racemization.[1] Trimethylamine, a potent racemizer, can be used successfully if an excess is avoided. N-Methylmorpholine was used by Wieland[2] in the synthesis of antamanide, a cyclic decapeptide of *Amanita phalloides*, which counteracts the lethal action of *Amanita* toxins.

[1]G. W. Anderson, J. F. Zimmermann, and F. M. Callahan, *Am. Soc.*, **88**, 1338 (1966); *idem, ibid.*, **89**, 5012 (1967)
[2]Th. Wieland, *Angew. Chem., internat. Ed.*, **7**, 204 (1968)

Methyl *trans*-2,4-pentadienoate, $CH_2=CHCH=CHCOOCH_3$ [**1**, 693, before 2-Methylpentane-2,4-diol]. Mol. wt. 112.12, b.p. 55–57°/14 mm.

Preparation. The acid is obtained by the reaction of acrolein with malonic acid and then esterified.[1]

Synthesis of 1,3-cyclohexadienes.[2] Pyrrolidine enamines of cyclic ketones and simple aldehydes undergo 1,4-addition with the reagent; under the reaction conditions the intermediate amino esters lose the elements of pyrrolidine to give methyl 3,4-dihydrobenzoate derivatives. Morpholine enamines give substantially lower yields.

[1]E. Adlerová *et al., Czech. Commun.*, **25**, 226 (1860)
[2]G. A. Berchtold, J. Ciabattoni, and A. A. Tunick, *J. Org.*, **30**, 3679 (1965)

3-Methyl-1-phenyl-3-phospholene-1-oxide [1, 695].

Correction: Hunger et al.,[1a] on the basis of spectroscopy and ozone degradation, showed that the substance is actually the isomeric 2-phospholene oxide (3a). More recently Quin and Barket[1b] found that the original adduct of isoprene and phenylphosphorous dichloride (2a) also has the 2-phospholene system (NMR spectrum).

The rearrangement is dependent on the substituents of the phosphorous dihalide; methyl phosphorous dichloride gives the expected 3-phospholene system.

[1a]K. Hunger, U. Hasserodt, and F. Korte, *Tetrahedron*, **20**, 1593 (1964)
[1b]L. D. Quin and T. P. Barket, *Chem. Commun.*, 914 (1967)

Methylphosphonic acid bis(dimethylamide), $CH_3PO[N(CH_3)_2]_2$ [1, 696, before 1-methyl-2-pyrrolidone]. Mol. wt. 147.19, b.p. 138°.

Preparation by reaction of methylphosphonyl dichloride[1] with dimethylamine[2]:

$$CH_3Cl + PCl_3 \xrightarrow{AlCl_3;\ H_2O} CH_3POCl_2 \xrightarrow{2\ (CH_3)_2NH} CH_3PO[N(CH_3)_2]_2$$

Corey's phosphonamide route to olefins.[3] When treated with 1 equivalent of *n*-butyllithium under nitrogen the reagent forms the α-lithio derivative (2), which reacts with a ketone (or aldehyde) to give a β-hydroxyphosphonic acid bisamide (3) in yield of 90–98%. The adducts are uniformly nicely crystalline substances which, when refluxed in benzene or toluene in the presence of Woelm silica gel, undergo

$$CH_3PO[N(CH_3)_2]_2 \xrightarrow[-BuH]{n-BuLi} LiCH_2PO[N(CH_3)_2]_2 \xrightarrow[90-98\%]{R_2CO} R_2\overset{\overset{\displaystyle OH}{|}}{C}CH_2PO[N(CH_3)_2]_2$$

$$\text{(1)} \qquad\qquad\qquad\qquad \text{(2)} \qquad\qquad\qquad\qquad \text{(3)}$$

$$\downarrow 53-93\%$$

$$R_2C{=}CH_2 + [(CH_3)_2N]_2POOH$$

$$\text{(4)}$$

elimination to form olefins (4). The method seems to be general. Thus ethylphosphonic acid bis(dimethylamide) and isopropylphosphonic acid bis(dimethylamide) have been used successfully. In addition the lithio derivatives can be alkylated with alkyl iodides or bromides which are not excessively prone to elimination:

$$\underset{\underset{\displaystyle Li}{|}}{\overset{\overset{\displaystyle H\quad O}{|\quad\ \parallel}}{H{-}C}{-}PN(CH_3)_2} \xrightarrow[\text{3) } \overline{C}_6H_5COC_6H_5]{\begin{array}{l}\text{1) } CH_3I\\ \text{2) } n{-}BuLi\end{array}} \underset{C_6H_5}{\overset{C_6H_5}{>}}\underset{\underset{\displaystyle H}{|}}{\overset{\overset{\displaystyle OH\ \ CH_3\ \ O}{|\quad\ |\quad\ \parallel}}{C{-}C{-}}}PN(CH_3)_2 \xrightarrow{\Delta} \underset{C_6H_5}{\overset{C_6H_5}{>}}C{=}CHCH_3$$

Another attractive feature of the phosphonamide route is that it can be controlled to give *cis*- and *trans*-olefins.[4] Formation of the adduct is not stereospecific, but the elimination reaction is stereospecific (*cis* cycloelimination). The synthesis of *cis*- and *trans*-1-phenylpropene is illustrative; the former was prepared from the reaction of benzaldehyde with the α-lithio derivative of ethylphosphonic acid bis(dimethylamide) to give two diastereoisomeric β-hydroxyphosphonamides (5) in the ratio of 3.5:1. The major isomer was separated by crystallization and on pyrolysis gave *cis*-1-phenylpropene. The isomeric olefin was prepared by reaction of the α-lithio

$$\underset{\underset{\displaystyle CH_3}{|}}{\overset{\overset{\displaystyle OH}{|}}{C_6H_5CHCHPO[N(CH_3)_2]_2}} \qquad\qquad \underset{\underset{\displaystyle CH_3}{|}}{C_6H_5COCHPO[N(CH_3)_2]_2}$$

$$\text{(5)} \qquad\qquad\qquad\qquad\qquad \text{(6)}$$

derivative of ethylphosphonic acid bis(dimethylamide) with methyl benzoate to give a β-ketophosphonamide (6). This was reduced stereospecifically by sodium borohydride to give the β-hydroxyphosphonamide (5), the isomer of the product obtained by the previous route. On pyrolysis it yields *trans*-1-phenylpropene. Alternatively (5) can be oxidized by active MnO_2 to the ketone and then reduced.

The phosphonamide route has some advantages over the Wittig reaction. The reagents are readily prepared and potentially cheaper. The products are readily isolated (separation from triphenylphosphine oxide is sometimes troublesome). The intermediate β-hydroxyphosphonic acid amides are readily purified. There is more opportunity to control the geometry and position of the double bond.

[1]A. M. Kinnear and E. A. Perren, *J. Chem. Soc.*, 3427 (1952)
[2]G. M. Kosolapoff and L. B. Payne, *J. Org.*, **21**, 413 (1956)
[3]E. J. Corey and G. T. Kwiatkowski, *Am. Soc.*, **88**, 5652 (1966)
[4]*Idem, ibid.*, **88**, 5653 (1966)

1-Methyl-2-pyrrolidone [**1**, 696, before references]. Henbest[5] used this solvent to advantage for the reaction of 3-keto-Δ^4-steroids with sodium cyanide to give 5α- and 5β-cyano-3-ketosteroids. The steric course of the addition is not strongly affected by the 17-substituent.

Aldehydes are converted into 1,1-difluoroethylenes by heating with triphenylphosphine and sodium chlorodifluoroacetate in glyme or diglyme. Under the same conditions, ketones do not react. However, Fuqua *et al.*[6] found that, if 1-methyl-2-pyrrolidone is used as solvent and tributylphosphine is used as base, satisfactory yields are obtained in reactions of ketones.

[5]H. B. Henbest and W. R. Jackson, *J. Chem. Soc.*, (C), 2465 (1967); *see also* M. Heller and S. Bernstein, *J. Org.*, **32**, 3978 (1967)
[6]S. A. Fuqua, W. G. Duncan, and R. M. Silverstein, *Tetrahedron Letters*, 521 (1965)

4-(Methylthio)phenol, $HOC_6H_4SCH_3$ [**1**, 696, before **1-Methyl-3-*p*-tolyltriazene**]. Mol. wt. 139.20, m.p. 86°. Supplier: Crown Zellerbach Corp.

Carboxy protection.[1] Under the influence of DCC, the reagent combines with an N-protected amino acid to give the 4-(methylthio)phenyl ester (1). This protected ester is converted by oxidation with excess hydrogen peroxide in acetic acid into the sulfone (2), which is an activated ester suitable for peptide synthesis.

In subsequent work[2] it was found more convenient to use *m*-chloroperbenzoic acid in dioxane in the oxidation step. The activation step can be carried out in the presence of N-Cb and *t*-butyl ester protective groups and in the presence of peptide bonds. The method was used successfully for the synthesis of the protected heptapeptide (A_{82}–A_{88}) of bovine chymotrypsinogen A.

(1)

(2)

The conversion of the 4-(methylthio)phenyl ester into the activated 4-(methyl-sulfonyl)phenyl ester is not accompanied by racemization.[3]

[1]B. J. Johnson and P. M. Jacobs, *Chem. Commun.*, 73 (1968)
[2]B. J. Johnson and E. G. Trask, *J. Org.*, 33, 4521 (1968)
[3]B. J. Johnson and P. M. Jacobs, *ibid.*, 33, 4524 (1968)

1-Methyl-3-*p*-tolyltriazine [1, 696–697, ref. 1]. *Change to*: E. H. White, A. A. Baum, and D. E. Eitel, *Org. Syn.*, 48, 102 (1968).

4-Methyl-1,2,4-triazoline-3,5-dione (2) [1, 697, before **Methyltriphenylphosphonium bromide**]. Mol. wt. 112.09, red crystals, m.p. 98–98.5°. Preparation[1] by oxidation of 4-methylurazole (1) with dinitrogen tetroxide.

(1)   (2)

Diels-Alder reaction. The reagent is one of the most reactive of dienophiles. Thus a solution of the red dione is decolorized instantly at −78° by cyclopentadiene.[2,3]

Reaction with monoolefins with allylic hydrogens.[4] The dione is extremely reactive toward monoolefins having allylic hydrogens, for example tetramethylethylene (3). The adduct (4) is of the addition-substitution type in which a shift of the double bond has occurred.

(3)   (2)   (4)

[1]J. C. Stickler and W. H. Pirkle, *J. Org.*, 31, 3445 (1966)
[2]R. C. Cookson, S. S. H. Gilani, and I. D. R. Stevens, *Tetrahedron Letters*, 615 (1962)
[3]B. T. Gillis and J. D. Hagarty, *J. Org.*, 32, 330 (1967)
[4]W. H. Pirkle and J. C. Stickler, *Chem. Commun.*, 760 (1967)

Methyl(tri-*n*-butylphosphine)copper complex, $CH_3CuP(n\text{-}Bu)_3$ [1, 697, before **Methyltriphenylphosphonium bromide**]. The reagent, developed by House,[1] is prepared by reaction of 1 equiv. of CH_3Li with 1 equiv. of the tri-*n*-butylphosphine complex of copper (I) iodide[2] in ether solution. The ethereal solution is essentially colorless and is stable at 0° for at least several hours. This reagent rapidly and selectively adds a methyl group to the β-carbon atom of an α,β-unsaturated ketone but is less reactive to isolated carbonyl groups. Thus it reacts with unsaturated ketone (1) to give three parts of the 1,4-adduct (2) to one part of the alcohol (3). In contrast, reaction of (1) with methylmagnesium bromide affords the tertiary alcohol (3) in high yield, and no conjugate addition was observed.

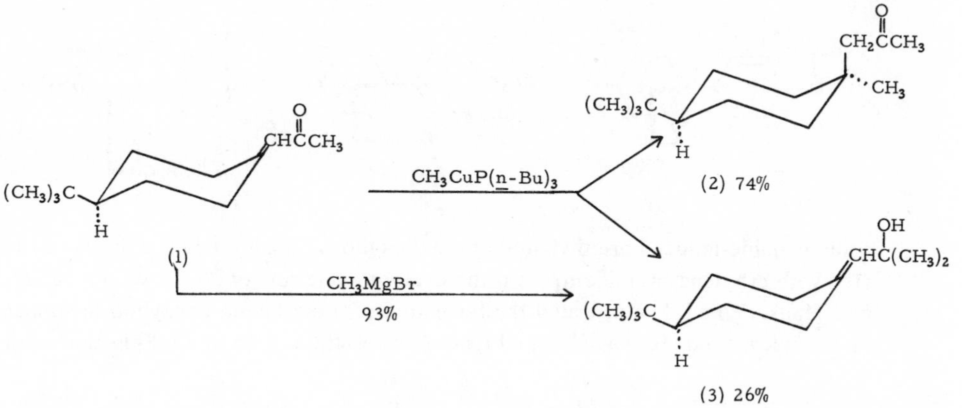

(2) 74%

(3) 26%

[1]H. O. House, W. L. Respess, and G. M. Whitesides, *J. Org.*, **31**, 3128 (1966)
[2]J. B. Kaufman and L. A. Teter, *Inorg. Syn.*, **7**, 9 (1963).

Methyltriphenoxyphosphonium iodide [1, 697, before Methyltriphenyl phosphonium bromide]. See **Triphenylphosphite methiodide (1, 1249).**

Methyl vinyl ketone [1, 697–703, before references].

Annelation of endocyclic enamines. Stevens and Wentland[20] prepared 1-phenyl-cyclopropanecarbonitrile (2a) by the sodium amide-induced bis-alkylation of phenyl-acetonitrile (1a) with ethylene dibromide. Controlled, partial reduction of the

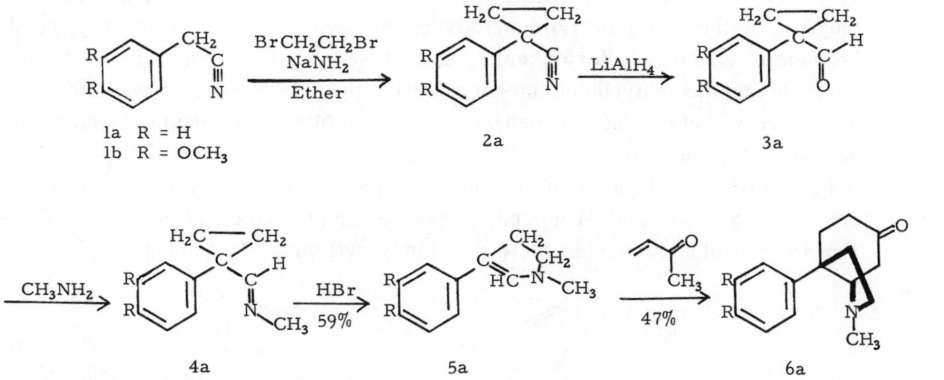

1a R = H
1b R = OCH₃

2a

3a

4a

5a

6a

nitrile 2a gave the aldehyde 3a, which was condensed with methylamine in the presence of magnesium sulfate to produce 4a. This cyclopropylaldimine was found to undergo a thermally induced acid-catalyzed rearrangement to the Δ^2-pyrroline 5a, an example of an efficient new general synthesis of pyrrolines. Stevens and Went-land[21] found, further, that the pyrroline 5a reacts with methyl vinyl ketone in ethylene glycol at 150° to give the product of annelation, 6a, in 47% yield. Compound

6a is of particular interest because the ring system corresponds to that present in the alkaloids crinine (7), mesembrine (8), and hasubanonine (9). An initial attempt to apply the new method to the synthesis of mesembrine (8) failed in the first step of

7   8   9

sodium amide-induced bisethylation of the dimethoxy-substituted phenylacetonitrile (1b) with ethylene bromide to form the cyclopropane ring of 2b. However, Kaiser and Hauser[22] had demonstrated the formation of a dilithiated benzylnitrile similar to 1c and, indeed, 1c was obtained readily by reaction of 1b in THF–hexane with

1b   1c   2b

n-butyllithium and it was found to react smoothly with ethylene dibromide to form the cyclopropane derivative 2b. The remainder of the synthesis proceeded as smoothly as with the model compounds and afforded (±)-mesembrine (8).

In a paper published along with that of Stevens and Wentland[20] and in agreement with these authors, Keely and Tahk[23] reported the independent synthesis of *dl*-mesembrine, also from 1-methyl-3-(3,4-dimethoxyphenyl)-2-pyrroline and methyl vinyl ketone. In their work the cyclopropyl derivative 3b was prepared from the reaction of the anion of 3,4-dimethoxyphenylacetonitrile (1c) with ethylene dibromide in dimethyl sulfoxide and its sodium salt as solvent and base. Reduction with ethereal diisobutylaluminum hydride gave the aldehyde, which was condensed with excess methylamine in benzene–ether solution with calcium oxide as the dehydrating agent.

In a further application of the methyl vinyl ketone annelation of endocyclic enamines, Stevens and Wentland[21] report a simple three-step synthesis of the *Erythrina* alkaloid model (±)-15,16-dimethoxyerythrinane-3-one (11).

(10)   (11)

Reaction with trialkylboranes. A trialkylborane (1), readily available by hydro-boration of an alkene, undergoes fast 1,4-addition to methyl vinyl ketone to give an enol borinate ester (2), which on hydrolysis affords a methyl ketone (3).[24]

$$R_3B + CH_2=CHCOCH_3 \longrightarrow RCH_2CH=\underset{\underset{CH_3}{|}}{C}-OBR_2 \xrightarrow{H_2O} RCH_2CH_2\underset{\underset{CH_3}{|}}{C}=O$$

(1)   (2)   (3)

Procedure A. A solution of 100 mmoles of 1-octene in 30 ml. of tetrahydrofurane was flushed with nitrogen and 33.3 ml. of a 1 M solution of borane in tetrahydrofurane was injected by hypodermic syringe to effect hydroboration. After 1 hr., 50 mmoles of methyl vinyl ketone in 15 ml. of tetrahydrofurane was added. After 2 hrs. at 40°, 15 ml. of water was added and the solution was heated at 40° for 1 hr. The solution was dried over magnesium sulfate for GLPC analysis:

$$\overset{8}{C}H_3CH_2CH_2CH_2CH_2CH_2\overset{1}{C}H=\overset{}{C}H_2 \xrightarrow{99\%} \begin{cases} (85)\ \overset{12}{C}H_3CH_2CH_2CH_2CH_2CH_2CH_2CH_2CH_2CH_2\overset{O}{\overset{\|}{C}}CH_3 \\[2mm] (15)\ \overset{11}{C}H_3CH_2CH_2CH_2CH_2CH_2\underset{\underset{5}{}}{\overset{\overset{CH_3}{|}}{C}}HCH_2CH_2\underset{\underset{2}{}}{\overset{O}{\overset{\|}{C}}}CH_3 \end{cases}$$

Procedure B. Hydroboration was carried out as above to form 40 mmoles of the organoborane. Then 100 mmoles of water was added, followed by 60 mmoles of methyl vinyl ketone, and the mixture was stirred for 1 hr. at 25°. GLPC analysis indicated a yield and isomer ratio substantially as before.

Since methyl ketones are convertible into acids by the haloform reaction, the present sequence provides a means of lengthening the chain by three carbon atoms.

[20]R. V. Stevens and M. P. Wentland, *Am. Soc.*, **90**, 5580 (1968)
[21]*Idem, Chem. Commun.*, 1104 (1968)
[22]E. Kaiser and C. Hauser, *Am. Soc.*, **88**, 2348 (1966)
[23]S. L. Keely, Jr., and F. C. Tahk, *ibid.*, **90**, 5584 (1968)
[24]A. Suzuki, A. Arase, H. Matsumoto, and M. Itoh; H. C. Brown, M. M. Rogić, and M. W. Rathke, *ibid.*, **89**, 5708 (1967)

Michler's ketone [4,4′-Bis(dimethylamino)benzophenone], [1, 703, before **Molecular sieves**]. Mol. wt. 268.36, m.p. 174–176°. Suppliers: E, Fl.

$$(CH_3)_2N-\!\!\left\langle\bigcirc\right\rangle\!\!-\underset{\underset{O}{\|}}{C}-\!\!\left\langle\bigcirc\right\rangle\!\!-N(CH_3)_2$$

Photochemical sensitizer. DeBoer, Turro, and Hammond[1] selected Michler's ketone as sensitizer for the photochemical dimerization of butadiene to *cis*- and *trans*-1,2-divinylcyclobutane; the *cis*-isomer undergoes thermal rearrangement to the higher boiling 1,5-cyclooctadiene. The choice of sensitizer depends upon the energy of the singlet-triplet transition, the intersystem crossing efficiency, and the absorption spectrum of the sensitizer.

[1]C. D. DeBoer, N. J. Turro, and G. S. Hammond, *Org. Syn.*, **47**, 64 (1967)

Molecular sieves [**1**, 703–705, before references]. Aromatic aldehydes and ketones react rapidly with N-aminotriphenylphosphinimine in the presence of Linde molecular sieves (pellets, 4A) as desiccant to yield triphenylphosphazines as principal products (40–90% yields):[13]

$$(C_6H_5)_3P{=}NNH_2 \ + \ O{=}CR_2 \ \xrightarrow[-H_2O]{} \ (C_6H_5)_3P{=}N{-}N{=}CR_2$$

The 4A pellet sieves have been used also for the preparation of the azomethine (2) from androsterone (1) and *n*-butylamine.[14] A mixture of androsterone (15 mg.), the sieve (0.5 g.), and *n*-butylamine (2 ml.) was kept under nitrogen in the dark at room temperature for 3 weeks, the liquid and washings from the sieve (3 ml. of *n*-butyl-

amine) were filtered through a kieselguhr pad, the solvent removed, and the residue crystallized.

Stern and Bolan[15] studied the esterification of benzoic acid (100 g.) with 2-butanol (300 ml.) and 2 ml. of sulfuric acid by refluxing the mixture under a Soxhlet condenser with 38 g. of Linde 5A sieve in the extraction thimble. A reflux period of about 4 hrs. sufficed to approach optimum yield. The method proved to be superior to a number of other methods employing water removal, such as the Dean-Stark trap.

In reply to an inquiry, Dr. Stern said "We did examine in our studies of the synthetic utility of molecular sieves the four Linde sieves, and found that while 4A and 5A sieves worked quite well, 7A and 15X were not as effective. We also did a limited study of some other sieves, and found that the Linde material gave the best results."

A Netherlands group[16] effected transesterification of the type $RCOOCH_3 + R'OH \rightleftharpoons RCOOR' + CH_3OH$ and found that it can be caused to go to completion by absorbing the methanol selectively on a molecular sieve type 3A. In ester interchange with secondary, tertiary or branched primary alcohols, sieve 5A is well suited.

[13]C. C. Walker and H. Shecter, *Tetrahedron Letters*, 1447 (1965)

[14]R. Bonnett and T. R. Emerson, *J. Chem. Soc.*, 4508 (1965)

[15]R. L. Stern and E. N. Bolan, *Chem. Ind.*, 825 (1967); *see also* H. R. Harrison, W. M. Haynes, P. Arthur, and E. J. Eisenbraun, *ibid.*, 1568 (1968)

[16]D. P. Roelofsen, J. A. Hagendoorn, and H. van Bekkum, *ibid.*, 1622 (1966)

Molybdenum hexacarbonyl, $Mo(CO)_6$ [**1**, 705, before **Morpholine**]. Mol. wt. 264.01, dec. around 150° without melting, b.p. 428°/760 mm. Suppliers, Matheson Co., Alfa Inorganics.

Epoxidation of olefins. Sheng and Zajacek[1] have worked out a procedure for the efficient monoepoxidation of 1,5-cyclooctadiene in which a mixture of 1 mole of the diene, 0.5 mole of 92% *t*-butyl hydroperoxide, and 0.1 g. of molybdenum hexacarbonyl is placed in a 500-ml. pendaclave (a cylindrical stainless steel pressure reactor sold by Pressure Products Industries, Inc., Hatboro, Penna. 19040). The reaction

mixture is heated gradually to 87°, when the exothermic reaction takes over and maintains a temperature of about 100° for 30 min. No work-up of the product is required other than distillation.

[1]M. N. Sheng and J. G. Zajacek, procedure submitted to *Org. Syn.*, 1967

N

Naphthalene–Lithium, $[C_{10}H_8]^-Na^+$ [**1**, 711, before **Naphthalene–Magnesium**].

Preparation in solution.[1,2] The reagent is prepared by stirring clean pieces of lithium (1 mole) with 0.3–0.5 mole of naphthalene in dry THF under nitrogen.

Dimerization of dienes. The reagent converts 1,3-cyclooctadiene into the dimer (3).[2] It dimerizes isoprene to a mixture of 2,6-dimethyl-2,6-octadiene (4) and 2,7-dimethyl-2,6-octadiene (5).[3]

The reagent reacts with ethyl vinyl ether to give 1-ethylnaphthalene in 40–60% yield.[1]

The reagent has also been used for the synthesis of acetylenic diols.[4] Thus 3-methyl-1-butyne-3-ol (6) is heated with two moles of the reagent to form the dilithio derivative. Cyclohexanone is added and the diol (7) is obtained in 60% yield. The reaction can also be carried out with acetylene and two different ketones.

The reaction of acetylenes with α,β-unsaturated ketones to give the corresponding acetylenic carbinols can be carried out conveniently with naphthalene–lithium.[5] An example is the reaction of β-ionone with lithium acetylide to give ethynyl-β-ionol.

β-Ionone   Ethynyl-β-ionol

Amines can be alkylated conveniently by alkyl halides using naphthalene–lithium in THF solution. Thus dibenzylamine is added to a solution of naphthalene–lithium in THF; addition of *n*-hexyl bromide yields N-hexyldibenzylamine in 90% yield.[6] The alkylation of higher amines usually has involved metallic sodium.

[1]K. Suga, S. Watanabe, and I. Torii, *Chem. Ind.*, 360 (1967); K. Suga, S. Watanabe, and T. P. Pan, *Australian J. Chem.*, **21**, 2341 (1968)
[2]K. Suga, S. Watanabe, and K. Kamma, *Canad. J. Chem.*, **45**, 933 (1967)
[3]K. Suga and S. Watanabe, *J. Chem. Soc. Japan, Ind. Chem.*, **69**, 354 (1966)
[4]S. Watanabe, K. Suga, and T. Suzuki, *Chem. Ind.*, 1489 (1968)
[5]K. Suga, S. Watanabe, and T. Suzuki, *Canad. J. Chem.*, **46**, 3041 (1968)
[6]K. Suga, S. Watanabe, T. P. Pan, and T. Fujita, *Chem. Ind.*, 78 (1969)

Naphthalene–Magnesium [**1**, 711, ref. 1] *Add: See also* P. Markov, D. Lasarov, and C. Ivanov, *Ann.*, **704**, 126 (1967).

Naphthalene–Sodium [**1**, 711–712, before references].

Sulfonamides are cleaved to amines in high yield by treatment with naphthalene-sodium. 1,2-Dimethoxyethane is preferred to THF as solvent.[8]

The reagent is exceptionally useful for dehalogenation of *vic*-dihalides, even when the resulting olefin is highly strained.[9] The yields noted were determined by VPC. Yields of isolated products were somewhat lower.

$$CH_3(CH_2)_4CHBrCH_2Br \xrightarrow[>90\%]{} CH_3(CH_2)_4CH=CH_2$$

[8]S. Ji, L. B. Gortler, A. Waring, A. Battisti, S. Bank, W. D. Closson, and P. Wriede, *Am. Soc.*, **89**, 5311 (1967)
[9]C. G. Scouten, F. E. Barton, Jr., J. R. Burgess, P. R. Story, and J. F. Garst, *Chem. Commun.*, 78 (1969)

Nickel-aluminum alloy [**1**, 718–720, before references].

Graham and Williams[9] found nickel-aluminum alloy with aqueous sodium hydroxide to be a useful reagent for the reduction of ketoximes to amines without rearrangements that often accompany aluminum hydride reductions.

[9]S. H. Graham and A. J. S. Williams, *J. Chem. Soc.*, (C), 655 (1966)

Nickel boride [**1**, 720, before references].

Clark *et al.*[4] compared nickel boride and Raney nickel for desulfurization of heterocyclic thiols and concluded that Raney nickel is usually superior in regard to yield.

[4]J. Clark, R. K. Grantham, and J. Lydiate, *J. Chem. Soc.*, (C), 1122 (1968)

Nickel carbonyl [1, 720–723].

Hydrocarboxylation of olefins [1, 721–722, after citation of ref. 8]. Nickel carbonyl reacts with 1,5-dienes in the presence of dilute acid to form cyclic ketones rather than the expected mono- and dicarboxylic acids. Thus hexadiene-1,5 is converted in 70% yield into a mixture of 2,5-dimethylcyclopentanone and 2-methyl-cyclohexanone.[8a]

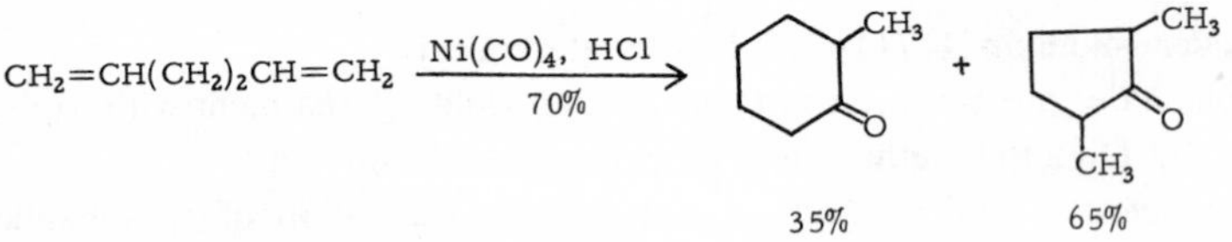

$$CH_2{=}CH(CH_2)_2CH{=}CH_2 \xrightarrow[70\%]{Ni(CO)_4,\ HCl}$$

35%   65%

Coupling of allylic compounds [1, 722–723, before references]; *revision and extension*. Bauld's observation of the coupling of allylic acetates by Ni(CO)$_4$ cited in ref. 12 was preceded by the discovery of Webb and Borcherdt[14] (du Pont) in 1951 that nickel carbonyl in methanol effects coupling of allylic chlorides in excellent yield, for example:

$$CH_3CH{=}CHCH_2Cl\ +\ CH_3OH\ +\ Ni(CO)_4 \xrightarrow{25^0} CH_3CH{=}CHCH_2CH_2CH{=}CHCH_3$$

223 g.   250 ml.   260 g.   74%

$$+\ 4\ CO\,(80\%)\ +\ NiCl_2$$

Caution: Webb and Borcherdt[14] emphasize that low-boiling nickel carbonyl is *extremely poisonous and flammable* and record precautions for its safe handling. Oxygen should be excluded rigorously with argon, either with a plastic glove bag or by the argon-line technique.

E. J. Corey achieved a major synthetic breakthrough by devising a succession of

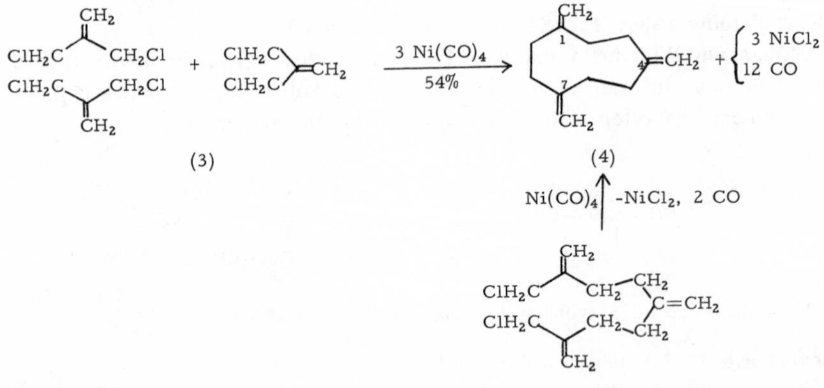

(3)   (4)

$$Ni(CO)_4\ {\uparrow}\ {-}NiCl_2,\ 2\ CO$$

(5)

schemes for utilizing the coupling reaction for the synthesis of unsaturated hydrocarbons, cyclic and acyclic. Thus Corey and Hamanaka[13] (1, 722–723) achieved the synthesis of all-*trans*-1,6-dimethyl-$\Delta^{1,5,9}$-cyclododecatriene (formula 2, 1, 723). Later Corey and Semmelhack[15] reported that nickel carbonyl cyclizes three molecules of 1,1-bischloromethylethylene (3) to produce 1,4,7-trimethylenecyclononane (4) in fair yield. The cyclononane (4) was obtained also in excellent yield by cyclization of the dihalide (5).

Nickel carbonyl in excess reacts in benzene with an allylic bromide to give a π-allylnickel (I) bromide, formulated as (6); removal of solvent and crystallization

$$2\ RCH{=}CHCH_2Br\ +\ 2\ Ni(CO)_4 \longrightarrow$$

(6)

from ether at $-70°$ affords the complex in yield of 80–95%. These complexes are rather inert toward alkyl halides in ether or hydrocarbon solvents but react readily with alkyl, vinyl, or aryl iodides in more polar, coordinating solvents (DMF, methylpyrrolidone, or hexamethylphosphoric triamide) to give coupled products:

$$RCH{=}CHCH_2Br\ +\ Ni(CO)_4 \longrightarrow \pi\text{-Complex} \xrightarrow[\text{DMF}]{R'I} R'CH_2C{=}CH_2$$
$$\underset{R}{|}$$

This new method was employed in an efficient synthesis of α-santalene (9):[16]

(7)   (8)   (9)

Corey and Wat[17] found that the method of forming cycloolefins from allylic dihalides and nickel carbonyl provides an unusually efficient route for the formation of large rings. Because it leads to cyclic 1,5-dienes, it makes available a variety of cyclic structures not obtainable in a practical way via the acyloin synthesis. Diacetylenic diols (10) were converted by selective reduction into the corresponding *cis,cis*- and *trans,trans*-ethylenic diols followed by reaction with PBr$_3$ to form the diallylic dibromides (12), which were then cyclized with nickel carbonyl.

$$HOCH_2C{\equiv}C(CH_2)_nC{\equiv}CCH_2OH \xrightarrow{4\ H} HOCH_2CH{=}CH(CH_2)_nCH{=}CHCH_2OH \xrightarrow{PBr_3}$$

(10)   (11)

$$BrCH_2CH{=}CH(CH_2)_nCH{=}CHCH_2Br$$

(12)

(12) n = 6	$\xrightarrow{\text{Ni(CO)}_4}$ 59%	(13) + Trace of cis, trans-isomer	(12) n = 8 $\xrightarrow{\text{Ni(CO)}_4}$ 70-74% (14) n = 12 + Trace of cis, trans-isomer

(12) n = 12 $\xrightarrow{\text{Ni(CO)}_4}$ 76-84%   (15)

Nickel carbonyl cyclization was the key step in a total synthesis of humulene (18) by Corey and Hamanaka.[18] When a solution of the dibromide (16) in N-methyl-

(16) $\xrightarrow{\text{Ni(CO)}_4}$ (17) $\xrightarrow[h\nu]{C_6H_5SC_6H_5}$ (18) Humulene

pyrrolidone was added slowly (automatic syringe drive) to 4 equivalents of nickel carbonyl in the same solvent at 50° under argon the major product formed was the 4,5-*cis*-isomer of humulene (17). Irradiation of the crude cyclization product and diphenyl disulfide[19] in cyclohexane at 25° caused isomerization of (17) to humulene (18), which was isolated from the reaction mixture by extraction with 50% aqueous silver nitrate.

Synthesis of β-epoxy ketones.[20,21] Nickel carbonyl reacts with an α-bromo ketone (DMF, argon, 30°, 5 hrs.) to give a β-epoxy ketone, for example (2). Yields are in the range 50–80%. The reaction is considered to proceed via an aldol-type condensation between the ketone and the nickel enolate followed by elimination of $NiBr_2$.

$2 \ (CH_3)_3C-\overset{O}{\overset{\|}{C}}CH_2Br \longrightarrow (CH_3)_3C-\overset{O}{\overset{\|}{C}}CH_2\overset{C(CH_3)_3}{\underset{O}{\overset{|}{C}}}CH_2 \xrightarrow{130°} (CH_3)_3C$

(1)   (2)   (3)

The products when heated undergo dehydration to give furanes, for example (2) → (3).

[8a] B. Fell, W. Seide, and F. Asinger, *Tetrahedron Letters*, 1003 (1968)
[14] I. D. Webb and G. T. Borcherdt, *Am. Soc.*, **73**, 2654 (1951); *see also* I. G. Farbenind. patent 448,884 [*C. A.*, **41**, 6576 (1947)]
[15] E. J. Corey and M. F. Semmelhack, *Tetrahedron Letters*, 6237 (1966)
[16] *Idem, Am. Soc.*, **89**; 2755 (1967)
[17] E. J. Corey and E. K. W. Wat, *Am. Soc.*, **89**, 2757 (1967)

[18]E. J. Corey and E. Hamanaka, *ibid.*, **89**, 2758 (1967)
[19]C. Monssebois and J. Dale, *J. Chem. Soc.*, (C), 260 (1966)
[20]E. Yoshisato and S. Tsutsumi, *ibid.*, **90**, 4488 (1968)
[21]M. F. Semmelhack, Ph.D. Thesis, Harvard Univ., 1967

Nickel catalysts (a), Raney type [1, 723–731].

Nitriles [1, 725–726, after citation of ref. 23]. The original method of Backeberg and Staskun[23] for conversion of a nitrile to an aldehyde does not proceed well with hindered nitriles; in this case, use of moist Raney nickel in formic acid is recommended.[23a] The formic acid serves as a source of hydrogen, and the nickel catalyzes both decomposition of the acid and reduction of the nitrile.

Disproportionation [1, 729–730]. In the absence of a hydrogen acceptor/donor, Raney nickel in boiling *p*-cymene brings about four different types of reactions on steroids: oxidation of a 3-hydroxyl group, hydrogenation of a 5,6-double bond, isomerization of a 5β-hydrogen to a 5α-hydrogen, and dimerization.[45a]

Aldehyde synthesis [1, 730, before references]. Gottstein *et al.*[48] developed an efficient method for the transformation of a tertiary amine salt of a penicillin (1) according to Scheme I into the thioacid salt (2) through the ethoxy formic anhydride. The salt is then desulfurized with No. 28 Raney nickel catalyst (W. R. Grace Co.)

SCHEME I

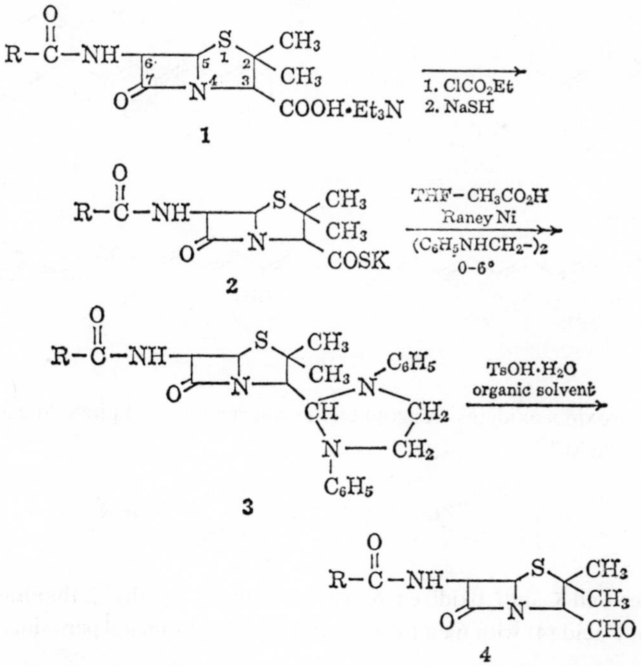

in THF–AcOH. The reaction is carried out in the presence of N,N'-diphenylene-diamine to trap the aldehyde through formation of the imidazoline derivative (3). The aldehyde group is regenerated (4) by treating (3) in ether–acetone–dichloromethane (3:1:1) with two equivalents of *p*-toluenesulfonic acid monohydrate instead of the customary mineral acid.

Stereoselectivity. Howard and Morley[49] examined the stereoselectivity of a range of catalysts in the hydrogenation of 2-cyclopentylidenecyclopentanol (1). The highest percentage of the *trans* product (2) was obtained with Raney nickel.

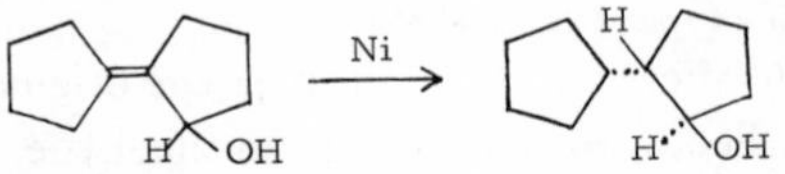

(1)   (2) 98%

The stereoselectivity of other catalysts were in the order nickel boride (Brown and Brown's P-1) > Ru/C > Pt > Rb/C > Pd/C.

[23a]B. Staskun and O. G. Backeberg, *J. Chem. Soc.*, 5880 (1964)
[45a]S. K. Banerjee, D. Chakravarti, R. N. Chakravarti, and M. N. Mitra, *Tetrahedron*, **24**, 6459 (1968)
[48]W. J. Gottstein *et al., J. Org.*, **31**, 1922 (1966); *idem, J. Med. Chem.*, **8**, 794.
[49]T. J. Howard and B. Morley, *Chem. Ind.*, 73 (1967)

Nickel peroxide [**1**, 731–732, before references]. The reagent proved effective for the selective oxidation of lutein (1) to 3-hydroxy-3′-keto-α-carotene (2).[8]

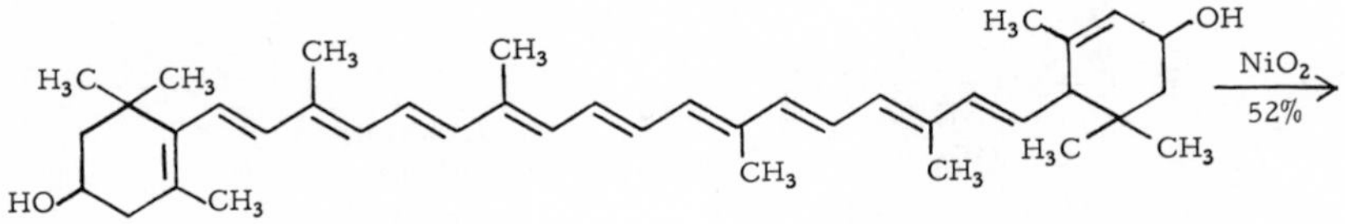

(1)

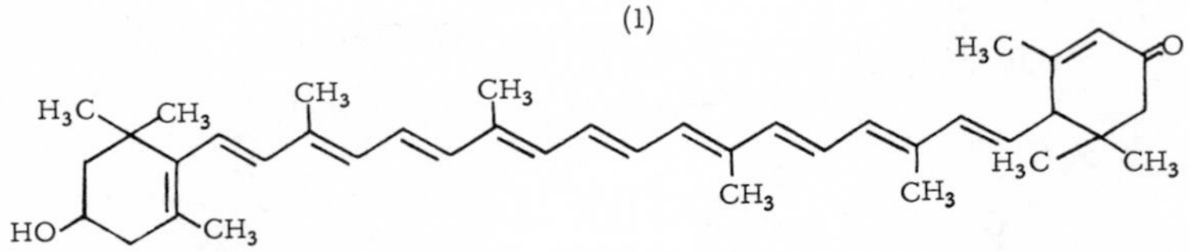

(2)

Nickel peroxide oxidizes benzophenone hydrazone to diphenyldiazomethane in quantitative yield.[9]

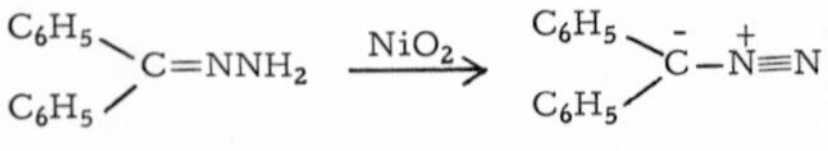

Warrener and Cain[10] oxidized 6-hydroxymethyl-1-methyl-2-thiouracil (3) to 1-methylorotic acid (4) with 6 equivalents of Nakagawa's nickel peroxide. The reagent

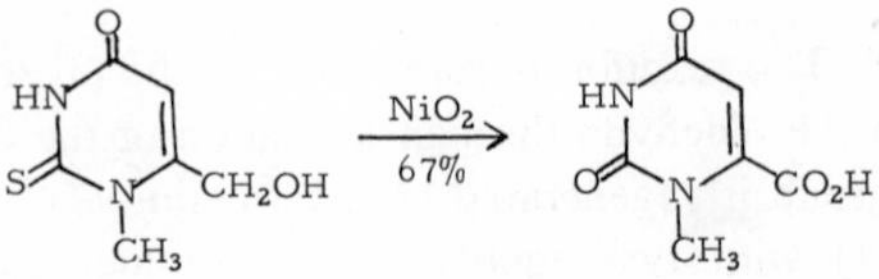

(3)   (4)

replaces doubly bound sulfur by oxygen and oxidizes the hydroxymethyl to a carboxyl group.

Belew and Tek-Ling[11] report that nickel peroxide prepared by ozonization of an alkaline solution of nickel (II) sulfate has oxidizing properties equal if not superior to Nakagawa's nickel peroxide. It is effective in smaller quantities but yields in some instances are lower.

The α,β-acetylenic alcohol (5) is oxidized by nickel peroxide in benzene at room temperature to the aldehyde (6) in 70% yield.[12] Oxidations of this type had been carried out previously, but in low yield, with manganese dioxide.[13] The aldehyde (6) can be deformylated by treatment with aqueous methanolic 2 N sodium hydroxide to give phenylacetylene in 70% yield.

$$\text{(5)} \xrightarrow[\text{70\%}]{\text{NiO}_2} \text{(6)}$$

[8]S. L. Jensen and S. Hertzberg, *Chem. Scand.*, **20**, 1703 (1966)
[9]K. Nakagawa, H. Onoue, and K. Minami, *Chem. Commun.*, 730 (1966)
[10]R. N. Warrener and E. N. Cain, *Tetrahedron Letters*, 4953 (1967)
[11]J. S. Belew and C. Tek-Ling, *Chem. Commun.*, 1100 (1967)
[12]R. E. Atkinson, R. F. Curtis, D. M. Jones, and J. A. Taylor, *ibid.*, 718 (1967)
[13]E. R. H. Jones, L. Skattebøl, and M. C. Whiting, *J. Chem. Soc.*, 1054 (1958)

Nitrobenzene, $C_6H_5NO_2$ [**1**, 736, before *p*-**Nitrobenzenesulfonoxyurethane**]. Mol. wt. 123.11, b.p. 210°, recovery by stream distillation (**1**, 25–26).

Synthesis of phenazines. Holliman et al.[1] used nitrobenzene as both solvent and oxidizing agent for the cyclization of 2-aminodiphenylamines to phenazines. The reaction rate is dependent upon substituents present and their positions.

Phenazines are of interest because they have been identified as metabolites of species of *Pseudomonas.*

[1]F. G. Holliman, B. A. Jeffery, and D. J. H. Brock, *Tetrahedron*, **19**, 1841 (1963)
[2]D. J. H. Brock and F. G. Holliman, *ibid.*, **19**, 1903 (1963); *see also idem, ibid.*, **19**, 1911 (1963)
[3]R. B. Herbert, F. G. Holliman, and J. D. Kynnersley, *Tetrahedron Letters*, 1907 (1968)

N-*p*-Nitrobenzenesulfonoxyurethane   [**1**, 736].

Further papers[2,3] discuss generation of carbo-ethoxynitrene in the singlet state (1), which then decays to the triplet state (2) in competition with addition to the olefin.

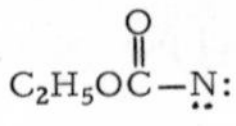

$$C_2H_5O\overset{O}{\overset{\|}{C}}-\underset{\cdot\cdot}{N}:$$
(1)

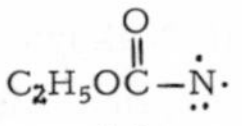

$$C_2H_5O\overset{O}{\overset{\|}{C}}-\underset{\cdot\cdot}{\overset{\cdot}{N}}\cdot$$
(2)

[2]W. Lwowski and T. J. Maricich, *Am. Soc.*, **87**, 3630 (1965)
[3]J. S. McConaghy, Jr., and W. Lwowski, *ibid.*, **89**, 2357 (1967); *ibid.*, **89**, 4450 (1967)

m-Nitrobenzenesulfonyl peroxide, $[m\text{-}O_2NC_6H_4SO_2O]_2$ [**1**, 736, before *p*-Nitrobenzoyl chloride]. Mol. wt. 404.33 m.p. 112°, dec.

The reagent has been prepared in 30% yield from *m*-nitrobenzenesulfonyl chloride and hydrogen peroxide.[1] It is relatively safe to handle and is suggested for use in the synthesis of phenols, for example:

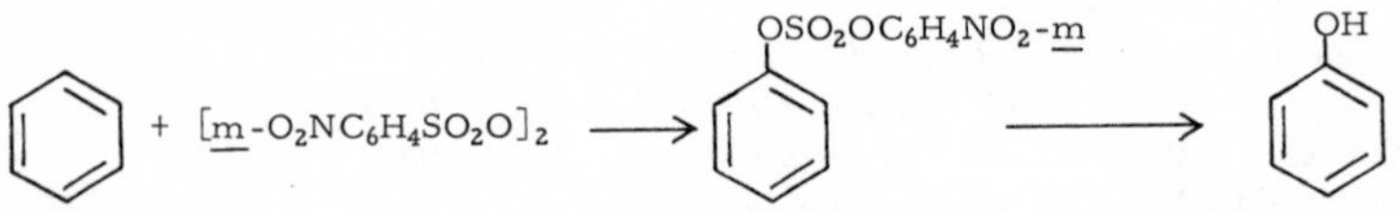

[1]R. L. Dannley and G. E. Corbett, J. Org., **31**, 153 (1966)

Nitronium tetrafluoroborate [**1**, 742–743,] replace the heading and first paragraph by:

Nitronium tetrafluoroborate, $NO_2^+BF_4^-$. Mol. wt. 132.83, dec. 170°. Supplier: Ozark-Mahoning Co., Tulsa, Okla.

Preparation. An initial procedure[1] involved interaction of nitric acid, hydrogen fluoride, and boron trifluoride in nitromethane, but mixtures of nitric acid and nitromethane are considered explosive. To avoid this hazard, Olah and Kuhn[2] developed the following modified procedure in which the medium is methylene chloride instead of nitromethane. A 1-l. three-necked polyolefin flask provided with a short inlet tube for nitrogen, a long inlet tube for gaseous boron fluoride, a drying tube, and a magnetic stirring bar is immersed in an ice-salt bath and flushed with dry nitrogen. Under a gentle stream of nitrogen and with stirring, the flask is charged with 400 ml. of methylene chloride, 41 ml. of red fuming nitric acid, and 22 ml. of cold, liquid hydrogen fluoride. Then 136 g. (2 moles) of gaseous boron trifluoride from a cylinder mounted on a scale is bubbled into the stirred mixture, the first mole is absorbed in about 10 min. and the second in about 1 hr. The mixture is allowed to stand in the cooling bath under nitrogen for 1.5 hrs. and then swirled and the suspended product

$$HNO_3 \ + \ HF \ + \ 2\,BF_3 \ \xrightarrow[64-80\%]{} \ O_2N^+BF_4^- \ + \ H_2O\cdot BF_3$$

separated on a sintered-glass Buchner funnel with the aid of two 50-ml. portions of nitromethane. The collected nitronium tetrafluoroborate is washed with two 100-ml. portions of nitromethane and two 100-ml. portions of methylene chloride. The yield of colorless product is 85–106 g.

Use in a nitration.[2] A flask dried by flaming and cooled with a stream of nitrogen passing through it is charged with tetramethylene sulfone and nitronium tetrafluoroborate and stirred at 10–20° during the addition of *o*-tolunitrile. Eventually the temperature is raised and kept at 100–115° for 1 hr.

[1] S. J. Kuhn and G. A. Olah, *Am. Soc.*, **83**, 4564 (1961)
[2] G. A. Olah and S. J. Kuhn, *Org. Syn.*, **47**, 56 (1967)

p-Nitrophenol [1, 743, before reference].

DeTar *et al.*[2] give a detailed procedure for the preparation of several *p*-nitrophenyl esters of carbobenzoxyamino acids.

[2] R. J. Albers, N. F. Estrin, and D. F. DeTar, procedure submitted to *Org. Syn.*, 1967

p-Nitrophenyl acetate, $CH_3COOC_6H_4NO_2$-*p* [1, 743, before **1-o-Nitrophenylbutadiene-1,3**]. Mol. wt. 181.15, m.p. 78°. Prepared from acetyl chloride and the sodium salt of *p*-nitrophenol. Suppliers: A, E. F.

N-Acetylation of basic amino acids. The reagent reacts with an aqueous solution of the copper salt of a basic amino acid to give the N-acetyl derivative.[1] The procedure is superior to the usual synthesis in which acetic anhydride is used because the reaction goes to completion. As applied to L-lysine, the method is simple and gives better yields of pure ε-N-acetyl-L-lysine. Excess cupric carbonate is added to a boiling aqueous solution of L-lysine (0.1 mole) and the solution is filtered and cooled to 25° and treated with sodium bicarbonate, *p*-nitrophenylacetate, and a few milliliters of ethyl acetate to keep the acetate in solution. After stirring for 15 hrs., the copper salt which separates is filtered, suspended in water, and freed of copper with H_2S. The solution is evaporated to dryness and the N-acetyllysine crystallized from water–ethanol.

For other basic amino acids, when the copper salt of the acetyl amino acid does not precipitate out, the product is desalted by absorbing on Dowex 50 resin which is then eluted with 3 *N* ammonium hydroxide.

[1] L. Benoiton and J. Leclerc, *Canad. J. Chem.*, **43**, 991 (1965); J. Leclerc and L. Benoiton, *ibid.*, **46**, 1047 (1967)

p-Nitrophenyl chloroformate, p-$O_2NC_6H_4OCOCl$ [1, 744, before **p-Nitrophenyl formate**]. Mol. wt. 201.57, m.p. 80–81°. Supplier: K and K Chemicals. Purified by sublimation.

The reagent is useful for blocking hydroxyl groups of nucleosides to give O-blocked derivatives of two useful types.[1] It reacts with the isolated hydroxyl group of 5′-tritylthymidine (1) in benzene in the presence of pyridine to give 5′-O-tritylthymidine-3′-*p*-nitrophenyl carbonate (2); on hydrolysis in refluxing aqueous acetic acid, this compound gave the 3′-blocked nucleoside, *p*-nitrophenylthymidine-3′-carbonate (3). As characteristic of nitrophenyl esters, (2) and (3) were converted rapidly and quantitatively into 5′-tritylthymidine and thymidine, respectively, by

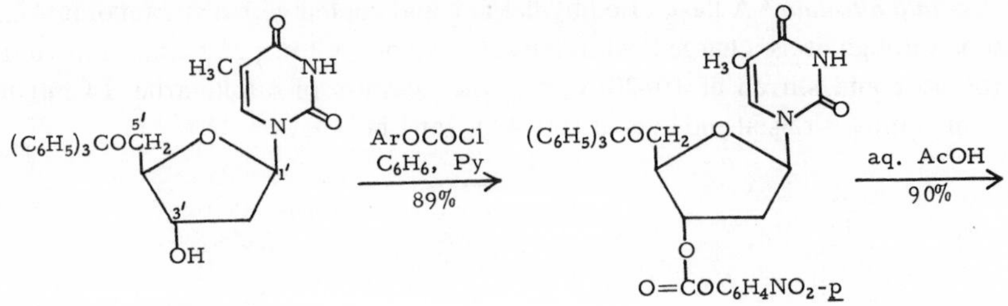

(1)   (2)

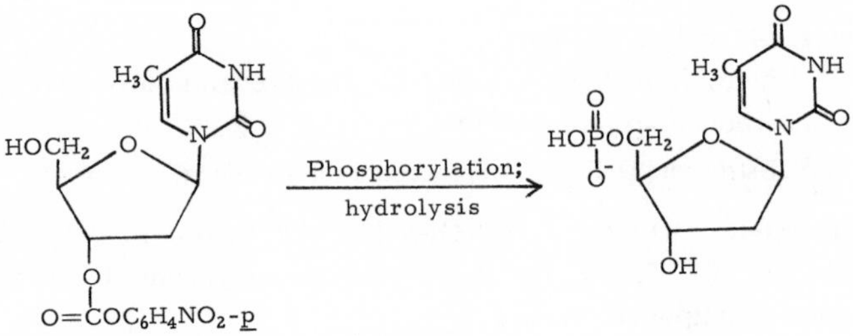

(3)   (4)

imidazole in organic solvents. The stability of the *p*-nitrophenylcarbonyl blocking group was demonstrated by phosphorylation of (3) with β-cyanoethyl phosphate and dicyclohexylcarbodiimide in pyridine; hydrolysis of the product afforded thymidine 5'-phosphate (4) in good yield.

The reaction of the reagent with a ribonucleoside such as uridine (5) takes a different course because of the presence in (5) of the 2',3'-*cis*-glycol group. Thus the

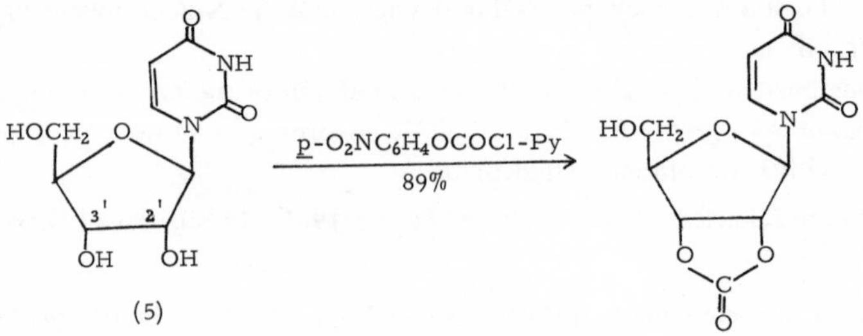

(5)   (6)

product, formed in high yield in pyridine solution, is the cyclic 2',3'-carbonate (6), 120–125°, dec. The cyclic carbonates are hydrolyzed by dilute sodium hydroxide in hot aqueous pyridine.

[1] R. L. Letsinger and K. K. Ogilvie, *J. Org.*, **32**, 296 (1967)

Nitrosyl chloride [**1**, 752, after line 4 from bottom].

Olefin addition. The reagent reacts with Δ²-chlolestene to give a greenish oil from which a pure nitroso chloride could not be isolated. After dehydrochlorination with pyridine, 2-nitro-Δ^2-cholestene was obtained in 46% yield. Reductive hydrolysis furnished cholestane-2-one.[24a]

[24a] A. Terada and A. Hassner, *Bull. Chem. Soc. Japan*, **40**, 1937 (1967)

Nitrosyl fluoride [**1**, 755]. Supplier: Ozark-Mahoning Co., Tulsa, Okla.

Reaction of steroid Δ^4-enes (1) gives 5α-fluoro-4-nitrimines (2), which on chromatography on alumina containing 6% water are converted into 5α-fluoro-4-ketones (3). Dehydrofluorination leads to the relatively inaccessible Δ^5-4-ketones (4).[3]

[3] G. A. Boswell, Jr., *J. Org.*, **33**, 3699 (1968)

Nitrosylsulfuric acid [**1**, 755], M.p. 70°. The reagent has been prepared[5] by bubbling dry SO_2 through fuming nitric acid and gradually raising the temperature to the boiling point. The reagent then solidifies on being cooled as low-melting, pale yellow crystals, which if protected from moisture are stable at room temperature for indefinite periods.

The reagent is superior to nitrosyl chloride for the nitrosation of an N-acylaryl-amine and conversion of the product to an unsymmetrical diaryl:[6]

The diazo oxide (2) is obtained in nearly quantitative yield by the action of the reagent on 2-amino-3-chloro-1,4-naphthoquinone (1).[7] No reaction occurred with 4-amino-3-bromo-1,2-naphthoquinone.

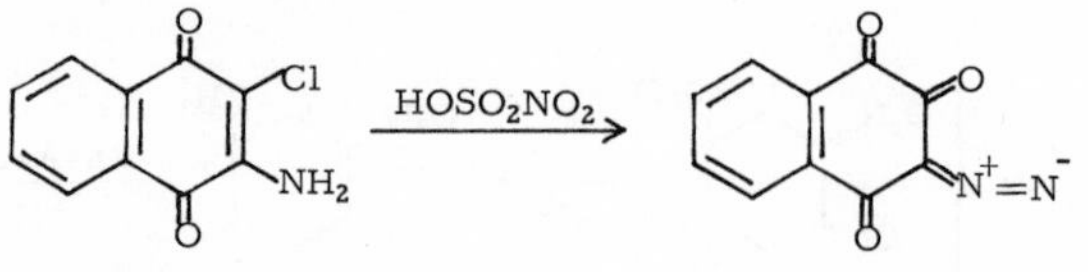

(1)   (2)

[6]Y. Ahmad, M. I. Qureshi, and M. I. Baig, *Canad J. Chem.*, **45**, 1539 (1967)
[7]W. L. Mosby and M. L. Silva, *J. Chem. Soc.*, 3990 (1964)

Nitryl chloride [**1**, 756–757, ref. 1] *Add:* R. B. Kaplan and H. Shechter, *Inorg. Syn.*, **4**, 52 (1953).

Nitryl iodide [**1**, 757, before reference]. ʼ

The reaction of unsaturated carbohydrates with the reagent has been reported.[2] Thus (1) reacts to give an unstable adduct (2) which on dehydrohalogenation is converted into (3).

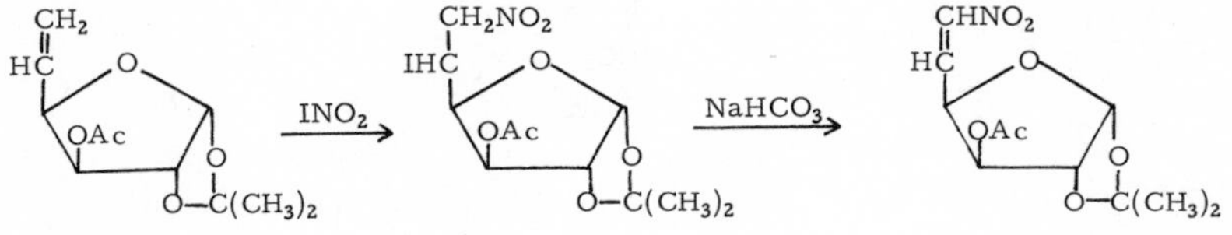

(1)   (2)   (3)

[2]W. A. Szarek, D. G. Lance, and R. L. Beach, *Chem. Commun.*, 356 (1968)

Norbornene [**1**, 757–758].

Bicyclo[3.2.1]octanone-3 [**1**, 758]. The procedure formulated occasionally failed as traces of *t*-butanol present in the potassium *t*-butoxide reacted with the product and fouled the otherwise straightforward reduction step. An improved procedure has been resubmitted[5] and the new flow sheet is as follows:

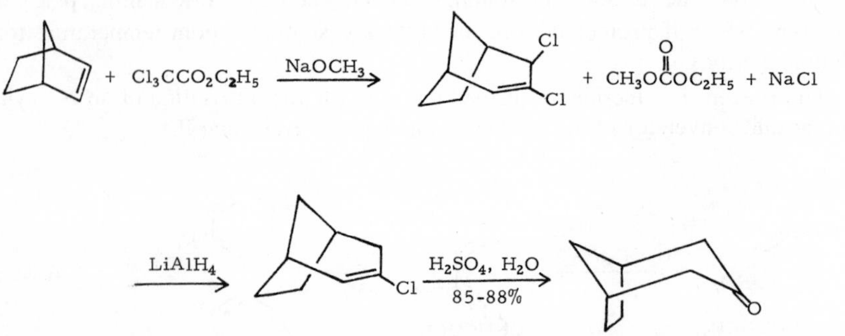

[5]Letter from Professor C. W. Jefford, Temple Univ.; C. W. Jefford, J. Gunsher, D. T. Hill, P. Brun, J. Le Gras, and B. Waegell, procedure submitted to *Org. Syn.*, 1968

O

Osmium tetroxide [**1**, 759–764, before references]. On oxidation of gibberellin A_{14} dimethyl ester (1) with osmium tetroxide in pyridine, followed by sodium periodate, Cross[13] obtained the expected norketone (2) as the major product but also isolated a small quantity of (3), a product of further oxidation of the secondary hydroxyl group present. A footnote states that "several similar examples of the oxidation of secondary alcohols by osmium tetroxide have been encountered."

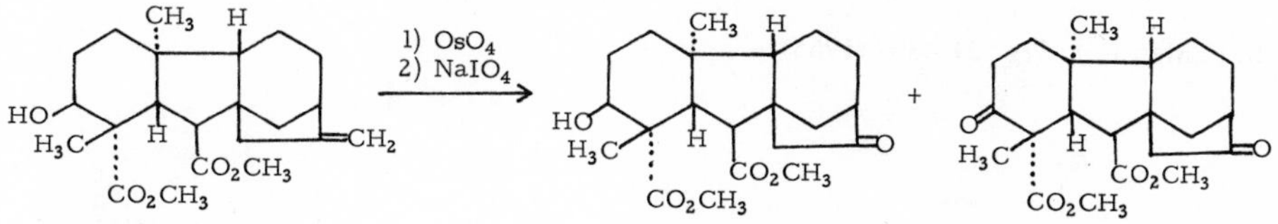

(1) 159 mg.   (2) 52 mg.   (3) 7.5 mg.

[13]B. E. Cross, *J. Chem. Soc.*, (C), 501 (1966)

Osmium tetroxide–Sodium chlorate [**1**, 764, before **Oxalic acid**].

In investigating the synthesis of diterpene alkaloids, Wiesner *et al.*[1,2] have used the combination of sodium chlorate with a catalytic amount of osmium tetroxide, for example:

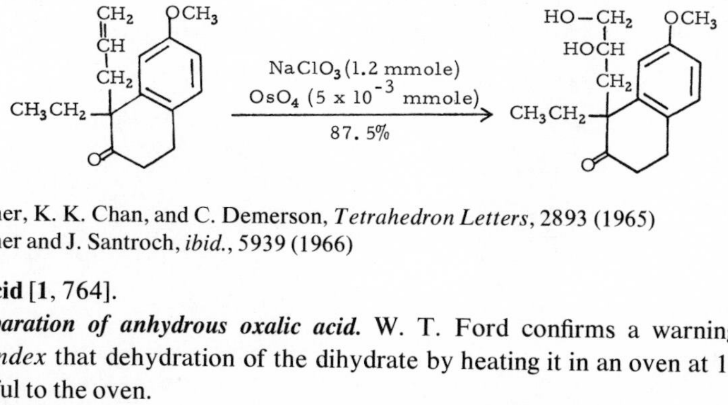

[1]K. Wiesner, K. K. Chan, and C. Demerson, *Tetrahedron Letters*, 2893 (1965)
[2]K. Wiesner and J. Santroch, *ibid.*, 5939 (1966)

Oxalic acid [**1**, 764].

Preparation of anhydrous oxalic acid. W. T. Ford confirms a warning in the *Merck Index* that dehydration of the dihydrate by heating it in an oven at 100° may be harmful to the oven.

Oxalyl chloride [**1**, 767–772, before references]. Brief refluxing of an N-carbobenzoxyamino acid (1) with 2 equivalents of oxalyl chloride in benzene gives the

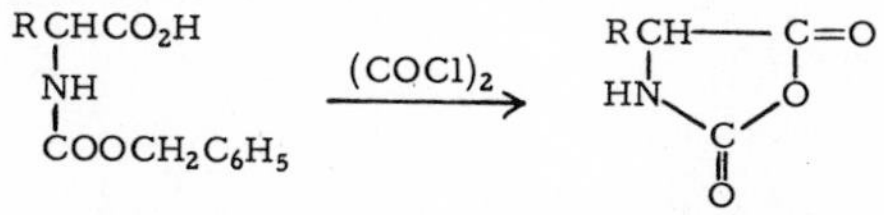

(1)   (2)

N-carboxy-α-amino anhydride (2), presumably through the acid chloride. Anhydrides of type (2) are useful starting materials for the synthesis of polypeptides.[24]

[24]D. Konopińska and I. Z. Siemion, *Angew. Chem. internat. Ed.*, **6**, 248 (1967)

Oxygen difluoride [1, 772–773, before references].

Merritt[4] established that tetramethylallene (1) consumes 1 equivalent of OF_2 at −78° to produce two volatile products assigned the structures (2) and (3).

$$(CH_3)_2C{=}C{=}C(CH_3)_2 \ + \ OF_2 \ \longrightarrow \ \underset{F\quad F}{(CH_3)_2C{-}\overset{O}{\overset{\|}{C}}{-}C(CH_3)_2} \ + \ \underset{F}{(CH_3)_2C{-}\overset{O}{\overset{\|}{C}}{-}C{\Big\langle}\,^{CH_2}_{CH_3}}$$

(1)   (2)   (3)

[4]R. F. Merritt, *J. Org.*, **30**, 4367 (1965)

P

Palladium acetate [**1**, 778, before references].

Oxidative dimerization of β-substituted α-olefins.[3] A Δ^1-olefin carrying alkyl or aryl groups at the 2-position is oxidized by the reagent in acetic acid in the presence of sodium acetate to a 1,1,4,4-tetrasubstituted 1,3-butadiene in yield of 20–90%.

$$\text{Example:} \quad \underset{\underset{C_6H_5}{|}}{CH_2{=}C{-}CH_3} \xrightarrow[91\%]{Pd(OAc)_2-NaOAc} \underset{\underset{C_6H_5}{|}}{CH_3C}{=}CH{-}CH{=}\underset{\underset{C_6H_5}{|}}{CCH_3}$$

Benzylic oxidation of toluenes. Toluene is oxidized by palladium acetate (equimolar) in acetic acid at 90° (13 hrs.) to benzyl acetate (80% yield), benzaldehyde (4%) and benzylidene diacetate (6%) with formation of palladium (O).[4] This oxidation is sensitive to electronic factors. Thus *p*-methoxytoluene is converted in 96% yield into *p*-methoxybenzyl acetate whereas *p*-nitrotoluene is essentially inactive.

[3]H. C. Volger, *Rec. trav.*, **86**, 677 (1967)
[4]C. H. Bushweller, *Tetrahedron Letters*, 6123 (1968)

Palladium catalysts [**1**, 778–782].

Hydrogenolysis [**1**, 779, after citation of ref. 4]. Horning and Reisner[4a] found palladium-on-charcoal very effective as a hydrogenation-hydrogenolysis catalyst without addition of perchloric or sulfuric acid. They found the catalyst effective also

$$\underset{}{C_6H_5}\overset{O}{\underset{}{C}}CH_2CH_2CO_2H \xrightarrow[90\%]{H_2, \ Pd-C} C_6H_5{-}CH_2CH_2CH_2CO_2H$$

for the reduction of β-benzoylpropionic acid to γ-phenylbutyric acid. Schimelpfenig[4b] employed Engelhard Industries 10% Pd-on-C in applying this procedure to the preparation of γ-phenylbutyric acid in greater than 90% yield over a dozen times.

Palladium catalyzed hydrogenation of 3β-acetoxy- or 3β-hydroxy-Δ^5-steroids affords 5–10% of the corresponding 3-desoxy steroids. The hydrogenation can be catalyzed by 70% perchloric acid. 3β-Acetoxy-5α-steroids are resistant to hydrogenolysis; hence the reaction probably involves partial isomerization of the Δ^5-double bond to the Δ^4-position, followed by hydrogenolysis of the allylic group.[4c]

[4a]E. C. Horning and D. B. Riesner, *Am. Soc.*, **71**, 1036 (1949)
[4b]C. W. Schimelpfenig, personal communication
[4c]G. R. Pettit, A. K. Das Gupta, and R. L. Smith, *Canad. J. Chem.*, **44**, 2023 (1966); G. R. Pettit, B. Green, and T. R. Kasturi, *J. Org. Chem.*, in press
[10a]*Add:* M. Crawford and V. R. Supanekar, *J. Chem. Soc.* (C), 2252 (1966)

Palladium (II) chloride, $PdCl_2$ [**1**, 782]. Additional supplier: Alfa Inorganics.

[Before reference]: Stern and Spector[2] found that the reaction of the π-complex

$$CH_2\!\!=\!\!CH_2 + CH_3COOH \longrightarrow CH_2\!\!=\!\!CHOCOCH_3 + Pd + 2\,HCl$$
$$\downarrow$$
$$PdCl_2$$

of ethylene and palladium chloride with acetic acid in isooctane containing dissodium hydrogen phosphate gives vinyl acetate in good yield. Baird[3] examined the reaction of the π-complex of norbornene (1) with sodium acetate and cupric chloride and obtained *exo*-2-chloro-*syn*-7-acetoxynorbornane (2) in 84% yield. Cupric chloride is used not only as a source of chloride ion but as an oxidation-reduction reagent for the palladium chloride. Treatment of (2) with potassium *t*-butoxide in DMSO gives

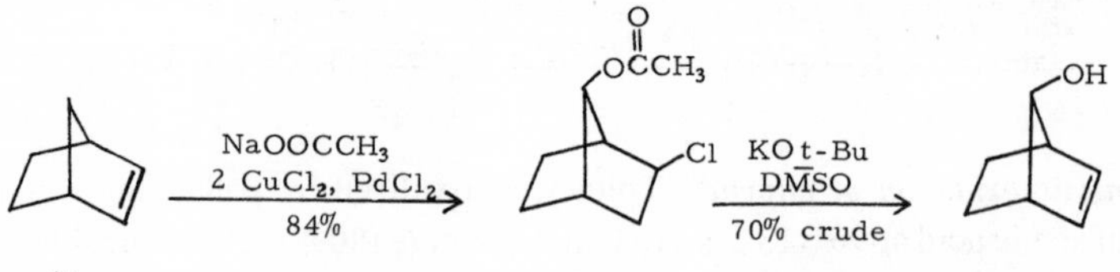

(1)   (2)   (3)

syn-7-norbornenol (3) in 70% yield (83% pure by VPC analysis). This two-step procedure is the most convenient route to (3).

Carbonylation of various unsaturated compounds in the presence of palladium chloride is described by Tsuji *et al.*[4-8] Since olefins form complexes with palladium chloride, these apparently are involved, but generally have not been prepared directly. In the case of simple olefins the general reaction is considered to be:

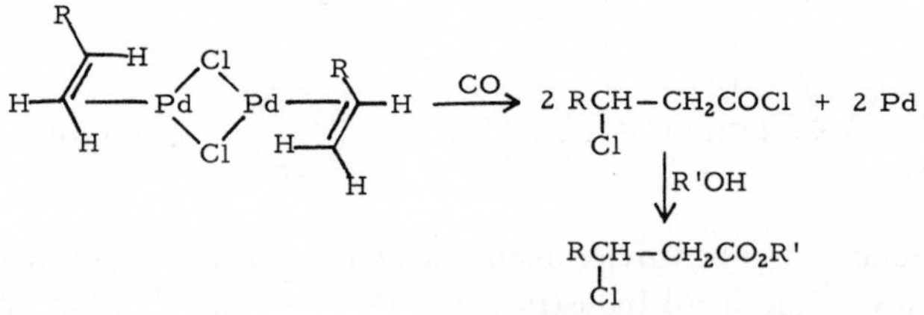

Yields are 5–40%. Study of allylic compounds[5] and of butadiene[6] has led to the following formulation of the complex of butadiene with palladium chloride and the two products obtained on carbonylation:

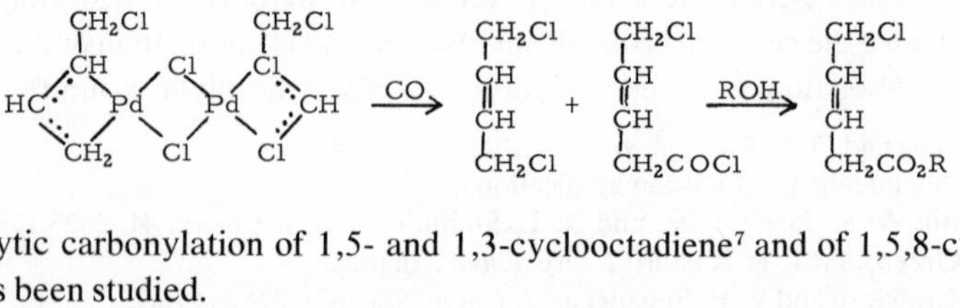

The catalytic carbonylation of 1,5- and 1,3-cyclooctadiene[7] and of 1,5,8-cyclodeca-triene[8] has been studied.

[2] E. W. Stern and M. L. Spector, *Proc. Chem. Soc.*, 370 (1961)
[3] W. C. Baird, Jr., *J. Org.*, **31**, 2411 (1966)
[4] J. Tsuji, M. Morikawa, and J. Kiji, *Am. Soc.*, **86**, 4851 (1964)

[5]J. Tsuji *et al, ibid.*, **86**, 4350 (1964); R. Long and G. H. Whitfield, *J. Chem. Soc.*, 1852 (1964)
[6]J. Tsuji *et al.*, *Tetrahedron Letters*, 605 (1964)
[7]J. Tsuji *et al.*, *Bull. Soc. Chem. Japan*, **39**, 141 (1966)
[8]J. Tsuji and T. Nogi, *ibid.*, **39**, 146 (1966)

Palladium hydroxide catalyst [1, 782, before **Pentachlorophenol**]. This hydrogenation catalyst is prepared by adding a slight excess of lithium hydroxide solution to a hot aqueous solution of palladium chloride; the precipitate is washed to neutrality with hot distilled water.[1] Reduction of cyclohexanones in an alcohol with prereduced palladium hydroxide as catalyst gives cyclohexyl ethers in high yield.[2] Thus 5α-cholestane-3-one gives β-methoxy-5α-cholestane in 91% yield when reduced in methanol. Hydrogenation of cyclohexanol in ethanol affords ethoxycyclohexane in 96% yield.

[1]S. Nishimura, M. Shimahara, and M. Shiota, *J. Org.*, **31**, 2394 (1966)
[2]S. Nishimura, T. Itaya, and M. Shiota, *Chem. Commun.*, 422 (1967)

Pentachlorophenol [1, 782–783, before reference].

Active pentachlorophenyl esters of amino acids have also been prepared by ester exchange of trialkylammonium salts of acylamino acids with pentachlorophenyl trichloroacetate or dichloroacetate.[2]

[2]M. Fujino and C. Hatanaka, *Chem. Pharm. Bull.*, **16**, 929 (1968)

Pentaethoxyphosphorane, $(C_2H_5O)_5P$ [1, 785, before **Peracetic acid**]. Mol. wt. 140.03.
The reagent is prepared conveniently by allowing triethyl phosphite to react

$$(C_2H_5O)_3P \ + \ (C_2H_5O)_2 \ \longrightarrow \ (C_2H_5O)_5P$$

(1)

with diethyl peroxide at room temperature for 15 days.[1] The concentration of (1) in the solution is then at a maximum of 60%. The reaction mixture can be enriched in (1) by distillation at low pressure.

Alkylations.[1] Pentaethoxyphosphorane is a powerful ethylating agent; no acidic or basic catalyst is required, and no acids or bases are generated. It converts acids quantitatively into ethyl esters; phenols into ethyl phenolates; enolic substrates into enol ethers. Diethyl malonate reacts slowly to give diethyl ethylmalonate in 88% yield.

[1]D. B. Denney and L. Saferstein, *Am. Soc.*, **88**, 1839 (1966)

Pentamethylbenzyl chloride, $(CH_3)_5C_6CH_2Cl$ [1, 785, before **Peracetic acid**]. Mol. wt. 196.72, m.p. 81–82°.

Preparation by chloromethylation of pentamethylbenzene with formaldehyde and concd. HCl in acetic acid.[1]

Peptide synthesis. Stewart[2] recommends use of pentamethylbenzyl esters in peptide synthesis because the protective group is cleaved rapidly by trifluoroacetic acid (also by HBr–AcOH). 2,4,6-Trimethylbenzyl esters are somewhat less labile.

[1]R. R. Aiken, G. M. Badger, and J. W. Cook, *J. Chem. Soc.*, 331 (1950); F. Bennington, R. D. Morin, and L. C. Clark, Jr., *J. Org.*, **23**, 2034 (1958)
[2]F. H. C. Stewart, *Australian J. Chem.*, **20**, 2243 (1967); *idem*, *Chem. Ind.*, 1960 (1967)

***trans*-3-Pentene-2-one,** $\begin{matrix} CH_3 \\ H \end{matrix} C=C \begin{matrix} H \\ C=O \\ H_3C \end{matrix}$ [**1**, 785, before **Peracetic acid**]. Mol. wt.

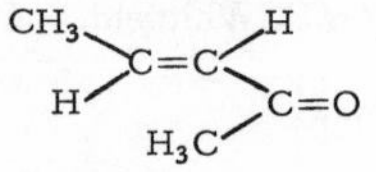

84. 11, b.p. 121–122.5°. Supplier: A.

Preparation. Noticing that the unsaturated ketone prepared by oxidation of the corresponding alcohol is difficult to obtain free from starting material, House *et al.*[1] found it preferable to prepare the reagent by a Wittig reaction between acetaldehyde and acetylmethylenetriphenylphosphorane.

$$CH_3CHO + CH_3COCH=P(C_6H_5)_3 \longrightarrow CH_3CH=CHCOCH_3 + (C_6H_5)_3PO$$

Robinson annelation. Marshall *et al.*[2] achieved the total synthesis of racemic isonootkatone (α-vetivone, formula 12) as follows. Diethyl isopropylidenemalonate (1) was reduced with lithium aluminum hydride to the diol (2), which was converted through the dibromide (3) and the ester (4) into the unsaturated diacid (5). The

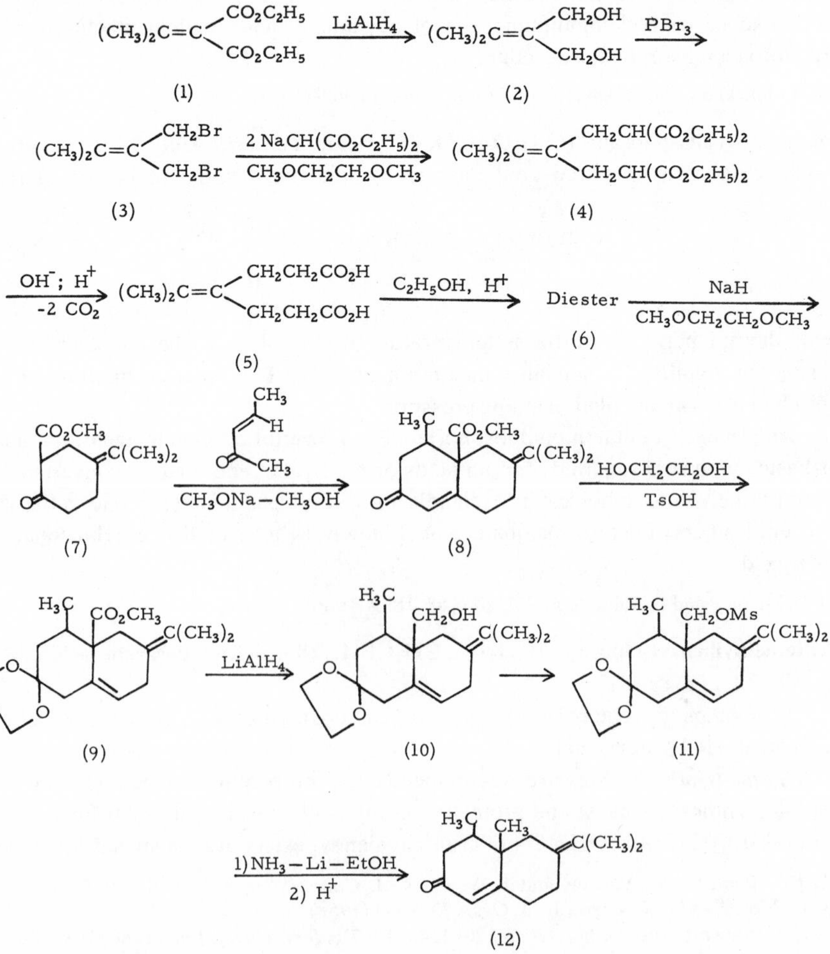

(1)   LiAlH₄ →   (2)   PBr₃ →

(3)   (4)

(5)   (6)

(7)   (8)

(9)   (10)   (11)

(12)

corresponding diethylester (6) on Dieckmann cyclization, effected by sodium hydride in 1,2-dimethoxyethane, gave the cyclic β-keto ester (7). Robinson annelation of (7) occurred smoothly upon treatment first with *trans*-3-pentene-2-one in the presence of 0.1 equiv. of sodium methoxide at 0° to effect Michael addition, and then with an excess of the same base at room temperature to complete aldol cyclization. Treatment with ethylene glycol and a trace of *p*-toluenesulfonic acid in refluxing benzene (Dean-Stark water trap) afforded the ethylene ketal (9). Reduction with lithium aluminum hydride to the alcohol (10) was followed by conversion to the mesylate (11). Reduction of the mesylate with lithium in ammonia–ethanol gave a mixture from which, after acid hydrolysis to effect deketalization, racemic isonootkatone (12) was isolated readily by chromatography on silica gel.

[1]H. O. House, W. L. Respass, and G. M. Whitesides, *J. Org.*, **31**, 3128 (1966)
[2]J. A. Marshall, H. Faubl, and T. M. Warne, Jr., *Chem. Commun.*, 753 (1967)

t-**Pentyl chloroformate (*t*-Amyl chloroformate)** [**1**, 785, before **Peracetic acid**]. Mol. wt. 150.61.

Preparation.[1]

$$CH_3CH_2\overset{\underset{\displaystyle CH_3}{|}}{\underset{|}{\overset{CH_3}{C}}}COH \ + \ Cl\overset{O}{\overset{\|}{C}}Cl \ \xrightarrow[60\%]{Py\ (-60°)} \ CH_3CH_2\overset{\underset{\displaystyle CH_3}{|}}{\underset{|}{\overset{CH_3}{C}}}O-\overset{O}{\overset{\|}{C}}Cl$$

Peptide synthesis.[1] The reagent is colorless and can be stored for over ten days in a deep freeze. It has been used as an alternative to carbobenzoxy chloride for the N-protection of amino acids. Condensation with an amino acid is carried out in chloroform in the presence of triethylamine. The blocking group is cleaved by trifluoroacetic acid or hydrogen chloride.

[1]S. Sakakibara, M. Shin, M. Fujino, Y. Shimonishi, S. Inoue, and N. Inukai,*Bull. Chem. Soc. Japan*, **38**, 1522 (1965); S. Sakakibara and M. Fujino, *ibid.*, **39**, 947 (1966)

Peracetic acid b[1, 785–787].

Epoxidation of olefins. [**1**, 785–786, at end]. The previously unknown monoepoxide (2) of the highly reactive cyclopentadiene (1) has been prepared in 70–75% yield.[3a] Since the unsaturated epoxide (2) is highly sensitive to acids the epoxidation

was done in methylene chloride in the presence of anhydrous sodium carbonate with 40% peracetic acid that had been treated with sodium acetate to neutralize traces of

mineral acid. This method was used by Crandall and Paulson[3b] to prepare the monoepoxide (4) of 1,2-bis(isopropylidene)-3,3-dimethylcyclopropane (3), and was
applied by Crandall et al.[3c] to cyclic conjugated C_6–C_8 dienes. Good yields were obtained with a 1 : 1 ratio of reactants with simplification in the separation of the epoxide
from excess diene. Reduction of the epoxide (6) with LiAlH$_4$ leads to the homoallylic
alcohol (7).

The method was also used for epoxidation of the alkenylidenecyclopropane (1);
the predominant product (64% yield) was the ketone (3). The minor product (27%
yield) was identified as (4). Both are considered to be formed from an intermediate
allene epoxide (2).[3d]

Buffered peracid oxidation of the allene (5) with two equivalents of peracid gives
the interesting spiro diepoxide (6) in high yield.[3e] Attempts to prepare the monoxide
by use of one equivalent of oxidant led to recovery of the allene (5) and formation

of the diepoxide (6). Epoxidation of the allene (7) unexpectedly led to the cyclopropanone (9). The allene epoxide (8) is considered to be an intermediate.[3f] Camp and Greene [3g] have obtained an allene oxide (11, m-chloroperbenzoic acid) and found that it rearranges to a cyclopropanone (12) when heated to 100°. Evidently in this case the cyclopropanone is also more stable than the epoxide.

$$\text{(CH}_3)_3\text{C} \underset{H}{\overset{}{\diagdown}} \text{C}=\text{C}=\text{C} \underset{H}{\overset{\text{C(CH}_3)_3}{\diagup}} \xrightarrow{\underline{m}\text{-ClC}_6\text{H}_4\text{COOOH, }25^0} \text{(CH}_3)_3\text{CCH} \underset{}{\overset{O}{\diagup\diagdown}} \text{C}=\text{CHC(CH}_3)_3$$

(10)   (11)

$$\xrightarrow{100^0} \quad \text{H}\cdot\cdot\overset{(CH_3)_3C}{\underset{}{\text{C}}}\overset{O}{\overset{\|}{\diagup\diagdown}}\text{C}\cdot\cdot\cdot\overset{}{\underset{H}{\text{C(CH}_3)_3}}$$

(12)

[3a]M. Korach, D. R. Nielsen, and W. H. Rideout, *Am. Soc.*, **82**, 4328 (1960)

[3b]J. K. Crandall and D. R. Paulson, *J. Org.*, **33**, 991 (1968)

[3c]J. K. Crandall, D. B. Parks, R. A. Colyer, R. J. Watkins, and J. P. Arrington, *ibid.*, **33**, 423 (1968)

[3d]J. K. Crandall, D. R. Paulson, and C. A. Bunnell, *Tetrahedron Letters*, 5063 (1968)

[3e]J. K. Crandall, W. H. Machleder, and M. J. Thomas, *Am. Soc.*, **90**, 7346 (1968)

[3f]J. K. Crandall and W. H. Machleder, *ibid.*, **90**, 7347 (1968)

[3g]R. L. Camp and F. D. Greene, *ibid.*, **90**, 7349 (1968)

Perchloric acid [1, 796–802].

A supplementary note on **Iodine as catalyst for dehydration** calls attention to the interesting finding that perchloric acid is a superior reagent for the rearrangement of benzopinacols.

Preparation of enol acetates [1, 800, after citation of ref. 18] It has been shown in at least two cases that the perchloric acid catalyzed acetic anhydride enol acetylation is thermodynamically controlled.[18a] Thus the 3-keto-5β-steroid, 17β-acetoxy-5β-androstane-3-one (1), on reaction with acetic anhydride–perchloric acid gives the two enol acetates (2) and (3) in the ratio 93.5 to 6.5. The calculated ratio derived from the relative stability of (2) and (3) is 96:4. If a mixture of 65% of (2)

(1)   (2)   (3)

and 35% of (3) is subjected to the reaction conditions, the equilibrium mixture of 94:6 of (2) to (3) is obtained after 3.5 hrs. Enol acetylation of (1) with isopropenyl acetate (kinetic control) gives (2) and (3) in the ratio 71:29. The presence of an 11β-hydroxyl group causes an increase in the proportion of (3).[18b]

Other catalytic effects [1, 801–802, at end]. Treatment of a steroid 5α,6α-diol (1) with a trace of perchloric acid in refluxing dioxane results in rearrangement to the 5-epimeric ketones (2) and (3). On treatment with sodium ethoxide in ethanol, (3) is converted into (2), the point of equilibrium being 93% of the 5α-ketone and 7% of the 5β-ketone.[24a]

(1)   (2) 10%   (3) 50%

Perchloric acid strongly accelerates aromatic mercuration in acetic acid solution; it converts mercuric acetate into a positively charged electrophile.[24b,c,d]

$$HClO_4 + Hg(OAc)_2 \rightleftharpoons \overset{+}{Hg}OAcClO_4^- + HOAc$$

Perchloric acid (70%) is superior to sulfuric acid or methanesulfonic acid for the isomerization of oleic acid to γ-stearolactone (2). The most satisfactory procedure is use of a 1 : 1 molar ratio and a temperature of 100° for 3 hrs.[24e]

(4)   (5)

Etherification [**1**, 802, before references]. 3β-Hydroxy-Δ⁵-steroids are etherified in 75–85% yield by treatment with a trialkyl orthoformate and 72% perchloric acid (2 : 1 equivalents).[26]

[18a]J. Champagne, H. Favre, D. Vocelle, and I. Zbikowski, *Canad. J. Chem.*, **42**, 212 (1964); A. J. Liston, *J. Org.*, **31**, 2105 (1966)

[18b]A. J. Liston and M. Howart, *J. Org.*, **32**, 1034 (1967)

[24a]M. Fétizon and P. Foy, *Bull. soc.*, 2653 (1967)

[24b]H. C. Brown and C. W. McGary, Jr., *Am. Soc.*, **77**, 2306 (1955)

[24c]R. M. Schramm, W. S. Klapproth, and F. H. Westheimer, *J. Phys. Colloid Chem.*, **55**, 843 (1951)

[24d]A. J. Kresge, M. Dubeck, and H. C. Brown, *J. Org.*, **32**, 745 (1967)

[24e]J. S. Showell, D. Swern, and W. R. Noble, *ibid.*, **33**, 2697 (1968)

[26]J. P. Dusza, J. P. Joseph and S. Bernstein, *Steroids*, **8**, 495 (1966)

Perchloryl fluoride [1, 802–808].

Fluorination of active-methylene compounds [**1**, 803, after citation of ref. 3]. Fluorination of an enolate activated by only one carbonyl group has been observed. Thus the sodioenolate of methyl isobutyrate on treatment with perchloryl fluoride gives 4-fluoro-3-keto-2,2,4-trimethylpentanoate as the only pure product in 30% yield. It is possible that this fluorination is successful only in the case of replacement of a tertiary hydrogen.[3a]

[**1**, after line 4 from bottom]: An investigation of the reaction of the reagent with testosterone enol diacetate in aqueous dioxane by Osawa and Neeman[12a] resulted in isolation of the five products formulated. The axial products predominated in the 6-fluoro series as well as in the 6-hydroxy series, implying that both reactions

involved electrophilic attack at C_6. The same investigators[12a] treated 19-nortestosterone enol diacetate with perchloryl fluoride in aqueous dioxane and isolated 6β-hydroxy-19-nortestosterone 17-acetate (3) in 15% yield. Pataki and Wlos[12b] added 85 ml. of water to a solution of 12.25 g. of 19-nortestosterone enol diacetate in 550 ml. of tetrahydrofurane and bubbled perchloryl fluoride into the stirred solution at room temperature for 40 min. Chromatography afforded the three products formulated.

[3a]W. J. Gensler, Q. A. Ahmed, and M. V. Leeding, *J. Org.*, **33**, 4279 (1968)
[12a]Y. Osawa and M. Neeman, *ibid.*, **32**, 3055 (1967)
[12b]J. Pataki and R. Wlos, *Steroids*, **11**, 225 (1968)

Periodates [1, 809–815].

Sulfides → sulfoxides [1, 810]. The oxidation of thioanisole to methyl phenyl sulfoxide by the method of Leonard and Johnson[5] has been described in detail.[5a] The procedure has been applied to the preparation of ten other sulfoxides with yields

$$C_6H_5SCH_3 \xrightarrow[91\%]{NaIO_4} C_6H_5\overset{\overset{O}{\|}}{S}CH_3 + NaIO_3$$

ranging from 65–99%. The method is said to be "excellent" for preparation of 1-

azulyl sulfoxides.[5b] Sodium periodate can be used successfully for oxidation of thio ethers containing a disulfide linkage.[5c] In the case illustrated use of chromium tri-

$$C_6H_5SS(CH_2)_2CONH(CH_2)_2SCH(C_6H_5)_2 \xrightarrow[\substack{71\%}]{\substack{NaIO_4, \\ CH_3OH, \ 0^0}} C_6H_5SS(CH_2)_2CONH(CH_2)_2\overset{O}{\overset{\|}{S}}CH(C_6H_5)_2$$

oxide, hydrogen peroxide, or m-chloroperbenzoic acid led to extensive decomposition.

Periodate–Permanganate oxidation [1, 810–812, at end]. In carrying out the oxidation of (R)-(+)-citronellol (8) to the 6-hydroxy-4-methylhexanoic acid (9) by the Lemieux–von Rudloff reagent, Overberger and Kaye[16a] used acetone–water as the medium in order to conduct the oxidation at a higher concentration.

(8)   (9)

Ogiso and Pelletier[16b] effected oxidative cleavage of the α,β-unsaturated ketone (10) with the reagent "under very carefully defined conditions."

(10)   (11)

Periodate–Osmium tetroxide oxidation [1, 812–813, after citation of ref. 22]. A British group has reported two cases where cleavage of an exocyclic methylene group is effected more cleanly by this reagent than by ozonolysis.[22a]

Shamma and Rodriguez[22b] found that catalytic oxidation of (1) to the aldehyde (2) by the original procedure of Lemieux-Johnson[18] (2 molar equivalents of NaIO$_4$ added over a period of 30–40 min.) proceeded in high yield when carried out on a small scale (less than 5 g.). Yields decreased constantly as the amount of (1) was increased. This difficulty was overcome by adding the periodate through a capillary over about 10 hrs. To a solution of (1, 0.09 mole) in dioxane was added 7.8 mmoles

(1)   (2)

of OsO_4. The mixture was stirred for 15 min. to allow formation of the osmate ester and then diluted with water. $NaIO_4$ (0.21 moles) in water was then added over a period of 10 hrs. The yield of (2) was 79%.

Oxidative cleavage [1, 814, before references]. Pyridine is recommended as the solvent for periodate oxidation of various vicinally disubstituted lipids. The oxidation occurs in high yield at room temperature. Thus *cis,cis*-9,12-octadecadiene-1-al has been obtained in 71% yield by oxidation of *cis,cis*-10,13-nonadecadiene-1,2-diol with sodium metaperiodate in dry pyridine.[27]

Review of the organic chemistry of periodates.[28]

[5a]C. R. Johnson and J. E. Keiser, *Org. Syn.*, **46**, 78 (1966)
[5b]L. L. Replogle and J. R. Maynard, *J. Org.*, **32**, 1909 (1967)
[5c]R. G. Hiskey and M. H. Harpold, *ibid.*, **32**, 3191 (1967)
[16a]C. G. Overberger and H. Kaye, *Am. Soc.*, **89**, 5640 (1967)
[16b]H. Ogiso and S. W. Pelletier, *Chem. Commun.*, 94 (1967)
[22a]K. H. Baggaley, J. R. Dixon, J. M. Evans, and S. H. Graham, *Tetrahedron*, **23**, 299 (1967); K. H. Baggaley, W. H. Evans, S. H. Graham, D. A. Jonas, and D. H. Jones, *ibid.*, **24**, 3445 (1968)
[22b]M. Shamma and H. R. Rodriguez, *Tetrahedron*, **24**, 6583 (1968)
[27]W. J. Baumann, H. H. O. Schmid, and H. K. Mangold, *J. Lipid Res.*, **10**, 132 (1969)
[28]B. Sklarz, *Quart. Rev.*, **21**, 3 (1967)

Periodic acid [1, 815–819].

vic-Glycol cleavage [1, 815–817, at end]. A new method for the stepwise degradation of the bile acid side chain[10a] involves α-bromination (2), hydrolysis, and periodate oxidation of the resulting α-hydroxy acid. In this step a solution of (3) in a 4:4:1 mixture of acetone:acetic acid:water was treated with excess sodium periodate

(1)   (2)

(3)   (4)

and stirred at 40–50° for 24 hrs. The aldehyde (4) was isolated in 90% yield. Replacement of acetone by ethanol as a component of the solvent mixture lowered the yield. Use of lead tetraacetate for cleavage of (3) gave a complex mixture from which (4) could be isolated in only about 50% yield.

The oxidation of methyl glycopyranosides with periodic acid in DMSO is unusual in that only 1 mole of oxidant is consumed. Most of the stereoselective oxidation observed can be explained on the assumption that *vic-cis*-diols (axial-equatorial) are more reactive than *vic-trans*-diols (diequatorial or diaxial).[10b]

Oxidative dimerization[18] [**1**, 818, before references]. Pyrene (1) is converted into bipyrene (2) by reaction with periodic acid in aqueous acetic acid at 48-51° for 45

min. The success of this simple synthesis is attributed to the specific ability of the oxidant to associate with pyrene molecules and abstract hydrogen to produce acetic acid-solvated radicals capable of dimerization to bipyrene.

Fatiadi[19] examined the behavior of other polycyclic hydrocarbons toward periodic acid and found that four of them are oxidized to quinones, not to dimeric products.

The oxidation of naphthalene is noteworthy, for the best yield of 1,4-naphthoquinone obtained with other reagents is 18–22% (CrO$_3$, see **1**, 144).

²*Add: See also* B. Sklarz, *Quart. Rev.*, **21**, 3 (1967)
[10a]Y. Yanuka, R. Katz, and S. Sarel, *Tetrahedron Letters*, 1725 (1968)
[10b]R. J. Yu and C. T. Bishop, *Canad. J. Chem.*, **45**, 2195 (1967)
[18]A. J. Fatiadi, *J. Org.*, **32**, 2903 (1967); *idem*, procedure submitted to *Org. Syn.*
[19]A. J. Fatiadi, *Chem. Commun.*, 1087 (1967)

Periodic acid–Chromic acid [1, 819 before Permaleic acid]. Perold and Pachler[1] used the combination of periodic and chromic acid to degrade the primary-secondary

glycol group of (1) to the carboxyl group of (3). The more powerful oxidant, periodic acid, specifically cleaves the *vic*-glycol bond and also regenerates the chromic acid utilized in oxidation of the intermediate aldehyde (2).

[1]G. W. Perold and K. G. R. Pachler, *J. Chem. Soc.*, (C), 1918 (1966)

Perlauric acid, C$_{11}$ H$_{23}$COOOH **[1, 819, before Permaleic acid].** Mol. wt. 216.31, m.p. 52°.

Preparation.[1] Long-chain aliphatic peracids are readily obtained by the reaction of the acid with 0.5-2.0 moles of 50–65% hydrogen peroxide in concentrated sulfuric acid solution. The conversion of lauric acid to perlauric acid is nearly quantitative.

Oxidation of sulfides to sulfoxides.[2] In initial experiments on the oxidation of the sulfide (1) to the sulfoxide (2). Jones and Green[2] used hydrogen peroxide in acetic acid. The reaction was slow and required 24 hrs. They then changed to perlauric acid in petroleum ether (40–60°) and reduced the time to 15 mins. There is some overoxidation to the sulfone, but this can be avoided by using less than one equivalent of the peracid and repeating the oxidation.

[1]W. E. Parker, C. Ricciuti, C. L. Ogg, and D. Swern, *Am. Soc.*, 77, 4037 (1955)
[2]D. N. Jones and M. J. Green, *J. Chem. Soc.*, (C), 532 (1967)

Pertrifluoroacetic acid [1, 821–827].

Pagano and Emmons[1a] describe a procedure for the oxidation of 2,6-dichloroaniline to 2,6-dichloronitrobenzene in which hydrogen peroxide (90%) is added

$$\xrightarrow[0.25°]{90\% \ H_2O_2, \ (CF_3CO)_2O, \ CH_2Cl_2}$$

without stirring to methylene chloride and the two-layer system is stirred with ice cooling and trifluoroacetic anhydride is added slowly. Stirring is continued at room temperature for 30 min. and a solution of 2,6-dichloroaniline is then added dropwise and the exothermic reaction mixture is allowed to reflux. Water is added and the organic layer is separated, washed, dried, and the solvent evaporated. Crystallization of the residue gives a light yellow product, m.p. 68–70°.

[1, 826]: *Correction*: Formula (4), top right, lacks one methyl group. It should be as shown:

Pertrifluoroacetic acid–Boron trifluoride [1, 826, after citation of ref. 13]. Hart and Lerner[13a] found that this combination is capable of oxidizing alkenes directly to ketones. It is postulated that the reaction proceeds by attack of OH^+ on the double bond and hydride migration in the resulting carbonium ion to give the ketone:

Other examples of this reaction have been reported.[13b]

[1a]A. S. Pagano and W. D. Emmons, procedure submitted to *Org. Syn.*
[13]*Add*: H. Hart, R. M. Lange, and P. M. Collins, *Org. Syn.*, 48, 87 (1968)
[13a]H. Hart and L. R. Lerner, *J. Org.*, 32, 2669 (1967)
[13b]H. Hart and R. M. Lange, *ibid.*, 31, 3776 (1966); P. M. Collins and H. Hart, *J. Chem. Soc.*, (C), 895 (1967); H. Hart and R. K. Murray, Jr., *J. Org.*, 32, 2448 (1967)

Phenacyl bromide, $C_6H_5COCH_2Br$ [1, 827, before **Phenanthrenequinone**]. Mol. wt. 199.05, m.p. 48–51°. Preparation, *see* 1, 32. Suppliers: A, E.

Peptide synthesis. Zervas and co-workers[1] prepared phenacyl esters of amino acids by treating a carbobenzoxyamino acid with phenacyl bromide and triethylamine in ethyl acetate. The phenacyl ester group is stable to acid but can be cleaved by catalytic hydrogenation or by treatment with sodium thiophenoxide in a nonaqueous medium under mild conditions. p-Bromophenacyl esters have been considered by Australian chemists[2] who, however, concluded that phenacyl-type esters may not be generally suitable for carboxyl protection in slow coupling procedures.

[1]G. C. Stelakatos, A. Paganou, and L. Zervas, *J. Chem. Soc.*, (C),1191 (1966)
[2]R. Ledger and F. H. C. Stewart, *Australian J. Chem.*, **20**, 787 (1967)

Phenanthrenequinone [**1**, 827–828, before references]. Phenanthrenequinone reacts specifically with arginine and with arginyl peptides to form the highly fluorescent 2-amino-1H-phenanthro[9,10-d]imidazole. This very sensitive test is useful for the detection of arginine-containing peptides.[6]

[6]S. Yamada and H. A. Itano, *Biochem. Biophys. Acta* **130**, 538 (1966)

p-Phenylazomaleinanil [**N-(p-phenylazophenyl)maleimide**] [**1**, 833]. Additional supplier: Eastman.

Phenylboronic acid [**1**, 833–834]. Correct mol. wt. 121.94. Additional suppliers: K.-L., Alfa Inorganics.

[Before references]: Brooks and Watson[5] have found the phenylboronate esters of 1,2- and 1,3-diols useful for characterization by gas chromatography and mass spectroscopy. The *cis*-diol system in the sesquiterpenoid (1) was confirmed by for-

(1)   (2)

mation of the cyclic ester (2) detected with a few micrograms of diol by gas chromatography and confirmed by combined gas chromatography-mass spectrometry.

Phenylboronate esters were used as protective derivatives in the oxidation of glycosides with DMSO–Ac$_2$O.[6] The particular advantage is the ease of removal from sensitive ketoglycosides and, of course, the stability to the oxidizing agent.

[5]C. J. W. Brooks and J. Watson, *Chem. Commun.*, 952 (1967)
[6]B. Lindberg and K. N. Slessor, *Chem. Scand.*, **21**, 910 (1967)

$$CH_2CH_3$$
$$|$$

α-Phenylbutyric anhydride, $(C_6H_5CHCO)_2O$ [**1**, 834, before **Phenylcyclone**]. Mol. wt. 310.38, oil.

Preparation. By refluxing α-phenylbutyric acid (suppliers: Aldrich, Eastman) with acetic anhydride for 6 hrs. and removal of the solvent.

Determination of configuration by asymmetric esterification. This method developed by Horeau[1,2] for determining the configuration of an optically active secondary alcohol is based upon the Cram[3]-Prelog[4] rule of asymmetric synthesis.

Horeau deduced that an alcohol of the R-configuration shown (L = large; M = medium; S = small) should react with an excess of α-phenylbutyric acid to give an ester and that the excess acid should be optically active and of the (+)-S-configuration. An alcohol of the S-configuration would lead to recovery of the R-acid.

Horeau and Kagan[5] applied the method to a large number of steroids and found that it led to the correct configurations. It has been applied successfully to terpenes,[1,2] to caryophyllene derivatives,[6] to grayanotoxin-I (1) and related toxins,[7] and to sesquiterpene lactones,[8] for example (2).

(1) Grayanotoxin-I

(2) 1-Epiallohelenalin

[1]A. Horeau, *Tetrahedron Letters*, 506 (1961)

[2]*Idem, ibid.*, 965 (1962)

[3]D. J. Cram and F. A. Abd Elhatez, *Am. Soc.*, **74**, 5851 (1952)

[4]V. Prelog, *Helv.*, **36**, 308 (1953)

[5]A. Horeau and H. B. Kagan, *Tetrahedron*, **20**, 2431 (1964)

[6]A. Horeau and J. K. Sutherland, *J. Chem. Soc.*, (C), 247 (1966)

[7]H. Kakisawa, T. Kuzima, M. Yanai, and K. Nakanishi, *Tetrahedron*, **21**, 3091 (1965)

[8]T. J. Mabry, W. Renold, H. E. Miller, and H. B. Kagan, *J. Org.*, **31**, 681 (1966); W. Herz and H. B. Kagan, *ibid.*, **32**, 216 (1967)

Phenyl chloroformate, $\overset{O}{\overset{\|}{Cl\,C}}OC_6H_5$ [**1**, 834, before **Phenylcyclone**]. Mol. wt. 156.57, b.p. 68–71°/9 mm. Supplier: E.

Cleavage of tertiary amines.[1] Tertiary aliphatic and alicyclic amines can be dealkylated by reaction with phenyl chloroformate in methylene chloride at 10–40°

$$R_3N + Cl\overset{O}{\overset{\|}{C}}OC_6H_5 - \left[\underset{\underset{R}{|}}{R_2\overset{+}{N}} - \overset{O}{\overset{\|}{C}}OC_6H_5 \right]Cl^- \longrightarrow R_2N\overset{O}{\overset{\|}{C}}OC_6H_5 + RCl$$

for 3–6 hrs. Yields are high (80–92%). The reagent compares favorably with cyanogen bromide in efficiency as well as convenience. The cleavage has been applied to several alkaloids, for example, to 21-desoxyajmaline (1). Reaction with this

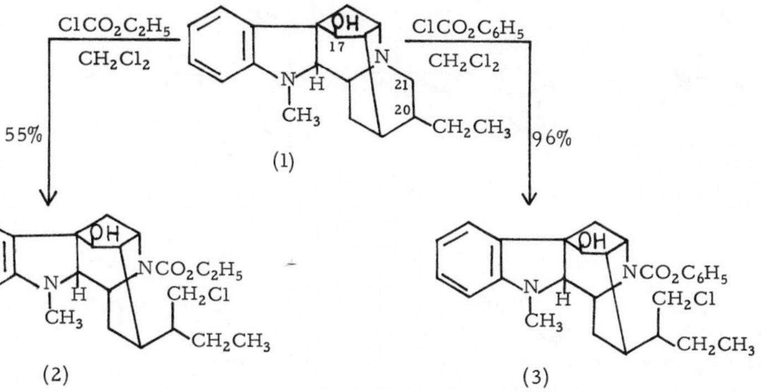

(1)

(2)   (3)

compound with ethyl or phenyl chloroformate (1.1 equiv.) in methylene chloride at 25° was complete after only 2 hrs. After removal of the water-soluble products, the chloro urethane (2) was obtained in 55% yield, whereas the N(b)-phenoxycarbonyl analog (3) was produced in virtually quantitative yield under the same conditions. Acylation of the 17-hydroxyl group did not occur to any significant extent with either ethyl or phenyl chloroformate. Ajmaline itself has another secondary alcoholic group at the 21-position (α), and in this case both reagents provide a useful means of achieving selective acylation at this position.

[1]J. D. Hobson and J. G. McCluskey, *J. Chem. Soc.*, (C), 2015 (1967)

1-Phenyl-5-chlorotetrazole, 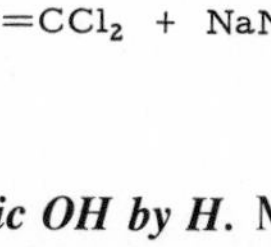 [**1**, 834, before **Phenylcyclone**]. Mol. wt. 180.60, m.p. 122–123. 50. Supplier: E.

Preparation from phenylisocyanide dichloride and sodium azide.[1]

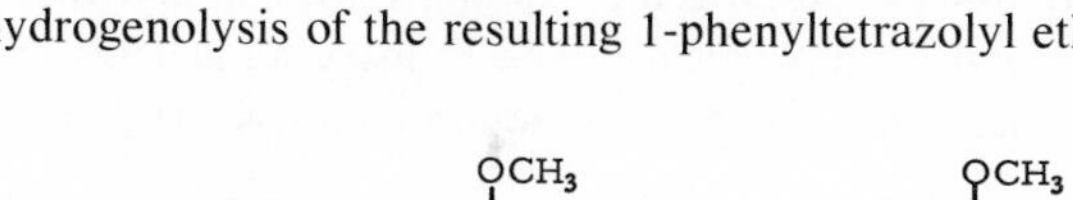

Replacement of phenolic OH by H. Musliner and Gates[2] describe a mild method for the smooth removal of a phenolic hydroxyl group involving condensation of 1-phenyl-5-chlorotetrazole with the phenol in acetone in the presence of potassium carbonate and hydrogenolysis of the resulting 1-phenyltetrazolyl ether with palladium–charcoal.

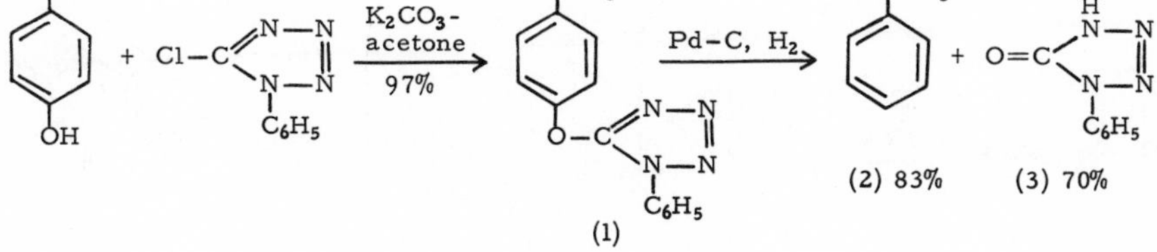

(1)   (2) 83%   (3) 70%

Another example is the conversion of *p*-phenylphenol into diphenyl.[3]

[1]C. A. Maggiulli and R. A. Paine, Belgian patent 671,402 (1966) [*C.A.*, **85**, 8926 (1966)]; Br. 1,128,025; Fr. 1,451,028; Ger. 1,251,327

[2]W. J. Musliner and J. W. Gates, Jr., *Am. Soc.*, **88**, 4271 (1966)

[3]*Idem*, procedure submitted to *Org. Syn.*

Phenylcyanate, $C_6H_5OC\equiv N$ [**1**, 834, before **Phenylcyclone**]. Mol. wt. 119.12, b.p. 82–83°/16 mm.

Preparation.[1] Liquid cyanogen chloride is added at 0° to a solution of phenol in acetone; triethylamine is added dropwise with stirring and cooling below 10°:

$$C_6H_5OH \ + \ Cl-C\equiv N \ \xrightarrow[94\%]{(C_2H_5)_3N} \ C_6H_5OC\equiv N$$

Use.[2] The reagent converts carboxylic acids, thiocarboxylic acids, and sulfonic acids into their anhydrides with formation of phenylcarbamate (sparingly soluble

$$2\ Cl_2CHCO_2H \ + \ C_6H_5OCN \ \xrightarrow[98\%]{} \ (Cl_2CHCO)_2O \ + \ C_6H_5O\overset{O}{\overset{\|}{C}}NH_2$$

in water or benzene). The substrate is refluxed with the reagent in benzene for 15–150 min. Yields are high.

[1]E. Grigat and R. Pütter, *Ber.*, **98**, 1168 (1965)

[2]*Idem, ibid.*, **98**, 1359 (1965)

Phenyldiazomethane [**1**, 834, before references].

Catalytic activity. Diazoalkanes, in particular phenyldiazomethane, catalyze the condensation of active hydrogen compounds, for example methyl salicylate (1), with isocyanates and isothiocyanates. The primary adduct (2) undergoes cyclization to (3). The rate of the catalyzed reaction parallels the proton mobility of the

(1) 1.15 g.   (2)   (3) 0.95 g.

active hydrogen compound. The effect is explained by the formation of a proton-bridge complex between the diazoalkane and the active hydrogen compound. The cyclization reaction of the primary adduct is explained in the same way.[3]

Other examples.

I[4]

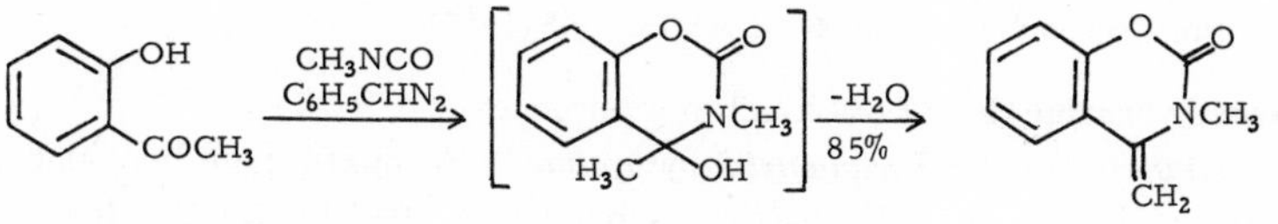

II[5]

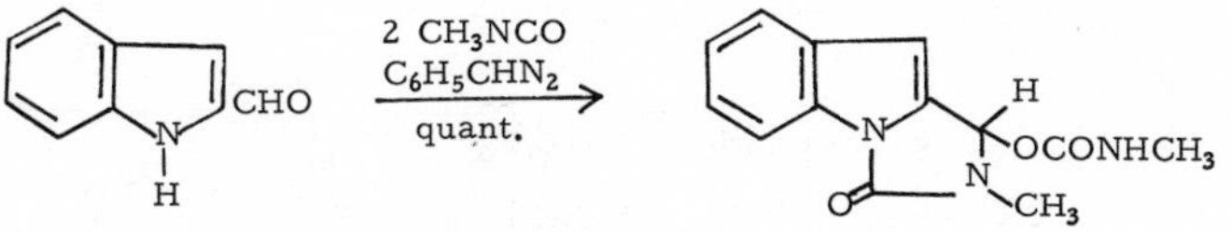

[2]Change to: J.-P. Anselme, *Org. Preparations Procedures* **1**, 73 (1969)
[3]L. Capuano and M. Zander, *Ber.*, **99**, 3085 (1966)
[4]*Idem, ibid.*, **100**, 3520 (1967)
[5]L. L. Capuano and M. Welter, *ibid.*, **101**, 3671 (1968)

o-Phenylene phosphorochloridate [1, 837].

Phosphorylation. Calderón used hydrogenolysis with Adam's catalyst for conversion of (4) to (5).[2a]

[2a]J. Calderón and G. Moreno, *Anales Real. Soc. Espan., Fis. Quim.* **56**, B, 603 (1960); M. A. Calama and J. Calderón, *ibid.*, **62**, B, 1015 (1966)

o-Phenylene phosphorochloridite,

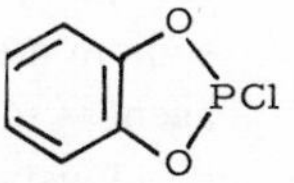

[1, 838, before *d*- and *1*-*α*-Phenyle-

thylamine]. Mol. wt. 174.52, m.p. 30°, b.p. 91°/18 min. *Preparation*[1] from catechol and PCl_3 (94% yield). Supplier: Eastman.

Conversion of alcohols to iodides.[2] An alcohol, for example cyclohexanol (1), is treated in ether solution with the cyclic phosphorochloridite (2) in the presence of pyridine to form the phosphite (3), which on treatment with iodine gives the

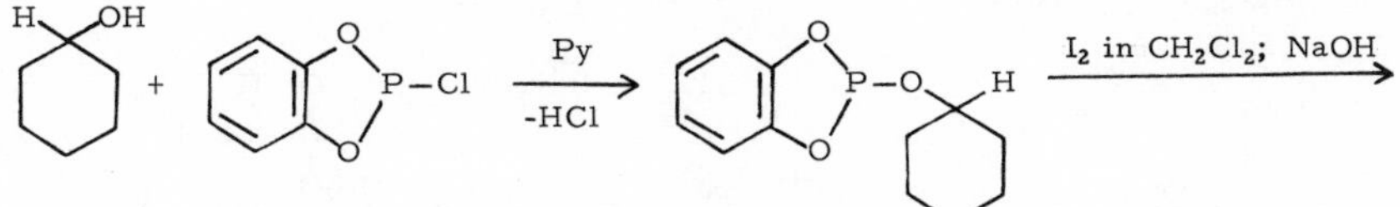

(1)   (2)   (3)

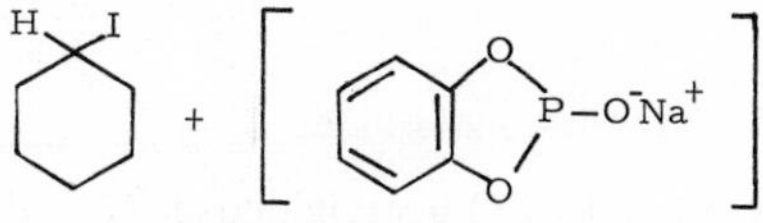

(4) 87%   (5) in H_2O

desired iodide (4) and *o*-phenylene iodophosphate, which is rapidly hydrolyzed to (5). The method is particularly valuable for alcohols that are prone to undergo elimination. This method is an improvement over that of Forsman and Lipkin,[3] who used diphenyl phosphorochloridite as the key reagent.

[1]P. C. Crofts, J. H. H. Markes, and H. N. Rydon, *J. Chem. Soc.*, 4250 (1958)
[2]E. J. Corey and J. E. Anderson, *J. Org.*, **32**, 4160 (1967)
[3]J. P. Forsman and D. Lipkin, *Am. Soc.*, **75**, 3145 (1953)

Phenylhydrazine [1, 838–842, before references].

Synthesis of 1,3,5-triphenyl-2-pyrazoline.[18] A mixture of benzalacetophenone, acetic acid, and phenylhydrazine is heated at 90–100° for 2–3 hrs. and then let cool to room temperature. The product separates in small yellow crystals of satis-

factory purity as judged by m.p. (130–131°) and UV absorption at 240 and 355 mμ (ϵ max 13,620, 16,950).

[18]S. R. Sandler, procedure submitted to *Org. Syn.*, 1968

Phenyl isocyanate [1, 842–843, before references].

Carbanilates.[5] Phenyl isocyanate reacts with carbohydrates having a free hydroxy group to give carbanilates, which generally are readily crystallized derivatives resistant to acid hydrolysis but cleaved by sodium methoxide in methanol. Since the reagent is readily hydrolyzed to the amine, the pyridine used as solvent must be scrupulously dry.

In an example described by Hearon *et al.*[6] methyl α-D-glucose was converted into the 6-trityl derivative (1) and this was converted by acetylation to (2) and by

detritylation into methyl α-D-2,3,4-tri-O-acetylglucose (3). Reaction of (3) in pyridine with phenyl isocyanate then gave methyl 2,3,4-tri-O-acethyl-α-D-glyco-pyranoside 6-carbanilate (4). This derivative was obtained by dissolving 50 g. (0.156 mole) of (3) in 40 ml. of pyridine, adding 0.234 ml. of phenyl isocyanate and heating at 100° for 1 hr. Work-up and two crystallizations from methanol afforded (4) in 84% yield.

[5]W. M. Hearon in R. L. Whistler and M. L. Wolfrom, *Methods Carbohydrate Chem.*, **2**, 239 (1963)

[6]W. M. Hearon, J. D. Hiatt, and C. R. Fordyce, *Am. Soc.*, **66**, 995 (1944)

Phenyl isothiocyanate [**1**, 844–845, before references].

An instrument which operates on the phenyl isothiocyanate degradation scheme has been developed for the automatic determination of amino acid sequences in proteins and peptides.[4]

[4]P. Edman and G. Begg, *European J. Biochem.*, **1**, 80 (1967)

Phenylmethanesulfonyl fluoride, $C_6H_5CH_2SO_2F$ [**1**, 846, before **N-Phenylmorpholine**]. Mol. wt. 174.20, b.p. 47°. Supplier: Calbiochem., Inc.

Enzyme modification. Polgar and Bender[1,2] report use of this reagent for transforming the "serine enzyme" subtilisin-OH into the "cysteine enzyme" subtilisin-SH by the following process:

$$\text{Subtilisin-OH} \xrightarrow{C_6H_5CH_2SO_2F} \text{Subtilisin-OSO}_2\text{CH}_2\text{C}_6\text{H}_5 \xrightarrow[-C_6H_5CH_2SO_3^-]{CH_3\overset{O}{\overset{\|}{C}}S^-}$$

$$\text{Subtilisin-SCOCH}_3 \xrightarrow{H_2O} \text{Subtilisin-SH}$$

Phenylmethanesulfonyl fluoride was chosen for the first step because the phenylmethanesulfonyl group is a better leaving group in the S_N2 displacement of the second step than the *p*-toluenesulfonyl group.

[1]L. Polgar and M. L. Bender, *Am. Soc.*, **88**, 3153 (1966)
[2]L. Polgar and M. L. Bender, *Biochemistry*, **6**, 610 (1967)

2-Phenyl-3-methyl-1,3,2-oxazapospholine (3) [**1**, 846, before **N-Phenylmorpholine**]. Mol. wt. 180.17, b.p. 72–75°/0.3 mm.

Prepared[1] by heating phenylphosphorous dichloride with 2-methylaminoethanol in the presence of 2 equiv. of triethylamine:

$$C_6H_5P\begin{array}{c}Cl\\Cl\end{array} + \begin{array}{c}\overset{CH_3}{\underset{|}{HN}}-CH_2\\ |\\ HO-CH_2\end{array} \xrightarrow[41\%]{2\ (C_2H_5)_3N} C_6H_5P\begin{array}{c}\overset{CH_3}{\underset{|}{N}}-CH_2\\ |\\ O-CH_2\end{array}$$

(1)   (2)   (3)

Use.[1] The reagent deoxygenates isocyanates to give isonitriles at low temperatures (20–30°) in 50–90% yield.

$$RN=C=O + C_6H_5P\begin{array}{c}\overset{CH_3}{\underset{|}{N}}-CH_2\\ |\\ O-CH_2\end{array} \longrightarrow R\overset{+}{N}\equiv\bar{C} + C_6H_5P\begin{array}{c}\overset{O}{\overset{\|}{}}\ \overset{CH_3}{\underset{|}{N}}-CH_2\\ |\\ O-CH_2\end{array}$$

[1]T. Mukaiyama and Y. Yokota, *Bull. Chem. Soc. Japan*, **38**, 858 (1965)

Phenylthiomethyllithium, $C_6H_5SCH_2Li$ [1, 849, before **4-Phenyl-1,2,4-triazoline-3,5-dione**]. Mol. wt. 130.13.

Preparation.[1] The reagent has been prepared in solution by several procedures, the most efficient of which is metalation of thioanisole by *n*-butyllithium in the presence of DABCO (yield 97%). In the absence of the amine the yield is about 35%.

Homologation of primary alkyl bromides or iodides. Corey and Jautelat[2] have developed a convenient two-step procedure for homologation of primary alkyl bromides or iodides, as illustrated for the conversion of 1-iododecane to 1-iodoun-

$$CH_3(CH_2)_8CH_2I \ + \ C_6H_5SCH_2^-Li^+ \longrightarrow CH_3(CH_2)_8CH_2CH_2SC_6H_5 \xrightarrow[\substack{93\% \ overall}]{\substack{CH_3I, \ NaI \\ DMF}}$$

$$CH_3(CH_2)_8CH_2CH_2I$$

decane. The iodide is treated with a slight excess of phenylthiomethyllithium in THF under nitrogen at $-70°$ to form phenyl *n*-undecyl sulfide. The phenylthio group is then replaced by iodine by treatment with a large excess of methyl iodide in 1 *N* sodium iodide in DMF under anhydrous conditions.

In the case of allylic halides somewhat higher yields are obtained if the complex of phenylthiomethyllithium and cuprous iodide is employed. This complex is prepared by stirring phenylthiomethyllithium with a slight excess of cuprous iodide in THF at $-50°$ to form a fine grey suspension of phenylthiomethylcopper. With this reagent allyl bromide is converted into 4-iodo-1-butene in 52% yield.

A more interesting application is the conversion of geranyl bromide (1) into homogeranyl iodide (2). In this case the second step is carried out in the presence of

(1)   (2)

a small amount of calcium carbonate and mercury to prevent formation of HI or I_2, which would catalyze isomerization of the Δ^3-double bond.

[1] E. J. Corey and D. Seebach, *J. Org.*, **31**, 4097 (1966)
[2] E. J. Corey and M. Jautelat, *Tetrahedron Letters*, 5787 (1968)

4-Phenyl-1,2,4-triazoline-3,5-dione [1, 849–850, before references].

Sauer and Schröder[4] isolated the red dione in crystalline form in 50% yield by oxidation of 4-phenylurazole with bromine water. A kinetic study indicated that it is somewhat more reactive than tetracyanoethylene as a dienophile.

Gillis and Hagarty[5] found that 4-phenylurazole is oxidized readily by lead tetraacetate in methylene chloride solution, and they developed a technique for carrying out a Diels-Alder reaction by generating the dienophile in the presence of the diene at a low temperature in methylene chloride or acetonitrile.

Stickler and Pirkle[6] report that nitrogen tetroxide is superior to all the previously cited oxidizing agents in convenience, yield, and purity of the isolated 1,2,4-triazoline-3,5-diones. Passage of gaseous nitrogen tetroxide into a suspension of a urazole in cold methylene chloride results in a rapid dissolution of the urazole and formation of a red solution of the dione, and evaporation of the solvent yields quantitatively the crystalline dione.

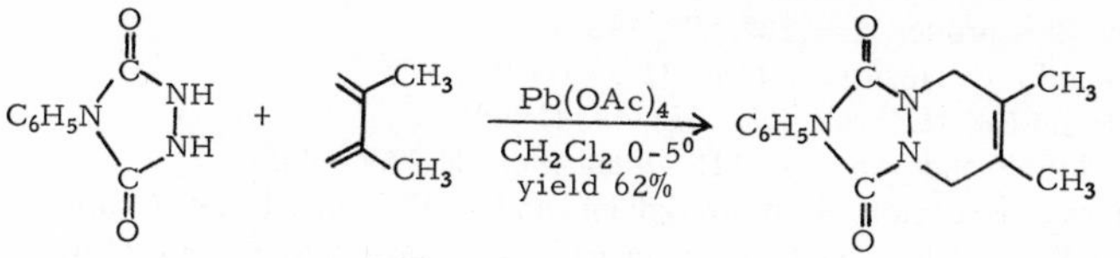

The dione reacts rapidly, even at room temperature, with the diene system of 3β-acetoxy-17-cyano-5,14,16-androstatriene (1) to give the adduct (2); however (2) decomposes rapidly at room temperature to the starting materials. In contrast, the adduct of (1) with maleic anhydride is stable at 180°.[7] The reagent also reacts rapidly

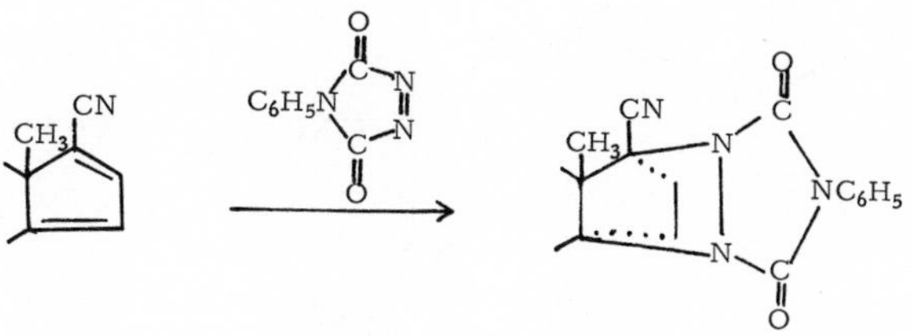

(1)   (2)

with 16-methylpregna-4,14,16-triene-3,20-dione (3) to give the isomeric adducts (4) and (5).[8]

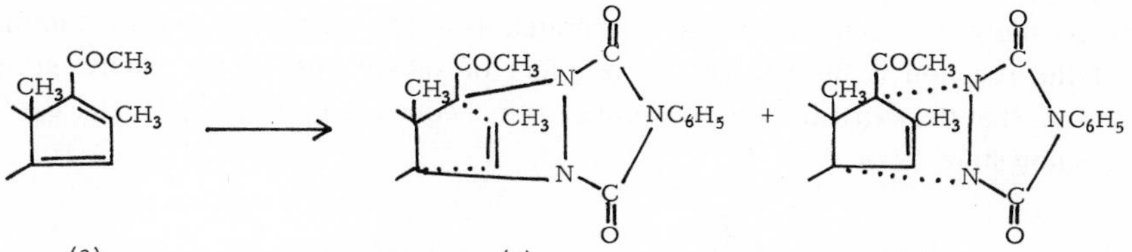

(3)   (4)   (5)

The dione reacts with cyclooctatetraene (6) to give (7). The result is interesting because examples of 1,4-cycloadditions to (6) are rare.[9]

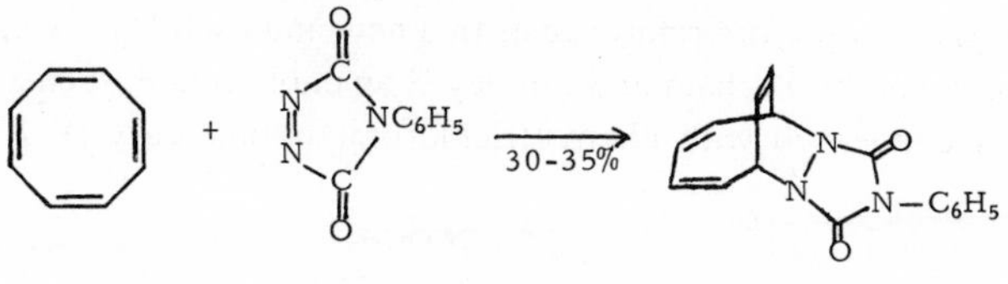

(6)   (7)

[1]Definitive paper: R. C. Cookson, S. S. H. Gilani, and I. D. R. Stevens, *J. Chem. Soc.*, (C), 1905 (1967)

[4]J. Sauer and B. Schröder, *Ber.*, **100**, 678 (1967)
[5]B. T. Gillis and J. D. Hagarty, *J. Org.*, **32**, 330 (1967)
[6]J. C. Stickler and W. H. Pirkle, *ibid.*, **31**, 3444 (1966)
[7]A. J. Solo, H. S. Sachdev, and S. S. H. Gilani, *ibid.*, **30**, 769 (1965)
[8]T. L. Popper, F. E. Carlon, H. M. Marigliano, and M. D. Yudis, *Chem. Commun.*, 1434 (1968)
[9]A. B. Evnin, R. D. Miller, and G. R. Evanega, *Tetrahedron Letters*, 5863 (1968)

Phenyl(trihalomethyl)mercury [1, 851–854]. Eastman supplies phenyl(trichloromethyl)mercury.

Generation of dihalocarbenes [1, 852–853, after citation of ref. 7]. Allylamines, in which the allyl chain contains at least four carbon atoms, react with phenyl(trichloromethyl)mercury to give a cyclopropane derivative (2) and cleavage products (3) and (4).[7a]

Early studies indicated that dichloro- and dibromocarbene (generated from haloform) do not react with hindered steroidal double bonds. However, Bond and Cornelia[7b] report that if phenyl(trihalomethyl)mercury precursors are used addition can be effected to Δ^7-, Δ^5-, and Δ^6-double bonds.

Kinetic studies of the reaction of phenyl(bromodichloromethyl)mercury with olefins show that dichlorocarbene is liberated as a free species. Moreover, the fact that the reaction is insensitive to the effect of substituents in the phenyl group suggests that the extrusion process proceeds in a concerted process through a cyclic transition state, 5a or 5b.[7c]

(5a)   (5b)

Pyrazole synthesis [before references]. In a new and useful two-step synthesis of pyrazoles developed by Parham and Dooley,[12] an enol acetate, such as isopropenyl acetate (1), is condensed with phenyl(trichloromethyl)mercury (1, 851) to give a

(1)   (2)   (3)

gem-dihalocyclopropyl acetate (2), which is treated with hydrazine (or a derivative) to form the pyrazole (3).

Suggested mechanism:

$$\ddot{N}H_2\ddot{N}H_2 \quad \overset{CH_3}{\underset{\overset{\|}{O}}{C}}{=}O$$

$$CH_3C{\overset{CH_2}{\underset{Cl}{\diagdown}}}{\underset{Cl}{\overset{C}{\diagup}}} \xrightarrow{-HCl} CH_3\underset{O}{\overset{\|}{C}}NHNH_2 \; + \; CH_3\underset{O}{\overset{\|}{C}}{-}\underset{Cl}{\overset{|}{C}}{=}CH_2$$

$$\left[\begin{array}{c} CH_3\underset{N}{\overset{\|}{C}}{-}\underset{CH_2}{\overset{|}{C}}HCl \\ \diagdown N \diagup \\ | \\ H \end{array} \right] \xrightarrow{-HCl} \begin{array}{c} CH_3C{-}CH \\ \| \quad \| \\ N \quad CH \\ \diagdown N \diagup \\ | \\ H \end{array}$$

An interesting application of the method was to the synthesis of the heterocyclic metacyclophane (8), 3,5-[10]-pyrazolophane.[13] Cyclododecanone (4) was converted into the enol acetate (5) and this was refluxed with phenyl(trichloromethyl)mercury in benzene under nitrogen for 48 hrs. to produce 1-acetoxy-2,2-dichlorobicyclo-[10.1.0]tridecane (6). Reaction with hydrazine gave as the chief product (49% yield)

$(4) \xrightarrow[\text{(TsOH)}]{\underset{81\%}{\overset{OCOCH_3 \atop | \atop CH_2C=CH_2}{}}} (5) \xrightarrow[59\%]{C_6H_5HgCCl_3} (6) \xrightarrow[49\%]{H_2NNH_2} (8)$

(9) $\xrightarrow{H_2NNH_2}$ (7) + (8)

a solid substance characterized as 3,5-[10]-pyrazolophane (8) by oxidation with neutral permanganate to 3,5-pyrazoledicarboxylic acid. However, the NMR spectra of the residue remaining after removal of acetyl hydrazide and most of (8) indicated the presence of two pyrazoles. One was additional (8) and the other was an unknown isomeric pyrazole identified as (7) by its synthesis from (9).

Metacyclophane synthesis. Parham and Rinehart[14] synthesized a new class of metacyclophanes by reaction of (1) with 2 equiv. of phenyl(trichloromethyl)mercury in boiling benzene; the intermediate dichlorocyclopropane (2) suffers spontaneous ring opening to give the cyclophane (3) in 73% yield (pure).

(1)   (2)   (3)

Diarylcyclopropenones. Diarylacetylenes react with phenyl(bromodichloromethyl)mercury to give, after hydrolysis of the reaction mixture, diarylcyclopropenones.[15] Analogous reactions with dialkylacetylenes could not be realized.

[7a]W. E. Parham and J. R. Potoski, *J. Org.*, **32**, 278 (1967)

[7b]F. T. Bond and R. H. Cornelia, *Chem. Commun.*, 1189 (1968)

[7c]D. Seyferth, J. Y.-P. Mui, and J. M. Burlitch, *Am. Soc.*, **89**, 4953 (1967); D. Seyferth, J. Y.-P. Mui, and R. Damrauer, *ibid.*, **90**, 6182 (1968)

[8]*Add:* D. Seyferth and J. Y.-P. Mui, *Am. Soc.*, **88**, 4672 (1966)

[12]W. E. Parham and J. F. Dooley, *Am. Soc.*, **89**, 985 (1967)

[13]W. E. Parham and R. J. Sperley, *J. Org.*, **32**, 926 (1967)

[14]W. E. Parham and J. K. Rinehart, *Am. Soc.*, **89**, 5668 (1967)

[15]D. Seyferth and R. Damrauer, *J. Org.*, **31**, 1660 (1966)

Phenyltrimethylammonium perbromide [1, 855, after citation of ref. 2]. The reagent can be prepared *in situ* by mixing molar equivalents of phenyltrimethylammonium bromide (Aldrich, mol. wt. 375.95) and bromine (mol. wt. 159.83) in THF in a solution of one molar equivalent of the ketone in THF.

Phosgene [1, 856–859].

Cyclic carbonates [**1,** 857–858, after line 1]. Plattner *et al.*[12a] cited the reaction of a steroidal *cis*-1,3-diol with phosgene in pyridine-chloroform to form a cyclic carbonate as evidence of the *cis* relationship of the groups. Another example is reported by Boulch, Raoul, and Ourisson.[12b]

Lactones [**1,** 858, after citation of ref. 14]. Lactonization of the hydroxy acid

(4) to (±)-didesoxyzearalane (5) was achieved using phosgene and triethylamine in benzene under high dilution.[14a] Cyclization of (4) could not be effected by the usual

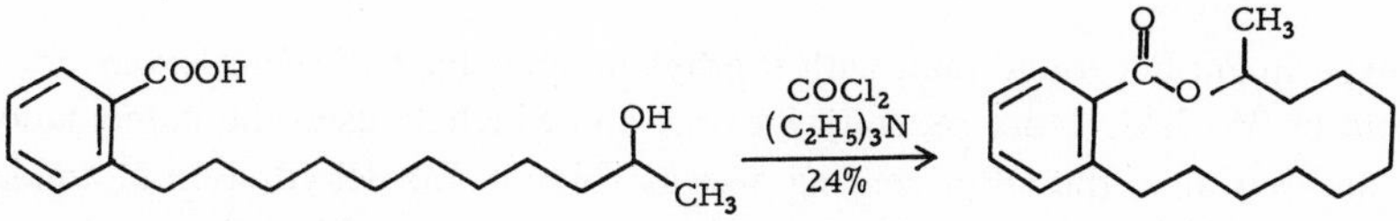

(4)   (5)

reagents: trifluoroacetic anhydride, DCC, thionyl chloride, or *p*-toluenesulfonyl chloride.

[12a] Pl. A. Plattner, A. Fürst, F. Koller, and W. Lang, *Helv.*, **31**, 1455 (1948)
[12b] N. L. Boulch, Y. Raoul, and G. Ourisson, *Bull. soc.*, 2413 (1967)
[14a] H. L. Wehrmeister and D. E. Robertson, *J. Org.*, **33**, 4173 (1968)

Phosphine [1, 859]. In the procedure cited for generation of the gas, phosphine is made by reaction of water with aluminum phosphide, available from Alfa Inorganics. Gokhale and Jolly[1a] made phosphine by pyrolysis of phosphorous acid: $4\ H_3PO_3 \rightarrow 3\ H_3PO_4 + PH_3$.

[Replacement, after first formulation]. "Note, however, . . ." and formulas (1)–(2):

Note, however, that under the same conditions 6-nitroquinoline (1) affords (2) and (3), while reduction of 2-nitronaphthalene yields (4) and (5).[1b]

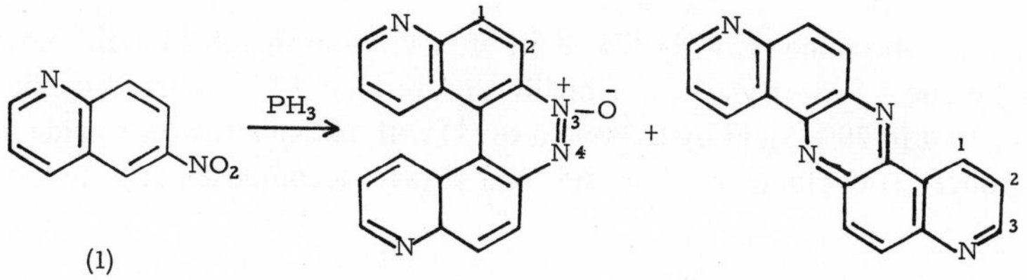

(1)   (2)   (3)

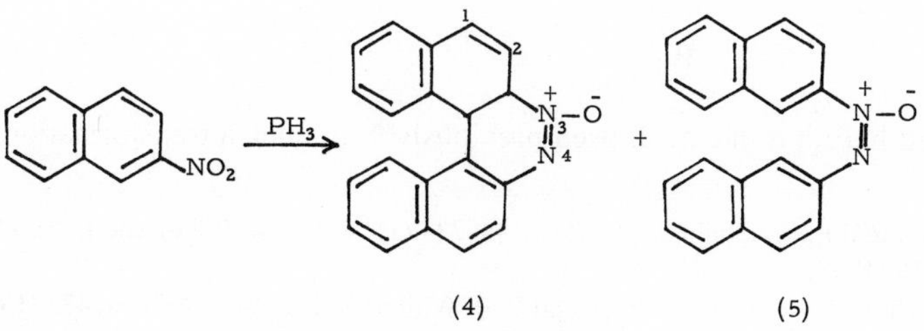

(4)   (5)

[1a] S. D. Gokhale and W. L. Jolly, *Inorg. Syn.*, **9**, 56 (1967)
[1b] A. C. Bellaart, *Rec. trav.*, **83**, 718 (1964); F. H. A. Rummens and A. C. Bellaart, *Tetrahedron*, **23**, 2735 (1967)

Phosphorus pentoxide–*t*-Amine [1, 872, before **Phosphorus pentoxide–Phosphoric acid**]. Scheibler *et al.*[1] used P_2O_5 in combination with quinoline for dehydration of the acid-sensitive diethoxyacetamide. McElvain and Clarke[2] were unable to repeat

$$(C_2H_5O)_2CHCONH_2 \xrightarrow[\text{\raisebox{-1ex}{\includegraphics{pyridine}}}]{P_2O_5} (C_2H_5O)_2CHC{\equiv}N$$

this experiment but found that, with triethylamine as base, the nitrile was obtained in yield of 76–79%. More recently Stevens and Singhal[3] used the combination of P_2O_5 and pyridine, the latter serving also as solvent, for dehydration of amides of type (1) to ketimines (2). In order to facilitate stirring, sand, Florisil, or alumina was

added as diluent. The same combination was used successfully for dehydration of ureas to carbodiimides:[4]

$$C_6H_{11}NHCONHC_6H_{11} \xrightarrow[75.6\%]{P_2O_5-Py} C_6H_{11}N{=}C{=}NC_6H_{11}$$

[1]H. Scheibler *et al.*, *Ber.*, **67**, 1507, but see 1513 (1934)
[2]S. M. McElvain and R. L. Clarke, *Am. Soc.*, **69**, 2661 (1947)
[3]C. L. Stevens and G. H. Singhal, *J. Org.*, **29**, 34 (1964)
[4]C. L. Stevens, G. H. Singhal, and A. B. Ash, *ibid.*, **32**, 2895 (1967)

Phosphorus tribromide [**1**, 873–874; 874, after citation of ref. 5] 1-Bromocyclotrideca-1,2-diene-4,8,10-triyne (2), a highly unsaturated 13-membered cyclic allene, was prepared in 20% yield by treatment of (1) with phosphorus tribromide in THF. The product (2) explodes at about 65° and slowly decomposes at 0° in the dark.[5a]

Concentrated hydrobromic acid, used previously[5b] for such a transformation, failed in this case.

[5a]C. C. Leznoff and F. Sondheimer, *Am. Soc.*, **90**, 731 (1968); G. M. Pilling and F. Sondheimer, *ibid.*, **90**, 5610 (1968)
[5b]D. K. Black, S. R. Landor, A. N. Patel, and P. F. Whiter, *Tetrahedron Letters*, 483 (1963)

Phosphoryl chloride [**1**, 876–882].

Phosphoryl chloride–Pyridine dehydration of alcohols [**1**, 878–879, at end]. Although thebaine (1) can be considered as the methyl enol ether of codeinone (2), no direct synthesis has been achieved. Rapoport[12a] has recently carried out a convenient indirect synthesis of (1) from Δ^6-dihydrothebaine (3). Addition of methyl hypobromite (generated from NBA in methanol) gave (4) in 62% yield, and this

(1)   (2)

was dehydrobrominated by potassium in *t*-amyl alcohol to give codeinone dimethyl

(3)   (4)   (5)

ketal (5). The most satisfactory reagent for elimination of methanol proved to be phosphoryl chloride in pyridine. Use of *p*-toluenesulfonic acid gave erratic yields, at the best, 40%.

Phosphoryl chloride–Stannous chloride–Pyridine [1, 881, before references]. Johnson[20] states that the stereoselectivity of the Cornforth olefin synthesis can be improved by carrying out the Grignard reaction (the first step) at a low temperature (−90°).

Phosphoryl chloride–Phosphoric acid–Phosphorus pentoxide [1, 881, before references]. A reagent originally used for cyclodehydration of arylbutyric and aryl-propionic acids was phosphorus pentoxide in phosphoric acid;[21] this reagent has been largely supplanted by commercial polyphosphoric acid. Birch[22] finds that the combination phosphoryl chloride–phosphoric acid–phosphorus pentoxide in at least two cases gives higher and more reproducible yields than the original reagent; with the newer reagent the acid chloride may be an intermediate. 5-Methoxyhydrin-

done is obtained in 85% yield from *m*-methoxyphenylpropionic acid,[22] whereas the yield by the earlier method was 55%.

[12a] H. Rapoport, C. H. Lovell, H. R. Reist, and M. E. Warren, Jr., *Am. Soc.*, **89**, 1942 (1967)
[20] S. F. Brady, M. A. Ilton, and W. S. Johnson, *Am. Soc.*, **90**, 2882 (1968)
[21] A. J. Birch, R. Jaeger, and R. Robinson, *J. Chem. Soc.*, 582 (1945)
[22] A. J. Birch and G. S. R. Subba Rao, *Tetrahedron Letters*, 2763 (1967)

1,4-Phthalazinedione (II) [1, 884, before *Picric acid*]. Mol. wt. 160. 13.

The reagent (II) was first prepared in acetonitrile solution by oxidation of phthal-hydrazide (I) at 0° with lead tetraacetate.[1] It was later obtained as a crystalline green solid by oxidation of the sodium salt of phthalhydrazide with *t*-butyl hypochlorite.[2]

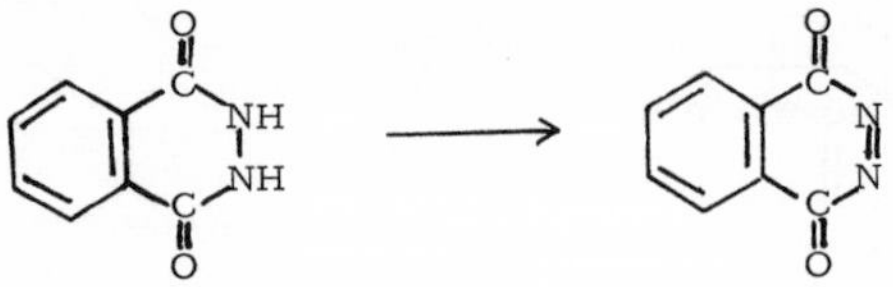

I   II

Like the related 4-phenyl-1,2,4-triazoline-3,5-dione, 1,4-phthalazinedione is a reactive dienophile. Thus the first known Diels-Alder adduct (III) of 1,3-cyclo-octadiene was obtained with this dienophile.[3]

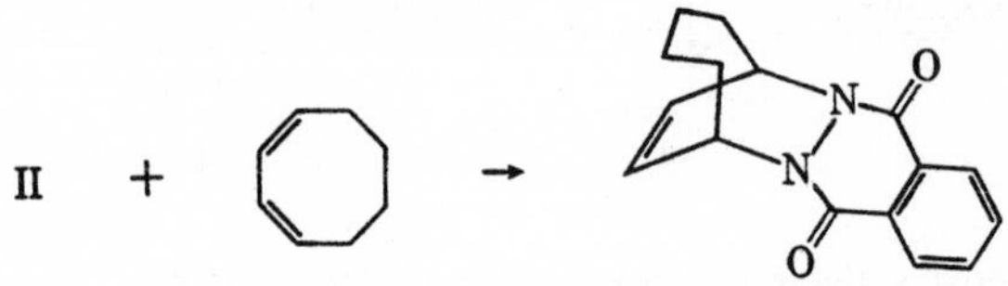

II   +   →

III

14α,17α- and 14β,17β-Adducts have been obtained from a steroidal $\Delta^{14,16}$-diene-20-one.[4]

[1]R. A. Clement, *J. Org.*, **25**, 1724 (1960); *idem, ibid.*, **27**, 1115 (1962)
[2]T. J. Kealy, *Am. Soc.*, **84**, 966 (1962)
[3]O. L. Chapman and S. J. Dominianni, *J. Org.*, **31**, 3862 (1962)
[4]T. L. Popper, F. E. Carlon, H. M. Marigliano, and M. D. Yudis, *Chem. Commun.*, 1434 (1968)

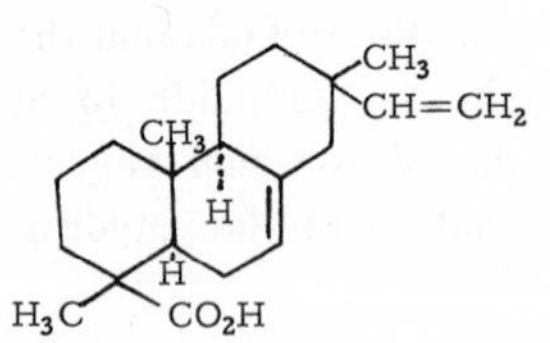

Piperidine [1, 886–890, before references].

Lawrence *et al.*[16] describe a method for isolation of isodextropimaric acid from the complex mixture of resin acids present in pine oleoresin and gum rosin by precipitation of the piperidine salt from *n*-heptane solution, followed by selective recrystallization from ethanol.

[16]N. M. Joye, Jr., V. M. Loeblich, and R. V. Lawrence, *J. Org.*, **30**, 654 (1965)

Platinum catalysts [1, 890–892].

[1, 890, after citation of ref. 3]: A freshly prehydrogenated platinum oxide catalyst plus oxygen was found to introduce a tertiary 12a-hydroxyl group into dedimethyl-amine-12a-desoxytetracycline (I) to produce dedimethylaminotetracycline (II) in satisfactory yield.[3a]

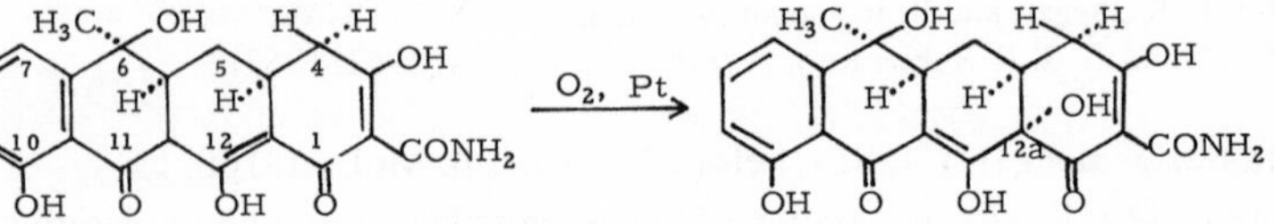

I   II

Brown and Brown catalyst [**1**, 890–891]. To ref. 10 add: C. A. Brown and H. C. Brown, *J. Org.*, **31**, 3989 (1966). H. Makata [*Bull. Chem. Soc. Japan*, **38**, 500 (1965)] finds that the catalyst is selective for hydrogenation of a steroidal α,β-unsaturated ketone.

[3a]H. Muxfeldt, G. Buhr, and R. Bangert, *Angew. Chem., internat. Ed.*, **1**, 157 (1962)

Polyhexamethylenecarbodiimide,[1]—$(CH_2)_6N=C=N$—$[(CH_2)_6N=C=N$—]— $(CH_2)_6$—[**1**, 892, before **Polyoxyethylatedlauryl alcohol**]. The polymer was obtained by catalytic decarboxylation of 1,6-diisocyanatohexane with 3-methyl-1-phenyl-3-phospholene-1-oxide as catalyst and N-methyl-2-pyrrolidone as solvent. The resulting polymer was treated with ethanol to block any terminal isocyanate groups present, filtered off, ground, and fractionated by extraction with boiling methylene chloride to remove any low-molecular-weight compounds and then treated with acetyl N-hydroxy-succinimide to acetylate any free amino groups liberated during the polymerization.

In a "reverse Merrifield" scheme of peptide synthesis the polymer is used as an insoluble condensing agent. The active ester of the N-blocked amino acid is bound to the insoluble polymer and the free peptide ester is in solution.

[1]Y. Wolman, S. Kivity, and M. Frankel, *Chem. Commun.*, 629 (1967)

Polyphosphate ester [**1**, 892, after formula (3)]. Further work indicates that the structure is actually more complicated than originally supposed.[4a]

[Before references]: Replace ref. 9 by definitive paper: *Chem. Pharm. Bull.*, **14**, 934 (1966).

Other work by this Japanese group is reported by Kanaoka *et al.*[10]

The aromatic azide with a *p*-substituent (1) decomposes thermally in the presence of a carboxylic acid in PPE to form the oxazole (2).[11] A nitrene intermediate is postulated.

Acid chlorides can be cyclized by PPE.[12] In the example formulated the mixture of the acid chloride from 4.65 g. of α-phenylbutyric acid with 23 g. of freshly pre-

pared PPE was heated at 70° for 15 min. and poured into water. α-Tetralone was recovered by extraction with ether. In a total synthesis of the phenolic noraporphine alkaloid *dl*-hernandine, the amide (3) was cyclized smoothly to the base (4) by PPE.[13]

(3)   (4)

[4a]J. R. Van Wazer and S. Norval, *Am. Soc.*, **88**, 4415 (1966)

[10]Y. Kanaoka *et al.*, *Chem. Ind.*, 2102 (1964); *idem, Chem. Pharm. Bull.*, **14**, 934 (1966); *idem, ibid.*, **15**, 101, 593 (1967)

[11]R. Garner, E. B. Mullock and H. Suschitzky, *J. Chem. Soc.*, (C), 1980 (1966)

[12]A. Bhati and N. Kale, *Angew. Chem. internat. Ed.*, **6**, 1086 (1967)

[13]K. S. Soh and F. N. Lahey, *Tetrahedron Letters*, 19 (1968)

Polyphosphoric acid (PPA) [1, 894–905].

Cyclodehydration [**1**, 894–897, at end]. PPA proved to be the most satisfactory acid for the cyclodehydration of (1) to a mixture of (3) and (4).[12a] The methoxy group was present in (1) in order to achieve adequate solubility in PPA.

(1)   (2)

(3)   +   (4)

Other cyclizations [**1**, 897–898, at end]. When the *p*-nitrophenylhydrazone of acetophenone (1) is heated with PPA, *p*-nitrophenylindazole (2) is formed.[15a]

(1)   (2)

1-Phenyl-2-acetonylisoquinolinium bromide (3) can be cyclized in good yield to (4) with PPA; it is not cyclized by hydrobromic acid or by sulfuric acid.[15b] Despite

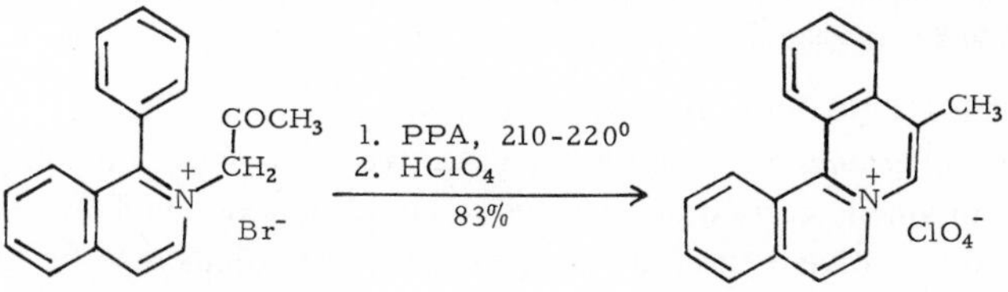

(3)   (4)

the drastic conditions required for cyclization, 5-methylbenzo[a]phenanthridizinium perchlorate was isolated in high state of purity and in good yield.

Aromatic sulfones can be obtained in good yield by stirring an aromatic hydrocarbon with an aromatic sulfonic acid and PPA at 80° (8 hrs.).[15c]

$$ArSO_3H + Ar'H \xrightarrow{PPA} ArSO_2Ar' + H_2O$$

Substitutions and Displacements [1, 904] Direct amidation of aromatic compounds can sometimes be achieved by reaction with a hydroxamic acid in PPA:[48a]

The product is isolated by ether extraction of the diluted reaction mixture. An interesting example is the intramolecular ring closure of hydrocinnamohydroxamic acid to hydrocarbostyril:

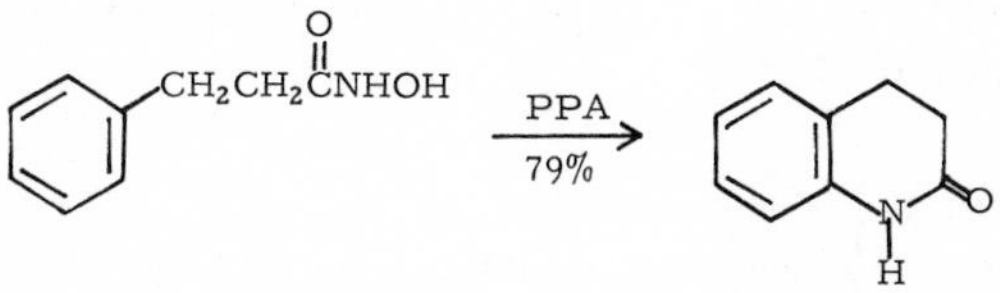

Hydroxy, methoxy, or acetoxy groups in the bridgehead carbon atom of the bicyclo[2.2.2]octane series can often be replaced by reaction with a halogenating

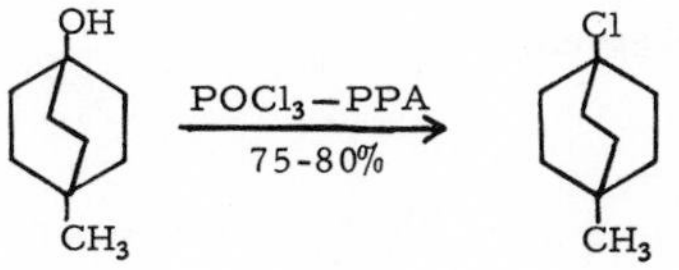

(1)   (2)

agent ($POCl_3$, PBr_3) in the presence of PPA,[48b] In the absence of PPA, reaction of (1) with $POCl_3$ results in replacement of OH by $OPOCl_2$.

[12a]H. W. Thompson, *J. Org.*, **33**, 621 (1968)
[15]*Change to read:* T. L. Emmick and R. L. Letsinger, *Org. Syn.*, **47**, 54 (1967)

[15a]E. B. Dennler and A. R. Frasca, *Tetrahedron*, **22**, 3131 (1966)
[15b]C. K. Bradsher and R. W. L. Kimber, *J. Org.*, **30**, 1848 (1965)
[15c]B. M. Graybill, *ibid.*, **32**, 2931 (1967)
[48a]F. W. Wassmundt and S. J. Padegimas, *Am. Soc.*, **89**, 7131 (1967)
[48b]J. Kopecký and J. Šmejkal, *Tetrahedron Letters*, 1931 (1967), *idem, ibid.*, 3889 (1967)

Potassium amide [**1**, 907–909, before references].

Nitration of ketones.[6] The nitration of active methylene compounds by alkyl nitrates was originally carried out with potassium *t*-butoxide in THF; the base was sublimed, and the solvent carefully purified. Feuer now finds that the reaction conditions can be considerably simplified without loss in yield by using potassium amide in liquid ammonia.

[6]H. Feuer, A. M. Hall, S. Golden, and R. L. Reitz, *J. Org.*, **33**, 3622 (1968)

Potassium *t*-butoxide [**1**, 911–927].

Dieckmann cyclization [**1**, 912, after citation of ref. 6]. In extending his work with Leonard,[6] Schimelpfenig[6a] used the reagent to effect Dieckmann condensation of esters of *p*-phenylenedicarboxylic acids to form ketones of paracyclophanes:

Isomerization of unsaturated compounds [**1**, 913–914]. Enynes and cumulenes are rapidly and smoothly isomerized to conjugated trienes by catalytic amounts of potassium *t*-butoxide in DMSO:[6b]

3-Dialkylamino-1-butynes (1), readily available from reaction of acetylene with secondary amines, are isomerized by this base to 2-dialkylamino-1,3-butadienes (2); no allenic products are observed.[6c]

A Schiff base (4) obtained from an α,β-unsaturated ketone, for example (3), is isomerized by the reagent to (5), in which the phenyl group is conjugated with the open-chain conjugated system.[6d] Hydrolysis of (5) gives benzaldehyde and the

$$C_6H_5CH_2NH_2 + O=\overset{\overset{\displaystyle R}{|}}{C}CH=CHR' \longrightarrow C_6H_5CH_2N=\overset{\overset{\displaystyle R}{|}}{C}CH=CHR' \xrightarrow{KOC(CH_3)_3}$$

(3)   (4)

$$C_6H_5CH=N-\overset{\overset{\displaystyle R}{|}}{C}=CHCH_2R' \xrightarrow{dil.\ AcOH} C_6H_5CHO + HN=\overset{\overset{\displaystyle R}{|}}{C}CH_2CH_2R' \longrightarrow O=\overset{\overset{\displaystyle R}{|}}{C}CH_2CH_2R'$$

(5)   (6)   (7)   (8)

saturated ketone (8). The overall process thus can be used for selective reduction of the double bond of (3) which is conjugated with the keto group.

The combination of potassium *t*-butoxide with dimethyl sulfoxide isomerizes the

$$(CH_2)_{10} \underset{CH}{\overset{CH}{\diagdown\diagup}} C \xrightarrow{KOC(CH_3)_3-DMSO} (CH_2)_{11} \overset{C}{\underset{C}{\diagdown}}\|$$

(9)   (10)

cyclic allene (9) to the acetylene (10).[6e] Other bases [KOC(CH$_3$)$_3$ in *t*-BuOH, KOH–C$_2$H$_5$OH, CH$_3$Li, and Al$_2$O$_3$] failed to effect isomerization.

Propargyl ethers, HC≡C—CH$_2$OR, are isomerized to pure allenyl ethers, CH$_2$=C=CHOR, in 80–90% yield by treatment with a catalytic amount of solid potassium *t*-butoxide (without a solvent) for 2–3 hrs. at 70°.[6f] Previous efforts to effect this transformation with solid potassium hydroxide or sodamide were unsuccessful.

[**1**, 914, before the last paragraph]: In contrast to Δ^4-3-ketosteroids, Δ^{1,4}-3-ketosteroids are not deconjugated by potassium *t*-butoxide in *t*-butanol, but they are deconjugated to Δ^{1,5}-3-ketones by this base in DMSO followed by quenching with water. Sodium hydride and sodamide in THF are also effective (in this case boric acid is used to effect neutralization).[15a] Treatment of a Δ^{4,6}-3-ketone with sodium methoxide in DMSO followed by neutralization with aqueous acetic acid gave the enol, a 3-hydroxy-3,5,7-triene, convertible into the Δ^{5,7}-3-ketone by treatment with ethyl acetate under nitrogen or by brief heat treatment above the melting point of the enol.[15b]

Dehydrohalogenation [**1**, 916–917, after citation of ref. 34]. 1,2-Dichloro-2,2-dimethyl-3-propylcyclopropane (1) on treatment with the potassium *t*-butoxide in DMSO at 30° is converted into 2,2-dimethylallylidenecyclopropane (2).[34a]

$$\underset{\underset{Cl}{\diagup}\overset{\diagup}{\diagdown}Cl}{\overset{\overset{H_3C}{\diagdown}\overset{CH_3}{\diagup}}{\diagdown}}-CH_2CH_2CH_3 \xrightarrow[60\%]{\underset{DMSO}{KOC(CH_3)_2}} \overset{H_3C}{\underset{}{\diagdown}}\overset{CH_3}{\diagup}=CH_2$$

(1)   (2)

A supplement entitled "Lithium dicyclohexylamide" describes the preparation by Traynham *et al.*[34b] of *trans*-cyclodecene by photochemical chlorination of cyclodecane to produce 1-chlorocyclodecane (4) and dehydrohalogenation of this substance with lithium dicyclohexylamide to form *trans*-cyclodecene in 70% yield.

Traynham *et al.* found further that dehydrohalogenation of (4) with potassium *t*-butoxide in dimethyl sulfoxide gives *cis*-cyclodecene (5) of excellent quality in high yield.

Dehydrohalogenation with rearrangement [**1**, 917–918, after "Gardner and co-workers.[36]"]. Dehydrochlorination of (2,2-dichloro-3,3-dimethylcyclopropyl)dimethylamine (7) with the reagent leads to the alkenynylamine (8) in 20–30% yield.[36a] The mechanism is not clear, but attempts to trap a cyclopropene intermediate failed.

Treatment of 1,4,5,8,9,10-hexahydroanthracene (10) with 2 equivalents of peracetic acid gives the diepoxide (11) in almost quantitative yield (*syn* and *anti* isomers).[36b] The diepoxide (11) is treated with 2 equivalents of NBS in CCl_4, and the crude bromination product is dehydrohalogenated by potassium *t*-butoxide in THF to give carmine-red crystals of (13), 1,6;8,13-diepoxy[14]annulene (*syn* or *anti*) in 5% yield.

The reaction of 1,1-dichloro-2,2,3-trimethylcyclopropane (14) with potassium *t*-butoxide in DMSO (inverse addition at 25°) results in two major products, 2-chloro-3,3-dimethylmethylenecyclopropane (16) and 2-methylpentene-1-yne-3 (17)[36c]

(14)   (15)   (16)   (17)

                                                 33.4%   30.5%

Mitchell and Sondheimer[36d] found potassium *t*-butoxide in *t*-butanol to be the most satisfactory reagent tried for dehydrobromination of the tetrabromide (7) to 1,8-diethynylnaphthalene (8). It was necessary to carry out the reaction at the reflux temperature, for at room temperature the main product was the ene-yne (10).

(1)   (2)   (3)   (4)

(5)   (6)   (7)

(8)   (9)   (10)

Oxidative coupling of (8) to the cyclic dimer (9) could be effected only in very poor yield. The best result (2%) was obtained when (8) was oxidized under Glaser conditions in benzene. The red cyclic dimer proved to be very unstable.

Phenylketene acetals can be obtained in yields of 20–80% by debromination of α-bromophenylacetaldehyde acetals, readily accessible by several general methods.[36e]

Dehydrotosylation. The combination of KOBu-*t* and DMSO is an excellent reagent for the dehydrotosylation of steroid 12α-tosyloxy esters to Δ^{11}-steroids.[36f]

Reusch and Frey[36g] state that 3,3,6,6-tetramethyl-1,4-cyclohexadiene (2) can be obtained in good yield by treatment of the ditosylate (1) with potassium *t*-butoxide in DMSO. The nonconjugated diene had been prepared previously by pyrolysis of

2,2,5,5-tetramethylcyclohexane-1,3-diacetate, but this method is hampered by thermal decomposition of (2) to *p*-xylene.

Dehalogenation with potassium *t*-butoxide – DMSO – *t*-butanol. Moyer[36h] found that 1,2,4-tribromobenzene when treated with *t*-BuOK in the mixed solvent gave *p*-dibromobenzene in 70% yield. This protodehalogenation has been confirmed and

extended by Bunnett.[36i] Dehalogenation occurs usually at a site *ortho* to other halogen atoms. Deiodination occurs more readily than debromination, and dechlorination has not been observed.

Esterification. Indole-3-acetyl chloride (1) is converted into *t*-butyl indole-3-

(1)   (2)

acetate by treatment with commercial potassium *t*-butoxide in *t*-butanol.[36j] The method is simpler than the more generally used reaction of the acid with isobutylene, transesterification, or reaction of the anhydride with *t*-butanol.

   Cleavage of α-hydroperoxy ketones. 17α-Hydroperoxy-20-ketosteroids are readily cleaved by potassium *t*-butoxide to 17-ketosteroids.[36k] For preparative purposes

the hydroperoxide need not be isolated. The 20-ketopregnane is oxygenated in THF–*t*-butanol containing potassium *t*-butoxide until 1.1 molar equivalent of oxygen has been consumed. Nitrogen is passed into the solution for a few minutes and the mixture is then warmed to 60–70°.

   Autoxidation [**1**, 921, after citation of ref. 51]. In the base-catalyzed autoxidation of ketones to α-hydroperoxides, the following factors have been shown to favor higher yields: short reaction times, temperatures below −8°, polar aprotic solvents (dimethoxyethane or DMF), and a mole ratio of base to ketone greater than 2.[51a]

   [After citation of ref. 52]: Schering chemists[52a] obtained low yields when applying the original procedure of Barton[52] to 20-ketosteroids and then turned to potassium *t*-butoxide in a mixture of DMF and *t*-butanol. These solvent systems had been used successfully for autoxidation of picolines[52b] which are not oxidized to a measurable extent in *t*-butanol. Autoxidation is rapid in DMF alone, but this solvent itself is oxidized; hence the combination solvent is recommended. THF–*t*-butanol can be used, but the oxidation is slower. The 17α-hydroperoxides were obtained in high yield. They then found that triethyl phosphite is superior to zinc–acetic acid for reduction to the 17α-ol. Actually the autoxidation and reduction can be carried out in a single step and yields of the α-ketols are in the range 60–70%.

   [After citation of ref. 57]: Both α- and β-tetralone and 1,2-dihydroxynaphthalene are autoxidized in *t*-butanol in the presence of potassium *t*-butoxide to give 2-

hydroxy-1,4-naphthoquinone in yields of 50–80%; the common intermediate is probably 1,2-naphthoquinone.[57a,b] The reaction was used for the synthesis of spinachrome D, 2,3,5,6,8-pentahydroxy-4-naphthoquinone.[57c]

Herz *et al.*[57d] assigned to the yellow adduct of levopimaric acid (1) and 1,4-benzoquinone the structure (2) and found that a solution of 5 g. of (2) in 75 ml. of *t*-butanol treated with a solution prepared from 0.7 g. of potassium and 50 ml. of *t*-butanol and then with a stream of oxygen for 3 hrs. developed a deep purple color. Addition of 60 ml. of water and removal of the solvent left a purple residue from which by acidification, solvent extraction, and chromatography a hydroxyquinone (3) was isolated in 20% yield. A distinction was not made between the two possible positions for the hydroxyl group.

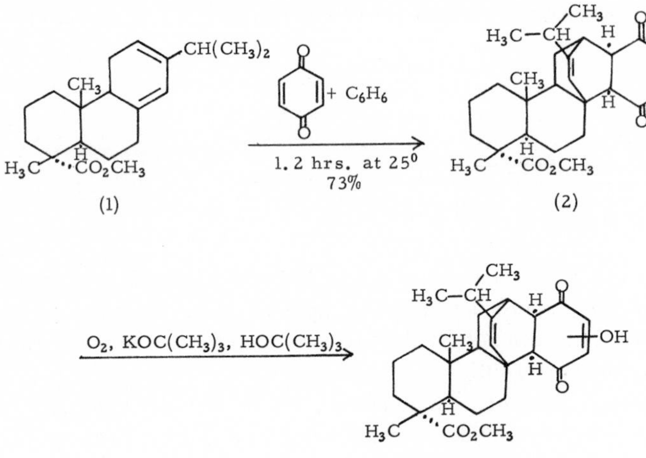

(1)

(2)

(3)

Autoxidation of either of the ketones (4) or (5) did not give the expected hydroperoxide but instead the phenol (6).[57e] The hydroperoxide was obtained in another way and shown not to be an intermediate.

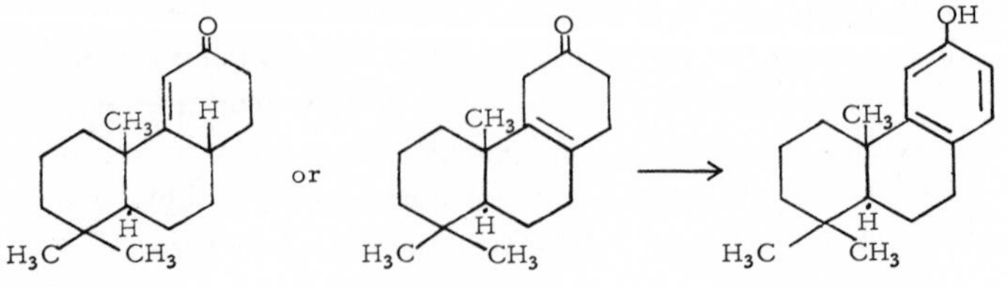

(4)   or   (5)   (6)

Cleavage of nonenolizable ketones [**1**, 923, after citation of ref. 60]. In further studies of ketone cleavage, Gassman, Lumb, and Zalar[60a] found that potassium *t*-butoxide–water in a 10:3 ratio in aprotic solvents such as DMSO, glyme, hexane, or diethyl ether was the most satisfactory reagent. The last solvent is usually preferred. With most ketones, high yields of acids were obtained after a few hours reaction time at room temperature.

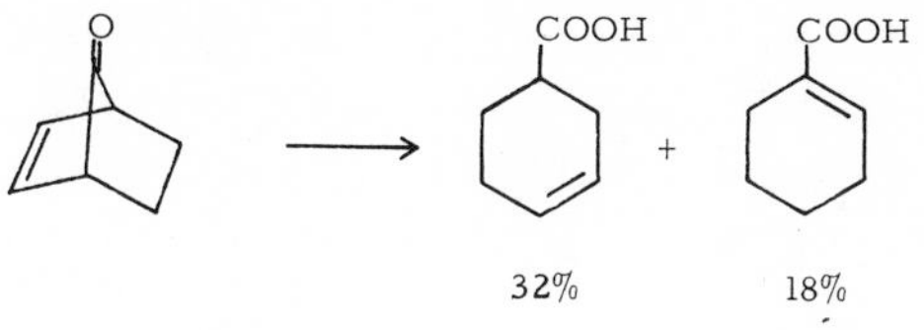

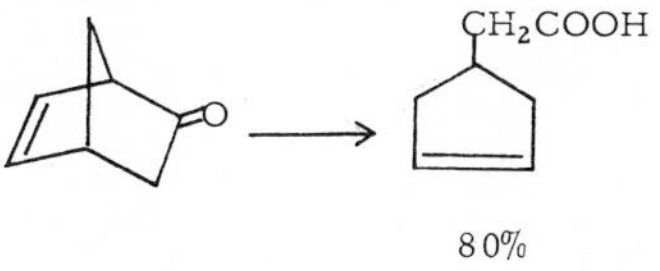

$$32\% \qquad 18\%$$

$$80\%$$

$$(C_6H_5)_2C=O \longrightarrow C_6H_5COOH$$

$$90\%$$

Activation of organolithium compounds [1, 926, before references]. Potassium *t*-butoxide enhances the reactivity of organolithium compounds. For example, benzene is not metalated by *n*-butyllithium at room temperature, but if potassium *t*-butoxide is present phenyllithium is formed in 77% yield as shown by the reaction with carbon dioxide to give benzoic acid. Triphenylmethane, diphenylmethane, and toluene are also rapidly metalated.[71]

α-Alkylation of ketones. Mono-α-alkylation of ketones is usually difficult, but can be achieved indirectly by reaction of trialkylboranes with α-bromo ketones under the influence of potassium *t*-butoxide in THF.[72] Thus α-bromocyclohexanone (1) reacts with triethylborane to give α-ethylcyclohexanone (2) in 68% yield:

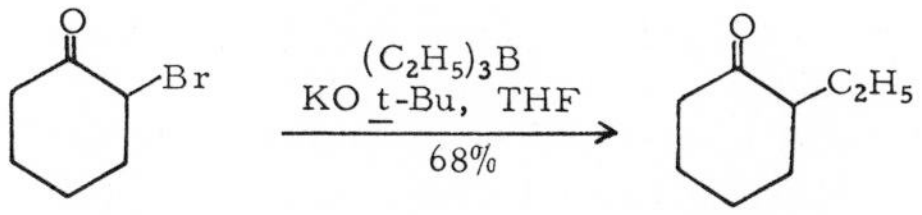

The reaction is considered to involve formation of the anion of the α-bromo ketone, reaction with the borane, and rearrangement. Use of potassium *t*-butoxide in *t*-butanol gave much lower yields. The α-bromo ketones were prepared by the reaction of ketones with cupric bromide in ethyl acetate–chloroform (method of L. C. King and G. K. Ostrum [*J. Org.*, 29, 3459 (1964)] *see* 1, 161–162).

A further example:

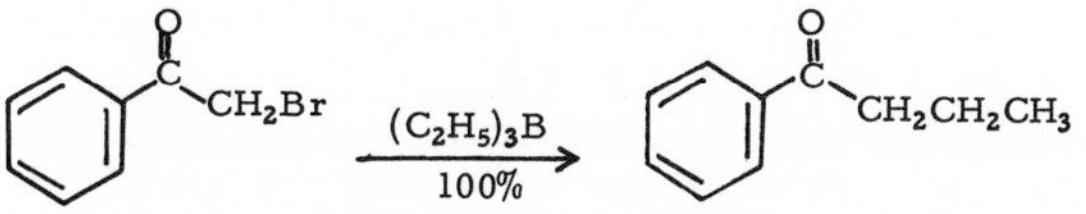

Pinacol-type rearrangement. The monotosylate (1), obtained by hydroxylation of α-pinene followed by tosylation, on treatment with potassium *t*-butoxide in *t*-butanol at 65° gives the ring-contracted ketone (2, 2α-acetyl-5,5-dimethylbicyclo[2.1.1]-

hexane) in 60% yield. In contrast the epimeric monotosylate (3) under the same conditions gives α-pinene oxide (4).[73]

[6a] C. W. Schimelpfenig, Y.-T. Lin, and J. F. Walker, Jr., *J. Org.*, **28**, 805 (1963)

[6b] J. P. C. M. Van Dongen, A. J. De Jong, H. A. Selling, P. P. Montijn, J. H. Van Boom, and L. Brandsma, *Rec. trav.*, **86**, 1077 (1967)

[6c] M. L. Farmer, W. E. Billups, R. B. Greenlee, and A. N. Kurtz, *J. Org.*, **31**, 2885 (1966)

[6d] S. K. Malhotra, D. F. Moakley, and F. Johnson, *Am. Soc.*, **89**, 2794 (1967)

[6e] H. Nozaki, S. Katô, and R. Noyori, *Canad. J. Chem.*, **44**, 1021 (1966)

[6f] S. Hoff, L. Brandsma, and J. F. Arens, *Rec. trav.*, **87**, 916 (1968)

[15a] E. L. Shapiro, T. Leggatt, L. Weber, E. P. Oliveto, M. Tanabe, and D. F. Crowe, *Steroids*, **3**, 183 (1964)

[15b] G. Kruger, *J. Org.*, **33**, 1750 (1968)

[34a] T. C. Shields, W. E. Billups, and A. R. Lepley, *Am. Soc.*, **90**, 4749 (1968)

[34b] J. G. Traynham, D. B. Stone, and J. L. Couvillion, *J. Org.*, **32**, 510 (1967)

[36a] T. C. Shields, W. E. Billups, and A. N. Kurtz, *Angew. Chem., internat. Ed.*, **7**, 209 (1968)

[36b] E. Vogel, M. Biskup, A. Vogel, and H. Günther, *ibid.*, **5**, 734 (1966)

[36c] T. C. Shields and W. E. Billups, *Chem. Ind.*, 1999 (1967)

[36d] R. H. Mitchell and F. Sondheimer, *Tetrahedron*, **24**, 1397 (1968)

[36e] J. E. Baldwin and L. E. Walker, *J. Org.*, **31**, 3985 (1966)

[36f] K. R. Bharucha and H. M. Schrenk, *Experientia*, **21**, 248 (1965)

[36g] W. Reusch and D. W. Frey, *Tetrahedron Letters*, 5193 (1967)

[36h] C. E. Moyer, Jr., *Dissertation Abstr.*, **25**, 4412 (1965)

[36i] J. F. Bunnett and R. R. Victor, *Am. Soc.*, **90**, 810 (1968)

[36j] P. M. Barna, procedure submitted to *Org. Syn.*, 1966

[36k] J. B. Siddall, G. V. Baddeley, and J. A. Edwards, *Chem. Ind.*, 25 (1966)

[51a] R. C. P. Cubbon and C. Hewlett, *J. Chem. Soc.*, (C), 2978 (1968)

[52a] J. N. Gardner, F. E. Carlon, and O. Gnoj, *J. Org.*, **33**, 1566, 3294 (1968)

[52b] W. Bartok, D. D. Rosenfeld and A. Scriesham, *ibid.*, **28**, 410 (1963)

[57a] A. C. Baillie and R. H. Thompson, *J. Chem. Soc.*, (C), 2184 (1966)

[57b] T. R. Kasturi and T. Arunachalam, *Canad. J. Chem.*, **44**, 1086 (1966); *see also* G. R. Pettit, W. C. Fleming, and K. D. Paull, *J. Org.*, **33**, 1089 (1968)

[57c] H. A. Anderson, J. Smith, and R. H. Thompson, *J. Chem. Soc.*, 2141 (1965)

[57d] W. Herz, R. C. Blackstone, and M. G. Nair, *J. Org.*, **32**, 2992 (1967)

[57e] K. Crowshaw, R. C. Newstead, and H. A. J. Rogers, *Tetrahedron Letters*, 2307 (1964)

[60a] P. G. Gassman, J. T. Lumb, and F. V. Zalar, *Am. Soc.*, **89**, 946 (1967)

[71] M. Schlosser, *J. Organometallic Chem.*, **8**, 9 (1967)

[72] H. C. Brown, M. M. Rogić and M. W. Rathke, *Am. Soc.*, **90**, 6218 (1968)

[73] R. G. Carlson and J. K. Pierce, *Tetrahedron Letters*, 6213 (1968)

Potassium ferricyanide [**1**, 929–933].

Oxidation of phenols [**1**, 929–931, after citation of ref. 6]. K. Dimroth *et al.*[6a] describe the preparation of 2,4,6-triphenylphenoxyl (4), a stable radical.

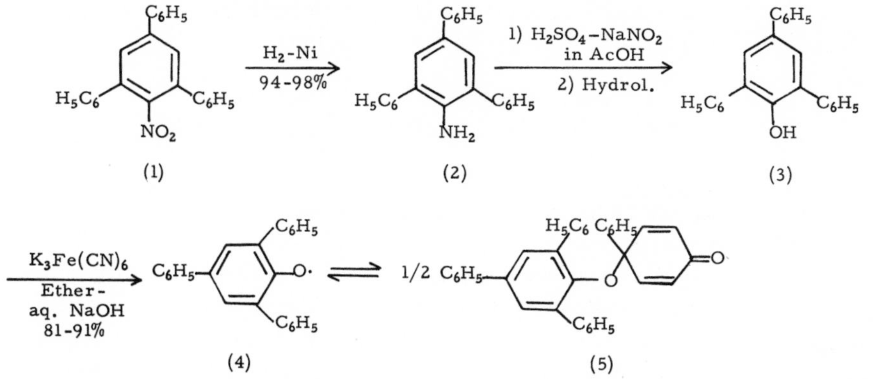

(1)   (2)   (3)

(4)   (5)

[**1**, 932, before references]: Alkaline potassium ferricyanide oxidizes 2,4,5,6-tetraphenylresorcinol (1) to tetracyclone (2) in 27% yield.[20] The oxidation can be effected also with lead dioxide or *o*-chloranil, but yields are lower. 2,4,6-Triphenyl-

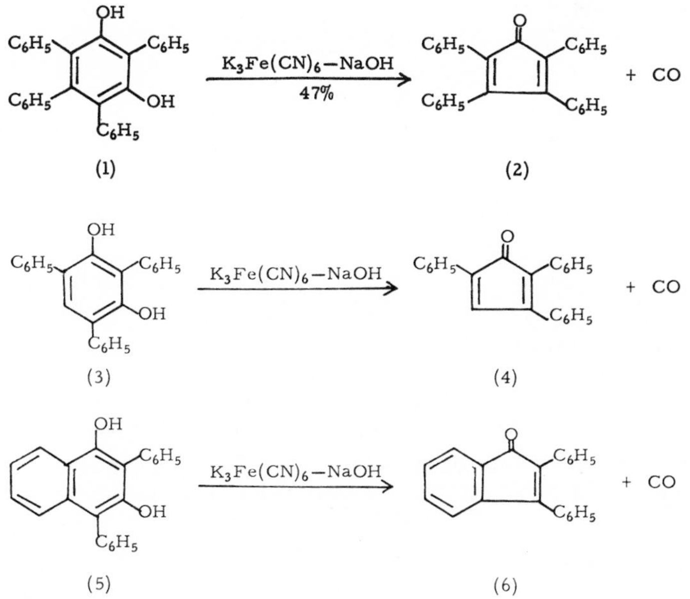

(1)   (2)

(3)   (4)

(5)   (6)

resorcinol (3) on oxidation gives 2,3,5-triphenylcyclopentadiene (4), and 2,4-diphenylnaphthoresorcinol (5) gives 2,3-diphenyl-1-indenone (6); yields of (4) and (6) are not given.

[6a]K. Dimroth, A. Berndt, H. Perst, and C. Reichardt, procedure submitted to *Org. Syn.*, 1967
[20]H. Güsten, G. Kirsch, and D. Schulte-Frohlinde, *Angew. Chem., internat. Ed.*, **6**, 948 (1967)

Potassium fluoride [1, 933–935].

Condensation catalyst [1, 933–934, after citation of ref. 5]. 4-Chlorobutyryl chloride (0.71 mole) when treated with potassium fluoride (2.74 moles) at 195–200° in tetramethylene sulfone is converted in 70% yield into cyclopropanecarboxylic acid fluoride.[5a] Evidence is presented that the reaction proceeds in two steps, first conversion of the acyl chloride into the fluoride, and then cyclization catalyzed

$$\text{Cl(CH}_2)_3\text{COCl} \xrightarrow[\text{195-200}^0]{\text{KF}} \text{Cl(CH}_2)_3\text{COF} \xrightarrow[\text{195-200}^0]{}$$

by KF acting as base. The yield was the same when potassium fluoride was replaced by the more expensive cesium fluoride.

Preparation of α,β-unsaturated aldehydes [1, 935, before references]. Elkik[11] treated the ethylene ketal of α-chloro and α-bromo aldehydes with potassium fluoride in refluxing ethylene glycol for 10–15 hrs. with the expectation of achieving halogen exchange. Instead dehydrohalogenation occurred in good yield (60–80%) to give the α,β-unsaturated ethylene ketal. The free aldehyde is liberated by exchange with acetone catalyzed by oxalic or citric acid (50–80% yield).

[5a]R. E. A. Dear and E. E. Gilbert, *J. Org.*, **33**, 1690 (1968)
[11]E. Elkik, *Bull. soc.*, 283 (1965)

Potassium hydride [1, 935].

Potassium hydride is superior to phenylsodium, phenylpotassium, or potassium for isomerization of cyclooctadienes to *cis*-bicyclo[3.3.0]octene-2.[1] Potassium

hydride is a more active catalyst than NaH for selective hydrogenation of 1,3-pentadienes and 2-pentyne to *n*-pentenes. It promotes the hydrogenation of nonconjugated dienes to monoolefins.

[1]L. H. Slaugh, *J. Org.*, **32**, 108 (1967)

Potassium hydroxide [1, 935–937, before references]. Lawrence *et al.*[10] charged Carius tubes with an ether-methanol solution of methyl levopimarate (1) and 5 mole percent of potassium hydroxide, removed the solvent under reduced pressure, sealed

(1)   (2) 23%   (3) cis 6. 2%
                                                  (4) trans 30%

the tubes *in vacuo* under nitrogen, and heated the tubes at 200° in an oil bath. Tubes were opened at intervals and the reaction followed by g.l.p.c. analysis. The reaction, which was found to be complete in 24 hrs., afforded four new compounds isomeric with levopimaric acid and three of these were identified as (2), (3), and (4). In all of these ring C has been aromatized; ring B has been opened and in (3) and (4) rings A and B have both been opened.

[10]H. Takeda, W. H. Schuller, and R. V. Lawrence, *J. Org.*, **33**, 3718 (1968)

Potassium nitrosodisulfonate [**1**, 940–942].

Preparation. Singh[1a] reports an improved procedure for the preparation based on a patent by H.-J. Teuber. Hydroxylamine disulfonate, $HON(SO_3Na)_2$, is prepared from sodium nitrite, sodium bicarbonate, and sulfur dioxide and then oxidized with potassium permanganate with pH-control. Manganese dioxide is removed by centrifugation followed by filtration. Fremy's salt separates from the filtrate after addition of KCl and is recrystallized from 1 N KOH. Material prepared in this way can be stored in the cold for several months.

[Before references]: 3-Hydroxy-4-methoxyphenylalanine methyl ester (1) is oxidatively cyclized by the reagent to the indole derivative (2).[9]

Experiments carried out with reagent in which the nitro group was labeled with O^{18} showed that the new oxygen function introduced in the quinone is derived from the reagent and supports the following mechanism:[10]

In studying the oxidation of the phenol (3), related to the mitomycin antibiotics, a Lederle group[11] found it necessary to employ excess reagent at a slightly elevated temperature and in this case the aldehyde group was partially converted into an oxime group (5).

(3) 3.95 g.   (4) 1.43 g. (crude)   (5) 1.20 g. (crude)

[1a]R. P. Singh, *Canad. J. Chem.*, **44**, 1994 (1966)
[9]M. E. Wilcox, H. Wyler, T. J. Mabry, and A. S. Dreiding, *Helv.*, **48**, 252 (1965)
[10]H.-J. Teuber and K. H. Dietz, *Angew. Chem., internat. Ed.*, **4**, 871 (1965)
[11]R. H. Roth, W. A. Remers, and M. J. Weiss, *J. Org.*, **31**, 1012 (1966)

Potassium permanganate [**1**, 942–952, before references].

The method was used also for the preparation of 1- and 2-anthraldehyde from the corresponding methyl ketones.[32a]

Oxidation of amines. Primary, secondary, and tertiary amines containing hydrogen on the carbon α to the nitrogen are oxidatively hydrolyzed to the corresponding aldehyde or ketone by buffered permanganate in warm aqueous *t*-butanol.[32b]

$$(CH_3)_2CHNH_2 \xrightarrow[82\%]{KMnO_4-aq.\ (CH_3)_3COH} (CH_3)_2C=O$$

$$\begin{array}{c} CH_2-CHNH_2 \\ |\qquad| \\ CH_2-CH_2 \end{array} \xrightarrow[71\%]{KMnO_4-aq.\ (CH_3)_3COH} \begin{array}{c} CH_2-CO \\ |\qquad| \\ CH_2-CH_2 \end{array}$$

[32a]J. L. Ferrari, I. M. Hunsberger, and H. S. Gutowsky, *Am. Soc.*, **87**, 1247 (1965)
[32b]S. S. Rawalay and H. Shechter, *J. Org.*, **32**, 3129 (1967)

Potassium persulfate [**1**, 952–954, before references].

Baeyer-Villiger reaction. 2-Alkylcyclopentanones are oxidized by the reagent in aqueous sulfuric acid to δ-lactones.[9]

R	%
CH_3	28.6
$\underline{n}$-C_5H_{11}	51.2
$\underline{n}$-C_8H_{17}	45.7

[9]T. H. Parliment, M. W. Parliment, and I. S. Fagerson, *Chem. Ind.*, 1845 (1966)

Potassium persulfate–Silver nitrate [**1**, 954, before **Potassium thiocyanate**]. This combination is about as satisfactory as Attenburrow manganese dioxide for the oxidation of 5-hydroxyuracil to uracil-5-aldehyde.[1]

$$\text{(HN—CH}_2\text{OH uracil derivative)} \quad \xrightarrow[\text{70-90\%}]{K_2SO_5-AgNO_3} \quad \text{(HN—CHO uracil derivative)}$$

[1]R. Brossmer and D. Ziegler, *Tetrahedron Letters*, 5253 (1966)

Potassium triethylmethoxide (Potassium *t*-heptoxide), $(C_2H_5)_3CO^-K^+$[1, 956, before **Potassium triphenylmethide**]. Mol. wt. 154.29.

Preparation. The red reagent is prepared from potassium and excess triethyl-methanol as solvent or from approximately equimolecular amounts of potassium and the alcohol in xylene or undecane as solvent.[1]

Dehydrohalogenation of aliphatic and alicyclic chlorides. Brown[2] noted that the bimolecular elimination of hydrogen halide from alkyl halides shifts to the Hofmann type by increasing the steric requirements of the base. Thus the elimination reaction

a) C_2H_5OK	30%
b) $(CH_3)_3COK$	72.5%
c) $(C_2H_5)_3COK$	88.5%

of *t*-amyl bromide with potassium ethoxide gave only a 30% yield of the 1-olefin but the yield increased to 88.5% with potassium triethylmethoxide. The reaction provides a convenient method for shifting a double bond to yield the less stable methylene derivatives.[2] The olefin is treated with hydrogen chloride in ether at $-70°$, the

$$\xrightarrow[\text{(overall)}]{60\%}$$

ether is removed at $0°$, and the tertiary chloride so obtained is treated with excess base at $60°$ (12 hrs.). The sequence was used to transform α-cedrene (1) into the less stable β-cedrene (2).[1]

$$\xrightarrow[\text{52\%}]{\substack{1)\ HCl \\ 2)\ (C_2H_5)_3CO^-K^+}}$$

(1)   (2)

[1]S. P. Acharya and H. C. Brown, *Chem. Commun.*, 305 (1968)
[2]H. C. Brown, I. Moritani, and Y. Okamoto, *Am. Soc.*, **78**, 2193 (1956)

Pyridine [1, 958–963].

Bromination [1, 960, after citation of ref. 16]. Perelman *et al.*[16a] found that 19-nor-$\Delta^{5(10)}$-3-ketosteroids (1) are converted in one step into conjugated 19-nor-$\Delta^{4,9}$-

(1) → Br₂–Py → (2)

(3) → C₅H₅NHBr₃⁺⁻ → (4)

3-ketosteroids (2) by bromination in pyridine solution. The related dehydrogenation of (3) → (4) is brought about with pyridinium hydrobromide perbromide in pyridine.[16b]

Reaction with 1,1-dihalocyclopropanes from enol ethers [1, 962, before references]. The cyclopropane (2), prepared from cyclohexanone (1) as shown, when refluxed in pyridine for 75 min. undergoes dehydrohalogenation and ring expansion to give (3)

in 83% yield. Further dehydrohalogenation to give (4) is carried out with potassium *t*-butoxide in DMSO. If (2) is treated with hot quinoline, (4) is formed directly but only in 38% yield. The ring expansion reaction is considered to be a carbonium ion process facilitated by the ether function.[26] The chlorodiene (3) provides a ready access to tropolone (5) and to 3,5-cycloheptadienone (6).

Similar reactions carried out starting with cycloheptanone and cyclooctanone lead to ring contraction products, presumably due to transannular reactions, but the reaction sequence has been applied successfully in the case of cyclododecanone.[27]

[16a]M. Perelman, E. Farkas, E. J. Fornefeld, R. J. Kraay, and R. T. Rapala, *Am. Soc.*, **82**, 2402 (1960)
[16b]W. F. Johns, *J. Org.*, **31**, 3780 (1966)
[26]W. E. Parham, R. W. Soeder, J. R. Throckmorton, K. Kuncl, and R. M. Dodson, *Am. Soc.*, **87**, 321 (1965)
[27]W. E. Parham and R. J. Sperley, *J. Org.*, **32**, 926 (1967)

Pyridine–Aluminum chloride [1, 963, before Pyridine borane].

Preparation.[1] Ninety-six grams of anhydrous aluminum chloride is added to 320 ml. of pyridine containing 2.5% of water warmed to 50°. The resulting melt is heated at 70° with 2 g. of a copper catalyst (prepared from copper sulfate solution and zinc dust according to Brewster and Groening[2]).

Dimeric condensations.[1] Typical reactions are formulated:

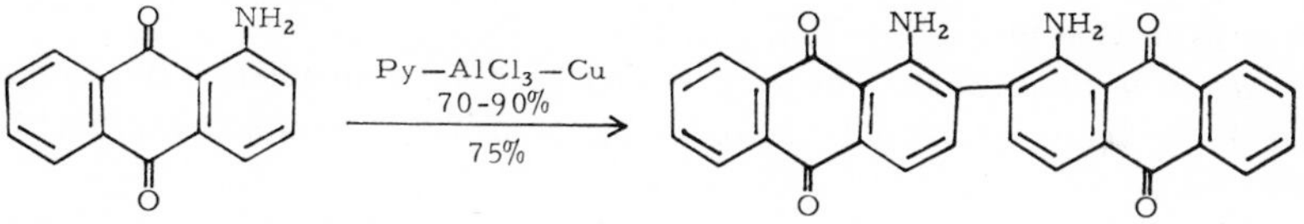

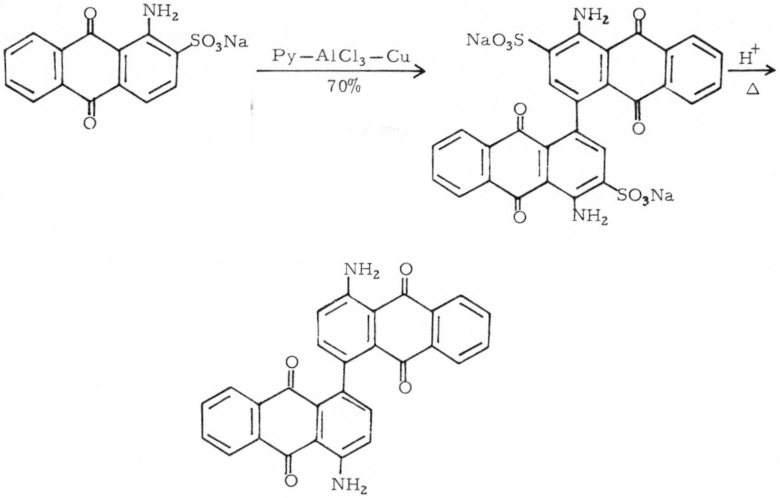

[1]A. K. Wick, *Helv.*, **49**, 1748, 1755 (1966)
[2]R. Q. Brewster and T. Groening, *Org. Syn., Coll. Vol.*, **2**, 445 (1963)

Pyridine–*n*-Butyllithium [1, 964, before Pyridine hydrochloride].

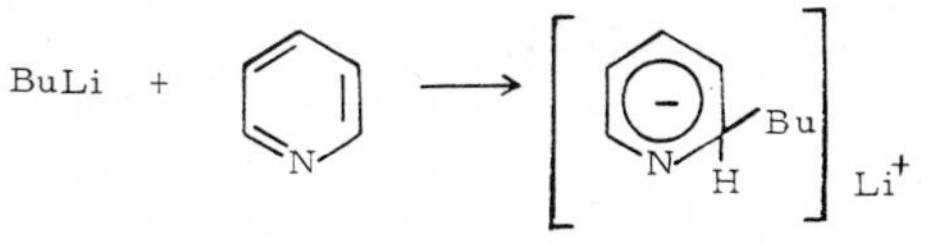

Preparation[1] by addition of *n*-butyllithium in ether in the cold to excess pyridine in dry ether. The reagent may find use in effecting reduction of ketones predominantly under nonequilibrating conditions to the equatorial alcohol where axial approach of the hydride ion is sterically difficult. Thus 3,3,5-trimethylcyclohexanone affords 79% of the equatorial alcohol and 21% of the axial alcohol. In contrast, reduction with complex hydrides gives predominantly the less stable axial alcohol.[2]

79%   21%

[1]R. A. Abramovitch, W. C. Marsh, and J. G. Saha, *Canad. J. Chem.*, **43**, 2631 (1965)
[2]H. Haubenstock and E. L. Eliel, *Am. Soc.*, **84**, 2363, 2368 (1962); J.-C. Richer, *J. Org.*, **30**, 324 (1965)

Pyridine hydrochloride [1, 964–966].

Addition to Preparation. The reagent can be dried conveniently by azeotropic distillation of benzene; it can be stored under benzene for protection against moisture.[1a]

Cleavage of phenol methyl ethers [1, 965, after line 2]. A disadvantage of the Prey procedure is that preparation of the reagent is a little troublesome. A group at St. Louis University[5a] has found that the reagent can be obtained very easily by distillation of a mixture of pyridine with a slight excess of concd. hydrochloric acid at 210°. The ether to be cleaved is stirred into the hot salt and then the reaction mixture is basified and steam distilled to remove pyridine. Yields for the most part are 80–90%.

Acetolysis [1, 966, before references]. Marker[11] discovered a method for utilizing the steroid sapogenin diosgenin (1) for the synthesis of steroid hormones consisting in acetolysis with acetic anhydride at an elevated temperature to the furostadiene diacetate (2), an unsaturated compound which is convertible in four simple steps into progesterone (6).

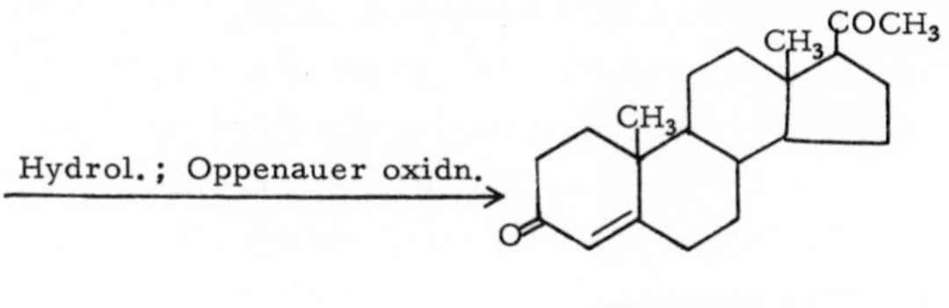

(6) Progesterone

Hershberg's group[12] at Schering found that the acetolysis (1) → (2) can be effected at the b.p. of acetic anhydride with improved yield in the presence of a Lewis acid catalyst ($AlCl_3$ or CH_3COCl). Dauben and Fonken[13] then found that the acetolysis of diosgenin acetate to (2) is improved still further (to a yield of 80%) by use of acetic anhydride catalyzed by pyridine hydrochloride. Wall et al.[14] report that this combination gave excellent results with a wide variety of sapogenins, including the reportedly recalcitrant 12-ketosapogenins.

Beckmann rearrangement. Aryl alkyl ketone oximes (acetophenone oxime) or diaryl ketone oximes (benzophenone oxime) undergo Beckmann rearrangement when refluxed with anhydrous or hydrated pyridine hydrochloride. If the ketone has a methoxyl group in the *para* position concomitant demethylation occurs.[15]

[1a]Dr. Everett E. Gilbert, Allied Chem. Corp., private communication
[5a]T. J. Curphey, E. J. Hoffman, and C. McDonald, *Chem. Ind.*, 1138 (1967)
[11]R. E. Marker and E. Rohrmann, *Am. Soc.*, **62**, 518 (1940)
[12]D. H. Gould, H. Staeudle, and E. B. Hershberg, *ibid.*, **74**, 3685 (1952)
[13]W. G. Dauben and G. J. Fonken, *ibid.*, **76**, 4618 (1954)
[14]M. E. Wall, H. E. Kenney, and E. S. Rothman, *ibid.*, **77**, 5665 (1955)
[15]R. Royer, P. Demerseman, G. Colin, and A. Cheutin, *Bull. soc.*, 4090 (1968)

Pyridine-N-oxide [**1**, 966]. α-Bromo and α-chloro carboxylic acids are oxidatively decarboxylated by treatment with pyridine-N-oxide (4 equiv.) in refluxing benzene or toluene.[3] Cohen et al.[4] note that, since pivalic acid is completely inert to pyridine-N-oxide, an α-hydrogen atom appears to be essential, for example in the reaction of phenylacetic acid. They suggest that an α-pyridinium ion is an intermediate:

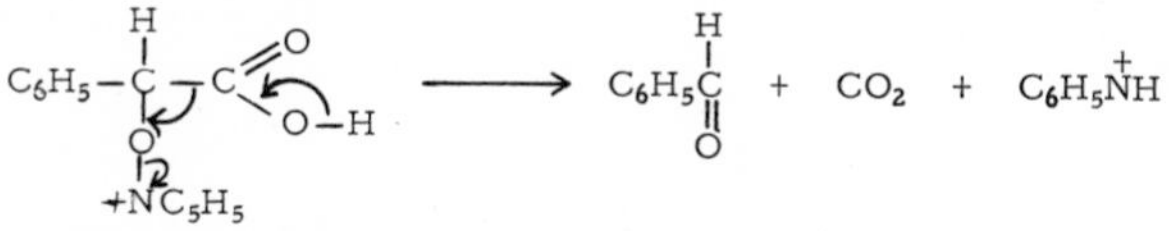

[3]T. Cohen and I. H. Song, *J. Org.*, **31**, 3058 (1966)
[4]T. Cohen, I. H. Song, J. H. Fager, and G. L. Deets, *Am. Soc.*, **89**, 4968 (1967)

Pyrophosphoryl tetrachloride [**1**, 971, after citation of ref. 2].

A more convenient preparation is the reaction of phosphorus pentoxide with phosphorus pentachloride (formed *in situ* from phosphorus trichloride and chlorine); yield 34%:[2a]

$$P_4O_{10} + 4\ PCl_5 \longrightarrow 2\ P_2O_3Cl_4 + 4\ POCl_3$$

Grünze and Koransky[3a] report further on use of the reagent for phosphorylation of nucleosides. The reagent is regarded by Merck chemists[3b] as superior to 2-cyanoethyl phosphate for phosphorylation of 21-hydroxy steroids, particularly those having a 16,17-acetonide group. The steroid is dissolved in the neat reagent at 0° and after one-half hour the reaction is quenched in ice-water, which precipitates the phosphate ester as a semicrystalline solid. By this technique the phosphate derivatives I and II were prepared quantitatively.

I, X = Y = H
II, X = OH; Y = F

The reagent gives a dimeric dehydration product in the case of cortisone and leads to extensive dehydration in the case of 11-hydroxylated steroids. Little or no phosphorylation was observed when the reaction was carried out in the presence of an organic diluent.

[2a]P. C. Crofts, I. M. Downie, and R. B. Heslop, *J. Chem. Soc.*, 3673 (1960)
[3a]H. Grünze and W. Koransky, *Angew. Chem.*, **71**, 407 (1959)
[3b]H. L. Slates, S. Weber, and N. L. Wendler, *Chem. Ind.*, 1174 (1967)

Pyrrolidine [1, 972–974].

Enamines [after citation of ref. 4]. Gadsby and Leeming[4a] used eniminium salts for protection of a Δ^4-3-keto grouping of steroids. The enamine (2) is formed as usual from pyrrolidine and treated with a strong acid such as hydrochloric or perchloric acid to form the eniminium salt (3). Various electrophilic reactions at C_{17} or

(1)   (2)   (3)

C_{21} can be carried out and then the parent Δ^4-3-keto system (1) is regenerated by the action of mild alkali. A British group[4b] prepared the 17-ethylene acetal of Δ^4-androstene-3,11,17-trione by conversion to the eniminium salt (2) to protect the Δ^4-3-keto grouping, ketalization with ethylene glycol (*p*-TsOH), and hydrolysis of the protective group. The overall yield was 72%. Direct ketalization of a 17-ketone had been effected earlier with ethylene glycol, but the yield was in the order of 25%.

Condensation catalyst, [**1**, 973–974, after citation of ref. 6]. The cyclization of (1) to (2) with pyrrolidine according to Newman[6] proceeded in poor yield. It was then found that the yield could be raised to 54% if the concentration of pyrrolidine was

(1)   (2)

kept constant. Thus the dione and the base were heated in benzene and fresh pyrrolidine in benzene was added at the same rate that the solvent distilled.[6a]

[4a]B. Gadsby and M. R. G. Leeming, *Chem. Commun.*, 596 (1968)

[4b]R. W. Kelly, I. McClenaghan, and P. J. Sykes, *J. Chem. Soc.*, (C), 2375 (1967)

[6a]J. N. Gardner, B. A. Anderson, and E. P. Oliveto, *J. Org.*, **34**, 107 (1969)

Q

Quinoline [1, 975, after second paragraph].

    Controlled hydrogenation. In a study of the controlled hydrogenation of acety-
lenes to *cis*-olefins, Cram and Allinger[3a] found palladium on barium sulfate with a
trace of pure quinoline (synthetic) to be superior to the Lindlar catalyst in repro-
ducibility and ease of preparation (a sample of quinoline from coal tar was found to
be unsuitable for this purpose). In one example 19.2 g of dimethyl 5-decynedioate
(1) was hydrogenated with use of 0.4 g. of 5% palladium on barium sulfate and
0.4 g. of synthetic quinoline in 100 ml. of methanol. The mildly exothermal reaction
ceased abruptly after 20 min., with absorption of exactly one equivalent of hydrogen.

In another example, 1,7-cyclodedecadiyne (3) afforded 1,7-*cis*,*cis*-cyclododecadiene
(4) in high yield.

[3a]D. J. Cram and N. Allinger, *Am. Soc.*, **78**, 2518 (1956)

R

Rhodium trichloride, $RhCl_3 \cdot 3H_2O$ [**1**, 983, before **Rochelle salt**]. Mol. wt. 263.33. Suppliers: Engelhard Industries, Inc.; Alfa Inorganics.

Rhodium trichloride catalyzes the addition of ethylene or propylene to a conjugated diene such as butadiene-1,3, for example:[1]

$$CH_2=CH_2 \; - \; CH_2=CHCH=CH_2 \xrightarrow[50^0]{RhCl_3} \begin{cases} CH_3CH=CHCH=CHCH_3 \; (67\%) \\ CH_3CH=CHCH_2CH=CH_2 \; (22\%) \end{cases}$$

It also catalyzes dimerization of olefins.

[1]T. Alderson, E. L. Jenner, and R. V. Lindsey, Jr., *Am. Soc.*, **87**, 5638 (1965)

Ruthenium tetroxide [**1**, 986–989].

[**1**, 988, after first paragraph]: Ruthenium tetroxide in a CCl_4–H_2O system was used for oxidation of the water-soluble alcohol (1) to the ketone (2); in this case platinum-catalyzed air oxidation failed.[3a]

The reagent, used in conjunction with sodium periodate, oxidizes phenyl groups to carboxylic acids:[3b]

and cyclobutanols to cyclobutanones:

Sulfur compounds [**1**, 988, after citation of ref. 4]. The statement that sulfides are inert to osmium tetroxide is not entirely correct. Some sulfides (e.g., diphenyl sulfide and dibenzyl sulfide) are inert, but thiacyclohexane, $S(CH_2)_5$, is converted into the sulfone $O_2S(CH_2)_5$ in 58% yield on treatment with osmium tetroxide at $-15°$ for 2 hrs.[4a]

Oxidation of carbohydrates [**1**, 988–989, before references]. In more recent work, Beynon *et al.*[11] report that the ruthenium tetroxide should be prepared from a hydrated form of ruthenium dioxide, $RuO_2 \cdot 2H_2O$, rather than the anhydrous form. The hydrated dioxide (0.001 mole) is added to an aqueous solution of sodium periodate (0.01 mole) and the mixture is shaken until the insoluble, black dioxide is converted into the tetroxide. This is then extracted into carbon tetrachloride and the solution is added to the substrate in carbon tetrachloride, dichloromethane, or acetone. Axial and equatorial hydroxyl groups on pyranoid rings were found to be oxidized with equal ease. Also *endo* and *exo* hydroxyl groups in 1,4;3,6-dianhydrides are oxidized equally well. Although reagents based on DMSO are more commonly used, the British group feels that ruthenium tetroxide still has a place when good yields of clean products are required quickly.

Horton and Jewell[12] have used RuO_4 in CCl_4 to a limited extent for oxidation of isolated secondary hydroxyl groups in carbohydrates to keto groups but seem to prefer DMSO–Ac_2O.

Oxidation of aromatic steroids and conjugated ketosteroids. In studies of the oxidation of various steroids by ruthenium tetroxide, Caspi *et al.*[13] generated the reagent *in situ* initially from ruthenium dioxide and sodium periodate and then regenerated the tetroxide during the reaction by addition of a sodium periodate solution. A mixture of acetone and water was employed as solvent. Since the dioxide is black and the tetroxide is yellow, the progress of the reaction can be followed visually. The tetroxide degrades aromatic steroids in satisfactory yield. Thus estrone (1) gives the diacid (2) in good yield. The reaction with estradiol diacetate is unexpected however. A

(1, 1.0 g.)   (2, 670 mg.)

(3)   (4)

diacid corresponding to (2) is obtained in only low yield, and the major product (4) results from oxidation doubly allylic to ring A. The reagent is useful for cleavage of conjugated and cross-conjugated steroidal ketones. In some cases, yields are higher than those obtained by ozonolysis. Thus testosterone acetate (5) is cleaved to the keto acid (6) in 80% yield. Oxidation of (7) gave the keto acid (8) by elimination of C_3

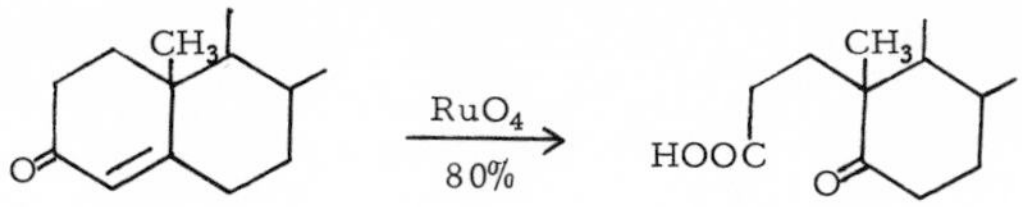

(5)   (6)

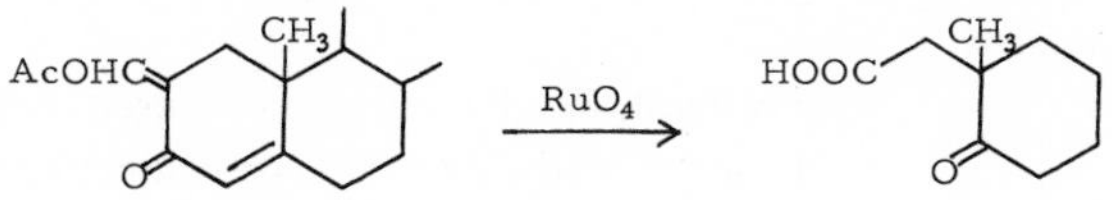

(7)   (8)

and C$_4$. Unexpectedly enediones are formed from 1,4-diene-3,11-diones, (9) → (10).

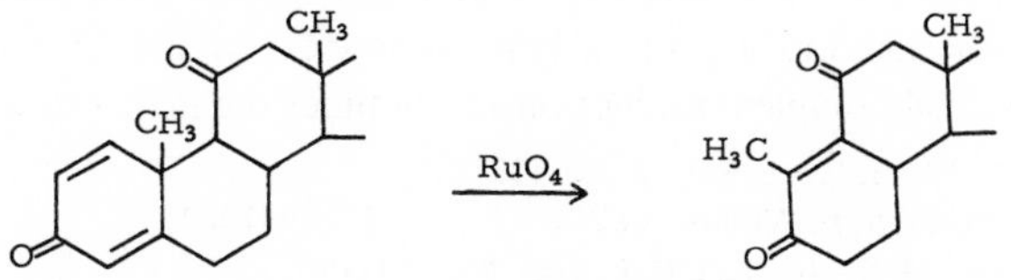

(9)   (10)

[3a]H. O. House and B. A. Tefertiller, *J. Org.*, **31**, 1068 (1966)

[3b]J. A. Caputo and R. Fuchs, *Tetrahedron Letters*, 4729 (1967)

[4a]H. B. Henbest and S. A. Khan, *Chem. Commun.*, 1036 (1968)

[11]P. J. Beynon, P. M. Collins, D. Gardiner, and W. G. Overend, *Carbohydrate Research*, **6**, 431 (1968)

[12]D. Horton and J. S. Jewell, *Carbohydrate Res.*, **2**, 251 (1966)

[13]D. M. Piatak, H. B. Bhat, and E. Caspi, *J. Org.*, **34**, 112 (1969); D. M. Piatak, G. Herbst, J. Wicha, and E. Caspi, *ibid.*, **34**, 116 (1969)

S

Salcomine [Bis(salicylidene)ethylenediiminocobalt (II)] [**1**, 990, before **Selenium**]. *Caution*: very toxic.

Preparation.[1] This maroon-colored chelate is prepared from N,N'-disalicylalethylenediamine and cobalt (II) chloride. It can bind oxygen reversibly ($1O_2 : 2Co$) both in the solid state and in various solvents.[2] Van Dort and Geursen[3] used it as a homogeneous catalyst for the oxidation of phenols by molecular oxygen. In methanol solution the main products from phenols with a free *para* position are the *p*-benzoquinones (yields 15–80%). In chloroform solution radical-complex products are sometimes the main products.

[1]H. Diehl and C. C. Hach, *Inorg. Syn.*, **3**, 196 (1950)
[2]H. M. Faigenbaum and S. E. Wiberley, *Chem. Revs.*, **63**, 269 (1963)
[3]H. M. Van Dort and H. S. Geursen, *Rec. trav.*, **86**, 520 (1967)

Selenium dioxide [**1**, 992–1000].

Oxidation [**1**, 993–994, at end]. Orotaldehyde (2) can be obtained in 58% yield by direct oxidation of 6-methyluracil (1) with selenium dioxide in acetic acid.[10a]

Allylic hydroxylation [**1**, 994–996, at end]. Oxidation of α-cyclodihydrocostunolide (I) with selenium dioxide unexpectedly results in attack of the allylic methine group to give (II) as the major product (30% yield).[18a]

One step in the production of (5), a key intermediate in a synthesis of the tetracyclic triterpene α-onocerin, involved allylic oxidation of the α,β-unsaturated ester (1). This was accomplished with SeO_2 in boiling acetic acid.[18b] The unsaturated hydroxy lactone produced (2) was next to be converted into the saturated keto acid (5), presumably by a stepwise process. However, the Israeli investigators were pleas-

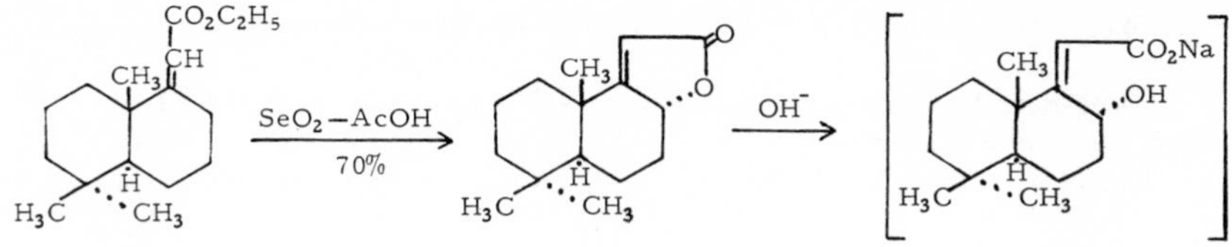

(1)   (2)   (3) 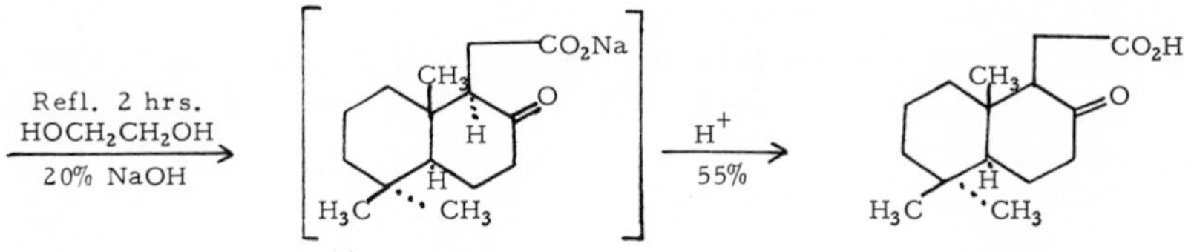   (4)   (5)

antly surprised with the discovery that mere refluxing of (2) with sodium hydroxide – ethylene glycol for 2 hrs. effects disproportionation of the unsaturated hydroxy salt (3) to the saturated keto salt (4), so that acidification gives the saturated keto acid (5) directly.

An Upjohn group[18c] found that steroid *cis*-unsaturated esters of type (6) undergo allylic hydroxylation at C_{16} when treated with selenium dioxide in THF in the presence of acetic acid. Both the α- and β-alcohols are formed. The products (7) and (8) were used for preparation of 16-halocorticoids.

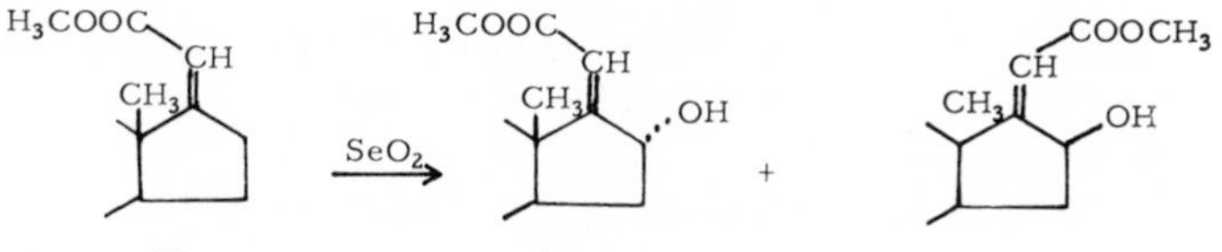

(6)   (7)   (8)

A key step in the partial synthesis of the steroidal insect hormone ecdysone is introduction of a 14α-hydroxyl group. Three groups [Schering (Berlin)–Hoffmann La Roche (Basel)[18d] and Syntex[18e]] achieved this end by allylic oxidation of Δ^7-6-keto-steroids, both 5α and 5β, by selenium dioxide in dioxane. Yields are high.

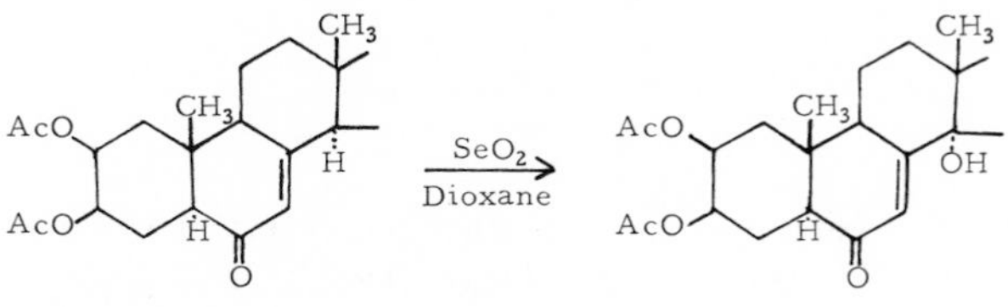

$5\alpha H$ or $5\beta H$ $5\alpha H$ or $5\beta H$

[10a]K.-Y. Zee-Cheng and C. C. Cheng, *J. Heterocyclic Chem.*, **4**, 163 (1967)
[16]*Add*: Idem, *Tetrahedron*, **22**, 3189 (1966)
[18a]S. P. Pathak and G. H. Kulkarni, *Chem. Ind.*, 913 (1968)
[18b]N. Danieli, Y. Mazur, and F. Sondheimer, *Tetrahedron*, **23**, 509 (1967)

[18c]J. E. Pike, F. H. Lincoln, G. B. Spero, R. W. Jackson, and J. L. Thompson, *Steroids*, **11**, 755 (1968)

[18d]A. Furlenmeier, A. Fürst, A. Langemann, G. Waldvogel, U. Kerb, P. Hocks, and R. Wiechert, *Helv.*, **49**, 1591 (1966)

[18e]J. B. Siddall, J. P. Marshall, A. Bowers, A. D. Cross, J. A. Edwards, and J. H. Fried, *Am. Soc.*, **88**, 379 (1966)

Selenium dioxide–Hydrogen peroxide [**1**, 1000, before **Selenium oxychloride**].

Coxon *et al.*[1] used this combination for oxidation of β-pinene (1) to *trans*-pinocarveol (2). The yield is higher than that obtained with selenium dioxide alone in molar quantity. Moreover the problem of eliminating selenium compounds from the product is minimized.

$$H_2O_2 + SeO_2$$
$$(0.66 \text{ m.}) \quad (13.3 \text{ mm.})$$
$$49-55\%$$

(1, 0.5 m.)   (2)

[1]J. M. Coxon, E. Dansted, and M. P. Hartshorn, procedure submitted to *Org. Syn.*, 1968

Silver acetate [**1**, 1002–1004].

cis-Hydroxylation [**1**, 1003, after citation of ref. 10]. The reaction, however, is not stereospecific in the case of alkyl-substituted olefins.[10a] Thus 1,2-dimethylcyclohexene gives, in 50% yield, a mixture of *cis*- and *trans*-1,2-dimethylcyclohexane-1,2-diol in which the *cis* isomer slightly predominates. Gunstone and Morris[10b] report their inability to oxidize tetramethylethylene or phenanthrene by the silver acetate-iodine-moist acetic acid method.

Reaction with gem-dihalocyclopropanes [**1**, 1004, before references]. *gem*-Dihalocyclopropanes react with electrophilic reagents, of which silver acetate–acetic acid or a mixture of sodium acetate and silver nitrate are most effective, to give products of chain extension.[12] In the case of *gem*-dihalocyclopropanes derived from cyclic olefins, ring enlargement results. Thus the reaction of 7,7-dichlorobicyclo-[4.1.0]heptane (1) with silver acetate–acetic acid gives 2-chloro-3-acetoxycyclo-

AgOAc
HOAc
26%

(1)   (2)

heptane (2) in 26% yield (pure). Chain extension is observed with *gem*-dihalocyclopropanes derived from olefins. Thus 1,1-dibromo-2,2-diphenylcyclopropane (3) is transformed into 1,1-diphenyl-2-bromo-3-acetoxy-1-propene (4).[13]

AgOAc
HOAc
72%

(3)   (4)

[10a]C. A. Bunton and M. D. Carr, *J. Chem. Soc.*, 770 (1963)
[10b]F. D. Gunstone and L. J. Morris, *ibid.*, 487 (1957)
[12]S. R. Sandler, *J. Org.*, **32**, 3876 (1967)
[13]S. R. Sandler, procedure submitted to *Org. Syn.*, 1968

Silver carbonate, Ag_2CO_3, [**1**, 1005, before reference].

Oxidation. In an attempted preparation of glycosides of codeine, Rapoport[2] found that codeine is oxidized to codeinone in 75% yield by silver carbonate, prepared by the reaction of silver nitrate with sodium carbonate. Kloetzel[3] later noted that commercial silver carbonate is also effective for this oxidation.

Fetizon[4] found that freshly prepared silver carbonate is a very active oxidizing reagent for alcohols but noted that it is difficult to filter and to wash the reagent. He eliminated this difficulty by precipitating the reagent in the presence of Celite (purified by washing with methanol containing 10% concd. hydrochloric acid, then with water to neutrality, and then drying at 120°). The reagent is prepared as follows. Silver nitrate (34 g.) is dissolved in 200 ml. of distilled water, the purified Celite (30 g.) is added, and the mixture stirred magnetically. Sodium carbonate · 10 H_2O (30 g.) in distilled water (300 ml.) is added. After stirring for 10 min. the yellow-green precipitate is filtered and washed to neutrality with distilled water and then dried several hours in a rotatory evaporator (steam bath). The reagent can be stored, but preferably should be prepared prior to use.

In the general procedure for oxidation of an alcohol (1 millimole), an excess of the reagent (8–15 millimoles) is suspended in a benzene solution (60 ml.) of the alcohol. Some of the benzene is distilled azeotropically and then the solution is refluxed. When the oxidation is complete, the solid is filtered and the aldehyde or ketone isolated from the benzene in the usual way.

Examples.
Androstanol-3β → Androstanone-3(87%)
Cholanol-24 → Cholanal-24 (94.5%)
Methyl cholanate → Methyl 3-keto-7α,12α-dihydroxycholanate (90%)
Geraniol → Geranial (97%)
Naphthohydroquinone → Naphthoquinone (100%)

The selective oxidation of the 3-hydroxyl group of methyl cholanate is noteworthy. Also acetyl, ethyleneketal, and ethylenethioketal groups are stable to the reagent.

The oxidation can also be carried out in toluene or, in the case of very reactive alcohols (allylic or benzylic), in chloroform or methylene chloride. Allylic alcohols can be selectively oxidized in acetone.

[2]H. Rapoport and H. N. Reist, *Am. Soc.*, **77**, 480 (1955)
[3]W. King, W. G. Penprase, and M. C. Kloetzel, *J. Org.*, **26**, 3558 (1961)
[4]M. Fetizon and M. Golfier, *Compt. rend.*, **267**, 900 (1968)

Silver chlorate [**1**, 1005, before references].

The reagent, in combination with a catalytic amount of osmium tetroxide in water solution was used for *cis*-hydroxylation of the unsaturated tetrol (1) to produce the rare alloinositol (2).[3]

McCasland *et al.*[4] attempted to convert 3-cyclohexenyl benzoate (3) into the 1,2-

(1)   (2)

cis-diol derivative with the combination reagent, benzoylated the crude reaction mixture, but obtained the keto dibenzoate (4) as the only isolable product. The

(3)   (4)

mechanism of this unexpected oxidation of a hydroxyl group is not known. 3-Cyclohexenol (5) reacted normally with the reagent to give, after benzoylation, the expected tribenzoate (6).

(5)   (6)

[3] S. J. Angyal and P. T. Gilham, *J. Chem. Soc.*, 375 (1958)
[4] G. E. McCasland, M. O. Naumann, and L. J. Durham, *J. Org.*, **31**, 3079 (1966)

Silver fluoride, AgF [**1**, 1007, before **Silver iododibenzoate**]. Mol. wt. 226.88. Supplier: Alfa Inorganics.

5,6-Unsaturated hexopyranosides, such as (2), are generally prepared by treating a 6-desoxy-6-iodo (or bromo) derivative (1) with silver fluoride in pyridine.[1]

(1) 1.2 g.   (2) 0.3 g.

The method has been extended to the synthesis of 5-desoxy-4,5-unsaturated furanosides[2] (3) → (4) and to the 4′,5′-unsaturated nucleoside (6).[3]

(3)   (4)

(5)   (6)

The reaction of an alkene with Br_2 or I_2 in the presence of finely powdered silver fluoride results in the addition of "BrF" or "IF," respectively. In the case of cyclohexene the addition is exclusively *trans*.[4] In the case of unsaturated carbohydrates

(pyranose glycals) both *cis* and *trans* additions are observed, but *trans* addition predominates:[5]

60%   6%

[1] B. Helferich and E. Himmen, *Ber.*, **61**, 1825; idem, ibid., **62**, 2136 (1929); Review: R. J. Ferrier, *Advan. Carbohydrate Chem.*, **20**, 122 (1965)
[2] L. Hough and B. Otter, *Chem. Commun.*, 173 (1966)
[3] J. P. H. Verheyden and J. G. Moffatt, *Am. Soc.* **88**, 5684 (1966)
[4] L. D. Hall, D. L. Jones, and J. F. Manville, *Chem. Ind.*, 1787 (1967)
[5] L. D. Hall and J. F. Manville, *Chem. Commun.*, 35 (1968)

Silver fluoroborate, $AgBF_4$ [**1**, 1007, before **Silver iododibenzoate**]. Mol. wt. 194.70.

Preparation.[1] Silver oxide (1.0 g.) is dissolved in 45% fluoroboric acid (7.2 g.).

Synthesis of a tropone.[1] The natural tropone nezukone (4) has been synthesized by addition of dichlorocarbene ($CHCl_3$–potassium t-butoxide) to 1-isopropyl-4-methoxycyclohexadiene-1,4 (2), obtained by Birch reduction of the anisole (1). The resulting adduct (3) was treated with silver fluoroborate to give the tropone (4) in

(1)   (2)   (3)   (4)

68% yield. When silver nitrate was used, the yield was 20%, probably as a result of secondary reactions due to the nitric acid produced.

Chromatography.[2] Reverse phase chromatography on glass fibre paper using silver fluoroborate solutions as eluants has proved useful for separation of sesquiterpenes, even of mixtures that appear homogeneous on alumina and by gas-liquid chromatography. Silver nitrate is too insoluble to be used.

[1] A. J. Birch and R. Keeton, *J. Chem. Soc.*, (C), 109 (1968)
[2] B. Wickberg, *J. Org.*, **27**, 4652 (1962); C. Enzell, *Chem. Scand.*, **15**, 1303 (1961); H. S. Barreto and C. Enzell, *ibid.*, **15**, 1313 (1961); J. Runeberg, *ibid.*, **14**, 1985 (1960); L. Westfelt and B. Wickberg, *Arkiv Kemi*, **26**, 545 (1967)

Silver nitrate [1, 1008–1011].

Complexes [1, 1010, after line 3 from bottom]. When a partly epoxidized fatty ester or glyceride carrying residual unsaturation is hydrogenated to the corresponding monohydroxy product at a low pressure over palladium-on-carbon catalyst in ethanol, the presence of silver nitrate in the solution provides complete protection to the ethenoid linkages, probably by π-complex formation.[17a]

$$-CH=CH-(CH_2)_n-CH\underset{O}{\overset{\diagdown \diagup}{\longrightarrow}}CH- \xrightarrow{AgNO_3} -CH=CH-(CH_2)_n-\underset{\underset{AgNO_3}{\uparrow}}{CH}\underset{O}{\overset{\diagdown \diagup}{\longrightarrow}}CH-$$

$$\xrightarrow{H_2,\ Pd-C} -\underset{\underset{AgNO_3}{\uparrow}}{CH}=CH-(CH_2)_n-\underset{\underset{OH}{|}}{CH}-CH_2-$$

Cope *et al.*[17b] pyrolyzed the N,N,N-trimethylammonium hydroxide (1) in a nitrogen atmosphere under evacuation to produce in 89% yield a mixture of cyclooctenes found by IR analysis to contain 40% of the *cis* isomer (2) and 60% of the *trans*

isomer (3). This mixture proved to be easily separable because the *trans* isomer (3) reacts with aqueous silver nitrate to form a water-soluble π-complex whereas the *cis* isomer does not. Thus the total hydrocarbon was distributed between *n*-pentane and 20% aqueous silver nitrate solution and the aqueous layer was extracted with *n*-pentane to remove *cis*-cyclooctene, which was distilled and obtained in yield of 29%. The aqueous AgNO$_3$ solution was added slowly to concentrated ammonium hydroxide containing cracked ice. The *trans*-hydrocarbon that separated was extracted with *n*-pentane and obtained by distillation in yield of 45.4%.

Sterols and their acetates have been separated by column and thin-layer chromatography on silica gel impregnated with silver nitrate.[17c]

In a newer preparation of cyclooctyne from 1-bromocyclooctene, Wittig and Dorsch[17d] isolated the product as the crystalline 2:1 complex with silver nitrate in

30% yield; 1,3-cyclooctadiene and cyclooctene remained unextracted. Treatment of the complex with ammonium hydroxide liberated pure cyclooctyne. Treatment of the complex with tetraphenylcyclopentadienone in benzene for 24 hrs. at room temperature and chromatography afforded the decarbonylated adduct in 87% yield.

Catalytic hydrogenation of 7-acetoxynorbornadiene yields primarily *syn*-7-acetoxynorbornene together with some of the *anti*-isomer. Franzus[17e] found that the *syn*-7-acetate forms a silver complex about ten times more stable than that of the *anti*-7-acetate. The difference is sufficient to permit efficient separation of the isomers. He attributes the effect to chelation of the silver ion with both the double bond and the acetoxy group (4). It was surprising that the complex (4) is even more stable than the complex of norbornene itself. However, the effect appears to be general. Thus *cis*-4-cyclooctene-1-ol is superior to *cis*-cyclooctene in coordinating ability. In acyclic terminally unsaturated alcohols, the complexing ability is highest when the double bond is in the Δ^4-relationship to the hydroxyl group, but a Δ^3- or Δ^6-relationship also enhances complexation.[17f]

Dehydrobromination [**1**, 1011, after formulas]. Kakis[19] has described a convenient procedure for the preparation of phenylbenzhydryl ketone (5) consisting in stirring a solution of triphenylethylene in chloroform, cooling in dry ice–isopropyl alcohol, and then adding all at once a solution of silver nitrate in methanol–water (12%).

$$(C_6H_5)_2C=CHC_6H_5 \xrightarrow[-40^0]{Br_2} (C_6H_5)_2C-CHC_6H_5 \xrightarrow[H_2O-CH_3OH]{AgNO_3}$$
$$\text{in } CHCl_3 \qquad\qquad\qquad \underset{Br\ \ Br}{|\ \ |}$$

(1)   (2)

$$\left[(C_6H_5)_2\underset{\underset{Br}{|}}{C}-\underset{\underset{OH}{|}}{C}HC_6H_5 \xrightarrow{-HBr} (C_6H_5)_2C=\underset{\underset{OH}{|}}{C}C_6H_5 \right] \xrightarrow{93-98\%} (C_6H_5)_2CH\underset{\underset{O}{\|}}{C}C_6H_5$$

(3)   (4)   (5)

Reaction with trialkylboranes. Trialkylboranes when treated with silver nitrate in the presence of either sodium hydroxide or potassium hydroxide undergo coupling.[20] For example, 1-hexene is hydroborated with sodium borohydride and boron trifluoride in diglyme. Aqueous potassium hydroxide is then added followed by aqueous silver nitrate. The major product is *n*-dodecane (66%). Other products are 5-methylundecane (5%) and a mixture of 1-hexene and *n*-hexane. Yields of coupled products are somewhat lower in the case of internal olefins. Coupling of mixed trialkylboranes is also possible.[21]

$$CH_3(CH_2)_3CH=CH_2 \xrightarrow{B_2H_6} [CH_3(CH_2)_3CH_2CH_2]_3B \xrightarrow{AgNO_3}$$

$$CH_3(CH_2)_3CH_2CH_2-CH_2CH_2(CH_2)_3CH_3$$

[17a]R. Subbarao, G. Venkateswara Rao, and K. T. Achaya, *Tetrahedron Letters*, 379 (1966)

[17b]A. C. Cope, R. A. Pike, and C. F. Spencer, *Am. Soc.*, **75**, 3212 (1953); A. C. Cope and R. D. Bach, procedure submitted to *Org. Syn.*, 1967

[17c]H. E. Vroman and C. F. Cohen, *J. Lipid Res.*, **8**, 150 (1967); J. A. Swoboda and M. J. Thompson, *ibid.*, **8**, 152 (1967); R. Kammereck, W.-H. Lee, A. Paliokas, and G. J. Schroepper, Jr., *ibid.*, **8**, 282 (1967)

[17d]G. Wittig and H.-L. Dorsch, *Ann.*, **711**, 46 (1968)

[17e]B. Franzus, W. C. Baird, Jr., E. I. Snyder, and J. H. Surridge, *J. Org.*, **32**, 2845 (1967)

[17f]D. Gray, R. A. Wies, and W. D. Closson, *Tetrahedron Letters*, 5639 (1968)

[18]*See* **1**, 1011: N. H. Cromwell, R. P. Ayer, and P. W. Foster, *Am. Soc.*, **82** 130 (1960)

[19]F. J. Kakis, procedure submitted to *Org. Syn.*, 1968

[20]H. C. Brown, N. C. Hébert, and C. H. Snyder, *Am. Soc.*, **83**, 1001 (1961)

[21]H. C. Brown, C. Verbrugge, and C. H. Snyder, *ibid.*, **83**, 1001 (1961)

Silver oxide [**1**, 1011–1015; 1013, after citation of ref. 12].

Diethyl diazomalonate is conveniently prepared from diethyl mesoxalate (**1**, commercially available) in 67% overall yield by condensation with hydrazine and oxidation of the hydrazone with silver oxide in THF.[12a]

$$\underset{EtOOC}{\overset{EtOOC}{>}}C=O \xrightarrow[75\%]{H_2NNH_2,\ aq.\ AcOH} \underset{C_2H_5OOC}{\overset{C_2H_5OOC}{>}}C=NNH_2 \xrightarrow[89\%]{Ag_2O;\ THF}$$

(1)   (2)

$$\underset{C_2H_5OOC}{\overset{C_2H_5OOC}{>}}C=\overset{+}{N}=\overset{-}{N}$$

(3)

[12a]E. Ciganek, *J. Org.*, **30**, 4366 (1965)

Silver (II) oxide (Argentic oxide) AgO [1, 1015, before **Silver sulfate**]. Mol. wt. 113.88.

Preparation:[1] A rapid and convenient process involves oxidation of 51 g. of silver (I) nitrate in an alkaline medium by means of potassium peroxydisulfate ($K_2S_2O_8$, supplied by Fisher):

$$4\ AgNO_3 + K_2S_2O_8 + 8\ NaOH \longrightarrow 4\ AgO + K_2SO_4 + 3\ Na_2SO_4 + 2\ NaNO_3 + 2\ KNO_3 + 4\ H_2O$$

The reaction is carried out with stirring at 85–90°. The precipitate of black silver (II) oxide is collected on a Büchner funnel and washed free of sulfate ion with water which has been made slightly alkaline. Yield, 35 g. (94%).

Properties.[1] The reagent appears to be a true oxide rather than a peroxide. It does not give free hydrogen peroxide when acidified but behaves in a manner characteristic of a compound in which the metal ion is present in a strongly oxidizing valence state, which may be stabilized by coordination. In dilute acid, oxygen is immediately evolved. The solution in concd. nitric acid is brown, that in concd. sulfuric acid is olive green.

Oxidant in organic chemistry. Syper,[2] of the Technical University, Wroclaw, Poland, found that, in aqueous solutions of acids (HNO_3, H_3PO_4, AcOH), silver (II) oxide oxidizes benzyl alcohols to benzaldehydes and allylic alcohols to allylic aldehydes. A methyl group or an aromatic ring is also oxidized to an aldehydic group, although when more than one group is present only one is oxidized.

T. G. Clarke *et al.*[3] found that the oxidation also proceeds in neutral or even mildly alkaline conditions. In this case the reaction is a two-electron process with formation of silver metal, which can be recovered easily.

Examples.

Benzaldehyde → Benzoic acid (57%)
Benzhydrol → Benzophenone (70%)
Anisyl alcohol → Anisaldehyde (44%)
Triphenyl phosphite → Triphenyl phosphate (30%)
Benzylamine → { Benzaldehyde (23%)
                Benzonitrile (77%)
DL-Valeric acid → Isobutyric acid (100%)

In connection with a study of the cyanide-catalyzed oxidation of allylic aldehydes to carboxylic acid esters by active MnO_2 (*see under* **Manganese dioxide (b) active,** this volume), Corey *et al.*[4] tried silver (II) oxide in place of manganese dioxide. Surprisingly, in this case the products are the free acids. This reagent, however, has the advantage that nonconjugated aldehydes are oxidized in the absence of cyanide ion in THF–water (9:1). Thus dodecanol and 3-cyclohexenylcarboxaldehyde are oxidized to the corresponding acids in 90 and 97% yields, respectively, by an excess of AgO.

[1] R. N. Hammer and J. Kleinberg, *Inorg. Syn.,* **4,** 12 (1953)
[2] L. Syper, *Tetrahedron Letters,* 4193 (1967)
[3] T. G. Clarke, N. A. Hampson, J. B. Lee, J. R. Morley, and B. Scanlon, *ibid.,* 5685 (1968)
[4] E. J. Corey, N. W. Gilman, and B. E. Ganem, *Am. Soc.,* **90,** 5616 (1968)

Silver perchlorate, $AgClO_4$ [1, 1015, before **Silver sulfate**]. Mol. wt. 207.34. Suppliers: Alfa Inorganics, Fl., Sch.

Preparation by reaction of Ag_2CO_3 with 10% perchloric acid, filtration, removal of water in vacuum, and drying by azeotropic distillation with benzene.

Methylation. 1-Methylthymine (3), previously very difficultly accessible, can be prepared easily in two steps as follows.[1] Thymine (1) is heated with hexamethyl-

(1)   (2)   (3)

disilazane to form the 2,4-bis-O-trimethylsilyl derivative (2), and this on treatment with methyl iodide and silver perchlorate gives 1-methylthymine (3).

Rearrangement. Benn[2] used silver perchlorate in refluxing acetone to rearrange the acetate of the ethynylcarbinol (4) to the isomeric allenes (5 and 6). Configurations were assigned on the basis of optical rotatory dispersion and NMR spectra.

(4)   (5)   (6)
                      42%   23%

Quasi-Favorsky reaction. Reaction of 4(e)-bromoadamantanone (1) with silver perchlorate in water–acetone (1:2) gives only minor amounts of the expected 4-hydroxyadamantanone (3), the major product being bicyclo[3.3.1]nonene-2-car-

(1)   (2, 71%)   (3, 3%)

boxylic acid-7 (2). The reaction is assumed to be related to known quasi-Favorsky reactions of some α-bromoketones; it is presumably favored by the rigid coplanar arrangement of (1).

[1]E. Wittenburg, *Ber.*, **99**, 2380 (1966)
[2]W. R. Benn, *J. Org.*, **33**, 3113 (1968)
[3]A. C. Udding, H. Wynberg, and J. Strating, *Tetrahedron Letters*, 5719 (1968)

Silver tosylate [1, 1018, after citation of ref. 1].

Hoffmann[1a] states that silver tosylate can be prepared much more easily *via* reaction (1) than (2).

1. $AgNO_3$ + NaOTs $\xrightarrow{H_2O}$ AgOTs + $NaNO_3$

2. Ag_2O + HOTs $\xrightarrow{CH_3OH}$ AgOTs + H_2O

"Firstly, $AgNO_3$ is more accessible than Ag_2O, which usually has to be made freshly from $AgNO_3$ and tends to decompose. Secondly, AgOTs is precipitated virtually instantaneously by simply mixing equimolar saturated solutions of $AgNO_3$ and NaOTs. The material is colorless when so prepared and ready for use. Also, it will not be decomposed by light at this temperature."

[1a]H. M. R. Hoffmann, private communication

Simmons-Smith reagent [1, 1019–1022, before references].

A modified reagent prepared by refluxing a large excess of zinc-copper couple with methylene iodide for 4–6 hrs. in ether reacts with 17β-acetoxy-11β-hydroxy-$\Delta^{5(10)}$-estrene-3-one (1) to give (2) and the spirocyclopropane (3).[17] The observation

of a Wittig reaction with this reagent is unprecedented. The corresponding 11-desoxy analog does not give this reaction. In contrast to the results cited with the modified reagent, the reaction of (1) with a reagent prepared *in situ* with an approximately 1:1 molar ratio of zinc and methylene iodide affords (4), a product of angular methylation at C_{10}.

The reaction of the Simmons-Smith reagent with α,β-unsaturated ketones is often unsuccessful.[18] Monti[19] devised a modification which appears to be general. An eneyne (5) is treated with red mercuric oxide, trichloroacetic acid, BF_3, and ethylene glycol to form the dioxolane (6); this reacts normally with the Simmons-Smith reagent, and the ketone (8) is obtained on acid hydrolysis.

Vidal, Dumont, and Arnaud[20] found that the Simmons-Smith reagent reacts with an acetylenic alcohol of the type (9) to give an α,β-unsaturated ketone (10) and a ketocyclopropane (II). Use as solvent in place of ether of a 1:1 mixture of ether and 1,1-dimethoxyethane accelerates the reaction and augments somewhat the formation of the α,β-unsaturated ketone (10).

(9)   (10) 10%   (11) 30%

Syntex chemists[21] report that $\Delta^{5(10)}$-estrene-$3\alpha,17\beta$-diol (12) does not react with the Simmons-Smith reagent in refluxing ether according to the procedure of Shank and Shechter[3] (**1**, 1022) but that the cyclopropane derivative (13) can be obtained in 85% yield if the ether is distilled to half volume and the reaction mixture then heated on the steam bath for 3 hrs. at 92° (steam-bath temperature in Mexico City).

(12)   (13)

[17]P. Turnbull, K. Syhora, and J. H. Fried, *Am. Soc.*, **88**, 4764 (1966)
[18]Y. Armand, R. Perraud, J.-L. Pierre, and P. Arnaud, *Bull. soc.*, 1893 (1965); J.-M. Conia and J.-C. Limasset, *Tetrahedron Letters*, 3151 (1965)
[19]H. Monti, *Compt. rend.*, **265** (C), 522 (1967)
[20]M. Vidal, C. Dumont, and P. Arnaud, *Tetrahedron Letters*, 5081 (1966)
[21]R. Guinsig and A. D. Cross, *Am. Soc.*, **87**; 4629 (1965); *see also* R. Rees, D. P. Strike, and H. Smith, *J. Med. Chem.*, **10**, 783 (1967)

Sodium aluminum chloride [**1**, 1027–1029, before references].

E. Ziegler et al.[10] prepared 4-hydroxycarbostyril by heating malondianilide with a mixture of 3 moles of $AlCl_3$ and 2 moles of NaCl at 250°. The mechanism of this reaction has been discussed.[11]

[10]E. Ziegler, R. Wolff, and T. Kappe, *Monatshefte*, **96**, 418 (1965)
[11]E. Ziegler and H. Sterk, *ibid.*, **98**, 1104 (1967)

Sodium amalgam [**1**, 1030–1033].

Preparation (2%) [**1**, 1030, after citation of ref. 4]. Blomquist *et al.*[4a] used the Merck procedure, but noted that it is not necessary to use a flame to initiate the reaction if the sodium is cut with scissors and added directly to the mercury.

Reduction of phthalic acid [before references]. A stirred solution of 1.02 moles of phthalic acid and 281 g. of sodium acetate trihydrate (2.07 moles) is cooled in ice and 3400 g. of 3% sodium amalgam is added in 50–100 g. portions.[14] Work-up, acidification, and crystallization affords *trans*-1,2-dihydrophthalic acid in 62% yield.

[4a]A. T. Blomquist, B. F. Hiscock, and D. N. Harpp, *J. Org.*, **31**, 4121 (1966)
[14]R. N. McDonald and C. E. Reineke, *J. Org.*, **32**, 1878 (1967); procedure submitted to *Org. Syn.*, 1967

Sodium amide [**1**, 1034–1041]. Another supplier: Farchan Research Labs.

Dehydrohalogenation [**1**, 1035–1037, at end]. In a general procedure for the conversion of alkenes into alkynes by bromination and dehydrobromination, Ward and van Dorp recommend sodium amide and liquid ammonia for the dehydrobromination step.[10a] The preparation of propargyl aldehyde diethyl acetal is an example:[10b]

$$CH_2=CHCHO + Br_2 \xrightarrow[72-80\%]{CCl_4} CH_2BrCHBrCHO \xrightarrow[80-82\%]{HC(OC_2H_5)_3} CH_2BrCHBrCH(OC_2H_5)_2$$

$$\xrightarrow[75-78\%]{NaNH_2-NH_3} HC\equiv CCH(OC_2H_5)_2$$

[**1**, 1040]: *Correction*: The formula of cyclopropene (3) as written contains an extra hydrogen atom.

1,4-Elimination of HOR [before references]. The 1,4-elimination of a molecule of an alcohol from an acetylenic ether of the type:

$$CH_3C\equiv C-COR' \quad \text{or} \quad RC-C\equiv CCH_2OR'$$

by reaction with an alkali metal in liquid ammonia constitutes a general method for forming the eneyne system, $HC\equiv C-CH=CH-$. An example is the synthesis of hept-3-ene-1-yne from methyl propargyl ether by Arens *et al.*[29]

$$HC\equiv CCH_2OCH_3 \xrightarrow{LiNH_2, \ NH_3} LiC\equiv CCH_2OCH_3 \xrightarrow[80-86\%]{n-C_4H_9Br}$$
$$(1) \hspace{5cm} (2)$$

$$CH_3CH_2CH_2CH[_2[C\equiv CCH_2[OCH_3] \xrightarrow{-HOCH_3} [CH_3CH_2CH_2CH=C=C=CH_2 \longrightarrow$$
$$(3) \hspace{5cm} (4)$$

$$CH_3CH_2CH_2CH=CHC\equiv CH] \xrightarrow{NaNH_2} CH_3CH_2CH_2CH=CHC\equiv CNa$$

(5)   (6)

$$H_2O \downarrow 63-67\%$$

$$CH_3CH_2CH_2CH=CHC\equiv CH$$

(7)

Cumulene synthesis. A second synthetic sequence developed by Arens *et al.*[30] is illustrated by the synthesis of 1-methoxy-4-methyl-1,2,3-pentatriene (5).

$$HC\equiv CCH_2OCH_3 \xrightarrow[\text{Ether}-\text{THF}]{C_4H_9Li} LiC\equiv CCH_2OCH_3 \xrightarrow{(CH_3)_2CO} Li\text{-derivative}$$

(1)   (2)

$$\xrightarrow[68-72\%]{H_2O} HO-\underset{\underset{CH_3}{|}}{\overset{\overset{CH_3}{|}}{C}}-C\equiv CCH_2OCH_3 \xrightarrow[82-88\%]{C_2H_5OCH(TsOH)} \left[C_2H_5O\underset{\underset{H}{|}}{\overset{\overset{CH_2}{||}}{C}}-O-\underset{\underset{H}{|}}{\overset{\overset{CH_3}{|}}{C}}-C\equiv C\underset{\underset{H}{|}}{\overset{\overset{H}{|}}{C}}OCH_3 \right]$$

(3)   (4)

$$\xrightarrow[58-64\%]{\substack{\text{liq. } NH_3 \\ 2\ NaNH_2}} \underset{CH_3}{\overset{CH_3}{>}}C=C=C=CHOCH_3 + C_2H_5ONa + \overset{ONa}{\underset{}{\overset{|}{CH}}}=CH_2$$

(5)

Homocyclic ring closures. Bunnett and Skorcz[31] found that several aliphatic esters, nitriles, sulfones, and ketones bearing an ω-o-chlorophenyl group react with potassium amide in liquid ammonia to form homocyclic products of ring closure by way of a benzyne intermediate. The procedure has since been modified to use sodium amide (commercially available).[32] The reaction is probably the method of choice for synthesis of 1-substituted benzcyclobutenes.

[10a] J. P. Ward and D. A. van Dorp, *Rec. trav.*, **85**, 117 (1966); **86**, 545 (1967)

[10b] *Idem*, procedure submitted to *Org. Syn.*, 1967

[17] *Change last entry to read:* E. M. Kaiser, W. G. Kenyon, and C. R. Hauser, *Org. Syn.*, **47**, 72 (1967).

[29] L. Brandsma, H. D. Verkruijsse, and J. F. Arens, procedure submitted to *Org. Syn.*, 1967

[30] *Idem, ibid.*, 1967

[31] J. F. Bunnett and J. A. Skorcz, *J. Org.*, **27**, 3836 (1962)

[32] J. A. Skorcz and F. E. Kaminski, *Org. Syn.*, **48**, 53 (1968)

Sodium-Ammonia [**1**, 1041, before references].

Reduction of unsaturated hydrocarbons. Gardner and co-workers[4,5] have found that allenes, both acyclic and cyclic, are reduced to enes in almost quantitative yield by sodium in liquid ammonia. The two-step allene synthesis of Doering and La-Flamme (**1**, 686) was found nicely adaptable to the synthesis of 1,2-cyclononadiene (3), from which *cis*-cyclononene (4) was obtained by reduction with sodium and ammonia.[4]

(1)　　　　　　(2)　　　　　　(3)　　　　　　(4)

The following is a summary of results obtained in a study of the reduction of open-chain allenes:[5]

Note that in the case of both (5) and (6) the more hindered of the two allenic double bonds is the one which is reduced to the greater extent.

As evident from example (4) above, cyclic allenes are reduced to *cis*-enes. A further example is reported by Indian workers[6] in describing a convenient synthesis of *cis,cis*-1,5-cyclononadiene (9). Starting with the readily available *cis,cis*-1,5-cyclooctadiene (7), they applied the method of Untch *et al.*[7] to expand the ring and

(7)　　　　　　(8)　　　　　　(9)

produce 1,2,6-cyclononatriene (8). Treatment of the triene (8) with sodium and liquid ammonia reduced the allene group to a *cis*-ene group and afforded (9) in high yield.

In the absence of added acids (water or alcohol), benzene is reduced exclusively to cyclohexene by sodium or potassium in neat, liquid ammonia at 60–130°.[8] Lithium gives predominantly cyclohexadienes.

[4]P. D. Gardner and M. Narayana, *J. Org.*, **26**, 3518 (1961)
[5]D. Devaprabhakara and P. D. Gardner, *Am. Soc.*, **85**, 648 (1963)
[6]R. Vaidyanathaswamy and D. Devaprabhakara, *J. Org.*, **32**, 4143 (1967)
[7]K. G. Untch, D. J. Martin, and N. T. Castelluci, *ibid.*, **30**, 3572 (1965)
[8]L. W. Slaugh and J. H. Raley, *ibid.*, **32**, 369 (1967)

Sodium azide [1, 1041–1044, before references].

Schmidt reaction. By the Schmidt reaction cyclobutanecarboxylic acid (Aldrich Chem. Co.) can be converted into cyclobutylamine in one step in high yield.[12] On addition of powdered sodium azide to a stirred mixture of chloroform, cyclobutane-carboxylic acid, and concentrated sulfuric acid and heating at 50° for 1.5 hrs., the

carboxylic acid is converted into the conjugate acid of the acyl azide (b), which loses nitrogen with rearrangement to the isocyanate (c). Neutralization with base and distillation affords pure amine, b.p. 80.5–81.5°.

Displacement of activated aromatic halogen.[13] In the synthesis of 4-chlorobenzo-furazane (4) from 2,6-dichloroaniline (1), the first step is oxidation to the nitroso compound (2). This crystallizes in buff-colored needles and dissolves in DMF (95°) to form an initially deep green solution. A solution of sodium azide in aqueous

dimethyl sulfoxide (1 : 4 v/v) is added over a period of 20 min., when the temperature rises to 115° and the color changes to brown. After 10 min. more the solution is cooled to 30° and poured into water to give 4-chlorobenzofurazane (4) as a white powder, m.p. 84–87°.

[12]N. W. Werner and J. Casanova, Jr., *Org. Syn.*, **47**, 28 (1967)
[13]P. B. Ghosh, procedure submitted to *Org. Syn.*, 1967

Sodium benzoate [**1**, 1044–1045, before references]. Angyal and Stewart[4] found that tosyl inositols react with sodium benzoate in DMF in four different ways, depending upon the nature of the neighboring groups, but not always predictably: displacement with inversion; direct displacement; elimination; and epoxide formation and opening (contrary to the rule of diaxial opening). Surprisingly, the Australians conclude that there is little difference in reactivity between axial and equatorial tosyloxy groups.

[4]S. J. Angyal and T. S. Stewart, *Australian J. Chem.*, **20**, 2117 (1967)

Sodium bisulfite [**1**, 1047–1049, before references].

Cleavage of oximes. A Merck group[17] found that oximes are cleaved by the reagent in near-quantitative yields at room temperature in a neutral aqueous medium. Brief treatment with acid is required only for isolation of the product. The reaction

$$CH_3(CH_2)_6\overset{H}{C}=NOH \xrightarrow[H_2O]{NaHSO_3} \left[CH_3(CH_2)_6\overset{SO_3Na}{\underset{H}{\underset{|}{C}}}OH \right] \xrightarrow[87\%]{H^+} CH_3(CH_2)_6\overset{H}{C}=O$$

was first described by von Pechmann[18] in 1887 but apparently has been overlooked in modern literature.

[17]S. H. Pines, J. M. Chemerda, and M. A. Kozlowski, *J. Org.*, **31**, 3446 (1966)
[18]H. von Pechmann, *Ber.*, **20**, 2539 (1887)

Sodium borohydride [**1**, 1049–1055, before references].

Conjugated double bonds. A double bond conjugated with an ester, nitrile, phenyl, or amide group can be selectively reduced in yields of the order of 60–80%.[34]

$$C_6H_5CH=C(CO_2C_2H_5)_2 \xrightarrow[69\%]{NaBH_4 \text{ in EtOH } (25^0)} C_6H_5CH_2CH(CO_2C_2H_5)_2$$

Reduction of tosylhydrazones. Caglioti (Univ. di Bologna, Italy) introduced a simple method for the deoxygenation of aliphatic aldehydes and ketones under mild and neutral conditions consisting in reaction of the tosylhydrazone with sodium borohydride in methanol.[35,36]

In the case of aromatic carbonyl compounds, the tosyl hydrazone is reduced with LiAlH$_4$. The procedure is indicated in the case of particular compounds such as sugars,[36] ketones bearing an asymmetric center in the α-position,[37] etc. If carried out with deuterated reagents, it allows the preparation of labeled compounds.[38]

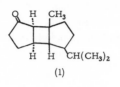

(1)

The method was used successfully for reduction of the hindered ketone (1); in this case, Wolff-Kishner reduction failed even though a hydrazone is formed.[39]

Other reactions. An alkyl halide can be prepared from either the alcohol or the ether by reaction with the halogen and sodium borohydride rather than by using free diborane.[40]

$$3\ ROH\ +\ 2\ X_2\ +\ NaBH_4\ \longrightarrow\ 3\ RX\ +\ H_3BO_3\ +\ NaX\ +\ 2\ H_2$$

The reaction with an ether provides a low-temperature method for cleavage of the ether:

$$3\ ROR'\ +\ 2\ I_2\ +\ NaBH_4\ \longrightarrow B(OR)_3\ +\ 3\ R'I\ +\ NaI\ +\ 2\ H_2$$

$$\downarrow 3\ H_2O$$

$$3\ ROH\ +\ H_3BO_3$$

Muxfeldt *et al.*[41] found that an acylmalonic ester (1), readily available by the method of Tarbell and Price,[42] is reductively cleaved by sodium borohydride to an aldehyde (2) and malonic ester.

$$R\overset{O}{\overset{\|}{C}}CH(CO_2C_2H_5)_2\ \xrightarrow{NaBH_4}\ R\overset{O}{\overset{\|}{C}}H\ +\ CH_2(CO_2C_2H_5)_2$$

(1)   (2)

[34]S. B. Kadin, *J. Org.*, **31**, 620 (1966)
[35]L. Caglioti, *Tetrahedron*, **22**, 487 (1966)
[36]*Idem*, procedure submitted to *Org. Syn.*, 1968
[37]A. N. De Belder and H. Weigel, *Chem. Ind.*, 1689 (1964)
[38]E. J. Corey and S. K. Gros, *Am. Soc.*, **89**, 4561 (1967); M. Fischer, Z. Pelah, D. H. Williams, and C. Djerassi, *Ber.*, **98**, 3236 (1965)
[39]J. D. White and D. N. Gupta, *Am. Soc.*, **90**, 6171 (1968).
[40]L. H. Long, G. F. Freeguard, *Chem. Ind.*, 223 (1965); *idem*, *Nature*, **207**, 403 (1965)
[41]H. Muxfeldt, W. Rogalski, and G. Klauenberg, *Ber.*, **98**, 3040 (1965)
[42]D. S. Tarbell and J. G. Price, *J. Org.*, **21**, 144 (1956); *idem, ibid.*, **22**, 245 (1957)

Sodium–*t*-Butanol–Tetrahydrofurane [**1**, 1056].

Dechlorination of (1) with this combination, equivalent to the original lithium–*t*-butanol–tetrahydrofurane combination (**1**, 604–606), led to reduction as well as dechlorination to give (2) and (3).[1]

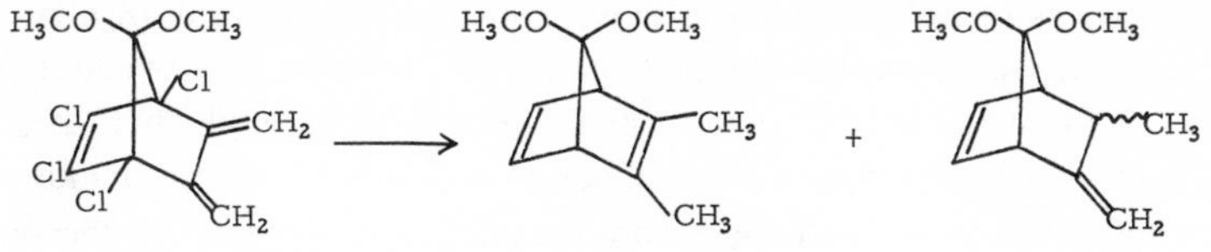

(1)   (2, 38%)   (3, 24%)

[1]P. G. Gassman, D. H. Aue, and D. S. Palton, *Am. Soc.*, **90**, 7271 (1968)

Sodium chlorodifluoroacetate, ClF_2CCO_2Na [1, 1058].

Preparation. The acid, mol. wt. 130.49, b.p. 122°, is supplied by Aldrich, Columbia, Fluka, K and K Laboratories. For conversion to the salt[1a] 60.7 g. of sodium hydroxide is stirred mechanically with 700 ml. of methanol until dissolved and the solution is cooled and kept below 40° during slow addition of a solution of 198 g. of chlorodifluoroacetic acid in 300 ml. of methanol. The methanol is removed under reduced pressure at 40°. The salt is pulverized and dried overnight at room temperature and 1 mm; it is obtained in essentially quantitative yield.

Synthesis of R(Ar)—CH=CF$_2$.[1a] The preparation of β,β-difluorostyrene involves the following reaction:

$$C_6H_5CHO + (C_6H_5)_3P + ClF_2CO_2Na \xrightarrow[67-79\%]{160°} C_6H_5CH=CF_2 + CO_2 + NaCl + (C_6H_5)_3PO$$

A mixture of benzaldehyde, triphenylphosphine, and diglyme is stirred magnetically and a solution of sodium chlorodifluoroacetate is prepared by stirring the finely divided salt in diglyme at 70° for about 5 min. The warm solution is placed in a heated (60°) dropping funnel for delivery into a reaction flask, and the system is purged with nitrogen. The reaction mixture is held at 160° while the solution of sodium salt is added over a period of 1.5–2 hrs. The diglyme and products are flash-distilled into a receiver, cooled with dry ice, and the distillate is fractionated through a spinning-band column; the yield of product collected at a head temperature of 52–54° (40 mm.) is 7.6–8.9 g.

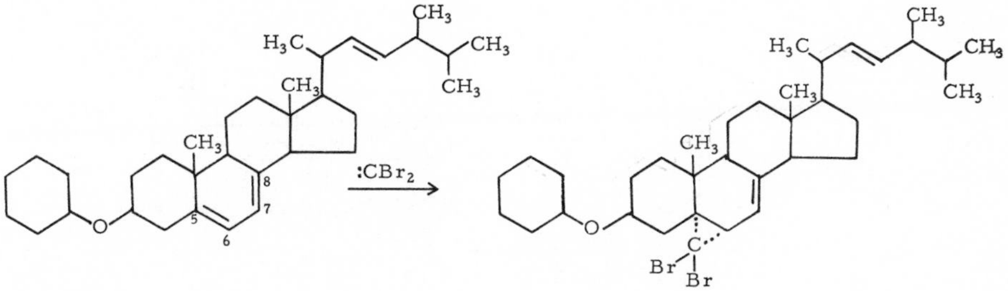

Precursor of difluorocarbene [before references]. In a study of the behavior of cholesterol to dihalocarbenes, a Syntex group[6] found that dichlorocarbene does not add to the somewhat unreactive double bond of cholesterol but that the less bulky difluorocarbene, generated from sodium chlorodifluoroacetate, does add to give a difluorocyclopropane which was assigned the $5\beta,6\beta$-orientation mainly on the basis of NMR correlations found later to have consistent application in many stereo-chemical problems. Nazer[7] found that dichloro- and dibromocarbene add to the more reactive 5,6-double bond of ergosterol, as the tetrahydropyranyl ether, and adduced unequivocal evidence of the 5α,6α-configuration. Catalytic hydrogenation afforded the corresponding 5α,6α-methylene compound. In commenting on the difference between these results and their own, the Syntex group say "We regard these results as fully compatible and see no inconsistency from electronic or steric considerations." —J. H. Fried, private communication.

The Palo Alto Syntex Research group[8] effected addition of difluorocarbene to the double bond of 17β-hydroxy-5α-Δ[1]-androstene-3-one acetate (1) by dropwise addition of a saturated solution of 20–50 equivalents of sodium chlorodifluoroacetate in diglyme or triglyme to a 10% solution of the enone in the same solvent at 165–

225° during ½ to 1 hr. Addition does not occur below 150°, even though decomposition of the salt is observed at 125°. That the reacting species has approached from the relatively unhindered rear[9] is supported by NMR and molecular rotation data. In the case of steroidal dienones and trienones,[10] addition occurs at the double

bond more distant from the ketone group; for example, the conjugated dienone (3) yields (4). The 2-methoxymethylene-3-ketosteroid (5) afforded both isomers of the 1,4-adduct (6).[11]

Slagel[12] reports that the lithium salt of chlorodifluoroacetic acid is superior to the sodium salt for generation of difluorocarbene and difluoromethylenetriphenylphosphorane. Thus the yield of 4,5-dicarbethoxy-1,1-difluoronorcarane from the lithium salt was 50.6% and from the sodium salt was 25.7%.

[1a]S. A. Fuqua, W. G. Duncan, and R. M. Silverstein, Org. Syn., 47, 49 (1967)

[5]Definitive paper: F. E. Herkes and D. J. Burton, J. Org., 32, 1311 (1967). In the early work it was assumed that the reaction of sodium chlorodifluoroacetate in the presence of triphenylphosphine involved formation of difluorocarbene, which then reacts with triphenylphosphine to form difluoromethylenetriphenylphosphorane, $(C_2H_5)_3P=CF_2$. However, addition of tetramethylethylene to the reaction in the presence of a ketone failed to yield any cyclopropane derivative. Herkes and Burton (loc. cit.) suggest that a phosphobetaine salt (a) is the intermediate which loses carbon dioxide to form the active reagent (b).

[6]L. H. Knox, E. Velarde, S. Berger, D. Cuadriello, P. W. Landis, and A. D. Cross, Am. Soc., 85, 1851 (1963)

[7]M. Z. Nazer, J. Org., 30, 1737 (1965)

[8]C. Beard, N. H. Dyson, and J. H. Fried, Tetrahedron Letters, 3281 (1966)

[9]L. F. Fieser, Experientia, 6, 312 (1950)

[10]C. Beard, I. T. Harrison, L. Kirkham, and J. H. Fried, Tetrahedron Letters, 3287 (1966) 3287 (1966)

[11]P. Hodge, J. A. Edwards and J. H. Fried, ibid., 5175 (1966)

[12]R. C. Slagel, Chem. Ind., 848 (1968)

Sodium cyanate [1, 1059, ref. 2].

Change to: B. Loev, M. F. Kormendy, and M. M. Goodman, Org. Syn., 48, 32 (1968).

Sodium cyanide–Dimethyl sulfoxide [1, 1059, before Sodium dichromate dihydrate]. gem-Dicarbethoxy compounds can be decarbethoxylated to ethyl esters in good yield by heating with sodium cyanide in DMSO at 160° for 4 hrs.; presumably 1 mole

each of carbon dioxide and ethylene are formed.[1] The classical procedure involves saponification, decarboxylation, and esterification.

The Johnson group[2] used this method for decarbethoxylation of the malonic ester (1).

(1)   (2)

The reaction was found to be useful in a total synthesis of dihydrocleavamines and related alkaloids. The key intermediate was (3, $R = COOC_2H_5$), but this contains an unwanted ethoxycarbonyl group. This group was removed by sodium cyanide in DMSO in 70% yield to give the desired intermediate (4, $R = H$).[3]

$$(3, \ R = COOC_2H_5)$$
$$(4, \ R = H)$$

[1] A. P. Krapcho, G. A. Glynn, and B. J. Grenon, *Tetrahedron Letters*, 215 (1967)
[2] W. S. Johnson, C. A. Harbert, and R. D. Stipanovic, *Am. Soc.*, **90**, 5279 (1968)
[3] J. Harley-Mason and Atta-Ur-Rahman, *Chem. Ind.*, 1845 (1968)

Sodium   dihydrobis-(2-methoxyethoxy)aluminate, $NaH_2Al(OCH_2CH_2OCH_3)_2$ [1, 1064, before **Sodium diisopropylamide**]. Mol. wt. 202.17. Supplier: Chemapol, Prague, Czechoslovakia.

Preparation.[1]

Reduction of nitroarenes.[2] The reagent has reducing properties similar to those of lithium aluminum hydride. Aromatic nitro compounds are reduced by two moles of the reagent to azo compounds (40–90% yield). The azoxy compound is obtained with 1.5 moles of the hydride.

[1] J. Vib, B. Casensky, and J. Machacek, French patent 1,515, 582 (1967)
[2] J. F. Corbett, *Chem. Commun.*, 1257 (1968)

Sodium fluoride [1, 1073–1074, before reference]. Sodium fluoride suspended in nonaqueous tetramethylene sulfone, acetonitrile, or DMF has been found to exchange halogen readily with carboxylic acid chlorides, α-chloro ethers, trichloromethanesulfenyl chloride, $POCl_3$, etc.[2]

[2] G. W. Tullock and D. D. Coffman, *J. Org.*, **25**, 2016 (1960)

Sodium hydride [1, 1075–1081].

Acylation of ketones [1, 1076 after first paragraph]. A related simplified procedure by Anselme[8a] using sodium hydride and DMSO affords dibenzoylmethane:

$$C_6H_5COCH_3 + C_6H_5CO_2CH_3 \xrightarrow[CH_3SOCH_3]{NaH} [C_6H_5\bar{C}HCOC_6H_5]Na^+ \xrightarrow[75-79\%]{H_3PO_4} C_6H_5COCH_2COC_6H_5$$

Carbomethoxylation [before references]. *See* **Dimethyl carbonate,** this volume.

Enol acetylation. An α-halo-α-arylacetophenone such as (1) cannot be converted into the enol acetate by reaction with isopropenyl acetate, and conversion into the sodium enolate by sodium methoxide followed by treatment with acetyl chloride gives low yields. However, Cooper and Owen[28] found that, if the ketone is treated with dry methanol and sodium hydride and the mixture let stand until evolution of hydrogen has ceased and then treated with acetyl chloride, the enol acetate is obtained in yield of 50–70%.

$$C_6H_5COCHBrC_6H_5 \xrightarrow{\text{NaH, CH}_3\text{OH}} [C_6H_5\underset{\underset{\text{ONa}}{|}}{C}{=}CBrC_6H_5] \xrightarrow[56\%]{\text{CH}_3\text{COCl}} C_6H_5\underset{\underset{\text{OCOCH}_3}{|}}{C}{=}CBrC_6H_5$$

(1)   (2)

Methylation of amino acids and peptides. Coggins and Benoiton[29] found that a series of N-acyl or N-alkyloxycarbonyl amino acids smoothly underwent N-methylation with methyl iodide in the presence of sodium hydride in refluxing tetrahydrofurane containing dimethylformamide. Benzoyl- or carbobenzoxy-L-leucine gave optically pure N-methylleucine in 96% yield after deblocking. No α-carbon alkylation occurred. Similar treatment of polyleucine followed by acid hydrolysis yielded 91% N-methylleucine and 1% leucine. Methylation of some acetyldipeptide esters and subsequent hydrolysis yielded over 80% of methylamino acids and less than 2% of amino acids.

$$C_6H_5CH_2OCO-\underset{\underset{C_4H_9}{|}}{\overset{\overset{H}{|}}{N}}-CHCOOH \xrightarrow[\substack{8\ CH_3I \\ THF-DMF \\ (10:1)}]{3\ NaH} C_6H_5CH_2OCO-\underset{\underset{C_4H_9}{|}}{\overset{\overset{CH_3}{|}}{N}}-CHCOOCH_3$$

$$\xrightarrow[96\%]{\substack{1.\ N\ NaOH \\ 2.\ \overline{H}Br/\text{acetic acid}}} \underset{\underset{C_4H_9}{|}}{\overset{\overset{CH_3}{|}}{HN}}-CHCOOH$$

[8a]J.-P. Anselme, *J. Org.,* **32,** 3716 (1967)
[28]D. J. Cooper and L. N. Owen, *J. Chem. Soc.,* (C), 533 (1966)
[29]J. Coggins and L. Benoiton, Abstracts, 156th Meeting, *Am. Soc. Div. Biol. Chem.,* Sept. 1968, No. 18.

Sodium hypobromite [1, 1083–1084, before references].

Dehydrogenation of aromatic aldoximes.[6] Unhindered aromatic nitrile oxides such as benzonitrile oxide (1) dimerize spontaneously to furoxazanes or 1,2,5-oxadiazole-1-oxides (2). If *o,o'*-substituents are present, as in (3), they tend to inhibit dimeriza-

(1)   (2)

tion and in this case sodium hypobromite dehydrogenates the compound to the nitrile oxide (4) in good to excellent yield.

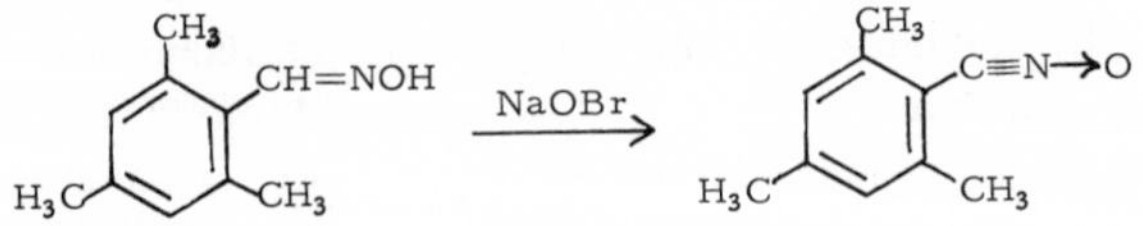

(3)   (4)

[6]C. Grundmann and J. M. Dean, *J. Org.*, **30**, 2809 (1965)

Sodium iodide [**1**, 1087–1090, before references].

Dealkylation of arylalkyl ethers. The method has been used for the demethylation of khellin (1) and visnagin (2).[18] In each case 1 g. of the methyl ether was heated with 5 g. of the alkali halide in 30 ml. of formic acid or acetic acid for 6 hrs. at 100°;

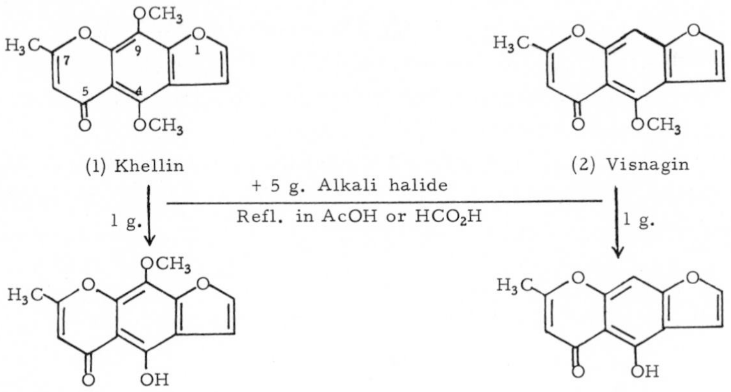

(1) Khellin   (2) Visnagin

+ 5 g. Alkali halide

1 g. | Refl. in AcOH or HCO$_2$H | 1 g.

(3a)   (3b)
AcOH: 90%   AcOH: 75%
HCO$_2$H: 90%   HCO$_2$H: 45%

sodium chloride and potassium chloride are inactive. The comparative results in the table show that potassium iodide is somewhat superior to sodium iodide.

Yield, %

Inorganic halide	In HCO$_2$H		In AcOH	
	3a	3b	3a	3b
NaBr	55	65	10	20
KBr	70	50	10	10
NaI	90	90	75	45
KI	ca. 100	ca. 100	80	60

[18]A. Mustafa, M. M. Sidky, and M. R. Mahran, *Ann.*, **704**, 182 (1967)

Sodium isopropoxide, $(CH_3)_2CHONa$ [**1**, 1090 before, **Sodium metabisulfite**]. Mol. wt. 82.09.

Preparation and use of the reagent are described in a procedure for the preparation of 1,3-cyclohexadiene by dehydrohalogenation of 1,2-dibromocyclohexane.[1] A mixture of 500 ml. of triglyme and 300 ml. of isopropanol is stirred mechanically and

2.23 moles of sodium hydride in a mineral oil suspension is added in small portions. A rapid stream of nitrogen is passed through the system and most of the isopropanol is removed by distillation. The flask is evacuated at the water pump and 1,2-dibromocyclohexane is then added at a rate adjusted to keep the temperature at 100–110°.

[1] J. P. Schaefer and L. Enders, *Org. Syn.*, **47**, 31 (1967)

Sodium-lead alloy [**1**, 1090, before **Sodium metabisulfite**]. Under the name "dri-Na," J. T. Baker Co. supplies in dry, granular form an alloy containing about 10% of sodium and 90% of lead.

Drying agent. Soroos[1] recommended use of this material in place of sodium wire for the drying of ether and comparable solvents. It reacts only slowly with air or water and yet dries ether as completely as sodium wire. It can be added directly to water or to dilute acid to give a nonviolent reaction without ignition of the hydrogen evolved. Typical drying performances are as follows:

	Water content (by Karl Fischer titration), % wt/wt	
	Before drying	After drying
Benzene, sample I	0.017	0.005
Benzene, sample II	0.049	0.007
Cyclohexane	0.006	0.006
Ether	0.048	0.001
Pyridine	0.069	0.035

Whereas disposal of metallic sodium residues presents a problem, "dri-Na" residues are easily disposed of, as the alloy may be placed directly in water.

[1] H. Soroos, *Ind. Eng. Chem., Anal. Ed.*, **11**, 657 (1939)

Sodium methoxide [**1**, 1091–1095, before references].

Treatment of 2-cyanomethyl-2′,4′-dimethoxybenzophenone (1) with sodium methoxide in DMSO under nitrogen gives a deep red solution, which when heated for 10 min. at 140° followed by acidification gives an almost quantitative yield of 9-cyano-2-methoxyanthracene-10-ol (3).[20] The reaction presumably proceeds through a carbanion (2). The anthranol can be oxidized to the anthraquinone (4) in 90% yield by alkaline hydrogen peroxide.

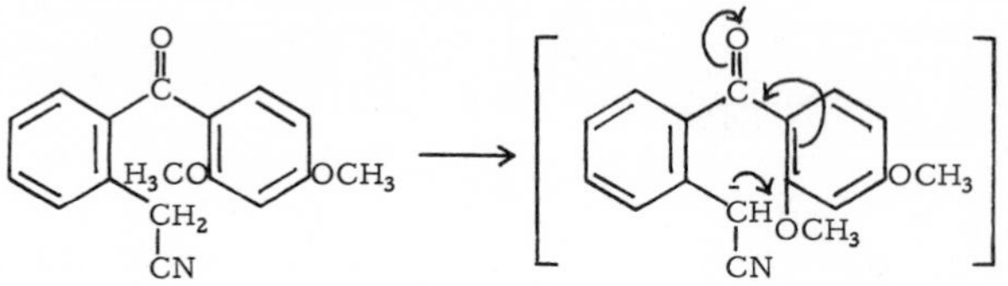

(1)   (2)

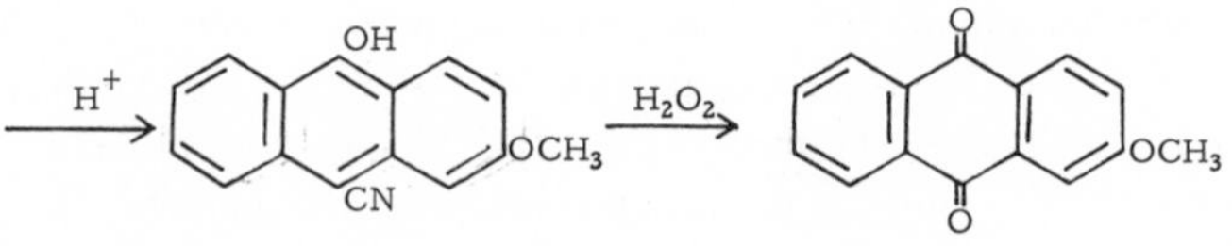

(3)   (4)

[20] J. S. Davies, V. H. Davies, and C. H. Hassall, *Chem. Commun.*, 1555 (1968)

Sodium 2-methyl-2-butoxide [1, 1096, before references].

Conia[7] recommends this base as a substitute for the usually employed phenyllithium or *n*-butyllithium for preparation of nonstabilized phosphonium ylides. The base is soluble in various organic solvents and the *t*-amyl alcohol formed apparently improves the yields in the Wittig reaction.

[7] J.-M. Conia and J.-C. Limasset, *Bull. soc.*, 1936 (1967)

Sodium methyl phosphorazidate, $CH_3O\overset{\underset{\displaystyle O}{\|}}{\underset{\underset{\displaystyle ONa}{|}}{P}}N_3$ **[1, 1097, before Sodium naphthalene].**

Mol. wt. 80.05, m.p., 146–148°.

Preparation.[1] Dimethyl phosphorazidate reacts with sodium iodide in acetone to give the crystalline reagent.

Use.[1] This is said to be a highly selective reagent for phosphorylation of amines even in dilute aqueous solution.

[1] N. K. Hamer, *Chem. Commun.*, 758 (1967)

Sodium nitrite [1, 1097–1101, before references].

Sodium nitrite–CF_3CO_2H–DMSO. Diazotization of a benzylamine (1) with sodium nitrite and trifluoroacetic acid in the molar ratio 1:2:3 in DMSO at 100° for 2 hrs.

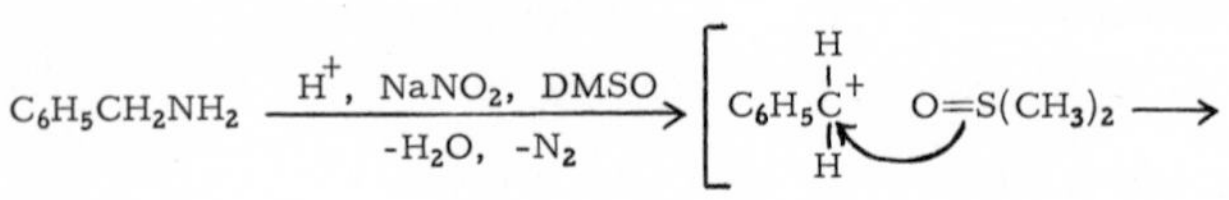

(1)   (2)

$$C_6H_5-\overset{\overset{\text{H}}{|}}{\underset{\overset{|}{\text{H}}}{C}}-O-\overset{+}{\underset{CH_3}{\overset{CH_3}{S}}} \longrightarrow C_6H_5-C\overset{\text{H}}{\underset{O}{\diagup}} + S(CH_3)_2$$

$$\text{(3)} \qquad\qquad\qquad\qquad \text{(4)}$$

gives the corresponding benzaldehyde (4) in yields of 60–80%.[25] Use of isoamyl nitrite reduces the yield.

[25] K. H. Scheit and W. Kampe, *Angew. Chem., internat. Ed.*, **4**, 787 (1965)

Sodium perborate [1, 1102, before references].

Quinone epoxides, for example the epoxide of juglone, have been obtained by reaction with sodium perborate.[3]

Juglone

[3] A. Rashid and G. Read, *J. Chem. Soc.* (C), 1323 (1967)

Sodium sulfite, Na_2SO_3 [1, 1105, before Sodium thiocyanate].

Photoreduction. Irradiation of 3,17β-estradiol (1) with a Hanovia mercury vapor lamp in an aqueous ethanol solution containing sodium sulfite gives as the major product 3β,17β-dihydroxy-5α,10β-estrane (2). Reduction in the presence of sodium borohydride gives (3) and (4) in low yield.[1] It is suggested that the reduction with sodium sulfite may proceed through a sulfinate intermediate. This novel photoreduction method was first observed with kynurenic acid (5), which is reduced in this way to kynurenine yellow (6).[2]

[1] J. A. Waters and B. Witkop, *Am. Soc.*, **89**, 1022 (1967)
[2] T. Tokuyama, S. Senoh, T. Sakan, K. S. Brown, Jr., and B. Witkop, *ibid.*, **89**, 1017 (1967)

Sodium telluride, Na_2Te [**1**, 1105, before **Sodium thiocyanate**]. Mol. wt. 173.61.

Preparation.[1] Liquid ammonia (5 l.) is poured over 716.4 g. of powdered tellurium in a 6-l. flask, then 273.2 g. of sodium is added slowly at $-60°$ with stirring.

Reduction of halogen substituents. The reagent effects reduction of halogen in aromatic and aliphatic compounds:

$$Cl_2C=CCl_2 + Na_2Te + CH_3OH \xrightarrow[51\%]{} Cl_2C=CHCl + Te + NaCl + NaOCH_3$$

[1]W. Mack, *Angew. Chem., internat. Ed.*, **6**, 1083 (1967)

Sodium trichloroacetate [**1**, 1107–1108]. This product, marketed as "Dow weed killer," is satisfactory for laboratory use.

Generation of dichlorocarbene [1107–1108, at end]. Peer and Schors[7] found that the reaction of allene (1) with dichlorocarbene generated from chloroform and potassium *t*-butoxide gave only tars, but that the reaction with dichlorocarbene generated under neutral conditions from sodium trichloroacetate gave 2,2-dichloromethylenecyclopropane (2) in about 20% yield. This reaction was used as the first step in a synthesis of dispiro[2.0.2.2]octene-7 (6).[8] When heated at 215° for 1 hour, (2) rearranges quantitatively to dichloromethylenecyclopropane (3); heating for a

longer period leads to 7,7,8,8-tetrachlorodispiro[2.0.2.2]octane (4), also in quantitative yield. Dechlorination to (5) is achieved by treatment with zinc in ethanol; the two chlorine atoms are then reduced by sodium–THF–*t*-butanol to give (6).

Trichloromethylation [before references]. Aldehydes and acid chlorides can also be trichloromethylated:[9]

$$C_6H_5CHO \xrightarrow[30\%]{CCl_3CO_2Na} C_6H_5\overset{\displaystyle |}{\underset{\displaystyle CCl_3}{C}HOH}$$

$$CH_3COCl \xrightarrow[20\%]{CCl_3CO_2Na} \underset{\underset{CCl_3}{|}}{CH_3C}=O$$

[7]H. G. Peer and A. Schors, *Rec. trav.*, **86**, 161 (1967)
[8]W. R. Dolbier, Jr., D. Lomas, and P. Tarrant, *Am. Soc.*, **90**, 3594 (1968)
[9]A. Winston, J. C. Sharp, K. E. Atkins, and D. E. Battin, *J. Org.*, **32**, 2166 (1967)

Sodium trithiocarbonate, Na_2CS_3 [**1**, 1109, before **Solvents**]. Mol. wt. 154.21.

Preparation.[1] A 33% aqueous solution of the reagent is prepared from sodium sulfide in water and carbon disulfide, followed by evaporation at reduced pressure.

Conversion of halides into mercaptans.[1] When a halide is heated at 60° for 1–5 hrs. with an aqueous solution of the reagent the corresponding mercaptan is obtained in 25–75% yield. The following mechanism is postulated:

$$R-Cl \ + \ Na_2CS_3 \longrightarrow RS\overset{\overset{S}{\|}}{C}S^-Na^+ \xrightarrow{H^+} RS\overset{\overset{S}{\|}}{C}SH \xrightarrow[-CS_2]{} RSH$$

[1]D. J. Martin and C. C. Greco, *J. Org.*, **33**, 1275 (1968)

Stannous chloride [**1**, 1113, after citation of ref. 7].

Peptide synthesis. The guanidine group of arginine is usually protected by nitration. In the original procedure of Bergmann and Zervas[7a] the protective group was removed by catalytic hydrogenation. Young *et al.*[7b] commented on limitations

$$O_2NN-\overset{\overset{NH}{\|}}{\underset{\underset{H}{|}}{C}}CH_2CH_2CH_2\overset{\overset{NH_2}{|}}{C}HCO_2H$$

Nitroguanidine

of this procedure and reported that electrolytic reduction gives excellent results. In a more convenient procedure, reduction is carried out in high yield with stannous chloride (8-fold excess) in 60% formic acid.[7c] The method was applied to the synthesis of poly-L-arginine hydrochloride from poly-L-nitroarginine (62.7% yield).

$$O_2NN-\overset{\overset{NH}{\|}}{\underset{\underset{H}{|}}{C}}CH_2CH_2CH_2\overset{\overset{NH_2}{|}}{C}HCO_2H \xrightarrow{H_2, \ Pt} HN-\overset{\overset{NH}{\|}}{\underset{\underset{H}{|}}{C}}CH_2CH_2CH_2\overset{\overset{NH_2}{|}}{C}HCO_2H$$

Nitroguanidine   Guanidine

[7a]M. Bergmann, L. Zervas, and H. Rinke, *Z. physiol.*, **224**, 40 (1934)
[7b]P. M. Scopes, K. B. Walshaw, M. Welford, and G. T. Young, *J. Chem. Soc.*, 782 (1965)
[7c]T. Hayakawa, Y. Fujiwara, and J. Nogucki, *Bull. Chem. Soc. Japan*, 40, 1205 (1967)

Sulfoacetic acid [**1**, 1117]. The correct formula is $HOOCCH_2SO_2OH$.

3-Sulfolene   (2-5-Dihydrothiophene-1,1-dioxide,   "Butadiene   sulfone")

[**1**, 1118, before **Sulfosalicylic acid**]. Mol. wt. 118.15, m.p. 64.5–65°. Basic sources: Shell Chem. Co., Phillips Petroleum Co. Suppliers: A, B, C, E, F, MCB, Fl.

Preparation.[1] Butadiene and sulfur dioxide in the ratio of 1:2 and with the addition of 1% of hydroquinone to retard polysulfone formation are allowed to react at 100° for 12 hrs. in a steel bomb or at room temperature for 2–3 weeks in pressure bottles (80–85% yield).[1] The product is purified by crystallization from water (Norit)[1] or methanol (Norit).[2]

Source of butadiene. When heated to a temperature of 110–130°, butadiene sulfone loses SO_2 and gives pure butadiene. Backer and Blaas[3] first noted that this substance can be used in place of 1,3-butadiene in Diels-Alder reactions with certain advantages: it is a crystalline solid, it is nonflammable, nontoxic, nonhygroscopic,

0.51 mole   0.50 mole   90 ml.   1 g.

odorless, and stable indefinitely. Sample and Hatch[2] described a procedure for the preparation of diethyl *trans*-Δ^4-tetrahydrophthalate in which a pressure vessel is charged with 0.51 mole of 3-sulfolene, 0.50 mole of diethyl fumarate, absolute ethanol, and a small amount of hydroquinone and heated at 100–105° for 8–10 hrs. Sample and Hatch[4] also worked out an undergraduate laboratory experiment for the reaction of 3-sulfolene (25 g.) with maleic anhydride (15 g.) in xylene (over a free flame!) to give *endo-cis*-4-cyclohexene-1,2-dicarboxylic anhydride (82–90%).

Benzyne does not act as a dienophile with butadiene, presumably because the diene exists in the transoid arrangement. However, benzyne and butadiene generated from 3-sulfolene react to give 1,4-dihydronaphthalene in low yield (9%). The reaction is carried out by decomposing benzenediazonium 2-carboxylate and 3-sulfolene at 100° in pentanone-2.[5] The reaction presumably occurs because the butadiene is generated in the cisoid conformation.

[1]O. Grummitt, A. E. Ardis, and J. Fick, *Am. Soc.*, **72**, 5167 (1950)
[2]T. E. Sample, Jr., and L. F. Hatch, procedure submitted to *Org. Syn.*, 1967
[3]H. J. Backer and T. A. H. Blaas, *Rec. Trav.*, **61**, 785 (1942)
[4]T. E. Sample, Jr., and L. F. Hatch, *J. Chem. Ed.*, **45**, 55 (1968)
[5]L. F. Hatch and D. Peter, *Chem. Commun.*, 1499 (1968)

"Sulfo-mix," a solution of *m*-nitrobenzenesulfonic acid in sulfuric acid [**1**, 1118, before **Sulfosalicylic acid**].

Preparation.[1,2] To 880 g. of 20% fuming sulfuric acid in a 2-l. flask is added drop-wise, with stirring, 197 g. of nitrobenzene. The temperature is raised slowly to 60–70° and this temperature is maintained for 6–8 hrs., or until a sample of the mixture is completely soluble in water.

Condensation catalyst. The reagent catalyzes the condensation of 4-amino-pyridine (1) with methyl vinyl ketone to give 4-methyl-1,6-naphthyridine (2) and with crotonaldehyde to give 2-methyl-1,6-naphthyridine (3) but the yields were low.

The condensation of 4-aminopyridine (1) with glycerol and sulfo-mix affords 1,6-naphthyridine (4) in modest yield.[2,3]

Similarly, 2-aminopyridine (5) affords 1,7-naphthyridine (6)[2] and 3-aminopyridine (7) gives 1,5-naphthyridine (8).[2]

[1]W. P. Utermohlen, Jr., *J. Org.*, **8**, 544 (1943)
[2]W. W. Paudler and T. J. Kress, procedure submitted to *Org. Syn.*, 1967
[3]T. J. Kress and W. W. Paudler, *Chem. Commun.*, 3 (1967)

Sulfur dichloride [**1**, 1121–1122, before references].

The reaction of sulfur dichloride with cyclic dienes has been extended to cyclic polyolefins.[5] The reagent reacts with cyclooctatetraene (5) to give (6) as the major product. The reaction is of interest because additions to cyclooctatetraene usually

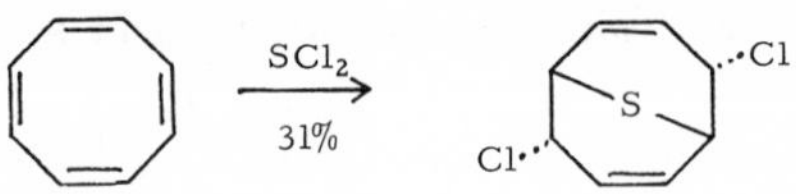

(5)   (6)

proceed with rearrangement of the carbon skeleton. Cycloheptatriene (7) gives (8) in 35% yield.

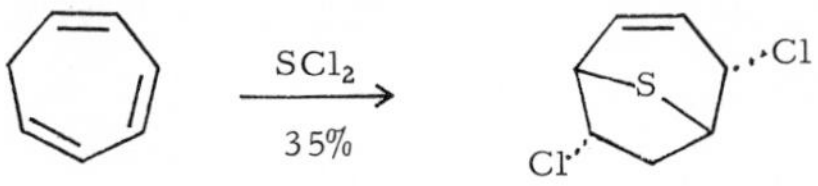

(7)   (8)

[5]F. Lautenschlaeger, *J. Org.*, **33**, 2627 (1968)

Sulfur dioxide [**1**, 1122, before reference].

Diels-Alder reaction. Sulfur dioxide adds 1,6 to *cis*-hexatriene in ether at room temperature to form the adduct 2,7-dihydrothiepin-1,1-dioxide (2).[2] The reaction is analogous to the 1,4-addition of sulfur dioxide to butadiene (*see* **Sulfolene**, this

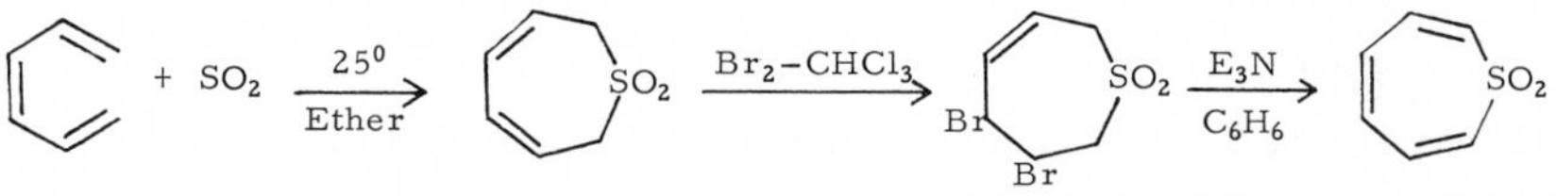

(1)   (2) m. p. 108°   (3)   (4)

volume). This product was converted into the hitherto unknown thiepin-1,1-dioxide (3) by bromination and dehydrohalogenation.

Deoxygenation of pyridine-N-oxides.[3] Introduction of a slow stream of sulfur dioxide into a refluxing solution of a pyridine-N-oxide in dioxane or water for a period of 3 hrs. affords the free base in yields of 21–78%. Nonaromatic N-oxides are not reduced.

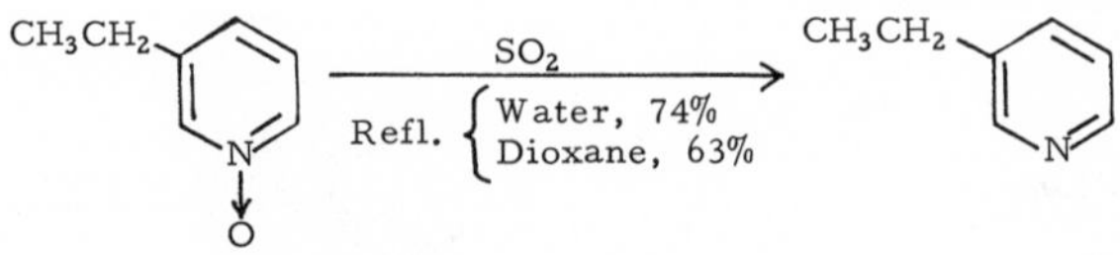

[2]W. L. Mock, *Am. Soc.*, **89**, 1281 (1967)
[3]F. A. Daniher and B. E. Hackley, Jr., *J. Org.*, **31**, 4267 (1966)

Sulfurous acid monomethyl ester N,N-diethylamide [**1**, 1123]. Third line: replace "chlorosulfonic acid methyl ester" by chlorosulfuric acid methyl ester.

Sulfur tetrafluoride [**1**, 1123–1125].

[**1**, 1124, after citation of ref. 7]: Boswell[7a] has prepared 6,6-difluoro-Δ^4-3-keto-steroids (4) by the following scheme. A 5α,6,6-trifluoro-3β-acetoxysteroid (2) is obtained by the reaction of sulfur tetrafluoride on a 5α-fluoro-6-ketone (1) (for preparation, *see* **Nitrosyl fluoride**, **1**, 755). The 3β-acetoxy group is hydrolyzed and the

(1)   (2)   (3)   (4)

resulting 3β-ol oxidized by Jones reagent. Dehydrofluorination is then accomplished by passage through neutral alumina to give (4).

[Before references]: Cram and Wingrove[9] found that there is no loss of deuterium in the reaction of the optically active (–)-acid with sulfur tetrafluoride and concluded that the reaction is stereospecific.

[7a]G. A. Boswell, Jr., J. Org., 31, 991 (1966)
[9]D. J. Cram and A. S. Wingrove, Am. Soc., 86, 5490 (1964); see also E. W. Della, ibid., 89, 5221 (1967)

Sulfur trioxide–Dioxane [bottom of 1, 1126].

Sulfonation of anthracene.[6a] Anthracene is sulfonated by the complex in dioxane almost completely to the 9-sulfonic acid. The equilibrium concentrations depend in a high degree on the temperature: a rise in temperature increases the amount of anthracene. However, by controlling the reaction temperature to 40°, sodium anthracene-9-sulfonate can be obtained in 70% yield in the reasonable reaction time of 20 hrs.

[6a]H. Zorn, O. Hinterhofer, and H. Schindlbauer, Monatshefte, 98, 2406 (1967)

Sulfur trioxide–Pyridine [1, 1127–1128].

Preparation [after (b), ref. 1]. Procedure (b) can be carried out with 6.17 g. of pyridine and 4.51 g. of chlorosulfonic acid in 15 ml. of carbon tetrachloride.[1a, 1b]

Sulfate esters [before references]. For the preparation of glucose-6-sulfate, Guiseley and Ruoff[9] recommend sulfur trioxide–pyridine in DMF. This procedure minimizes polysulfation. Although the salt so obtained gave the correct analysis for

(1) 0.12 m.   in HCON(CH$_3$)$_2$ + Py·SO$_3$ in HCON(CH$_3$)$_2$
                     300 ml.   0.12 m.   125 ml.

Stir 2 1/2 hrs.
Work-up, conversion to crude salt
40% + 14%

Crude

barium, paper chromatography showed the presence of glucose, glucose-6-sulfate, and glucose disulfate.

Oxidizing agent. Parikh and Doering[10] report a novel reagent consisting of sulfur trioxide, conveniently in the form of the pyridine complex, and DMSO in the presence of triethylamine. The reagent oxidizes primary and secondary alcohols to aldehydes and ketones rapidly at room temperature. It oxidizes allylic alcohols to the corresponding α,β-unsaturated carbonyl compounds.

(1)   (2)

This combination has been used with success for the oxidation of norbornadiene-7-ol-iron tricarbonyl (1) to the ketone (2), the simplest stable derivative of the elusive norbornadiene-7-one.[1b] Use of CrO_3 leads to formation of benzaldehyde.

[1a]L. F. Fieser, *Am. Soc.*, **70**, 3232 (1948); *idem, Org. Expts.*, third edition, D. C. Heath and Co., Boston, Mass., 1955, p. 337
[1b]J. M. Landesberg and J. Sieczkowski, *Am. Soc.*, **90**, 1655 (1968)
[9]K. B. Guiseley and P. M. Ruoff, *J. Org.*, **26**, 1248 (1961)
[10]J. R. Parikh and W. von E. Doering, *Am. Soc.*, **89**, 5505 (1967)

Sulfuryl chloride [**1**, 1128–1131].

Chlorination of aromatics [at end]. de la Mare and Suzuki[15a] examined the chlorination of naphthalene, 1-methylnaphthalene, and 2-methylnaphthalene with sulfuryl chloride and concluded that the main products are generally those of electrophilic substitution. The results are similar to those obtained with molecular chlorine.

Chlorination of methyl sulfides and methyl ethers [**1**, 1130]. The procedure of Davis and Lougheed cited in ref. 22 has now been published in *Org. Syn.*, **47**, 23 (1967), but Dr. Lougheed has informed us that it contains an error first noted by Dr. H. Gross of the German Academy of Sciences, Berlin, and confirmed by Dr. Lougheed: the product is not "α-chloroanisole" but rather *p*-chloroanisole. *See also* M. Shamma, L. Novak, and M. G. Kelley, *J. Org.*, **33**, 3335 (1968).

Chlorination of cyclohexene epoxide [**1**, 1131]. The reagent reacts with cyclohexene epoxide and 1 equiv. of pyridine in chloroform at the reflux temperature to give in 70% yield a product consisting to the extent of 99% of *cis*-1,2-dichlorocyclohexane.[23a] Thionyl chloride–pyridine was less effective; the total yield of dichlorides was 50% and the *cis* isomer predominated to the extent of 93.5%.

[15a] P. B. D. de la Mare and H. Suzuki, *J. Chem. Soc.*, (C), 1586 (1967)

[23a] J. R. Campbell, J. K. N. Jones, and S. Wolfe, *Canad. J. Chem.*, **44**, 2339 (1966)

T

Tetrachlorocyclopentadienone ethylene ketal,   [1, 1132, before

Tetrachlorofurane]. Mol. wt. 261.93, m.p. 64.5–65.5°, b.p. 78–80°/0.13 mm.

Preparation. The reagent is prepared in good yield by reaction of hexachloro-cyclopentadiene with ethylene glycol and potassium hydroxide.[1,2]

Diels-Alder diene.[1–3] This is a reactive Diels-Alder diene, but has the disadvantage of competitive dimerization of the reagent. However, the desired adduct can be dechlorinated easily by the Winstein procedure (Li + t-butanol),[4] and removal of the protective ethylene ketal group presents no problem. Thus Stedman and Miller[3]

report two synthetic routes to the bird-cage ketone (6), hexacyclo[5.4.1.0.^{2,6}0.^{3,10}-0.^{5,9}0.^{8,11}]dodecane-4-one. In the preferred one (Scheme I) the first step involves the Diels-Alder reaction of tetrachlorocyclopentadienone ethylene ketal (1) with 1,2,3,4,7,7-hexachloronorbornadiene (18% yield). Later steps involved photochemical cyclization of (3) to the cage compound (4); dechlorination by the Winstein procedure (5), and hydrolysis of the ketal group.

[1]W.-H. Chang, *J. Chem. Soc.*, 2305 (1965)
[2]D. M. Lemal, E. P. Gosselink, and A. Ault, *Tetrahedron Letters*, 579 (1964)
[3]R. J. Stedman and L. S. Miller, *J. Org.*, **32**, 35 (1967)
[4]P. Bruck, D. Thompson, and S. Winstein, *Chem. Ind.*, 405 (1960)

Tetracyanoethylene[**1**, 1133]. Additional suppliers: EGA-Chemie KG, Fl.
  Review: D. N. Dhar, *Chem. Rev.*, **67**, 611 (1967).

Tetraethylammonium acetate [**1**, 1136–1137, before references].
  Cope and Nealy[5] epimerized the *cis*-hydroxy ester (1) by conversion to the tosylate (2), S_N2 displacement by tetraethylammonium acetate (with inversion), followed by alkaline hydrolysis of the ester.

[5]A. C. Cope and D. L. Nealy, *Am. Soc.*, **87**, 3122 (1965)

Tetraethylammonium periodate, $(C_2H_5)_4N^+IO_4^-$ [**1**, 1138, before **Tetraethyl orthocarbonate**]. Mol. wt. 261.19, m.p. 176–177°.

  Preparation.[1] A solution of 0.034 mole each of periodic acid (H_5IO_6) and 26% tetramethylammonium hydroxide in 20 ml. of water is evaporated under reduced pressure, and the solid residue extracted with hot *t*-butanol, precipitated with diisopropyl ether, and crystallized from *t*-butanol (8.5 g., 82%). Soluble in water, acetic acid, acetone, pyridine, DMF, $CHCl_3$.

  Oxidant.[1] The oxidant is equivalent to periodate salts but the great solubility in water may be useful in some cases. It may find use as a co-oxidant in homogeneous aqueous phase. It has been used specifically for oxidation of hydroxylamines such as (1).

[1]A. K. Qureshi and B. Sklarz, *J. Chem. Soc.*, (C), 412 (1966)

Tetramethyl pyrophosphite [**1**, 1138–1139, before references]. A German group[4] has used the reagent for cyclization of a peptide by activation of the amino group. The reaction is carried out at 140° with high dilution.

[4]M. Rothe, I. Rothe, H. Brünig, and K.-D. Schwenke, *Angew. Chem.*, **71**, 700 (1959)

Tetrafluoroboric acid [**1**, 1139, before references].
  Dimerization of carbodiimides.[4] Aliphatic carbodiimides (1) when mixed with 0.5

molar equivalent of anhydrous ethereal tetrafluoroboric acid in methylene chloride dimerize rapidly to the salts (2). The salts were not isolated but were converted by basification into the diazetidines (3).

$$R = \underline{n}\text{-}C_3H_7, \ \underline{i}\text{-}C_3H_7, \ C_6H_{11}$$

Aromatic carbodiimides (4) also dimerize; however, they afford substituted quinazolium salts (5), which on basification give 3-aryl-2-arylamino-4-aryliminoquinazolines (6).

[4]K. Hartke and F. Rossbach, *Angew. Chem., internat. Ed.*, **7**, 72 (1968)

Tetraheptylammonium chloride, $[CH_3(CH_2)_6]_4N^+Cl^-$ [**1**, 1140, before **Tetrahydrofurane**]. Mol. wt. 446.25. Suppliers: E, F.

Use.[1] A solution of this oil-soluble quaternary ammonium salt in chloroform or ethyl acetate quantitatively extracts polar, anionic lipids such as steroid conjugates from aqueous solution by a process of anion exchange.

[1]A. F. Hofmann, *J. Lipid Res.*, **8**, 55 (1967)

Tetrahydrofurane [**1**, 1140–1141].

Solvent effects [**1**, 1141, after line 10]. Sodium acetylide can be prepared conveniently by the reaction of sodium with acetylene in THF.[11a] The classical procedure using liquid ammonia is experimentally inconvenient.

[11a]J.-F. Normant, *Bull. soc.*, 859 (1965)

Tetrahydrophthalazine (5) [**1**, 1142, before **Tetrakis-(N-dihydropyridyl)-aluminate**]. Mol. wt. 134.18, m.p. 196.5–197.5°.

Preparation. Detailed procedures are given[1] for photochemical chlorination of

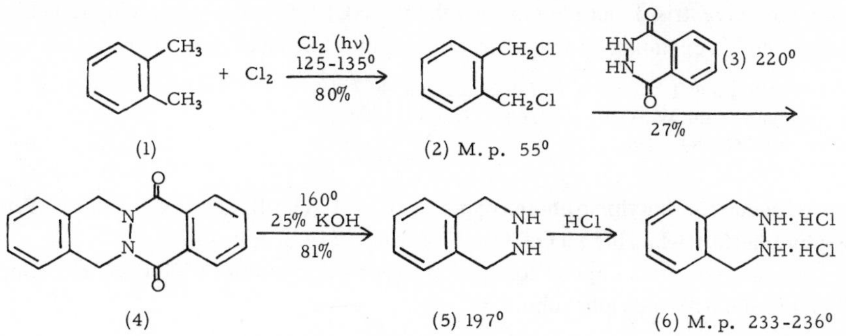

(1)   (2) M. p. 55°

(4)   (5) 197°   (6) M. p. 233-236°

o-xylene to produce α,α'-dichloro-*o*-xylene (2) and for its condensation with phthal-hydrazide (3) to form 1,2,3,4-tetrahydrophthalazino[2.3 : b]phthalhydrazide (4).

Selective precipitation of formaldehyde. In a dilute aqueous solution weakly acidified with acetic acid, tetrahydrophthalazine precipitates formaldehyde as the sparingly soluble hexahydrotetrazine (7). The precipitation is quantative, and by this means formaldehyde can be detected without difficulty at a concentration of only

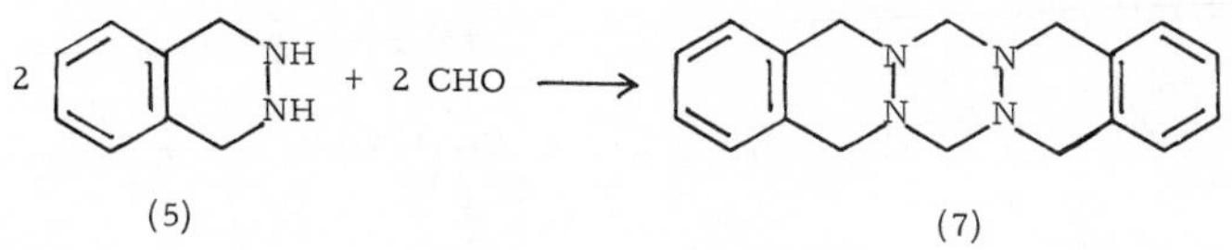

(5)   (7)

8.6×10^{-6} g./ml. Other aldehydes do not interfere with the test. Methanol can be detected by first oxidizing it to formaldehyde with a glowing copper wire or with potassium peroxydisulfate.

[1] R. Ohme and E. Schmitz, *Z. anal. Chem.*, **220**, Vol. 2, 105 (1966)

Tetrakis(dimethylamino)titanium, $Ti[N(CH_3)_2]_4$ [**1**, 1142, before **Tetrakis-phosphorus trichloride-nickel(O)**]. Mol. wt. 225.20, orange liquid, b.p. 50°/0.05 mm. Prepared in 85% yield by reaction of titanium tetrachloride with lithium dimethyl-amine.[1]

Uses. The reagent converts even hindered ketones into enamines, for example:[2]

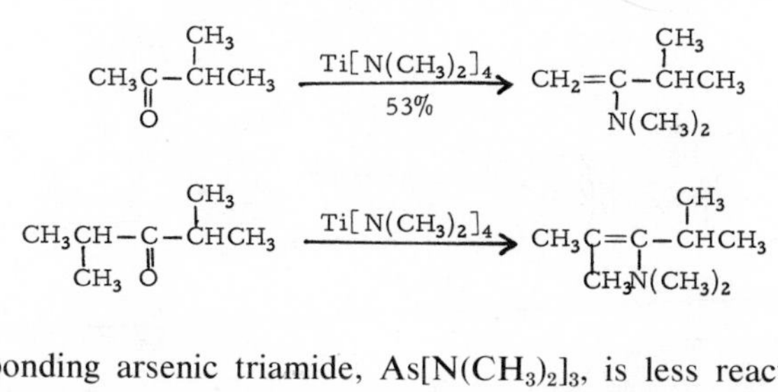

The corresponding arsenic triamide, $As[N(CH_3)_2]_3$, is less reactive and reacts only with unhindered ketones. In contrast, the phosphorus analog gives epoxides (*see* **Hexamethylphosphorous triamide**).

The reagent reacts with carboxylic acids or derivatives (esters, amides, anhydrides) to give tris(dimethylamino)methane, $HC[N(CH_3)_2]_3$, or a vinylidinebisdimethylamine, depending upon the structure of the starting compound.[3]

[1]D. C. Bradley and T. M. Thomas, *J. Chem. Soc.*, 3857 (1960)
[2]H. Weingarten and W. A. White, *J. Org.*, **31**, 4041 (1966)
[3]*Idem, ibid.*, **31**, 2874 (1966)

Tetrakisiodo(tri-*n*-butylphosphine)copper, $[ICuP(C_4H_9)_3]_4$ [**1**, 1142, before **Tetra-kis-phosphorus trichloride-nickel (O)**]. Mol. wt. 1575.08, m.p. 75°.

Preparation.[1] This copper complex is prepared in about 50% yield from copper (I) iodide and tri-*n*-butylphosphine:

$$4\ (\underline{n}\text{-}C_4H_9)_3P\ +\ 4\ CuI\ \longrightarrow\ [ICuP(C_4H_9)_3]_4$$

The reagent decomposes in several days when refrigerated. It is extremely soluble in chloroform, benzene, toluene, and ether, and moderately soluble in ethanol or water.

Oxidative coupling. Organolithium and organomagnesium compounds react with the complex in THF or dimethoxyethane at $-78°$ to give copper(I) ate complexes, which in the presence of atmospheric oxygen undergo coupling.[2] The reaction of *n*-butyllithium is typical:

$$2\ C_4H_9Li\ +\ [ICuP(C_4H_9)_3]_4\ \xrightarrow[-78^0]{THF}\ (C_4H_9)_2CuLi\ \xrightarrow[-78^0]{O_2}\ C_8H_{18}$$

The main product is octane (84% yield); 1-butene (14%) and 1-butanol (5%) are minor products. The reaction is applicable to primary, secondary, vinyl, and aryl groups, but tertiary alkyl compounds give low yields. Organolithium compounds give somewhat higher yields than corresponding Grignard reagents. Oxidants other than oxygen are effective, for example, nitrobenzene or $Cu(II)Cl_2 \cdot TMEDA$ (**2**, 403). Also, two different lithium reagents can be used but, as expected, mixtures of products are obtained.

The final step in the synthesis of the natural fulvene fulvoplumierin (3), involved condensation of the vinyl chloride (1) with lithium di(*trans*-1-propenyl)cuprate (2), prepared by the above method.[3]

[1]G. B. Kauffman and L. A. Teter, *Inorg. Syn.*, **7**, 9 (1963)
[2]G. M. Whitesides, J. SanFilippo, Jr., C. P. Casey, and E. J. Panek, *Am. Soc.*, **89**, 5302 (1967)
[3]G. Büchi and J. A. Carlson, *Am. Soc.*, **90**, 5336 (1968)

Tetramethoxyethylene, $(CH_3O)_2C=C(OCH_3)_2$ [**1**, 1142, before **Tetramethylammonium acetate**]. Mol. wt. 148.16, b.p. 140°, m.p. 2–4°.

Review.[1]

Preparation.[2] The reagent (2) is prepared by pyrolysis of 5-phenyl-1,2,3,4-tetrachloro-7,7-dimethoxynorbornadiene (1) at 130°, N_2, evacuation to 4 torr. (*The pyrolysis can lead to an explosion on a scale larger than 25 g.*)

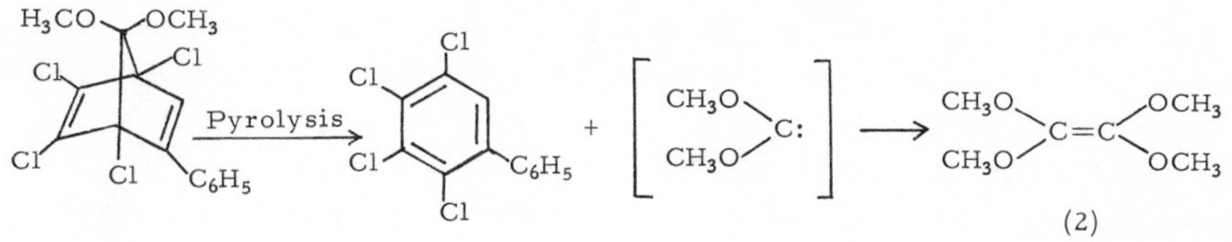

(1)   (2)   50–60%

Properties. The reagent, with four electron-donating substituents, is the counterpart of tetracyanoethylene, with four electron-attracting groups. Thus it forms charge-transfer complexes with weak π-acids, e.g., fumaronitrile and 1,3,5-trinitrobenzene. One interesting use in synthesis is as a strong reducing agent that is soluble in organic solvents. During the process the reagent is oxidized to the dication, $(CH_3O)_2\overset{+}{C}-\overset{+}{C}(OCH_3)_2$, which is a strong methylating agent. Thus reduction of chloranil (3) gives tetrachlorohydroquinone dimethyl ether (4) in 88% yield. Benzoyl peroxide (5) gives methyl benzoate (6) in 74% yield.[3]

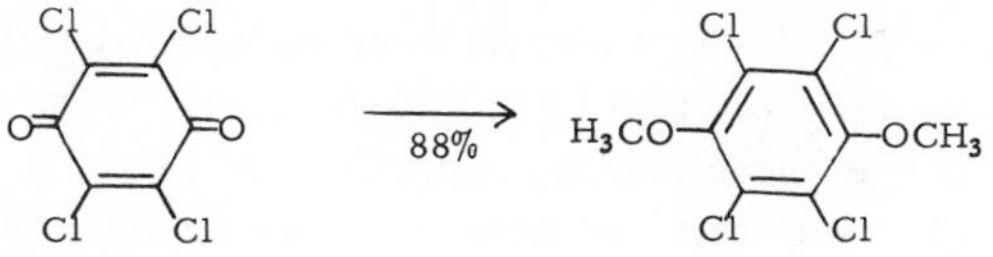

(3)   (4)

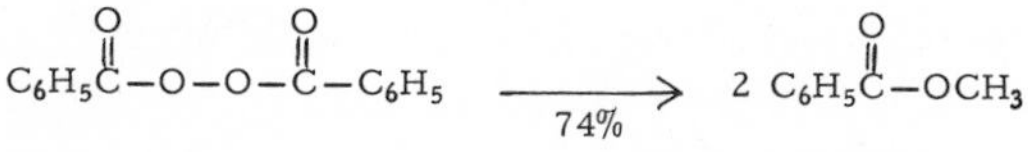

(5)   (6)

Tetramethoxyethylene readily undergoes $2+2$ cycloadditions with electrophiles to give carbocyclic and heterocyclic four-membered rings.[4] Thus it reacts at 0° with

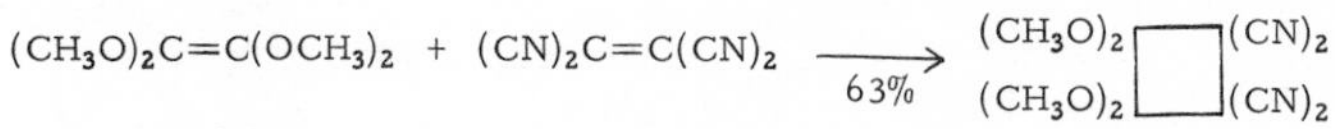

(2)   (7)

tetracyanoethylene to give the adduct (7) in 63% yield. Addition to diethyl azodi-

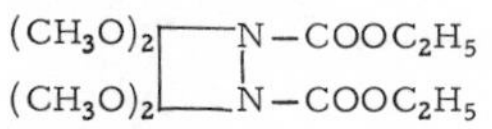

(8) 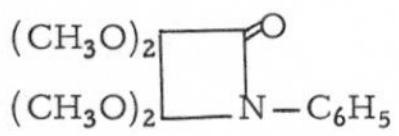   (9)

carboxylate yields the diazetidine (8) in 98% yield, and addition to phenyl isocyanate gives (9) in 76% yield.

[1]R. W. Hoffmann, *Angew. Chem., internat. Ed.*, **7**, 754 (1968)
[2]R. W. Hoffmann and H. Häuser, *Tetrahedron*, **21**, 891 (1965)
[3]R. W. Hoffmann and J. Schneider, *Ber.*, **100**, 3689 (1967)
[4]R. W. Hoffmann and H. Häuser, *Angew. Chem., internat. Ed.*, **3**, 380 (1964)

Tetramethylene sulfone (Sulfolane) [**1**, 1144–1145, before references].

Lhomme and Ourisson,[11] in working on the oxidation of camphanols with lead tetraacetate in benzene found that there was considerable risk that very volatile products would be entrained during removal of the benzene by distillation. Since sulfolane has been used in the industry for the extraction of aromatics from hydrocarbon mixtures, they tried adding pentane and then extracting the solution several times with the nonmiscible sulfolane. The residual pentane solution could then be washed with water for the removal of sulfolane and recovery of the volatile cyclic ethers formed in the oxidation. The procedure was verified by showing that more than 70% of camphene could be recovered in this way.

Acceleration of acid-catalyzed reactions. Whiting and co-workers[12–15] have used this solvent for reaction of aliphatic and aromatic hydrocarbons under acidic conditions. Thus $\Delta^{1,9}$-octalin and *trans*-Δ^1-octalin are rapidly isomerized to a mixture of Δ^9-octalin, $\Delta^{1,9}$-octalin, and four other isomers in the ratio of 90:9:1 by tetrafluoroboric acid (HBF_4, an equimolecular mixture of BF_3 and anhydrous HF) in benzene–sulfolane. Substitution of acetic acid for sulfolane decreases the rate and the yield markedly.[12] Solutions of 85% H_2O_2, HF, and BF_3 in sulfolane probably contain the conjugate cation $H_3O_2^+$. This is a powerful but unselective oxidant, effecting extensive or total breakdown of benzene or cyclohexane at room temperature.[13] The cation $C_6H_5N\overset{+}{H}$ has been generated from phenylhydroxylamine by treatment with tetrafluoroboric acid in sulfolane and used for aromatic aminophenylation.[14] Total yields are 20–55%, but a multitude of isomers is formed. Aromatic arylaminocarbonylation has been achieved with aryl isocyanates by treatment with hexafluorophosphoric acid (HPF_6, prepared from PF_5 + HF) in sulfolane.[15]

$$ArH + Ar'NCOH^+ \longrightarrow ArCONHR'$$

Condensation catalyst. In seeking a practical synthesis of 3,4-benzphenanthrene, an Oxford group[16] effected the cyclodehydration of 2-phenylethyl-1,2,3,4-tetra-hydro-1-naphthol (1) with a combination of polyphosphoric acid (PPA) and sulfolane at 125° for 1 hr. and isolated the hexahydrobenzophenanthrene (2) in 74% yield. In a trial with PPA alone at the same temperature, the sole product was the tricyclic hydrocarbon (3), isolated in only a trace amount. The results suggest that sulfolane is an effective condensation catalyst.

[11]J. Lhomme and G. Ourisson, *Tetrahedron*, **24**, 3201 (1968)
[12]J. W. Powell and M. C. Whiting, *Proc. Chem. Soc.*, 412 (1960)
[13]R. W. Alder and M. C. Whiting, *J. Chem. Soc.*, 4707 (1964)
[14]J. H. Parish and M. C. Whiting, *ibid.*, 4713 (1964)
[15]R. W. Alder, G. R. Chalkley, and M. C. Whiting, *ibid.*, (C), 52 (1966)
[16]N. A. Burditt, M. C. Whiting, and L. M. Venanzi, *ibid.*, (C), 2273 (1967)

N,N,N′,N′-Tetramethylethylenediamine (TMEDA), $(CH_3)_2NCH_2CH_2N(CH_3)_2$

[**1**, 1145, before **Tetramethylguanidine**]. Mol. wt. 116.21, b.p. 120–122°. Suppliers: E, A.

Metalation of dialkyl sulfides.[1] *n*-Butyllithium and N,N,N′,N′-tetramethyl-ethylenediamine form a highly reactive complex which can metalate dimethyl sulfide to give methylthiomethyllithium:

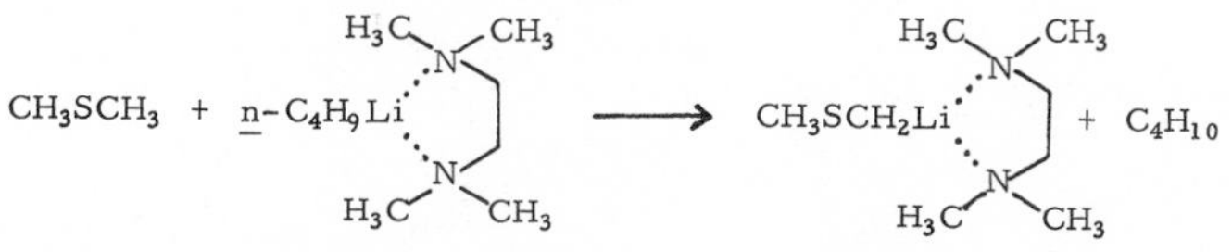

The carbanion is useful for the synthesis of functionally substituted organosulfur compounds in the sulfide oxidation state. Dialkyl sulfides containing a β-hydrogen atom are converted mainly into olefins.

[1]D. S. Peterson, *J. Org.*, **32**, 1717 (1967)

Tetramethylguanidinium azide (2) [**1**, 1145, before **Tetramethylthiourea**]. Mol. wt. 158.21, m.p. 90–93°.

Preparation.[1] A dried ethereal solution of hydrazoic acid (prepared by adding 80 ml. of concd. HCl to a cold solution of 1 mole of sodium azide in 200 ml. of water over 30 min. and then extracting with ether) was added to a solution of 1 mole of tetramethylguanidine (1) in 750 ml. of ether at 0°. The product (2) was slurried with two portions of ether and crystallized from chloroform–ether.

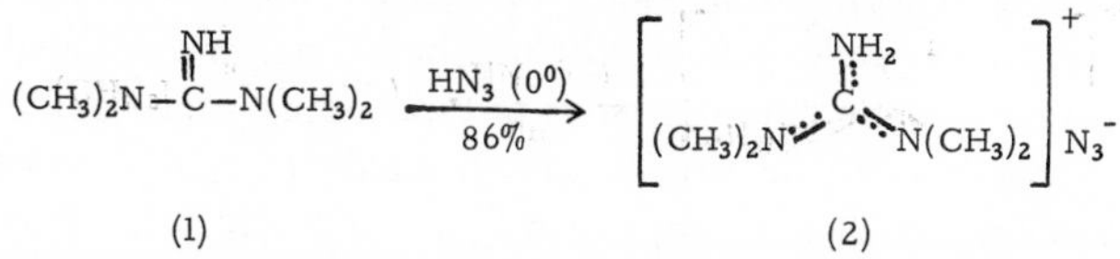

Preparation of alkyl azides.[1] Because it is easy to prepare, stable, and soluble in low-boiling organic solvents such as $CHCl_3$, it is the reagent of choice for reaction with alkyl halides to form the corresponding alkyl azides in yields of 60–96%. With the more reactive alkyl halides, in particular alkyl bromides, the reaction is exothermic and requires cooling in the initial stages. The solubility of (2) in chloroform simplifies isolation of the product. Added ether precipitates tetramethylguanidine hydrochloride, leaving the desired alkyl azide in chloroform–ether solution.

5-Substituted tetrazoles.[1] When heated with an aryl nitrile in 100–125°, the reagent affords a 5-aryltetrazole in good yield.

$$C_6H_5C{\equiv}N \quad + \quad (2) \quad \xrightarrow[75\%]{3 \text{ hrs. } 100°} \quad C_6H_5-C\underset{\underset{H}{N-N}}{\overset{N-N}{\Vert}}$$

[1]A. J. Papa, *J. Org.*, **31**, 1426 (1966)

(+)- and (−)-α-(2,4,5,7-Tetranitro-9-fluorenylideneaminooxy)propionic acid [1, 1147, before references].

The reagent served successfully for the resolution of 15- and 16-methylcholanthrene:[3]

$$CH_2-CH \qquad\qquad CH-CH_2$$
$$CH_3 \qquad\qquad\qquad CH_3$$

[1]*Change to*: P. Block, Jr., and M. S. Newman, *Org. Syn.*, **48**, 120 (1968)
[3]M. S. Newman, R. W. Wotring, Jr., A. Pandit, and P. M. Chakrabarti, *J. Org.*, **31**, 4293 (1966)

Tetranitromethane [1, 1147–1148, before references]. A preliminary communication reports unusual results in the reaction of tetranitromethane with cyclohexene, 1-methylcyclohexene, 1-methylcycloheptene, and cycloocta-1,5-diene.[7]

[6]*Change to read*: J. F. Riordan, M. Sokolovsky, and B. L. Vallee, *Am. Soc.*, **88**, 4104 (1966); M. Sokolovsky, J. F. Riordan, and B. L. Vallee, *Biochemistry*, **5**, 3582 (1966); J. F. Riordan, M. Sokolovsky, and B. L. Vallee, *ibid.*, **6**, 358 (1967)
[7]R. W. Bradshaw, *Tetrahedron Letters*, 5711 (1966)

Tetraphenylethylene, $(C_2H_5)_2C{=}C(C_6H_5)_2$ [1, 1150, before **Thallium triacetate**]. Mol. wt. 332.45, m.p. 222–224°. Supplier: A.

Wurtz coupling catalyst. Müller and Röscheisen[1] noted that low yields in the Wurtz coupling of two molecules of a benzyl halide may be because the reaction proceeds in part at least in heterogeneous phase on the surface of the metal. They found that tetraphenyl ethylene forms a disodium adduct which is sufficiently soluble in THF or glyme for the efficient coupling of 2 moles of benzyl chloride:

$$(C_6H_5)_2\underset{Na}{C}-\underset{Na}{C}(C_6H_5)_2 + 2\ C_6H_5CH_2Cl \xrightarrow{82\%} C_6H_5CH_2CH_2C_6H_5 + (C_6H_5)_2C{=}C(C_6H_5)_2$$

With $C_6H_5CH_2F$, $C_6H_5CH_2Br$, and $C_6H_5CH_2I$ the yields were 68, 76, and 74%. A disadvantage is that the molecular weights are such that the weight of tetraphenyl-ethylene required is about eight times the weight of benzyl chloride. However, if a vibro-mixer is used, tetraphenylethylene can be taken in catalytic amount, that is, some 0.05 mole instead of 1 mole. The hydrocarbon thus accepts sodium and gives it up again and so functions as metal-transfer agent.

$$2 \ C_6H_5CH_2X \ + \ 2 \ Na \ \xrightarrow{(C_6H_5)_2C=C(C_6H_5)_2} \ C_6H_5CH_2CH_2C_6H_5 \ + \ 2 \ NaX$$

Boekelhëide *et al.*[2] found this modified Wurtz reaction serviceable in the synthesis of [2.2]metacyclophanes, for example, 4,12-dimethyl[2.2]metacyclophane (2). In the case of the dibromide corresponding to (1) but lacking the two methyl groups, cyclization is accomplished in yield of 77%.

(1) 5.0 g.

(2)

[1]E. Müller and G. Röscheisen, *Ber.*, **90**, 543 (1957)
[2]W. S. Lindsay, P. Stokes, L. G. Humber, and V. Boekelheide, *Am. Soc.*, **83**, 943 (1961)

Thallium (I) bromide, TlBr [1, 1150, before **Thallium triacetate**]. Mol. wt. 284.31. Supplier: Alfa Inorganics, Thallium, Ltd.

Coupling of aryl and alkyl Grignard reagents.[1] Aryl- and *sec*-alkylmagnesium bromides undergo coupling when refluxed with thallium (I) bromide in THF–benzene for a few hours. Optimum conditions require 1.5–2.0 moles of thallium (I) bromide per mole of Grignard reagent. Thus a mixture of 4-tolylmagnesium bromide (0.0675 m.) and thallium (I) bromide (0.135 m.) was stirred and refluxed under nitrogen for four hours. After acidification with dilute hydrochloric acid and usual puri-fication procedures, 4,4'-dimethylbiphenyl was obtained in 91% yield. However, *ortho*-substituted Grignard reagents fail to give coupled products; thus mesityl-

magnesium bromide gives dimesitylthallium (III) bromide, Ar_2TlBr. Where applic-able, the new procedure is equal to or even superior to the classical Ullmann synthesis of biaryls. Secondary alkyl Grignard reagents give coupled products in about 50% yield. The reaction of primary aliphatic Grignard reagents gives only traces of coupled alkanes; the major products are dialkylthallium (III) bromides.

[1]A. McKillop, L. F. Elsom, and E. C. Taylor, *Am. Soc.*, **90**, 2423 (1968)

Thallium triacetate [1, 1150–1151]. Supplier: Thallium Ltd.

Preparation. Kochi and Bethea[1a] have developed a procedure for the preparation of 97% pure reagent on a large scale (467 g., 61%) starting with thallium (III) oxide obtained from the American Smelting and Refining Co., New York, N.Y. The brown oxide was dissolved in acetic acid (2 l.)–acetic anhydride (110 ml.) by stirring at 80–90° and the solution was filtered (sintered-glass funnel) and let cool. The product separating was recrystallized as before.

Oxidation of enamines[6] [before references]. Enamines are oxidized by thallium triacetate at room temperature in glacial acetic acid or chloroform to give, after hydrolysis, the α-acetoxy derivative of the parent ketone. Thus morpholinocyclohexene is converted into 2-acetoxycyclohexanone in about 70% yield. The reaction can also be carried out on a combination of cyclohexane and morpholine (*in situ* generation of the enamine). Pyrrolidine enamines give somewhat lower yields.

Yields are generally higher than those obtained by direct oxidation of the ketones with thallium triacetate or lead tetraacetate. The reaction is also stereospecific. Thus oxidation of the morpholine enamine of 4-*t*-butylcyclohexanone gives only *trans*-2-acetoxy-4-*t*-butylcyclohexanone.

Oxidative rearrangement of chalcones. 4-Methoxychalcone (1) on treatment with thallium triacetate in boiling methanol is converted into the 1,2-diaryl-3,3-dimethoxy-

(1)   (2)

propanone-1 (2). The reaction is of interest because the biosynthesis of isoflavonoids from chalcone precursors has been shown to involve a 1,2-aryl migration.[7]

[1a]J. K. Kochi and T. W. Bethea, III, *J. Org.*, **33**, 75 (1968)
[6]M. E. Kuehne and T. J. Giacobbe, *ibid.*, **33**, 3359 (1968)
[7]W. D. Ollis, K. L. Ormand, and I. O. Sutherland, *Chem. Commun.*, 1237 (1968)

Thallous ethoxide,[1] $TlOC_2H_5$ [**1**, 1151, before N,N'-**Thiocarbonyldiimidazole**]. Mol. wt. 249. Suppliers: A, E, KK, Thallium Ltd.

$$
\begin{array}{c}
H_5C_2\cdots O \longrightarrow Tl \\
Tl \longrightarrow O \longrightarrow C_2H_5 \\
Tl \longrightarrow O \cdots C_2H_5 \\
H_5C_2 \longrightarrow O \longrightarrow Tl
\end{array}
$$

(1)

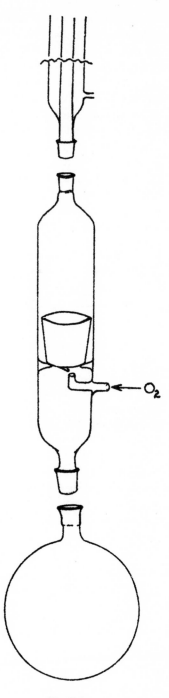

Preparation.[2] Thallous ethoxide is readily prepared by refluxing ethanol over thallium shot while simultaneously passing oxygen over the surface of the thallium:

$$2\ Tl(\text{metal}) + 1/2\ O_2 \longrightarrow Tl_2O$$

$$Tl_2O + 2\ C_2H_5OH \longrightarrow 2\ TlOC_2H_5 + H_2O$$

(1)

Thallium metal (m.p. 303°) is available from Alfa Inorganics in the form of $\frac{3}{8}$ in. rods. A clean section of it is grasped in tongs and melted with a propane blow torch and the molten metal let fall into a 2-l. beaker full of cold water.

The oxidation of the metal is carried out in the apparatus shown in Fig. T-1, which consists of a 5×30-cm. tube fitted with a 24/40 female joint at the top and a 24/40 male joint at the bottom. A porcelain Gooch filter crucible with a perforated base is supported on a series of indentations made in the middle of the tube. The oxygen inlet tube is located some 4–5 cm. below the indentations and is bent upwards so that the end of the tube is approximately 1 cm. below the crucible. The perforated base of the Gooch crucible is covered with a pad of glass wool to retain black particles of thallium oxide or metal, and then thallium shot is dried by pressing between wads of filter paper, and 100 g. of dried metal is placed in the crucible.

The 500-ml. boiling flask is charged with 350 ml. of ethanol and the reflux condenser is fitted with a drying tube filled with Ascarite (or soda lime) to exclude carbon dioxide, which reacts rapidly with thallous ethoxide. The ethanol is then refluxed over the thallium shot while a vigorous stream of oxygen is passed

Fig. T-1

through the tube. Some ethanol is carried out of the system in the oxygen flow; if this amounts to more than 100 ml., the level of ethanol in the boiling flask should be adjusted to about 300 ml. Refluxing is continued for 12–16 hrs., during which time the thallium gradually dissolves to give thallous ethoxide as a heavy colorless oil which runs down the reaction tube into the refluxing ethanol. When shiny metallic thallium can no longer be observed, the reaction is stopped. Thallous ethoxide can be removed with a pipet and used directly in the following reactions. It should be noted that the supernatant ethanol is saturated with thallous ethoxide (it contains about 9 g. of thallous ethoxide/100 ml.) and may also be used directly in many of the reactions described below.

Uses. Thallous ethoxide is soluble in most organic solvents, including heptane, and thus possesses the considerable advantage over sodium ethoxide of effecting homogeneous base-catalyzed reactions in nonpolar solvents. Thallous ethoxide converts most β-dicarbonyl compounds into stable, crystalline, light-insensitive, colorless, 1:1 salts (2) which may be subsequently mono-C-alkylated in almost quantitative yield by heating with alkyl iodides.[3] The salts are readily prepared by addition

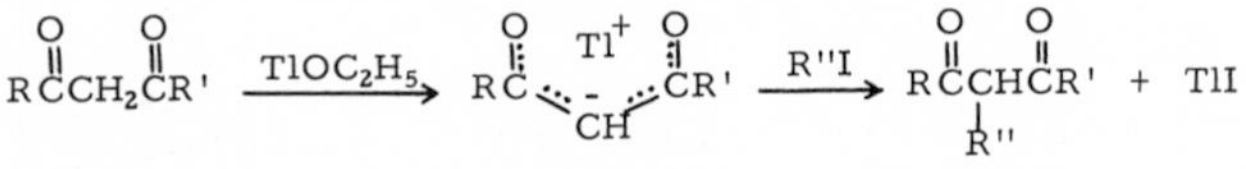

$$\underset{\text{(2)}}{\overset{\overset{O}{\parallel}\ \overset{O}{\parallel}}{RCCH_2CR'}} \xrightarrow{TlOC_2H_5} \underset{\text{(2)}}{\overset{O\ Tl^+\ O}{\underset{CH}{RC \cdots - \cdots CR'}}} \xrightarrow{R''I} \underset{\overset{|}{R''}}{\overset{\overset{O}{\parallel}\ \overset{O}{\parallel}}{RCCHCR'}} + TlI$$

of thallous ethoxide to a solution of the β-dicarbonyl compound in an inert solvent such as benzene or petroleum ether. Heating these thallous salts with an excess of an alkyl iodide followed by removal of thallous iodide by filtration and distillation yields the mono-C-alkylated products (3). The reaction fails with *t*-butyl iodide, but proceeds quantitatively with isopropyl iodide and with primary alkyl iodides. This alkylation procedure, which is carried out under neutral conditions, avoids *all* the normally observed side reactions which accompany the alkylation of sodium or potassium enolates (dialkylation, O-alkylation, β-diketone cleavage, Claisen condensations, oxidative couplings, etc.).

Thallous salts of β-dicarbonyl compounds may also be acylated, and the reaction can be controlled to give either O-or C-acylation. Thus reaction of the thallous salt

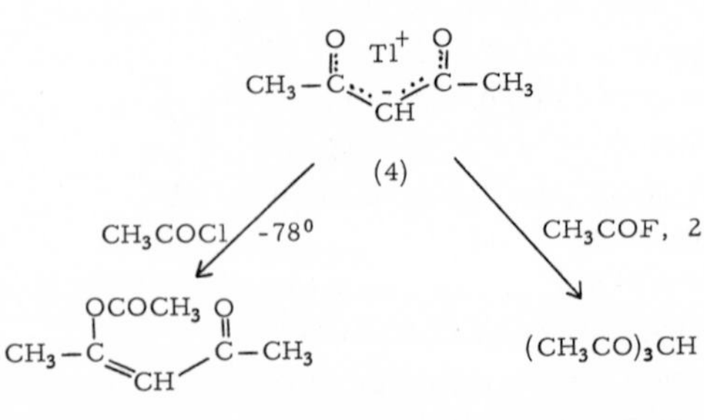

$$\underset{\text{(4)}}{\overset{O\ Tl^+\ O}{\underset{CH}{CH_3-C\cdots - \cdots C-CH_3}}}$$

$$\underset{CH_3COCl}{\nearrow}{}^{-78^0} \qquad \underset{CH_3COF,\ 25^0}{\searrow}$$

$$\underset{CH}{\overset{OCOCH_3\ O}{CH_3-C \diagdown\ \diagup C-CH_3}} \qquad (CH_3CO)_3CH$$

of acetylacetone (4) with acetyl chloride at $-78°$ in ether suspension gives the enol acetate in greater than 90% yield, uncontaminated by triacetylmethane. On the other hand, treatment of the same thallous salt with acetyl fluoride at room temperature, again in ether suspension, gives triacetylmethane in greater than 95% yield, uncontaminated by the enol acetate. 1,1,1-Triacetylethane (5) may be prepared in an overall yield of greater than 90% from acetylacetone either by (a) methylation of the thallous salt (4) with methyl iodide followed by reconversion to the thallous salt and subsequent C-acetylation with acetyl fluoride, or (b) initial acetylation of (4) with acetyl fluoride to give triacetylmethane, followed by reconversion to the thallous salt and subsequent C-methylation with methyl iodide.

$$(4)$$

$$CH_3I \quad\quad CH_3COF$$

$$CH_3CH(COCH_3)_2 \quad\quad\quad (CH_3CO)_3CH$$

$$TlOC_2H_5 \quad\quad\quad TlOC_2H_5$$

$$CH_3COF \quad CH_3I$$

$$(CH_3CO)_3C-CH_3$$

$$(5)$$

Such alkylations and acylations utilizing thallous salts have been termed Taylor-McKillop reactions.

The same workers have shown that a wide variety of acidic substrates form thallous salts by treatment with thallous ethoxide, and that these salts offer unique advantages either in yields, specificity of reactions, or convenience or simplicity in handling over alkali or other heavy-metal salts.[4] Thallous salts of phenols, for example, are readily prepared in quantitative yield by the addition of thallous ethoxide to a solution of the phenol in benzene or ethanol. These salts are crystalline, sharp-melting, colorless

$$ArOH \xrightarrow{TlOC_2H_5} ArO^-Tl^+ \begin{array}{c} \xrightarrow{TsCl} ArOTs \\ \\ \xrightarrow{RCOCl} ArOCOR \end{array} \quad (\sim100\%)$$

solids which are recrystallizable from water or aqueous ethanol and are indefinitely stable. Treatment of an ether suspension of these phenol salts with an equimolar quantity of an acyl or aroyl halide at room temperature, followed by filtration of the precipitated thallous halide and evaporation of solvent, affords pure phenol esters in yields seldom lower than 97%. Similarly, treatment of thallous salts of phenols with tosyl chloride in DMF at room temperature gives crystalline, pure phenol tosylates in 92–96% yield.

Thallous salts of carboxylic acids are also readily prepared in quantitative yield by addition of thallous ethoxide to a solution of the acid in ether or ethanol.[5] Treatment of these crystalline, light-insensitive, sharp-melting stable salts with a stoichiometric amount of an acyl or aroyl chloride, followed by removal of thallous chloride by filtration and evaporation of solvent, affords crystalline carboxylic anhydrides in quantitative yield. This procedure, which employs stoichiometric amounts of both reactants and proceeds quantitatively at room temperature or below, appears to

$$R COO^- Tl^+$$

$$\overset{O}{\overset{\|}{R C}} - O - \overset{O}{\overset{\|}{C R'}}$$

(100%)

$$\overset{O}{\overset{\|}{R C}} - O - \overset{O}{\overset{\|}{C R}} \ (+ SO_2 + TlCl)$$

(100%)

utilize the minimal conditions requisite for mixed anhydride formation and preservation (avoidance of disproportionation reactions).

Symmetrical anhydrides are alternatively prepared by direct treatment of thallous carboxylates with thionyl chloride in ether suspension at room temperature. The intermediate diacyl or diaroyl sulfites spontaneously lose sulfur dioxide to give the symmetrical anhydrides in 96–98% yield after distillation.

Thallous carboxylates have also been utilized by Taylor and McKillop[6] in the Hunsdiecker reaction; yields of primary aliphatic bromides are extremely high. Be-

$$2 \ RCO_2^- Tl^+ + 3 \ Br_2 \longrightarrow 2 \ RBr + 2 \ CO_2 + Tl_2Br_4$$

cause of the ease of preparation, light-insensitivity, and purity of thallous carboxylates, their use in the Hunsdiecker reaction would appear to have advantages over the traditional silver salt procedure.

Alkylation of thallous salts of cyclic amides (i.e., 2-pyridone) with alkyl iodides results in exclusive N-alkylation[5] and in most cases offers no synthetic advantage over the use of sodium or potassium salts. In some instances, however, striking simplifications have been observed. Phenanthridinone can be alkylated extremely

readily by addition of a stoichiometric amount of thallous ethoxide to a stirred DMF suspension at room temperature; after 30 sec, the suspension becomes homogeneous, at which time one equivalent of methyl iodide is added. Filtration of the precipitated thallous iodide followed by dilution of the filtrate with water gives 6-methyl-5(6 H)-phenanthridinone in quantitative yield.

Treatment of the thallous salt of 2-pyridone (6) with an acyl or aroyl chloride in ether suspension, at room temperature, results in quantitative conversion to a 2-acyloxy- or 2-aroyloxypyridine (7). The latter compounds are extremely reactive acylating and aroylating agents which possess the advantage over the starting acid chlorides of eliminating 2-pyridone rather than chloride ion in the acylation step.[5]

9-Unsubstituted purines are also readily converted into thallous salts which appear

$$\text{(6)} \xrightarrow{\underset{\text{RCCl}}{\overset{O}{\parallel}}} \text{(7)}$$

to undergo alkylation predominantly, if not exclusively, at position 9.[7] The thallous salts of purine and 6-chloropurine are prepared by addition of thallous ethoxide to stirred ethanol solutions. The thallous salt of adenine is similarly prepared in dimethylacetamide solution. Both benzylation and methylation of these salts give 9-alkylated derivatives only. Nebularine and adenosine have been prepared by ribosidation of the thallous salts of purine and adenine, respectively. The ease of formation, stability, high purity, solubility, and reactivity of these purine thallous salts, coupled with alkylation at position 9 independent of the substituent at position 6,

suggest that they may be prominsing intermediates for the preparation of nucleosides.

Taylor and McKillop[5] have also found that the thallous salts of trichloroacetic acid and chlorodifluoroacetic acid decompose in the presence of olefins to give di-

$$\text{CCl}_3\text{COO}^-\text{Tl}^+ \xrightarrow{\text{Cyclohexene}} \quad (30\%)$$

$$\text{CClF}_2\text{COO}^-\text{Tl}^+ \xrightarrow{\text{Cyclohexene}} \quad (60\%)$$

chlorocarbene and difluorocarbene adducts, respectively. Decomposition of these thallous salts to give the carbenes is reported to take place some 100° lower than decomposition of the respective sodium or potassium salts.

[1]Contributed by Edward C. Taylor
[2]M. J. Zelesko, E. C. Taylor, and A. McKillop. procedure to be submitted to *Org. Syn.*
[3]E. C. Taylor, G. H. Hawks, III, and A. McKillop, *Am. Soc.*, **90**, 2421 (1968)
[4]E. C. Taylor, G. W. McLay, and A. McKillop, *ibid.*, **90**, 2422 (1968)
[5]Unpublished work
[6]A. McKillop, D. Bromley, and E. C. Taylor, *J. Org.*, in press
[7]E. C. Taylor, Y. Maki, and A. McKillop, *J. Org.*, in press

N,N'-Thiocarbonyldiimidazole [1, 1151–1152, before references].

Fox *et al.*[3] report that they experienced difficulties when following the preparative procedure of Staab and Walther;[1] they prefer the procedure of Reid and Beck[4] slightly modified in that the preparation was carried out under nitrogen with strictly anhydrous conditions (yield 80–90%).

In an alternative synthesis,[5] trimethylsilylimidazole[6] in anhydrous benzene is treated with thiophosgene at 0°. After 1 hr. the benzene and trimethylchlorosilane are pumped off and the yellow residual powder, N,N'-thiocarbonyldiimidazole, is used directly.

[3] J. J. Fox, N. Miller, and I. Wempen, *J. Med. Chem.*, **9**, 101 (1966)
[4] W. Reid and B. M. Beck, *Ann.*, **646**, 96 (1961)
[5] T. J. Pullukat and G. Urry, *Tetrahedron Letters*, 1953 (1967)
[6] L. Birkoffer and A. Ritter, *Angew. Chem., internat. Ed.*, **4**, 427 (1965)

Thionyl chloride [1, 1158–1163].

Amino acid ester [1160, after citation of ref. 16]. The preparation of L-aspartic acid β-methyl ester hydrochloride by use of methanol and thionyl chloride is described by DeTar et al.[16a] This method is the most satisfactory for esterification of ethylenediamine tetraacetic acid.[16b]

Cyclic anhydrides [1, 1163, before references]. Merck chemists[30] prepared L-

glutamic anhydride hydrochloride for the first time by stirring a solution of L-glutamic acid in trifluoroacetic acid and slowly adding thionyl chloride. Ether was added until the precipitate no longer dissolved, and the product was then allowed to crystallize. L-Aspartic anhydride hydrochloride was prepared similarly in 70% yield.

[16a] H. Bach, M. Gouge, W. Honsberg, U. Honsberg, and D. F. DeTar, procedure submitted to *Org. Syn.*, 1967
[16b] D. J. Alner, P. A. Claret, and A. G. Osborne, *Chem. Ind.*, 1565 (1968)
[30] J. Kollonitsch and A. Rosegay, *Chem. Ind.*, 1867 (1964)

Thiourea [1, 1164–1167].

Thiourea inclusion complexes. As noted in the second paragraph beginning on 1, 1165, a Delft group (Verkade et al.[9]) reported an efficient separation of cis- and trans-4-isopropylcyclohexane-1-carboxylic acid based on their observation that the trans-acid forms a thiourea inclusion complex whereas the cis isomer does not. However, they failed to account for the difference. A simple explanation became

trans, m.p. 94-95°   cis, m.p. 40-41°

apparent to us on examining models and seeing if they can be fitted into a cylinder of cellulose acetate of diameter scaled to represent the available space in the channel of a thiourea inclusion complex (*see* **1**, 1262–1263). A cylinder made to fit snugly around the model of the *trans*-acid has a diameter of 20.6 cm., a little less than that of a cylinder just capable of accommodating adamantane (which forms a complex with thiourea but not with urea). The model of *cis*-4-isopropylcyclohexane-1-carboxylic acid, with one axial and one equatorial substituent, cannot be fitted into the 20.6-cm. cylinder. Figure T-2 shows that a 20.6-cm. cylinder accommodates a model of the *trans*-acid (a) but not a model of the *cis*-acid (b).

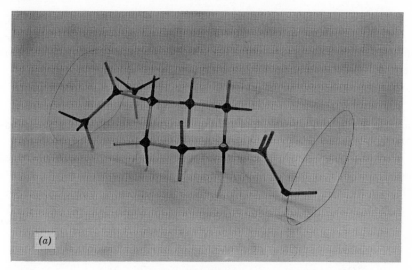

(a)

Fig. T-2a

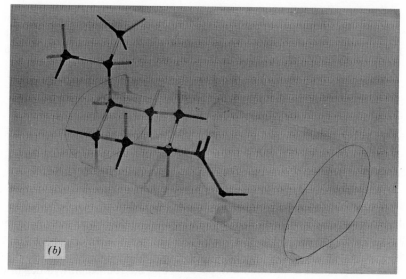

(b)

Fig. T-2b

Tin [**1**, 1168–1169].

Debromination [**1**, 1169, after formulation]. 6-Bromo-2-naphthol is readily prepared by dibromination of 2-naphthol in acetic acid and removal of the more

144 gs. (1 m.)   400 ml.

reactive α-bromo substituent by reduction with mossy tin and the hydrobromic acid formed in the bromination.[8a] The reduction has been effected also with stannous chloride,[8b] but it is not clear whether or not one reagent has advantages over the other.

[8a]C. F. Koelsch, *Org. Syn., Coll. Vol.*, **3**, 132 (1955)
[8b]K. Fries and K. Schimmelschmidt, *Ann.*, **484**, 245 (1930), *see* p. 293

Titanium tetrachloride [**1**, 1169–1171]. Other suppliers: Alfa Inorganics, Fl., Riedel-de Haën, Sch.

Aldehyde synthesis [before references]. A fairly general route to aromatic aldehydes is illustrated by the synthesis of mesitylaldehyde by $TiCl_4$-catalyzed reaction of mesitylene with dichloromethyl methyl ether (*which see*, this volume).

Enamine synthesis. Monsanto chemists White and Weingarten[9] found the reagent useful for the synthesis of enamines; it not only functions as an effective water scavenger but also acts as a Lewis acid catalyst:

$$2 \ RCH-\overset{O}{\overset{\|}{C}}R' \ + \ 6 \ HNR'' \ + \ TiCl_4 \ \longrightarrow \ 2 \ RCH=\overset{NR''}{\overset{|}{C}}R' \ + \ 4 \ R''_2NH_2Cl \ + \ TiO_2$$

Ketimines. Weingarten, Chupp, and White,[10] finding shortcomings in available procedures for the preparation of some ketimines from substituted cyclohexanones and primary amines, devised a more powerful new method capable of application to a

highly hindered ketone such as camphor. A solution of the ketone and isopropylamine in toluene was treated at 0–5° with $TiCl_4$ in toluene and the mixture was refluxed for 7 hrs., with slow separation of amine hydrochloride. The mixture was let stand at room temperature, treated with pentane, filtered from amine hydrochloride, and distilled to afford the product.

[5]*Add:* H. L. Finkbeiner and G. D. Cooper, *J. Org.*, **27**, 3395 (1962)
[9]W. A. White and H. Weingarten, *J. Org.*, **32**, 213 (1967)
[10]H. Weingarten, J. P. Chupp, and W. A. White, *ibid.*, **32**, 3246 (1967)

Titanium trichloride, $TiCl_3$ [**1**, 1171, before **Tollens reagent**]. Mol. wt. 104.27. Suppliers: Alfa Inorganics, MCB.

Reaction with methyllithium. Titanium trichloride is reported to react in glyme at $-50°$ to $-80°$ with methyllithium in ether to give a dark green solution of unisolated product—presumed to be triethyltitanium—which decomposes above $-20°$ to gas and "black needles" which react with water to yield methane.[1]

Coupling of allyl alcohols to 1,5-dienes. van Tamelen *et al.*[2] found that treatment of allyl alcohol in glyme with $TiCl_3$ (0.5 mole) and methyllithium (1.5 moles) at $-78°$, warming the mixture to room temperature, and eventually refluxing (b.p. 83°) for 15 min., effects conversion to the 1,5-diene:

$$CH_2=CHCH_2OH + HOCH_2CH=CH_2 \xrightarrow{\text{TiCl}_3 + \text{CH}_3\text{Li}} CH_2=CHCH_2CH_2CH=CH_2$$

Geraniol gives in 80% yield a hydrocarbon mixture consisting of C-1 to C-1′ and C-1 to C-3′ units in the ratio of 7:1. Benzyl alcohol is transformed into dibenzyl (78%). Other alkyl and aryllithium compounds can be used. Mixed coupling can be achieved by using one allylic alcohol in excess.

[1]K. Clauss and C. Beerman, *Angew. Chem.*, **71**, 627 (1959)
[2]K. B. Sharpless, R. P. Hanzlik, and E. E. van Tamelen, *Am. Soc.*, **90**, 209 (1968)

p-**Toluenesulfonyl azide (Tosyl azide)** [**1**, 1178–1179].

Diazo compounds. Review.[2a]

Preparation of diazocyclopentadiene according to Doering and DePuy.[2] Weil and Cais[2b] found that phenyllithium can be replaced by other bases, preferably diethylamine or ethanolamine. A mixture of cyclopentadiene, tosyl azide, and diethylamine was allowed to stand at 0° for three days; then, after addition of water, diazocyclopentadiene was extracted with ether (73% yield). The yield is somewhat higher when acetonitrile is used as solvent.[2c]

Azide synthesis[6] [before references]. The reaction of a halomagnesium salt of

aniline with tosyl azide gives phenyl azide in moderate yield. The reaction is considered to involve an intermediate triazene anion. Benzyl azide was obtained in the same way in 20% yield.

Diazoacetic acid t-butyl ester.[7]

$$CH_3\underset{O}{\overset{O}{C}}CH_2\underset{O}{\overset{O}{C}}OC(CH_3)_3 \ + \ H_3C-\!\!\!\!\left\langle\!\!\!\!\bigcirc\!\!\!\!\right\rangle\!\!\!\!-\underset{O}{\overset{O}{S}}N_3 \quad \xrightarrow[\substack{94-98\% \\ -\,TosNH_2}]{\substack{38-40^0 \\ Et_3N}} \quad CH_3\underset{O}{\overset{O}{C}}-\underset{\underset{N}{\overset{N^+}{\|}}}{C}-\underset{O}{\overset{O}{C}}-OC(CH_3)_3$$

$$\xrightarrow[68-70\%]{CH_3OH-CH_3ONa} \quad \underset{\underset{N^-}{\overset{N^+}{\|}}}{HC}-\underset{O}{\overset{O}{C}}OC(CH_3)_3$$

Reaction with acylmethylenetriphenylphosphoranes.[8] Tosyl azide reacts with acylmethylenetriphenylphosphoranes (1) at room temperature to give 1,5-disubstituted 1,3,5-triazoles (5) in good yield.

$$(C_6H_5)_3P = \underset{\overset{\|}{O}}{CHCR} \ + \ R'N_3 \ \rightarrow \ \left[\begin{array}{c}(C_6H_5)_3\overset{+}{P}\diagdown\;\;\overset{O}{\diagup} \\ CH-C-R \\ N\diagdown\;\;\diagup \\ N\diagdown N-R'\end{array}\right]$$

$$(1) \qquad\qquad (2)$$

$$R = C_6H_5, \ \underline{p}-NO_2C_6H_4,$$
$$\underline{p}-BrC_6H_4$$
$$R' = \underline{p}-CH_3C_6H_4SO_2$$

$$(3)$$

$$\Updownarrow$$

$$(C_6H_5)_3PO \ + \ \overset{R}{\underset{N\diagup\diagdown N-R'}{\diagup\diagdown}} \ \longleftarrow \ \left[\begin{array}{c}(C_6H_5)_3\overset{+}{P}\diagup\overset{-}{O} \\ \diagdown\!\!\!\swarrow R \\ N\diagdown\diagup\diagdown N-R'\end{array}\right]$$

$$(5) \qquad\qquad (4)$$

$$(C_6H_5)_3P = \overset{R}{\underset{\overset{\|}{O}}{C}}-C-R' \ + \ N_3SO_2-\!\!\!\left\langle\!\!\!\!\bigcirc\!\!\!\!\right\rangle\!\!\!-CH_3 \ \rightarrow$$

(6) a, R = H; R' = OC_2H_5
    b, R = CH_3; R' = OC_2H_5
    c, R = H; R' = N(C_2H_5)_2

$$\left[\begin{array}{c}\overset{R}{\overset{|}{C}}\;\overset{O}{\overset{\|}{C}} \\ (C_6H_5)_3\overset{+}{P}-C-C-R' \\ \diagup \\ Ts-\bar{N}\quad N \\ \diagdown\diagup \\ N\end{array}\right]$$

$$(7)$$

$$\Updownarrow$$

$$(C_6H_5)_3P{=}NTs + N_2{=}\overset{R}{\underset{\underset{O}{\|}}{\overset{|}{C}}}{-}C{-}R' \leftarrow \left[\begin{array}{c} (C_6H_5)_3P{-}\overset{R}{\underset{Ts{-}N}{\overset{|}{C}}}\overset{CR'}{\underset{N:}{\overset{\|}{O}}} \\ N \end{array} \right]$$

(10)   (9)   (8)

When the carbonyl group of the ylide is weakly electrophilic, as in an ester or an amide, the reaction takes a different course and leads to an α-diazo ester (9) or amide and N-tosyltriphenylphosphinimine (10). This reaction is very facile and can be carried out in aprotic solvents.

[2a]M. Regitz, *Angew. Chem., internat. Ed.*, **6**, 733 (1967)
[2b]T. Weil and M. Cais, *J. Org.*, **28**, 2472 (1963)
[2c]M. Regitz and A. Liedhegener, *Tetrahedron*, **23**, 2701 (1967)
[6]W. Fischer and J.-P. Anselme, *Am. Soc.*, **89**, 5284 (1967)
[7]M. Regitz, J. Hocker, and A. Liedhegener, *Org. Syn.*, **48**, 36 (1968)
[8]G. R. Harvey, *J. Org.*, **31**, 1587 (1966)

p-**Toluenesulfonylhydrazine (Tosylhydrazine)** [**1**, 1185]. This name is to replace "*p*-Toluenesulfonylhydrazide," which we now believe to be less appropriate and less widely used. It identifies the compound more clearly as structurally related to phenylhydrazine and not to semicarbazide or to acethydrazide. Some suppliers have used the name "*p*-toluenesulfonylhydrazide," and this is the name under which the compound is indexed in *Chemical Abstracts*. The name is used also by *Organic Syntheses* in describing a procedure based on one originated by K. Freudenberg and F. Blümmel [*Ann.*, **410**, 45 (1924)], who, however, describe the reagent as "*p*-Toluolsulfo-hydrazin." We now urge general acceptance of the preferred "hydrazine" name.

Preparation [**1**, 1185] *Correction.*[1a] Change second line after formulas to read: After 15 min. the two-phase mixture is separated; the lower aqueous layer is discarded. The THF layer is filtered by suction through a Celite bed and two volumes of water is added to the stirred filtrate.

Elimination reactions [**1**, 1186, after line 11]. In the original procedure (Cava[6]), elimination of TsO⁻ was accomplished with dilute sodium hydroxide solution in a two-phase system. Muchowski[6a] reported that basic alumina, pH 10–10.5 (McArthur Chemical Co., Montreal) suspended in methylene chloride or ethyl acetate can be used advantageously; yields are generally in the range 80% to quantitative. Toluene-sulfonylhydrazones of simple aldehydes and ketones do not decompose under these conditions. Meinwald *et al.*[6b] used this method in an interesting synthesis of the acetoxy diazoketone (5) starting with 1-bornylacetate (1, Aldrich Chem. Co.). In this case the alumina used was Fisher Scientific Co. adsorption alumina 80–200 mesh, Cat. No. A-540.

In the Bamford-Stevens reaction,[2] sodium methoxide is commonly used as base. Kirmse *et al.*[6c] have shown that use of sodamide or sodium hydride converts tosyl-hydrazones of aliphatic ketones and cyclic ketones into 1-olefins. Thus the tosyl-hydrazone of pentanone-2 gives pentene-1 in 83% yield together with small amounts of *cis*- and *trans*-pentene-2.

$$CH_3CH_2CH_2CH_2\underset{\overset{\shortparallel}{NNHSO_2C_6H_5}}{C}CH_3 \xrightarrow{NaH} CH_3CH_2CH_2CH=CH_2 \;+\; CH_3CH_2CH=CHCH_3$$

$$\qquad\qquad\qquad\qquad\qquad\qquad\qquad\qquad\quad 83\% \qquad\qquad\quad 14\%\ \underline{trans},\ 3\%\ \underline{cis}$$

p-Toluenesulfonylhydrazine reacts with an ortho ester (6) at room temperature with elimination of two moles of methanol and formation of methyl N'-*p*-tosylhydraz-

$$+ \ 2\ CH_3OH$$

imidoformate (7) in good yield.[6d] The product is of interest as a possible precursor of 1-methoxycarbene.

New Olefin Synthesis. Shapiro and Heath[6e] report a new synthesis in which an aliphatic tosylhydrazone having an α-hydrogen is treated with an alkyllithium in ether or hexane to give an olefin in high yield. Examples:

$$3)^{6f} \quad CH_3\overset{\overset{\displaystyle CH_3NNHTs}{|}}{\underset{\underset{\displaystyle CH_3}{|}}{C}}-\overset{\overset{\displaystyle ||}{}}{C}CH_3 \quad \xrightarrow{\quad 2 \ BuLi \quad} \quad CH_3\overset{\overset{\displaystyle CH_3}{|}}{\underset{\underset{\displaystyle CH_3}{|}}{C}}-CH=CH_2$$

(Use of 2 equivalents of butyllithium obviates formation of an array of products arising by cationic and carbenic processes.[6f])

The method was used by Meinwald[6g] for the synthesis of the highly strained bicyclo[2.1.1]hexene-2 from the tosylhydrazone of bicyclo[2.1.1]hexane-2-one (4). In this case the Hofmann-elimination sequence failed.

Bond and Scerbo[6h] have reported an alternative synthesis of bicyclo[2.1.1]hexene-2 also from bicyclo[2.1.1]hexane-2-one (1). The ketone is reduced to the alcohol (2). The hydroxyl group is replaced by bromine in high yield by PBr_3 (3), and then de-

hydrobromination is effected with potassium *t*-butoxide in DMSO at 50°. The overall yield is somewhat lower than that obtained by Meinwald and Uno, but the olefin could be isolated by distillation rather than by preparative GLC.

Shapiro and Duncan[6i] have described use of the method for the synthesis of 2-bornene (6) from camphor tosylhydrazone (5).

The olefin synthesis has been extended to the preparation of conjugated dienes from the tosylhydrazones of α,β-unsaturated ketones.[6j] The reaction is particularly useful for preparation of 1,3-cyclohexadienes as shown by the preparation of (8). β-Ionone tosylhydrazone was converted into the triene (9). The method cannot be used to prepare allenes. Further experiments indicated that the eliminated α-hydrogen must be part of a methylene or methyl group. Methyllithium was found to be superior to *n*-butyllithium.

Fragmentation of α,β-epoxyketones. This fragmentation reaction is a powerful and widely applicable new synthetic method which incorporates in a novel way

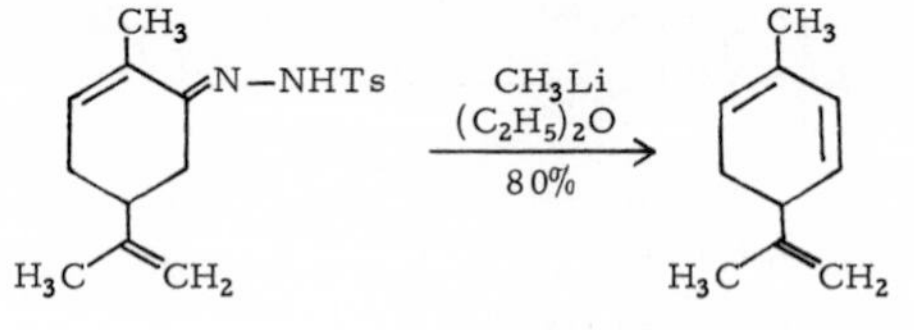

(7)

CH₃Li
(C₂H₅)₂O
80%

(8)

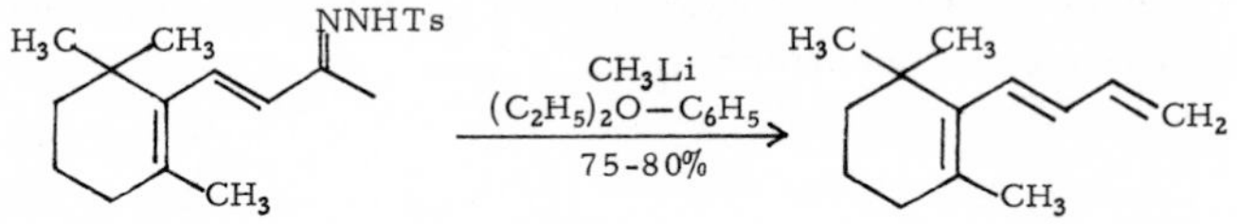

(9)

CH₃Li
(C₂H₅)₂O—C₆H₅
75-80%

(10)

the tosylhydrazine olefin synthesis just discussed. The striking advances here summarized represent joint work of Swiss groups at the Eidgenossische Technische Hochschule, Zurich, the perfume firm Firmenich Cie., successor of Chuit, Naef Cie., Geneva, and Ciba AG, Basel.[6k-6m]

Cyclododecanone (1) serves particularly well as a starting material because it is obtainable by a simple process and is available commercially in any quantity (Hüls). In work on the synthesis of muscopyridine cited previously, Biemann, Büchi, and

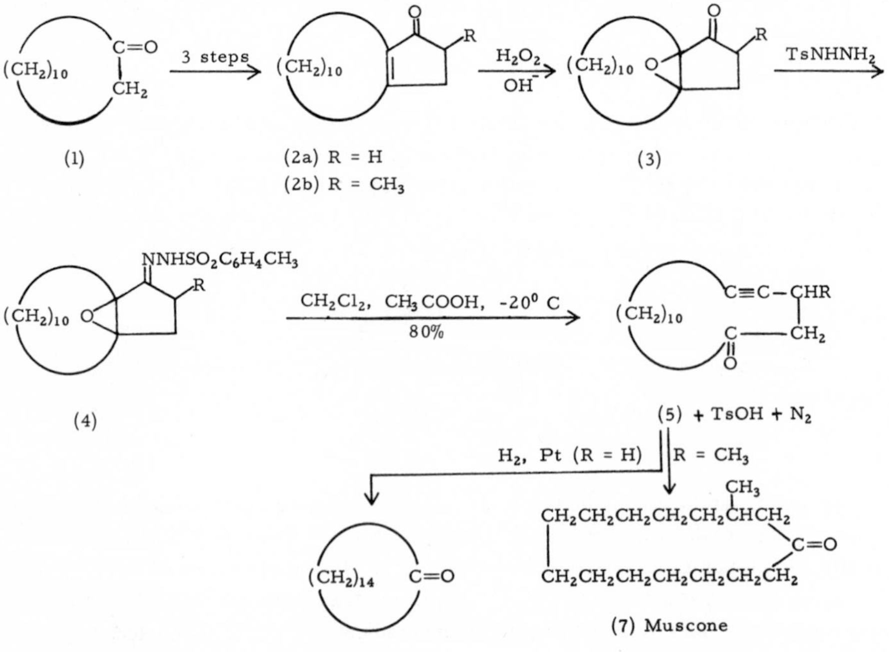

(1)   3 steps   (2a) R = H
(2b) R = CH₃
H_2O_2 / OH^- (3) $TsNHNH_2$

(4) CH_2Cl_2, CH_3COOH, $-20°$ C
80%   (5) + TsOH + N₂

H_2, Pt (R = H)   R = CH₃

(6) Exaltone

(7) Muscone

Walker[6n] had developed an efficient three-step process for the conversion of commercially available cyclododecanone[6o] into bicyclo[10.3.0]$\Delta^{1(12)}$-pentadecene-13-one

(2). This α,β-unsaturated ketone reacts readily with hydrogen peroxide in a basic medium to form the bicyclic α,β-epoxy ketone (3), and this on reaction with toluene-sulfonylhydrazine gave the derivative (4); addition of 2 equivalents of sodium methoxide in methanol or dimethyl sulfoxide affords 4-cyclopentadecyne-1-one (5) in 60–65% yield. Unexpectedly the acidic conditions shown in the formulation give a higher yield (80%). Exaltone (6) is readily obtained from (5) by catalytic hydrogenation. For the production of muscone (7), a methyl group β to the carbonyl function was introduced by methylation of the bicyclic α,β-unsaturated ketone (2a) to produce a second series (2b), R = CH$_3$.

A group at the Stanford Research Institute[6p] applied the fragmentation reaction to the preparation of various secosteroid acetylenic ketones, for example (2). This

(1)   (2)

(3)   (4)

substance (2) can be reconverted into the original α,β-unsaturated ketone (4) by hydration of the triple bond and cyclization with potassium *t*-butoxide. They report also that the two steps of the fragmentation can be reversed; that is, epoxidation (*m*-chloroperbenzoic acid) of the *p*-toluenesulfonylhydrazone of the α,β-unsaturated ketone gives the fragmented ketone. This procedure is useful when the direct epoxidation of the α,β-unsaturated ketone is difficult. Methanesulfonylhydrazine can be used with equally good results. Other examples have been described by the Stanford Research Institute group, for example:[6q]

These workers note, however, that 2,3-epoxycyclohexanone does not yield the corresponding 1-hexyne-6-ol, which indicates that the presence of a β-hydrogen atom alters the reaction.

The fragmentation reaction may be limited to cyclic substrates, since treatment of *trans*-chalcone oxide (5) with tosylhydrazine in acidic ethanol for 5 min. at 50° gives 4-hydroxypyrazoline (6).[6r] Probably the tosylhydrazone is formed and then undergoes intramolecular ring opening and closure to form the pyrazoline.

(5)   (6)

Generation of a carbene.[6s] When the *p*-tosylhydrazone V is treated with sodium acetamide (aprotic medium) at 175°, 10-carbenabicyclo[5.2.1]decane is formed and undergoes transannular cyclization to give tricyclo[5.2.1.0^{4,10}]decane (VI) in 87% yield. The high yield in this carbene reaction is attributed to restricted conformational

IV

86%

87%

VI   V

mobility of the cyclic carbene (8-membered ring) and to strain in the various alternative products.

[6a]J. M. Muchowski, *Tetrahedron Letters*, 1773 (1966)

[6b]J. Meinwald, J. C. Shelton, G. L. Buchanan, and A. Courtin, *J. Org.*, **33**, 99 (1968)

[6c]W. Kirmse, B.-G. von Bülow, and H. Schepp, *Ann.*, **691**, 41 (1966)

[6d]R. M. McDonald and R. A. Krueger, *J. Org.*, **31**, 488 (1966)

[6e]R. H. Shapiro, and M. J. Heath, *Am. Soc.*, **89**, 5734 (1967)

[6f]G. Kaufman, F. Cook. H. Shechter, J. Bayless, and L. Friedman, *ibid.*, **89**, 5736 (1967)

[6g]J. Meinwald and F. Uno, *ibid.*, **90**, 800 (1968)

[6h]F. T. Bond and L. Scerbo, *Tetrahedron Letters*, 2789 (1968)

[6i]R. H. Shapiro and J. H. Duncan, procedure submitted to *Org. Syn.*, 1968

[6j]W. G. Dauben, M. E. Lorber, N. D. Vietmeyer, R. H. Shapiro, J. H. Duncan, and K. Tomer, *Am. Soc.*, **90**, 4762 (1968)

[6k]G. Ohloff, J. Becker and K. H. Schulte-Elte (Firmenich), *Helv.*, **50**, 705 (1967)

[6l]A. Eschenmoser, D. Felix (ETH), and G. Ohloff (Firmenich), *ibid.*, **50**, 708 (1967)

[6m]J. Schreiber, D. Felix, and A. Eschenmoser (ETH), M. Winter, F. Gautechi, K. H. Schulte-Elte, E. Sundt, and G. Ohloff (Firmenich), J. Kalvoda, H. Kaufmann, P. Wieland, and G. Anner (Ciba, Basel), *ibid.*, **50**, 2101 (1967)

[6n]K. Biemann, G. Büchi, and B. H. Walker, *Am. Soc.*, **79**, 5558 (1957)

[6o]G. Wilke, *Angew. Chem.*, **69**, 397 (1957); *idem, ibid.*, **75**, 10 (1963)

[6p]M. Tanabe, D. F. Crowe, R. L. Dehn, and G. Detre, *Tetrahedron Letters*, 3739 (1967)
[6q]M. Tanabe, D. F. Crowe and R. L. Dehn, *ibid.*, 3943 (1967)
[6r]A. Padwa, *J. Org.*, **30**, 1274 (1965)
[6s]T. Jacobson, *Chem. Scand.*, **21**, 2235 (1967)

s-Triazine,  [**1**, 1188, before **1,2,4-Triazole**]. Mol. wt. 81.08, b.p. 78–80°.

Suppliers: A, Fl.

s-Triazine can be used in place of hydrogen cyanide in the Gattermann aldehyde synthesis.[1] In the furane and pyrrole series, and in the case of particularly reactive benzenoid compounds, no Friedel-Crafts catalysts are required, for example:

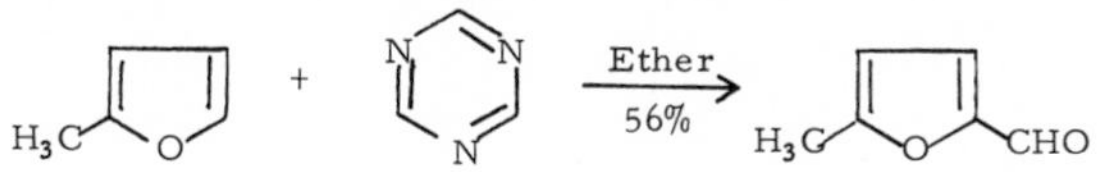

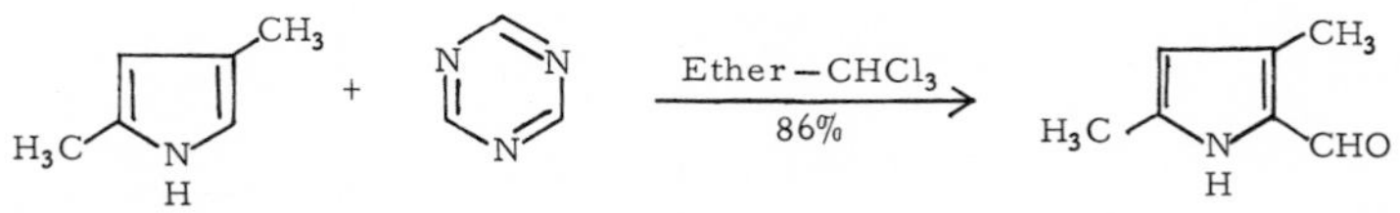

In the case of phenol ethers and the less reactive aromatic compounds, aluminum chloride is required as well as an elevated temperature.

[1]A. Kreutzberger, *Angew. Chem., internat. Ed.*, **6**, 940 (1967)

1,2,4-Triazole [**1**, 1188]. Additional supplier: Eastman.

Preparation. The reagent is prepared conveniently in 70% yield[1a] from 3-amino-1,2,4-triazole (Aldrich, Eastman) by deamination by the method of Henry and Finnegan,[1b] which involves diazotization and reduction with hypophosphorous acid.

[**1**, 1188, before references]: Wieland and Kahle[4] found this polar compound to be the best of several substances investigated for catalysis of coupling reagents of p-thiocresyl esters in peptide synthesis.

[1a]W. M. van der Brink, personal communication
[1b]R. A. Henry and W. G. Finnegan, *Am. Soc.*, **76**, 290 (1954)
[4]Th. Wieland and U. Kahle, *Ann.*, **691**, 212 (1966)

β,β,β-Tribromoethyl chloroformate, CBr_3CH_2OCOCl [**1**, 1188, before **Tri-i-butyl-aluminum**]. Mol. wt. 345.25, b.p. 47–50°/0.05 mm.

The reagent is prepared by reaction of β,β,β-tribromoethanol with phosgene in benzene. It reacts with primary and secondary hydroxyl groups of nucleosides to give β,β,β-tribromoethoxycarbonyl compounds (1). The protective group is removed by β-elimination with a zinc–copper couple.[1]

$$ROH + CBr_3CH_2OCOCl \longrightarrow CBr_3CH_2O\overset{O}{\overset{\|}{C}}OR \xrightarrow{Zn-Cu} CBr_2{=}CH_2 + CO_2 + ROH$$

(1)

[1]A. F. Cook, *J. Org.*, **33**, 3589 (1968)

2,4,6-Tribromophenol [**1**, 1188, before **Tri-*i*-butylaluminum**]. Mol. wt. 330.82, m.p. 93–95° Suppliers: A, E, F.

Esters of this hindered phenol have been prepared from N-carbobenzoxy amines and tribromophenol in the presence of DCC.[1]

[1]T. Scott-Burden and A. O. Hawtrey, *Tetrahedron Letters*, 4831 (1967)

Tri-*n*-butyltin hydride [**1**, 1192–1193].

Correction to first formulation. The ratios of the two products should be reversed.

[**1**, 1193, before references]: *gem*-Halofluorocyclopropanes are reduced stereo-specifically to fluorocyclopropanes:[10]

X = Br, Cl
n = 3, 4

Cyclopropenone (3) has been prepared for the first time by reduction of tetra-chlorocyclopropene (1) with 2 equivalents of tri-*n*-butyltin hydride;[11] careful hydroly-

(1)   (2)   (3)

sis gives cyclopropenone (3). Under appropriate conditions it is possible to obtain 3-chlorocyclopropene in 22% yield.[12]

Both *trans*- and *cis*-α-chlorodecalin are reduced by tri-*n*-butyltin hydride to the same mixture of *trans*- and *cis*-decalin in which the *trans* isomer predominates. Greene and Lowry[13] note that this method is useful for reduction of tertiary halides; it is particularly valuable for preparation of specifically labeled deuterated or tritiated compounds.

Review.[14]

[10]T. Ando, F. Namigata, H. Yamanaka, W. Funasaka, *Am. Soc.*, **89**, 5719 (1967)
[11]R. Breslow and G. Ryan, *Am. Soc.*, **89**, 3073 (1967)
[12]R. Breslow, J. T. Groves, and G. Ryan, *ibid.*, **89**, 5048 (1967)
[13]F. D. Greene and N. N. Lowry, *J. Org.*, **32**, 882 (1967)
[14]H. G. Kuivila, *Accounts Chem. Res.*, **1**, 289 (1968)

Trichloramine, [**1**, 1193–1194, before references].

m-Xylene is 6–8 times as reactive as the other isomers in the amination reaction; hence coal-tar xylene can be converted into 3,5-dimethylaniline in modest yield

(20–30%).[3] Amination of diphenyl with trichloramine in o-dichlorobenzene in the presence of aluminum chloride gives 3-aminodiphenyl in up to 27% yield.[4]

The amination reaction is not limited to aromatic hydrocarbons; it is also applicable to t-alkanes. t-Butyl chloride reacts with trichloramine in the presence of aluminum chloride to give t-butylamine in 88% yield.[5] Methylcyclohexane is converted into 1-amino-1-methylcyclohexane in yields as high as 67% (based on trichloramine). The most satisfactory conditions use C_7H_{14}–$AlCl_3$–NCl_3 in a 2:2:1 ratio with methylene chloride as solvent and a temperature of $0 \pm 5°$.[6] Under the same conditions adamantane gives 1-aminoadamantane in nearly quantitative yield.[7]

[3]P. Kovacic et al., J. Org., **32**, 585 (1967)
[4]P. Kovacic and A. K. Harrison, ibid., **32**, 207 (1967)
[5]P. Kovacic and M. K. Lowery, Chem. Commun., 651 (1966)
[6]P. Kovacic and S. S. Chaudhary, Tetrahedron, **23**, 3563 (1967); idem, Org. Syn., **48**, 4 (1968)
[7]P. Kovacic and P. D. Roskos, Tetrahedron Letters, 5833 (1968)

Trichloroacetic acid [**1**, 1194, before references]. Trichloroacetic acid reacts with the cyclic enamine 1-morpholino-1-cyclohexene in ethylene dichloride with elimination of carbon dioxide and formation of N-[1-(trichloromethyl)cyclohexyl]morpholine,

which on hydrolysis yields 1-cyclohexene-1-carboxylic acid (3).[3]

[3]G. H. Alt and A. J. Speziale, J. Org., **31**, 1340 (1967); idem, procedure submitted to Org. Syn., 1967

Trichloroacetyl isocyanate, CCl_3CONCO [**1**, 1195, before **Trichloromethanesulfonyl bromide**]. Mol. wt. 188.40, b.p. 80–85°. Suppliers: E; F.

Preparation.[1]

Classification of alcohols. The reagent reacts with an alcohol in a few minutes to form a carbamate, the NMR spectrum of which can be used to determine whether the alcohol is primary, secondary, or tertiary.[2] In the case of a tertiary alcohol, loss of the hydroxyl peak and appearance of an NH peak provide evidence. Secondary and primary alcohols can be distinguished by measuring the areas of the peaks which shift and thereby determining the number of hydrogens α to the hydroxyl group.

The method has been applied to steroid alcohols, even to 11β- and 17α-hydroxyl functions.[3] Some information about the environment of a hydroxyl group can be obtained by comparison of the NMR spectrum before and after addition of the reagent. Allylic alcohols are readily distinguished by the downfield shift of vinyl protons β to the hydroxyl group.

[1] A. J. Speziale and L. R. Smith, *J. Org.*, **27**, 3742 (1962)
[2] V. W. Goodlett, *Anal. Chem.*, **37**, 431 (1965)
[3] I. R. Trehan, C. Monder, and A. K. Bose, *Tetrahedron Letters*, 67 (1968)

$β,β,β$-Trichloroethyl chloroformate, CCl_3CH_2OCOCl (TrOCOCl) [**1**, 1195, before **Trichloromethanesulfonyl bromide**]. Mol. wt. 211.88, b.p. 171–172°/760 mm., 75–76°/60 mm. Supplier: A.

Prepared by passing phosgene into a solution of trichloroethanol in benzene–diethylaniline, this stable chloroformate acylates hydroxyl and amino groups in pyridine at room temperature or under Schotten-Baumann conditions (1–3).[1] The protective group is removed by treatment with zinc dust in methanol. The group is stable to the conditions of Sarett and of Jones oxidations, to dioxane–HCl, to CF_3-

(1) M. p. 150–152°   (2) M. p. 123–124°   (3) M. p. 140–141°

CO_2H for 30 min., and to hydrogenation. Reversal conditions are illustrated by the following experiment. A 107-mg. sample of the epiandrosterone derivative (1) was stirred with 107 mg. of zinc dust in 1 ml. of acetic acid for 70 min. After filtration, the filtrate was diluted with water, extracted with chloroform, and the recovered material on crystallization gave 56 mg. (84%) of epiandrosterone.

[1] T. B. Windholz and D. B. R. Johnston, *Tetrahedron Letters*, 2555 (1967)

Trichloroisocyanuric acid, (1) [**1**, 1195, before **Trichloromethanesulfonyl bromide**]. Mol. wt. 232.42, m.p. 145°.

   Preparation.[1]

(1)

Conversion of ethers to esters.[2] The reagent in the presence of an excess of water converts ethers of the type RCH$_2$OR' into carboxylic acid esters. Benzyl ethyl ether

$$CH_3CH_2OC_2H_5 \xrightarrow[49\%]{} CH_3COOC_2H_5$$

is converted into benzaldehyde as the major product.

[1] E. M. Smolin and L. Rapoport, "*s*-Triazines and Derivatives," 391, Interscience, New York, 1959

[2] E. C. Juenge and D. A. Beal, *Tetrahedron Letters*, 5819 (1968)

Triethylaluminum [1, 1197–1198].

Addition of hydrogen cyanide. As one step in a total synthesis of *dl*-atisine, Nagata *et al.*[3a] wanted to effect conjugate addition of hydrogen cyanide to the intermediate

$$(C_2H_5)_2AlCl-HCN \xrightarrow[72-75\%]{THF}$$

(1)   (2)   (3)

(1). Use of potassium cyanide and ammonium chloride in DMF was unsuccessful; use of triethylaluminum and hydrogen cyanide gave the desired crude cyano ketone, but in a yield of only 11%. They then used the less basic diethylaluminum chloride in place of triethylaluminum in combination with hydrogen cyanide and obtained a crystalline mixture of epimers (2) and (3) in 72–75% yield.

The hydrocyanation to 3β-acetoxy-Δ^5-cholestene-7-one to give 3β-acetoxy-5α-cyanocholestane-7-one has been described in detail.[3b] In this case the reaction shows high stereoselectivity.

$$(C_2H_5)_3Al-HCN \xrightarrow[92.5\%]{THF}$$

[3a] W. Nagata, T. Sugasawa, M. Narisada, T. Wakabayashi, and Y. Hayase, *Am. Soc.*, **89**, 1483 (1967)

[3b] W. Nagata and M. Yoshioka, procedure submitted to *Org. Syn.*, 1969

Triethylamine [1, 1198–1203].

Purification. R. Breslow and J. Posner [*Org. Syn.*, **47**, 62 (1967)] recommend that commercial triethylamine be purified to remove primary and secondary amines and water either by distillation from acetic anhydride and then from barium oxide or by reaction with phenyl isocyanate. F. F. Rogers, Jr., R. J. Albers, and D. F. DeTar (procedure submitted to *Org. Syn.*) recommend refluxing with phthalic anhydride followed by distillation.

Anhydride synthesis [1, 1200, after line 2). In a procedure by H. Rinderknecht and M. Gutenstein [*Org. Syn.*, **47**, 89 (1967)] a suspension of nicotinic acid is stirred at 5° and treated with a cold 12.5% solution of phosgene in benzene. After 45 min. at room temperature the mixture is heated to the boiling point and the triethylamine

hydrochloride removed by suction filtration. Nicotinic anhydride of good purity is recovered from the benzene solution in several crops and high yield.

The mixed anhydride synthesis is illustrated further in a procedure by DeTar *et al.* (*loc. cit.*) for synthesis of benzyloxycarbonyl-L-serylglycine *p*-nitrophenyl ester.

Dehydrohalogenation [**1**, 1202, first paragraph]. *Correction*: Dicyanocarbene is probably not generated in the reaction cited in ref. 16. Boldt *et al.*[16a] have found that bromomalononitrile reacts with tetramethylethylene at room temperature to give the adduct (3) in practically quantitative yield in a light-initiated reaction. In the presence of triethylamine the adduct loses hydrogen bromide to give the cyclopropane derivative (4).

Breslow and Posner (*loc. cit.*) give a detailed procedure for the conversion of α,α'-dibromodibenzyl ketone to diphenylcyclopropenone cited in ref. 17.

A simple preparation of γ-crotonolactone (7, $\Delta^{\alpha,\beta}$-butenolide) has been described.[18a] Vinylacetic acid (5) is converted into the dibromide (6) and the crude product is refluxed in chloroform with excess triethylamine. Elimination of hydrogen bromide and lactonization take place to give (7) in 54% overall yield.

Intermolecular dehydrohalogenation [**1**, 1203, before references]. A solution of cyclohexanecarbonyl chloride (Eastman) in benzene is stirred and swept with

Dispiro[5.1.5.1]tetradecane-
7,14-dione

nitrogen, triethylamine is run in, and the mixture is refluxed overnight.[24] The amine hydrochloride that separates is filtered and the benzene solution is washed with dilute hydrochloric acid and water, dried, and evaporated. Crystallization of the residue from ligroin–ethanol gives pure dispirocyclodiketone, m.p. 161–162°.

Hydrogenolysis. In the removal of halogen from an organic molecule by hydrogenolysis, the hydrogen halide formed poisons the catalyst unless neutralized. Reinecke[25] found that triethylamine can be used and is sometimes superior to sodium

hydroxide. Overberger and Kaye[26] found these conditions the most satisfactory for the hydrogenolysis of the α-bromolactone (3).

Orientation in Aromatic Substitution. One objective in research set by D. E. Pearson[27] was to manipulate orientation in various ways to obtain any isomer desired. An example cited on **1**, 32–33 is the *meta*-bromination of acetophenone, described by Pearson as a "swamping catalyst effect." In the bromination of a phenol, *para* substitution ordinarily predominates over *ortho* substitution, but considerable increase in the proportion of *ortho* isomer can be achieved by operating at −70° in the presence of a strongly basic aliphatic amine.[28] The best procedure was to add bromine to a cold solution of *t*-butylamine in toluene, cool to about −70°, and add a phenol dropwise over a short period of time. By this procedure, phenol was converted by 1 equivalent of bromine into 2-bromophenol in 60% yield and by 2 equivalents of bromine into 2,6-dibromophenol in 87% yield. Tertiary amines such as DABCO and triethylamine serve also for enhanced *o*-bromination of phenols. Chlorination under the same conditions gave a mixture of *o*- and *p*-chlorophenols in the ratio 2:1.

[16a]P. Boldt, L. Schulz, and J. Etzemüller, *Ber.*, **100**, 1281 (1967)
[18a]M. Franck-Neumann and C. Berger, *Bull. soc.*, 4067 (1968)
[24]N. J. Turro, P. A. Leermakers, and G. F. Vesley, *Org. Syn.*, **47**, 34 (1967)
[25]M. G. Reinecke, *J. Org.*, **29**, 299 (1964)
[26]C. G. Overberger and H. Kaye, *Am. Soc.*, **89**, 5640 (1967)
[27]D. E. Pearson, *J. Tenn. Acad. Sci.*, **40**, 97 (1965)
[28]D. E. Pearson, R. D. Wysong, and C. V. Breder, *J. Org.*, **32**, 2358 (1967)

Triethylenediamine [**1**, 1203]. This name has become obsolete; the compound is more generally known as 1,4-Diazabicyclo[2.2.2]octane, *which see* (this volume).

Triethyl orthoformate [1, 1204–1210]. A simplified method of preparation[1a] consists in dropwise addition of 1 mole of benzoyl chloride to a stirred mixture of 180 ml. of absolute ethanol, 45 g. of formamide, and 200 ml. of ligroin (70–80°) with cooling. After 2 hrs. the crystallizate of benzoic acid and ammonium chloride is removed, and the filtrate is washed with ice-cold 3 N alkali, dried over potassium carbonate, and distilled; yield 40–44%.

[**1**, 1205, after citation of ref. 6]: Treibs[6a] reports that the simplest route to an azulene aldehyde from an azulene is by reaction with triethyl orthoformate in petroleum ether solution in the presence of BF_3-etherate. Yields are 86–90%. Previously the Vilsmeier reaction had been used, but it is less convenient.

10 g. (Blue)   10 g.   150 ml.   10 g.   (Red)

[**1**, 1210, before references]: The reagent reacts with 1,2-dianilinoethane to give bis(1,3-diphenylimidazolidinylene-2) in 91–95% yield.[28]

in 91–95% yield. [28]

[1a]R. Ohme and E. Schmitz, *Ann.*, **716**, 207 (1968)
[6a]W. Treibs, *Tetrahedron Letters*, 4707 (1967)
[28]H.-W. Wanzlick, *Org. Syn.*, **47**, 14 (1967)

Triethyloxonium fluoroborate [1, 1210–1212, (**Trimethyl salt, 1**, 1232)].

Reduction of secondary and tertiary amides[8] [before references]. Treatment of a secondary or tertiary amide (1) with the reagent in CH_2Cl_2 gives the imino ether

(1)   (2)   (3)

fluoroborate (2) in excellent yield. For reduction to the amine (3) the methylene chloride is removed under reduced pressure and a solution of the residue in absolute ethanol is treated with excess sodium borohydride at 0–25°. Overall yields are 81–94%.

Attempted reduction of the imino ether (5) from the primary amide (4) led instead to the corresponding nitrile (6) in overall yield of 30–60%.

$$C_6H_5CONH_2 \xrightarrow{(C_2H_5)_3O^+BF_4^-} \underset{(5)}{\overset{OC_2H_5}{C_6H_5\overset{|}{C}=NH}} \xrightarrow[30-60\%]{NaBH_4} \underset{(6)}{C_6H_5C\equiv N}$$

$$\text{(EtONa) } 60°, \text{ 1 hr.} \uparrow 95\%$$

Alkylation of sulfides. In a study of the possible role of sulfonium ylides in the coupling of allyl units to give squalene and related terpenes, Baldwin et al.[9] examined the alkylation of the sulfide (1). The only product was the symmetrical salt (2).

(2)   (1)

(3)   (4)   (5)

They then turned to the less hindered reagent trimethyloxonium fluoroborate in nitromethane and obtained the desired salt (3). The product is rearranged to (4) on treatment with n-butyllithium, and reduction with sodium in liquid ammonia gives the squalenelike hydrocarbon (5). Desulfurization with Raney nickel gives complex mixtures in the case of allylic sulfides.

O-Alkylation of enolate ions by the reagent occurs to some extent in aprotic, polar solvents (1,2-dimethoxyethane), but may become the major reaction in DMSO or DMF.[10]

Deacetylation. N-Acetyl groups of acetamido desoxysugars are selectively cleaved under mild conditions by treatment with triethyloxonium fluoroborate, followed by hydrolysis of the intermediate O-ethyl acetamidium fluoroborate.[11] Ester, acetal, and glycosidic linkages are not affected.

[8]R. F. Borch, *Tetrahedron Letters*, 61 (1968)
[9]J. E. Baldwin, R. E. Hackles, and D. P. Kelly, *Am. Soc.*, **90**, 4758 (1968)
[10]G. J. Heiszwolf and H. Kloosterziel, *Chem. Commun.*, 51 (1966)
[11]S. Hanessian, *Tetrahedron Letters*, 1549 (1967)

Triethyl phosphite [1, 1212–1216].

Phosphonate modification [bottom of 1, 1212]. *trans*-3-Stilbazole is conveniently prepared by the phosphonate modification of the Wittig reaction:[4a]

Reduction of hydroperoxides [1, 1213]. The original procedure (1, 921) for conversion of steroid C_{20}-ketones into 17α-hydroxy-20-ketones involved two steps: autoxidation in the presence of potassium *t*-butoxide, followed by reduction of the resulting 17α-hydroperoxide with zinc dust in acetic acid. A Schering group[8a] in an application of this reaction obtained a yield of only 22% and investigated an alternative method. Since the original work, reduction of hydroperoxides by trialkyl phosphites had been reported. Hence they investigated a one-step procedure: autoxidation with sodium hydride as base in DMF–*t*-butanol in the presence of triethyl phosphite at −20° to −25°. Average yields of 60–70% were obtained. They also applied the method to Δ^{16}-pregnene-20-ones (1); in this case several products were formed, the main products being (2) and (3), both in low yield.

Reaction with ascaridole. The natural *endo*-peroxide ascaridole (1) when heated with triethyl phosphite at 160–170° is converted into *p*-cymene (2).[8b] This conversion was first carried out by Horner[8c] using triethylphosphine; the product was then

believed to be *p*-Δ^2-menthene-1,4-oxide, formed by removal of one oxygen atom.

Reduction of N-functions [**1**, 1215–1216]. *Correction*: The correct name of the first formula (2) is 2-*p*-methoxyphenylindazole.

The preparation of 2-phenylindazole itself by the same procedure has been described.[23a]

Smolinsky and Feuer[26a] suggest that the deoxygenation of aromatic nitro compounds is a two-step process involving reduction to the nitroso stage and then to the nitrene:

Review.[26b]

[4a]F. J. Villani and T. A. Mann, procedure submitted to *Org. Syn.*, 1967
[8a]J. N. Gardner, F. E. Carlon, and O. Gnoj, *J. Org.*, **33**, 3294 (1968); J. N. Gardner, T. L. Popper, F. E. Carlon, O. Gnoj, and H. L. Herzog, *ibid.*, **33**, 3695 (1968)
[8b]T. Kametani and K. Ogasawara, *Chem. Ind.*, 1772 (1968)
[8c]L. Horner and W. Jurgeleit, *Ann.*, **591**, 138 (1955)
[23a]J. I. G. Cadogan and R. K. Mackie, *Org. Syn.*, **48**, 113 (1968)
[26a]G. Smolinsky and B. I. Feuer, *J. Org.*, **31**, 3882 (1966)
[26b]J. I. G. Cadogan, *Quart. Rev.*, **22**, 222 (1968)

Triethylsilane [**1**, 1218, before references]. Pettit *et al.*[4] report a case where cleavage of a carbobenzoxy group with triethylsilane – palladium chloride in the presence of triethylamine proceeded in 70% yield. Hydrogenolysis was effected in somewhat lower yield (60%), and the yield obtained by solvolysis with CF_3CO_2H was only 22%.

[4]G. R. Pettit, R. L. Smith, A. K. Das Gupta, and J. L. Occolowitz, *Canad. J. Chem.*, **45**, 501 (1966)

Trifluoroacetic acid [**1**, 1219–1221].

Condensation-cyclization [bottom of **1**, 1219]. Flavones can be prepared in one step by the condensation of a phenol with malonic acid in the presence of trifluoroacetic acid.[3a]

Condensation of ethane-1,2-dithiol [**1**, 1220, before references]. Coffen[13] states that trifluoroacetic acid is an excellent reagent for the condensation of ketones with ethanedithiol to form ethylenethioketals. He found, however, that in the absence of a carbonyl compound the acid condenses with ethanedithiol to produce in high yield the crystalline orthothiol ester formulated.

M.p. 85°

Cleavage of an oxide. A Merck group[14] found that the ketoxide (1) when treated

(1)   (2)

with trifluoroacetic acid is converted into the 16-methylene-17α-hydroxy compound (2).

Hydrolysis of acetal groups. Acetal groups attached to sugars and nucleosides are hydrolyzed in 5–10 min. at room temperature by 90% (v/v) aqueous trifluoroacetic acid. Acetic acid is not effective.[15]

[3a]L. L. Woods and J. Sapp, *J. Org.*, **29**, 3445 (1964)
[13]D. L. Coffen, *Chem. Commun.*, 1089 (1967)
[14]D. Taub, R. D. Hoffsommer, and N. L. Wendler, *J. Org.*, **29**, 3486 (1964)
[15]J. E. Cristensen and L. Goodman, *Carbohydrate Res.*, **7**, 510 (1968)

Trihydridobis(triphenylphosphine)iridium (III), $IrH_3[P(C_6H_5)_3]_2$ [1, 1228, before **Triisopinocampheyldiborane**]. Mol. wt. 731.79, m.p. 184–185°, dec. **Preparation.**[1,2]

Hydrogenation catalyst.[3] This complex is an active catalyst for homogeneous hydrogenation of aldehydes (acetic acid is necessary).

[1]J. Chatt, R. S. Coffey, and B. L. Shaw, *J. Chem. Soc.*, 7391 (1965)
[2]L. Vaska, *Am. Soc.*, **83**, 756 (1961)
[3]R. S. Coffey, *Chem. Commun.*, 923 (1967)

Trimethylamine oxide [1, 1231].

Aldehyde synthesis [before references]. Franzen[5] gives a procedure for drying trimethylamine oxide dihydrate (supplied by Beacon Chemicals) by mixing with dimethylformamide and distillation, eventually in vacuum, until the solvent is all removed. A solution of the residue in chloroform is treated with *n*-octyl iodide, added dropwise with stirring in 20–30 min. After refluxing for 20 min., the solution is cooled and treated with 2 N aqueous sulfuric acid at 50°. The chloroform layer is

$$\underline{n}\text{-}C_8H_{17}I + (CH_3)_3N\!\rightarrow\!O \xrightarrow[41.5\text{-}43\%]{CHCl_3} \underline{n}\text{-}C_7H_{15}CHO + (CH_3)_3N^+HI^-$$

separated, washed, dried, and concentrated. Two distillations of the residue afforded 10.6–11.0 g. of *n*-octanal.

[5]V. Franzen, *Org. Syn.*, **47**, 96 (1967)

Trimethylammonium formate (Trimethylamine formate) [**1**, 1231]. Supplier: Eastman.

Trimethyl borate $(CH_3O)_3B$ [**1**, 1231, before **Trimethylboroxine**]. Mol. wt. 103.92, b.p. 67–69°. Suppliers: A, B, Fl, MCB.

The use of this ester for the indirect conversion of an aryl halide to the corresponding phenol is illustrated by the preparation of 6-methoxy-2-naphthol (4) from 6-bromo-2-methoxynaphthalene (1).[1] A mixture of the aryl halide (1), magnesium,

tetrahydrofurane, and a small crystal of iodine is refluxed to form the Grignard reagent (2). Reaction of the reagent (2) with trimethyl borate in THF then affords the ester (3), and in the next step this ester is oxidized with hydrogen peroxide–acetic acid to the desired 6-methoxy-2-naphthol and dimethyl borate.

[1]R. L. Kidwell, M. Murphy, and S. D. Darling, procedure submitted to *Org. Syn.*, 1968

Trimethylchlorosilane [**1**, 1232]. Additional suppliers: Alfa Inorganics; Fl.

Acyloin condensation [before reference]. Schräpler and Rühlmann[2] found that, if the acyloin condensation is carried out in the presence of trimethylchlorosilane, the intermediate enediol can be isolated as the trimethylsilyl derivative with improvement in yield. Hydrolysis is accomplished with hydrochloric acid in tetrahydrofurane.

n = 3, 4, 8; yield = 91–93%, 55–89%, 20–54%

Bloomfield[3] made the remarkable finding that the method, as applied to (1) closes a highly strained cyclobutene ring to give (2) in excellent yield. The silyl ether groups are readily hydrolyzed to the acyloin (3) by refluxing methanol. A further advantage of the method is that it inhibits Dieckmann condensation which often competes with acyloin condensation.[4] Thus attempted cyclization of the esters

(1)   (2)   (3)

(4) and (6) with excess sodium–potassium alloy had given mixtures of several components from which crystalline material was not obtainable,[5] but in the presence of the silane the acyloin derivatives (5) and (7) were obtained in excellent yields.[4]

(4)   (5)

(6)   (7)

Other trimethylsilyl enol ethers. Stork and Hudrlik[6] developed a process for the conversion of 2-methylcyclohexanone into its two sodium enolates by refluxing with sodium hydride in glyme, cooling and adding excess triethylamine and trimethylchlorosilane, and then diluting with pentane and washing successively with dilute HCl and with aqueous bicarbonate. The two isomeric silyl ethers are separated by

73:29

preparative VPC. These trimethylsilyl enol ethers are ideally suited for generation of metal enolates by reaction with an organometallic reagent, since an inert tetra-

$$\text{OSi(CH}_3)_3 \quad \xrightarrow{\text{LiCH}_3} \quad \text{OLi} \quad + \ (\text{CH}_3)_4\text{Si}$$

alkylsilane is the only by-product. The lithium enolate from (1) has been methylated in 80% overall yield.[7]

$$\text{(1)} \xrightarrow[\text{80\%}]{\begin{array}{l}1)\ \text{CH}_3\text{Li}\\2)\ \text{CH}_3\text{I}\end{array}} \text{(2)}$$

Protection of a terminal acetylene group. Earborn *et al.*[8] found that treatment of the Grignard reagent (1) with trimethylchlorosilane in THF gave (2). Conversion

$$\underset{\text{(1)}}{p\text{-BrC}_6\text{H}_4\text{C}{\equiv}\text{CMgBr}} \xrightarrow[87\%]{(\text{CH}_3)_3\text{SiCl}} \underset{\text{(2)}}{p\text{-BrC}_6\text{H}_4\text{C}{\equiv}\text{CSi(CH}_3)_3} \xrightarrow[\text{THF}]{\text{Mg}}$$

$$\underset{\text{(3)}}{[\text{BrMgC}_6\text{H}_4\text{C}{\equiv}\text{CSi(CH}_3)_2]} \xrightarrow[70\%]{\text{CO}_2} \underset{\text{(4)}}{p\text{-HO}_2\text{CC}_6\text{H}_4\text{C}{\equiv}\text{CSi(CH}_3)_2}$$

into the Grignard reagent (3) and carbonation gave (4).

Russian investigators[9] found that a silyl substituent on one carbon atom of a triple bond protects this unsaturated center from hydrogenation. Schmidt and Arens,[10] seeking to selectively reduce the central triple bond of I without disturbance of the two terminal triple bonds or of the two double bonds present, made use of the

$$\text{HC}{\equiv}\text{C}-\text{CH}{=}\text{C(CH}_3)-\text{CH}_2-\text{C}{\equiv}\text{C}-\text{CH}_2-\text{C(CH}_3){=}\text{CH}-\text{C}{\equiv}\text{CH} \qquad \textbf{(I)}$$

$$83\% \ \begin{array}{l}1.\ \text{EtMgBr}\\2.\ \text{Me}_3\text{SiCl}\end{array} \Big\downarrow$$

$$\text{Me}_3\text{Si}-\text{C}{\equiv}\text{C}-\text{CH}{=}\text{C(CH}_3)-\text{CH}_2-\text{C}{\equiv}\text{C}-\text{CH}_2-\text{C(CH}_3){=}\text{CH}-\text{C}{\equiv}\text{C}-\text{SiMe}_3$$
$$\textbf{(II)}$$

$$80\% \ \Big\downarrow \ \text{H}_2/\text{Pd-BaSO}_4$$

$$\text{Me}_3\text{Si}-\text{C}{\equiv}\text{C}-\text{CH}{=}\text{C(CH}_3)-\text{CH}_2-\text{CH}{=}\text{CH}-\text{CH}_2-\text{C(CH}_3){=}\text{CH}-\text{C}{\equiv}\text{C}-\text{SiMe}_3$$
$$\textbf{(III)}$$

$$90\% \ \begin{array}{l}1.\ \text{AgNO}_3\\2.\ \text{KCN/H}_2\text{O}\end{array} \Big\downarrow$$

$$\text{HC}{\equiv}\text{C}-\text{CH}{=}\text{C(CH}_3)-\text{CH}_2-\text{CH}{=}\text{CH}-\text{CH}_2-\text{C(CH}_3){=}\text{CH}-\text{C}{\equiv}\text{CH} \qquad \textbf{(IV)}$$

Russian finding by converting I via the MgBr-derivative into the bis-trimethylsilyl derivative II. Hydrogenation over palladium catalyst then reduced the central triple bond selectively, leaving untouched the two $\equiv$C—Si(CH$_3$)$_3$ groups and the two =CH— groups. The protective groups were then split by treatment with alcoholic silver nitrate to form the silver acetylide, which was treated with concentrated aqueous KCN to give IV.

Acylation of malonic esters. Monoacylation of sodiomalonic esters is usually accompanied by diacylation. This disadvantage can be eliminated by reaction of the sodiomalonate with trimethylchlorosilane to give a "ketene acetal" (1). This reacts readily with an acid chloride or anhydride to give an acylmalonic ester (2).[11] Yields are in the range 50–80%.

$$(C_2H_5OOC)_2CHNa \xrightarrow{ClSi(CH_3)_3} C_2H_5OOCCH{=}C\underset{OC_2H_5}{\overset{OSi(CH_3)_3}{\big<}} \xrightarrow[-ClSi(CH_3)_3]{ROCl} RCOCH(COOC_2H_5)_2$$

$$(1) \qquad\qquad (2)$$

Synthesis of isocyanates.[12] Thermal cleavage of urethanes gives low yields of isocyanates because of the high temperatures necessary (200–300°). However, if the urethane is N-silylated, cleavage occurs at much lower temperatures. Thus the urethane (1) is treated with trimethylchlorosilane and triethylamine in refluxing

$$RNH\overset{O}{\overset{\|}{C}}OR' \xrightarrow{(CH_3)_3SiCl} R\underset{Si(CH_3)_3}{N}\overset{O}{\overset{\|}{C}}OR' \xrightarrow{\Delta} RN{=}C{=}O + R'OSi(CH_3)_3$$

$$(1) \qquad\qquad (2) \qquad\qquad (3) \qquad (4)$$

toluene for two hours. After cooling, the triethylammonium chloride is filtered and the isocyanate (3) isolated from the filtrate by fractionation. In the case of carbamoyl chlorides, RNHCOCl, trimethylsilylacetamide is used for N-silylation, and the cleavage to the isocyanate occurs at $-20°$ to $0°$.

[2]U. Schräpler and K. Rühlmann, *Ber,* **97**, 1383 (1964)
[3]J. J. Bloomfield, *Tetrahedron Letters*, 587 (1968)
[4]*Idem, ibid.*, 591 (1968)
[5]J. J. Bloomfield, and J. R. S. Irelan, *J. Org.*, **31**, 2017 (1966)
[6]G. Stork and P. F. Hudrlik, *Am. Soc.*, **90**, 4462 (1968)
[7]*Idem, ibid.*, **90**, 4464 (1968)
[8]C. Earborn, A. R. Thompson, and D. R. M. Walton, *J. Chem. Soc.*, (C), 1364 (1967)
[9]B. G. Shakovski, M. D. Stadnichuk, A. A. Petrov, *J. Gen. Chem. USSR*, **35**, 1036 (1965)
[10]H. M. Schmidt and J. F. Arens, *Rec. trav.*, **86**, 1138 (1967)
[11]U. Schmidt and M. Schwochau, *Tetrahedron Letters*, 4491 (1967)
[12]G. Greber and H. R. Kricheldorf, *Angew. Chem. internat. Ed.*, **7**, 941 (1968)

Trimethyloxonium fluoroborate [1, 1232]. In the preparation cited in ref. 1, the reagent was prepared by the reaction of dimethyl ether with triethyloxonium fluoroborate. In a new procedure,[2] the reagent is prepared by the reaction of epichlorohydrin with dimethyl ether and boron trifluoride etherate. This procedure dispenses with the intermediate preparation of triethyloxonium fluoroborate. Prepared by the newer method, the salt can be stored for as long as a year in a dessicator over Drierite at $-20°$.

[2]T. J. Curphey, procedure submitted to *Org. Syn.*, 1968

Trimethyloxonium 2,4,6-trinitrobenzenesulfonate [1, 1232–1233, before reference]. This stable alkylating agent is prepared by the method cited[1] and also by reaction of the acid with trimethyloxonium fluoroborate (71–76% yield).[2] The salt can be kept for about 4 weeks in a closed container at 5–10° with only about 10% decomposition. It is not hygroscopic.

Alkylating agent. The reagent reacts with cyclooctene sulfide to give S-methyl-sulfonium 2,4,6-trinitrobenzenesulfonate:[2]

As compared with methyl iodide, this more reactive alkylating agent gives less dialkylation with lithium enolate anions; on the other hand, more O-alkylated products are formed.[3]

	CH₃I:		
CH_3I:	79–92%	8–21%	<1%
$(CH_3)_3\overset{+}{O}SO_3^-C_6H_2(NO_2)_3$:	88%	<3%	ca. 10%

[2]D. J. Pettitt and G. K. Helmkamp, *J. Org.*, **29**, 2702 (1964)
[3]H. O. House and B. M. Trost, *ibid.*, **30**, 2503 (1965); H. O. House, *Record Chem. Progress*, **28**, 98 (1967)

Trimethyl phosphite [1, 1233–1235].

Olefin synthesis [1, 1233–1234, after formula (5)]. Corey's group has extended the olefin synthesis to the preparation of relatively unstable olefins.[4a] Treatment of *trans*-1,2-cyclooctenethionocarbonate (6) with triisooctyl phosphite at 135° for 24 hrs., while passing a steady stream of argon through the reaction mixture to effect rapid

removal of the volatile product, afforded *trans*-cyclooctene (7) in 75% yield.

When an attempt was made to produce *trans*-cycloheptene from *trans*-1,2-cyclo-heptenethionocarbonate (8) by the same procedure, only *cis*-cycloheptene was obtained. However, the reaction of *trans*-1,2-cycloheptenethionocarbonate (8) with trimethyl phosphite in the presence of 2,5-diphenyl-3,4-isobenzofurane (9) as trapping agent gave an adduct (10), m.p. 150°, isomeric with the known adduct of the benzofurane with *cis*-cycloheptene, m.p. 185°. It is apparent, therefore, that *trans*-cycloheptene is the primary product from *trans*-1,2-cycloheptenethionocarbonate.

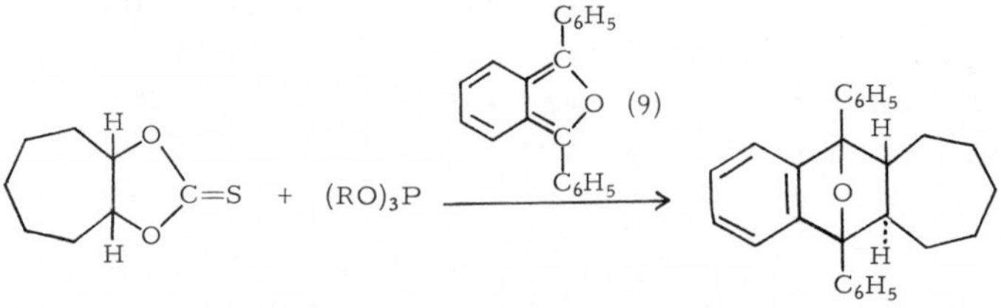

(8)   (10)

1,2-Trithiocarbonates also undergo elimination when heated with a trialkyl phosphite to form olefins by stereospecific *cis* elimination, as illustrated by a practical synthesis of *trans*-cyclooctene from the *cis* isomer:

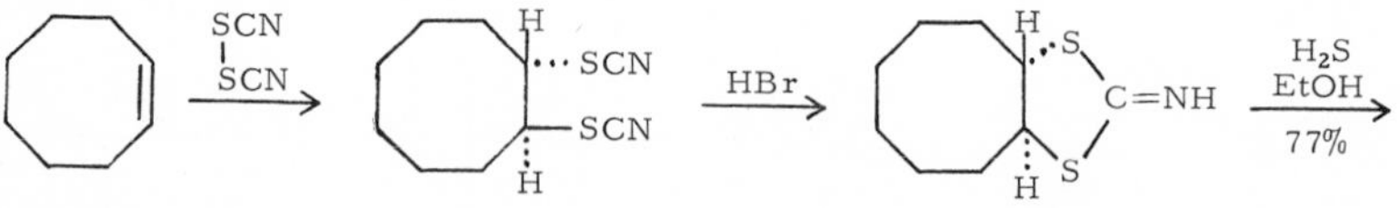

(11)   (12)   (13)

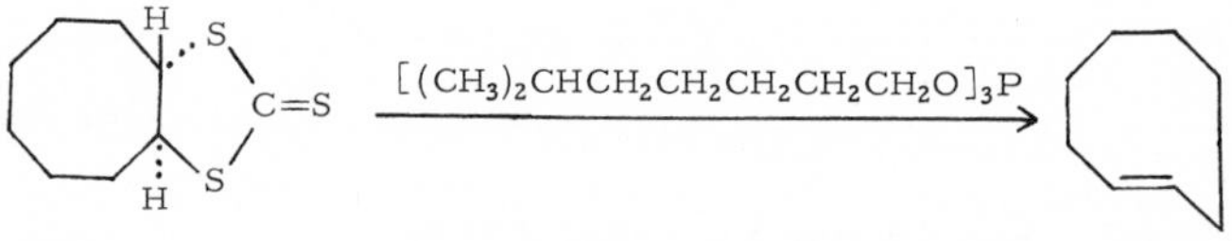

(14)   (15)

Addition of thiocyanogen to *cis*-cyclooctene affords *trans*-1,2-dithiocyanocyclooctane (12), which is converted quantitatively into the imino dithiocarbonate (13) by refluxing for 2 hrs. with 47% hydrobromic acid, followed by neutralization with sodium carbonate. The *trans*-thiocarbonate (14) is produced from this imine by reaction with hydrogen sulfide in ethanol and converted into *trans*-cyclooctene (15) by heating with triisooctyl phosphite at 135° (41 hrs.), using the entrainment technique to remove product as formed.

Another route to intermediate trithiocarbonates is the reaction of *cis*- and *trans*-1,2-epoxides with potassium methyl xanthate to give, with Walden inversion, *trans*- or *cis*-1,2-trithiocarbonates, respectively.

Corey and Shulman[4b] achieved the following direct synthesis of optically pure *trans*-cyclooctene. Optically active (+)-*trans*-1,2-cyclooctanediol (16) was prepared

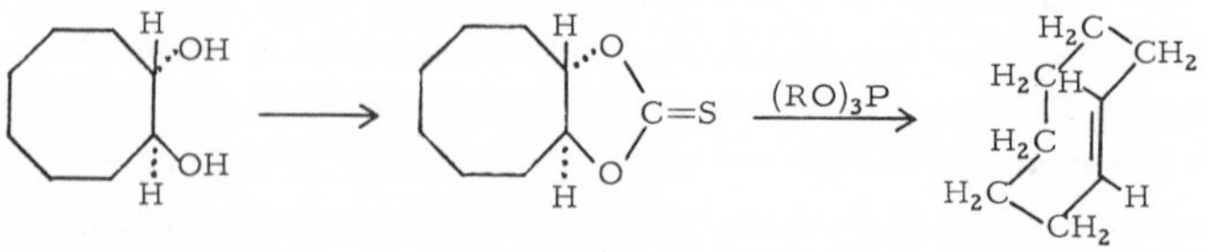

(16)   (17)   (18)

(+)-antipode   (+)-antipode   (−)-antipode

by treatment of a solution of racemic diol in THF with a slight molar excess of *n*-butyllithium followed by one equivalent of phthalic anhydride. The resulting mono-phthalate half-ester was then converted into the strychnine salt, which was purified by several recrystallizations and then converted via the optically active diol into the thionocarbonate (17). Reaction of (17) with triisooctyl phosphite was effected in 17 hrs. at 130° to give (−)-*trans*-cyclooctene (18) in 84% yield and > 99% optical purity.

Conversion of RCHO into RCH$_2$COOH [**1**, 1234, before references]. 1,3-Dithio-cyclohexane-2-thione (1)[9] reacts quantitatively with trimethyl phosphite (N$_2$, 55°,

$$(4)$$

(1)   (2)   (3)

3 hrs.), to give the ylide (2). This reacts rapidly and exothermally with an aldehyde, for example, benzaldehyde, to give the ketene thioacetal (3). Since ketene thioacetals on hydrolysis yield carboxylic acids, this method provides a means of transformation of an aldehyde into the homologous acid.[10] Ketones do not react with (2).

[4a]E. J. Corey, F. A. Carey, and R. A. E. Winter, *Am. Soc.*, **87**, 934 (1965)
[4b]E. J. Corey, and J. I. Shulman, *Tetrahedron Letters*, 3655 (1968)
[9]Prepared in over 60% yield by the reaction of trimethylene dibromide with sodium trithio-carbonate: W. H. Mills and B. C. Saunders, *J. Chem. Soc.*, 537 (1931)
[10]E. J. Corey and G. Märkl, *Tetrahedron Letters*, 3201 (1967)

Trimethyl phosphite–Methylcopper complex [(CH$_3$O)$_3$P]$_3$CuCH$_3$ [**1**, 1235, before **Trimethylsilane**]. Mol. wt. 450.80, b.p. 110–111°.

The *preparation* of this relatively stable, partially water-soluble, ether-soluble complex of methylcopper (I) is conducted as follows:[1]

$$CH_3Cu + 3 (CH_3O)_3P \longrightarrow [(CH_3O)_3P]_3CuCH_3$$

Use.[1] The reagent has been used in the same way as dimethylcopperlithium for conjugate addition to α,β-unsaturated ketones; however, with the present reagent various salts (lithium iodide, lithium bromide, etc.) must be present. The tri-*n*-butyl phosphite and tri-*n*-butyl phosphine complexes have been prepared but are less use-ful.

98% trans   2% cis

[1]H. O. House and W. F. Fischer, Jr., *J. Org.*, **33**, 949 (1968)

Trimethylphosphonoacetate, $(CH_3O)_2\overset{\overset{O}{\|}}{P}CH_2CO_2CH_3$ [1, 1235, before **Trimethyl-silane**]. Mol. wt. 182.11. Preparation: from trimethyl phosphite and methyl bromo-acetate (compare triethylphosphonoacetate).

Synthesis of olefins[1] (*see* **Triethylphosphonoacetate, 1,** 1217). The trimethyl ester was used in two key steps in the synthesis of the juvenile hormone of *Hyalophora cecropia*, methyl *trans,trans,cis*-10,11-epoxy-7-ethyl-3,11-dimethyl-2,6-tridecadieno-ate (formula I); the reagent was used in the preparation of *cis*-II and of *trans,cis*-VII.

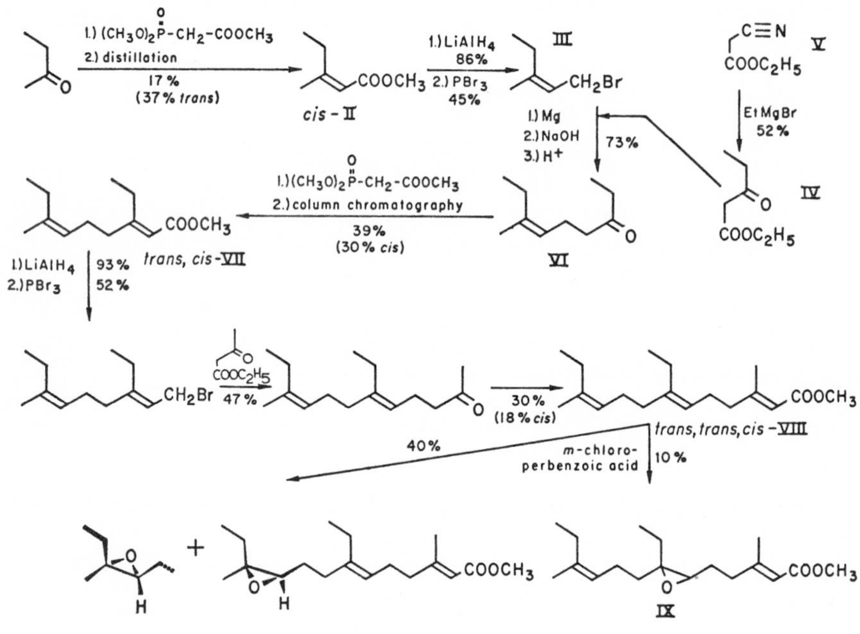

I (*d l*-mixture)

[1]K. H. Dahm, B. M. Trost, and H. Röller, *Am. Soc.*, **89**, 5292 (1967)

Trimethyl(trifluoromethyl)tin [1, 1237–1238, ref. 2]. Definitive paper: D. Seyferth, H. Dertouzos, R. Suzuki, and J. Y.-P. Mui, *J. Org.*, **32**, 2980 (1967).

2,2,2-Triphenyl-1,2-oxaphosph(V)olane (1) [1, 1238, before **Triphenylphosphine**]. Mol. wt. 320.36, m.p. 116–117°.

Preparation.[1]

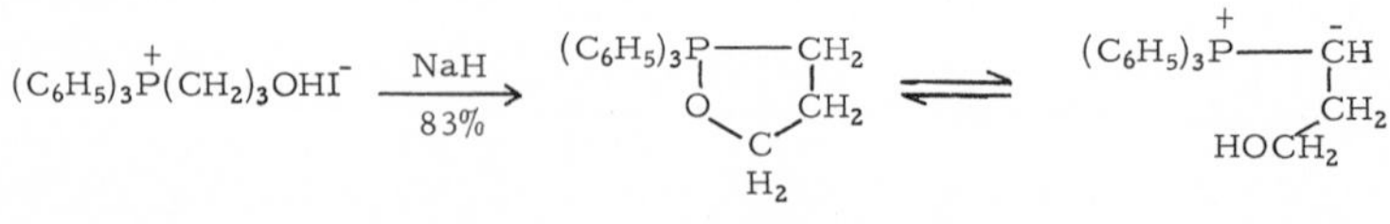

Wittig reaction.[2] The reagent (in its ylide form, 1b) adds to aldehydes to give

γ,δ-unsaturated alcohols in about 1:1 *cis-trans* ratios. Ketones react much less readily.

$$RCHO + (C_6H_5)_3\overset{+}{P}-\overset{-}{C}H(CH_2)_2OH \longrightarrow (C_6H_5)_3PO + \underset{H}{\overset{R}{>}}C=C\underset{H}{\overset{CH_2CH_2OH}{<}} + \underset{H}{\overset{R}{>}}C=C\underset{CH_2CH_2OH}{\overset{H}{<}}$$

[1] A. R. Hands and A. J. H. Mercer, *J. Chem. Soc.*, (C), 1099 (1967)
[2] *Idem, ibid.*, (C), 2448 (1968)

Triphenylphosphine [1, 1238–1247].

Wittig reaction [1, 1239–1243; p. 1239, after first paragraph]. Burton and Krutzsch[6a] generated triphenylphosphinechlorofluoromethylide for reaction with a carbonyl compound in the following two ways:

(1) $(C_6H_5)_3P + CFCl_2CO_2Na \xrightarrow{\text{Triglyme, } 85^0} (C_6H_5)_3P=CFCl \xrightarrow{>C=O}$

$(C_6H_5)_3PO + >C=CFCl$

(2) $(C_6H_5)_3P + CFCl_2H \xrightarrow[\text{Heptane}]{\text{t-BuOK, } 0^0} (C_6H_5)_3P=CFCl \xrightarrow{>C=O}$

$(C_6H_5)_3PO + >C=CFCl$

Usually the first method gives somewhat higher yields with aldehydes or reactive ketones, whereas the second method is better for less reactive ketones because the ylide is generated under milder conditions. Both *cis-* and *trans*-olefins are formed, and the method of generation of the ylide has no effect on the isomer ratio.

Deoxygenation [1, 1242–1244; p. 1244, after citation of ref. 22]. Deoxygenation of nitrosobenzene by triphenylphosphine or tributylphosphine in the presence of diethylamine results in ring enlargement to 2-diethylamino-3H-azepine:[22a]

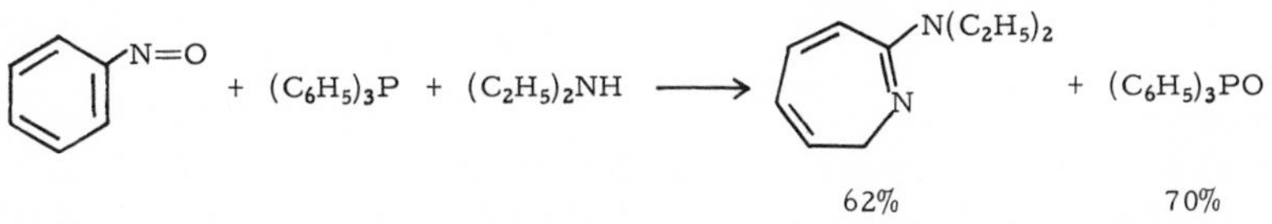

The ring enlargement is presumed to result from an intermediate nitrene, as in a similar reation observed on photolysis of phenyl azide in the presence of an amine.

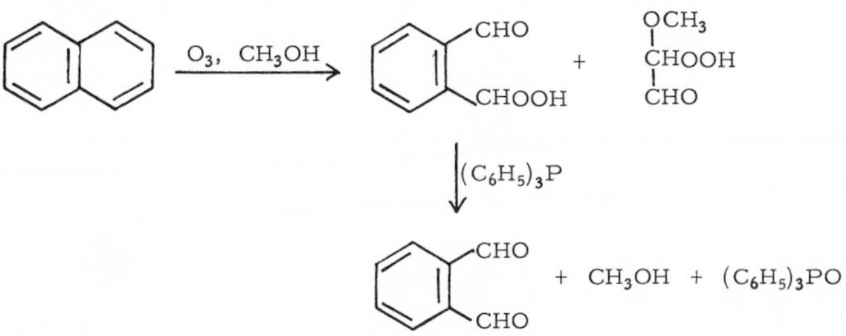

Reduction of ozonides [**1**, 1244, after citation of ref. 23]. Pappas *et al.*[23a] found triphenylphosphine the most satisfactory reducing agent for ozonides derived from nephthalenic compounds.

Dehalogenation [**1**, 1245, after citation of ref. 28]. Darling and Kidwell[28a] obtained diphenylketene in 81.5% yield by debromination of α-bromodiphenylacetyl bromide with triphenylphosphine:

$$(C_6H_5)_2CBrCOBr \ + \ (C_6H_5)_3P \xrightarrow[81.5\%]{} (C_6H_5)_2C{=}O{=}O \ + \ (C_6H_5)_3PBr_2$$

Perchloro-3-pentanone (1) is dehalogenated to perchlorodivinyl ketone (2) by triphenylphosphine.[28b] The triphenylphosphine dichloride formed is advantageously

converted into triphenylphosphine oxide by addition of water before isolation of the ketone (2).

Peptide synthesis [**1**, 1246, before references]. In the presence of triphenylphosphine, copper salts of carboxylic acids undergo condensation with sulfenamides:[33]

$$[CH_3(CH_2)_4COO]_2Cu \ + \ 2\ C_6H_5SN(CH_2CH_2CH_2CH_3)_2 \ + \ 2\ (C_6H_5)_3P \longrightarrow$$

$$2\ CH_3(CH_2)_4CON(CH_2CH_2CH_2CH_3)_2 \ + \ (C_6H_5S)_2Cu \ + \ 2\ (C_6H_5)_3P{=}O$$
$$95\% \qquad\qquad\qquad\qquad\qquad\qquad 93\%$$

The reaction has been applied in the synthesis of peptides, for example, benzyloxycarbonyl-L-phenylalanylglycine ethyl ester (96% yield).

The **Beckmann rearrangement** of 1-chloro-1-nitrosocyclohexane (2) proceeds in

good yield.[34] Thus (2), prepared from cyclohexanone oxime by chlorination, reacts with triphenylphosphine in benzene solution, followed by hydrolysis, to give ε-caprolactam (3) in 96% yield.

[6a]D. J. Burton and H. C. Krutzsch, *Tetrahedron Letters*, 71 (1968)
[22a]R. A. Odum and M. Brenner, *Am. Soc.*, **88**, 2074 (1966)
[23a]J. J. Pappas, W. P. Keaveney, M. Berger, and R. V. Rush, *J. Org.*, **33**, 787 (1968)

[28a]S. D. Darling and R. L. Kidwell, J. Org., 33, 3974 (1968)
[28b]K. Pilgram and H. Ohse, Angew. Chem. internat. Ed., 5, 837 (1966)
[33]T. Mukaiyama, M. Ueki, H. Maruyama, and R. Matsueda, Am. Soc., 90, 4490 (1968)
[34]M. Ohno and I. Sakai, Tetrahedron Letters, 4541 (1965)

Triphenylphosphine–Carbon tetrachloride [1, 1247, before references].

The reagent is well suited to use in the carbohydrate field, particularly since protective groups commonly used with carbohydrates (acetal, ether, ester groups) are stable to the reagent.[3]

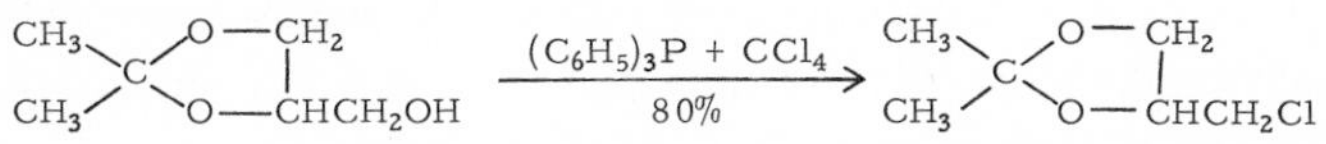

The reagent has been used successfully for conversion of hydroxy carboxylic acid esters into the corresponding chloro esters.[4] Bromo esters are obtained if CBr_4 is used. The replacement occurs with inversion. The method is applicable to hindered α-hydroxy esters. Hooz and Gilani[5] state that the reaction is more rapid if tri-n-octylphosphine is used in place of triphenylphosphine.

Primary and secondary alcohols are converted into nitriles on refluxing with triphenylphosphine, carbon tetrachloride, DMSO, and sodium cyanide.[6] Thus a

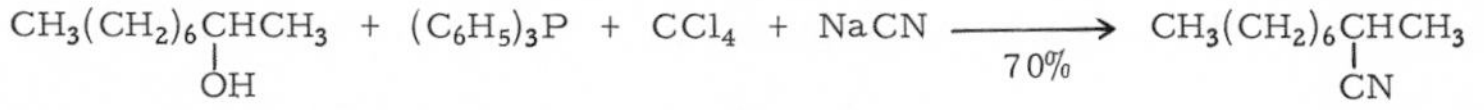

$$CH_3(CH_2)_6\underset{OH}{CHCH_3} + (C_6H_5)_3P + CCl_4 + NaCN \xrightarrow[70\%]{} CH_3(CH_2)_6\underset{CN}{CHCH_3}$$

mixture of 2-octanol, CCl_4, and triphenylphosphine was refluxed briefly, dimethyl sulfoxide was added, and the solution was distilled until a temperature of 90° was obtained; sodium cyanide was then added, and the solution was refluxed and stirred for 2 hrs. longer. The cooled solution was then poured onto ice plus aqueous ferrous sulfate solution and extracted with chloroform. Distillation afforded 2-methyloctanonitrile. The reaction has been applied for introduction of the primary amino group in carbohydrates via the nitrile:

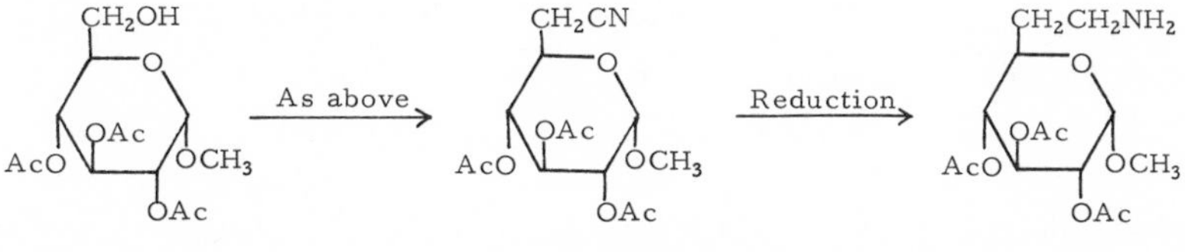

In some instances Downie et al.[7] found difficulty in separating the alkyl chloride from triphenylphosphine oxide. In such cases, triphenylphosphine can be replaced by hexamethylphosphorous triamide, $[(CH_3)_2N]_3P$, which is converted into hexamethylphosphoric triamide, $[(CH_3)_2N]_3PO$.

[3]J. B. Lee and T. J. Nolan, Canad. J. Chem., 44, 1331 (1966); idem. Tetrahedron, 23, 2789 (1967)
[4]J. B. Lee and I. M. Downie, ibid., 23, 359 (1967)
[5]J. Hooz and S. S. H. Gilani, Canad. J. Chem., 46, 86 (1968)
[6]D. Brett, I. M. Downie, and J. B. Lee, J. Org., 32, 855 (1967)
[7]I. M. Downie, J. B. Lee, and M. F. S. Matough, Chem. Commun., 1350 (1968)

Triphenylphosphine dibromide [**1**, 1247–1249]. Supplier: Alfa Inorganics.

[**1**, 1248, after citation of ref. 7]: The reagent is recommended for the conversion of phenols into aryl bromides.[7a] Triphenylphosphine reacts with bromine in acetonitrile at 0°, and addition of the phenol produces a complex which when heated decomposes to the aryl halide, triphenylphosphine oxide, and hydrogen bromide.

[7]*Change to*: J. P. Schaefer, J. G. Higgins, and P. K. Shenov, *Org. Syn.*, **48**, 51 (1968)

[7a]J. P. Schaefer and J. Higgins, *J. Org.*, **32**, 1607 (1967)

Triphenyl phosphite [**1**, 1249, before references].

Rydon[4] gives details of a procedure (A), which is the simplest and the best for use with sterically hindered alcohols (e.g., neopentyl alcohol) and another (B) which is preferable for sensitive alcohols.

[4]H. N. Rydon, procedure submitted to *Org. Syn.*, 1967

Triphenyl phosphite dibromide [**1**, 1249, ref. 1]. Definitive paper: D. K. Black, S. R. Landor, A. N. Patel, and P. F. Whiter, *J. Chem. Soc.*, (C), 2260 (1967).

Triphenyl phosphite methiodide [**1**, 1249–1250, ref. 4]. *Add: See also* J. P. H. Verheyden and J. G. Moffatt, *Am. Soc.*, **88**, 5684 (1966)

Triphenylphosphoranylideneketene, $(C_6H_5)_3P{=}C{=}C{=}O$ [**1**, 1250, before **Triphenyltin chloride**]. Mol. wt. 302.29, m.p. 172–173.5°.

Preparation. The preparation of this stable but reactive organophosphorus com-

$$2\ (C_6H_5)_3P\ +\ CH_2Br_2(N_2)\ \xrightarrow[36\%]{\substack{22.5\ \text{hrs.}\\86\text{-}110^0}}\ (C_6H_5)_3\overset{+}{P}{-}CH_3{-}\overset{+}{P}(C_6H_5)_3\ \xrightarrow{\substack{\text{aq.}\\Na_2CO_3}}$$

$$\underset{Br^-}{}\ \underset{Br^-}{}$$

(1)   (2)

$$(C_6H_5)_3P\overset{H}{\cdots}C\cdots P(C_6H_5)_3\ \xrightarrow[74\%]{K,\ \text{diglyme}\ (150^0)}\ (C_6H_5)_3P{=}C{=}P(C_6H_5)_3$$
$$\underset{Br^-}{+}$$

(3)   (4)

$$\xrightarrow[96.5\%]{CO_2,\ \text{diglyme}}\ \begin{matrix}(C_6H_5)_3P\\ \\ (C_6H_5)_3P\end{matrix}\overset{+}{\underset{\cdots}{C{-}C}}\overset{O}{\underset{O}{}}\ \xrightarrow[19.5\%]{145^0}\ (C_6H_5)_3P{=}C{=}C{=}O\ +\ (C_6H_5)_3PO$$

(5)   (6)   (7)

pound was described first by a Monsanto group. Of several procedures now in the literature, those recommended[1] are formulated. First, triphenylphosphine (1) is heated with methylene bromide under nitrogen to produce methylenebis(triphenylphosphonium)bromide (2).[2] Then, following a procedure of Ramirez *et al.*,[3] the bisbromide is treated with aqueous sodium carbonate to produce the monobromide (3). In the first of two further steps due to Birum and Matthews,[4] the monobromide (3) is treated in diglyme solution with metallic potassium to form hexaphenylcarbodiphosphorane (4), a yellow solid. This product is then stirred with diglyme under nitrogen and carbon dioxide is introduced. As the reaction progresses, the yellow color of (4) gradually gives way to the white of the product (5). The final step of the synthesis involves warming of (5) in diglyme at 14.5° to effect fission to triphenylphosphoranylideneketene (6) and triphenylphosphine oxide (7). The product (6) requires five crystallizations to produce white needles of satisfactory purity (m.p. 172–173.5°), with consequent sacrifice in yield.

Birum and Matthews[1] state that "in most of our work (involving 5), an adduct of (4) with carbon dioxide was heated in diglyme at about 120–125° rather than at the reported temperature of 140–145°. The resulting yellow solution containing an approximately equimolar mixture of (6), and triphenylphosphine oxide can then be used directly as a source of (6), since triphenylphosphine oxide is separated more readily from adducts of (6) than from (6) itself."

Reactions. Novel reactions and structures encountered by the Monsanto workers are indicated by titles of current papers:

"Mesomeric phosphonium dications."[4]
"Reaction with nucleophiles to form ylides."[4]
"Mesomeric phosphonium inner salts."[5]
"A stable four-membered ring ylid-ketone adduct."[6]
"Reactions of triphenyl-2,2-bis(trifluoromethyl)vinylidenephosphorane, synthesized from a cyclic ylide-ketone adduct."[7]
"Cycloaddition reactions of triphenylphosphoranylideneketene."[8]
"Synthesis of triphenylphosphoranylidene-ketenimines."[9]

[1]G. H. Birum and C. N. Matthews, private communication; the page numbers cited are those containing the material cited and not the first page of each communication.
[2]J. S. Driscoll, D. W. Grisley, Jr., J. V. Pustinger, J. E. Harris, and C. N. Matthews, *J. Org.*, **29**, 2429 (1964)
[3]F. Ramirez, N. B. Desai, B. Hansen, and N. McKelvie, *Am. Soc.*, **83**, 3539 (1961)
[4]G. H. Birum and C. N. Matthews, *ibid.*, **88**, 4198 (1966); *Tetrahedron Letters*, 5707 (1966)
[5]C. N. Matthews, J. S. Driscoll, and G. H. Birum, *Chem. Commun.*, 736 (1966)
[6]G. H. Birum and C. N. Matthews, *ibid.*, 137 (1967)
[7]*Idem, J. Org.*, **32**, 3554 (1967)
[8]*Idem, Am. Soc.*, **90**, 3842 (1968)
[9]*Idem, Chem. Ind.*, 653 (1968)

Triphenylpropargylphosphonium bromide (1) [**1**, 1250, before **Triphenyltin chloride**]. Mol. wt. 381.24, m.p. 156–158°.

Preparation in 56% yield from triphenylphosphine, hydrogen bromide, and propargyl bromide:[1]

$$(C_6H_5)_3P \ + \ HBr \ + \ HC{\equiv}CCH_2Br \ \longrightarrow \ [(C_6H_5)_3\overset{+}{P}CH_2C{\equiv}CH]Br^-$$

$$(1)$$

Wittig-type reaction. The reagent reacts with benzaldehyde in liquid ammonia to give a mixture of enynes (2) and (3). Cinnamaldehyde, also expected to give a mix-

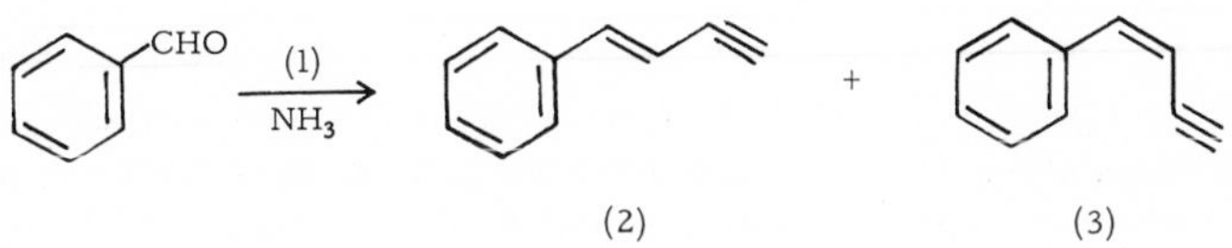

(2)   (3)

ture, gave a product which crystallized readily and was shown by IR spectrum to be the isomer (6).

[1]K. Eiter and H. Oediger, *Ann.*, **682**, 62 (1965)

Triphenyltin hydride [**1**, 1250–1251, before references].
The double bond of mesityl oxide is selectively reduced in quantitative yield:[10]

$$(CH_3)_2C=CHCOCH_3 \xrightarrow{2\ (C_6H_5)_3SnH} (CH_3)_2CHCH_2COCH_3 + (C_6H_5)_3Sn-Sn(C_6H_5)_3$$

The reaction of a ketone with an acid chloride and triphenyltin hydride results in reductive acylation of the ketone in high yield:[11]

$$C_6H_5COCH_3 + CH_3COCl + (C_6H_5)_3SnH \xrightarrow[\text{quant.}]{} C_6H_5\overset{OCOCH_3}{\underset{|}{C}}HCH_3 + (C_6H_5)_3Sn-Sn(C_6H_5)_3$$

[10]M. Pereyre and J. Valade, *Compt. rend.*, **260**, 581 (1965)
[11]L. Kaplan, *Am. Soc.*, **88**, 1833, 4970 (1966)

Note. The section that follows combines, replaces, and corrects errors in entries which appeared on pp. 140 and 1252 of Vol. 1.

Tris(triphenylphosphine)chlororhodium known also as chlorotris(triphenylphosphine)rhodium, $[(C_6H_5)_3P]_3RhCl$ [**1**, 1252]. Mol. wt. 952.20, m.p. 140°, dec. Suppliers: Alfa Inorganics; Fl.; John Matthey, Ltd., Halton Garden, London, England.

This is a crystalline solid which exists in both red and yellow forms of identical chemical properties and which probably differ only in state of subdivision. The complex is soluble in chloroform or methylene chloride to the extent of about 20 g./l. at 25°. The solubility in benzene or toluene is about 2 g./l. at 25°, but is much lower in acetic acid, acetone, or lower aliphatic alcohols. The complex is virtually insoluble in *n*-hexane or cyclohexane. Preparation by interaction of ethanolic solutions of $RhCl_3 \cdot 3H_2O$ and a sixfold molar excess of triphenylphosphine, acting as both complexing and reducing agent and as suppressor of dissociation.[1,2]

Homogeneous catalytic hydrogenation. Wilkinson *et al.*[1] at Imperial College found that the complex is an active catalyst for hydrogenation in homogeneous solution; it promotes exceedingly rapid hydrogenation of alkenes and alkynes.[2,3] Djerassi and Gutzwiller[4] prepared the complex by a different method and investigated its suitability for homogeneous hydrogenation in the steroid series. With this catalyst, unhindered disubstituted double bonds are reduced readily in high yield:

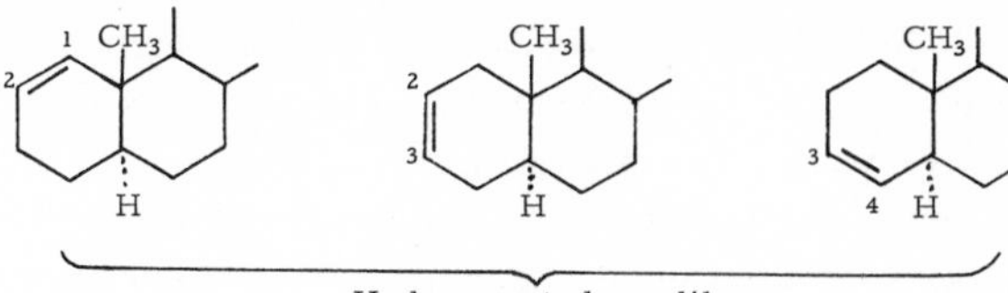

Hydrogenated readily

The unhindered, disubstituted conjugated 1,2-double bond of a Δ^1-3-ketosteroid (a) was reduced readily, but β,β-disubstituted conjugated ketones (b) proved unreactive under the same conditions.

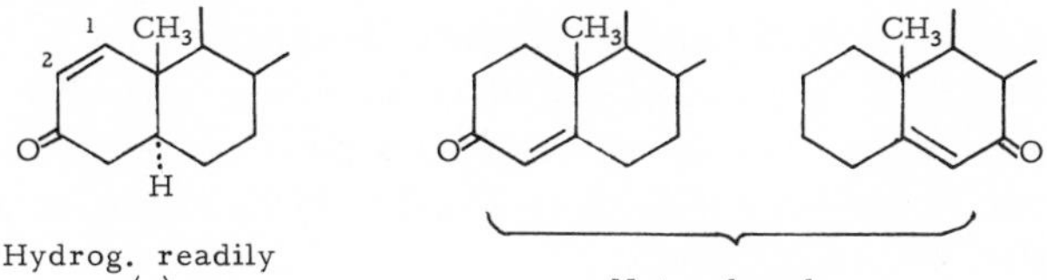

Hydrog. readily
(a)

Not reduced
(b)

An observation along the same lines was made by Piers and Cheng[5] with respect to the dienone ester (1). For the synthesis at hand, they desired to selectively reduce the disubstituted 1,2-double bond without attack of the trisubstituted 4,5-double bond.

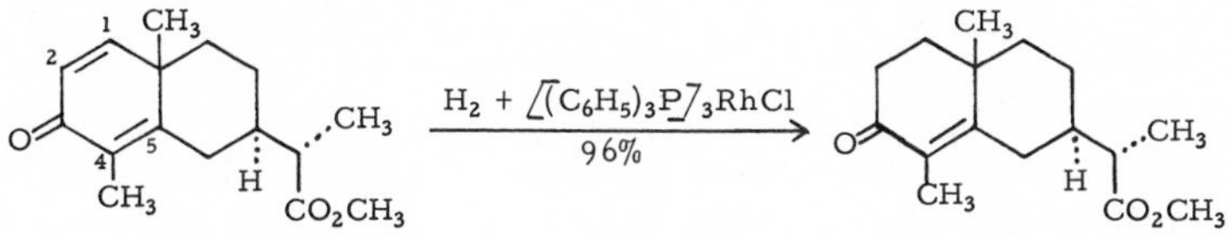

$$H_2 + [(C_6H_5)_3P]_3RhCl$$
96%

(1)   (2)

From results of previous studies, it appeared highly unlikely that usual methods of heterogeneous catalytic hydrogenation would effect the change desired, and so trial was made of the newer method of homogeneous catalytic hydrogenation. Indeed,

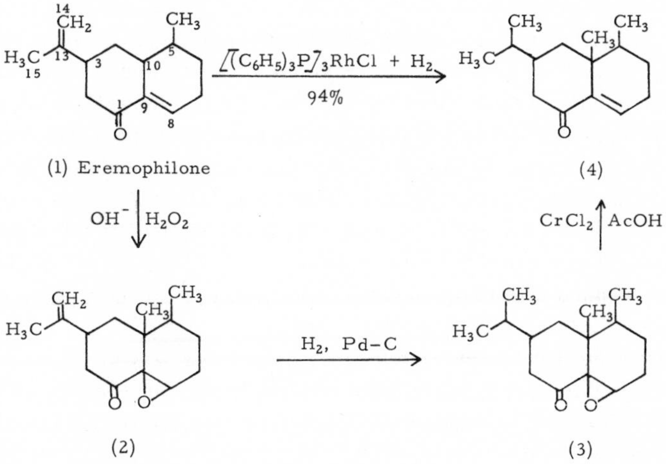

$$[(C_6H_5)_3P]_3RhCl + H_2$$
94%

(1) Eremophilone

(4)

$OH^- \Big| H_2O_2$

$CrCl_2 \uparrow AcOH$

H_2, Pd–C

(2)   (3)

hydrogenation of (1) in benzene solution containing tris(triphenylphosphine)chloro-rhodium proceeded smoothly and afforded the desired monounsaturated ketone (2) in nearly quantitative yield. The catalyst has been used successfully on a micro scale for the hydrogenation of unsaturated aldehydes to saturated aldehydes.[6]

Brown and Piszkiewicz[7] first found a lengthy, indirect route from eremophilone (1) to (4) by selective epoxidation in a basic medium to (2), selective hydrogenation of the 13, 14-double bond (3), and deoxygenation with chromous chloride in acetic acid to give 13,14-dihydroeremophilone (4) in 63% overall yield. They then tried the new technique of homogeneous hydrogenation with the complex rhodium chloride catalyst and obtained the desired 13,14-dihydride (4) in 94% yield. The result accords with the order of reactivity of isolated and conjugated double bonds evident from results for the hydrogenation of steroids (Djerassi and Gutzwiller,[4] above).

Homogeneous catalytic hydrogenation of 1-hexyne in ethanol–benzene proceeds rapidly at 1 atm. pressure and 0° to give n-hexane.[8] If the hydrogenation is stopped short of complete saturation, the mixture contains both hexene-1 and hexane.

Birch and Walker[9] found that 1,4-naphthoquinone is reduced in the presence of the complex catalyst to 1,2,3,4-tetrahydro-1,4-dioxonaphthalene. 1,4-Benzoquinone is

$$\text{H}_2, \; \angle(\text{C}_6\text{H}_5)_3\text{P}\angle_3\text{RhCl}$$
$$70\%$$

converted initially into quinhydrone. Quinones of high oxidation potential cause destruction of the catalyst.

Another example is the hydrogenation of β-nitrostyrene in methyl ethyl ketone to give 1-phenyl-2-nitromethane.[10] The hydrogenation vessel is a round-bottomed

$$\text{C}_6\text{H}_5\text{CH}=\text{CHNO}_2 \; + \; \text{H}_2 \; \xrightarrow[41\%]{\angle(\text{C}_6\text{H}_5)_3\text{P}\angle_3\text{RhCl}} \; \text{C}_6\text{H}_5\text{CH}_2\text{CH}_2\text{NO}_2$$

flask with a magnetic stirrer and a polytetrafluoroethylene catalyst bucket sus-pended from a hook in a side tube. The system is flushed three times with hydro-gen and deaerated between each addition, and the catalyst bucket is dropped into the solution by rotating the hook. The catalyst soon dissolves in the solution and uptake of hydrogen commences. At ambient temperature and an initial hydrogen pressure of about 85 cm., the reaction is complete after about 90 hrs. The bulk of the solvent is distilled off and the catalyst precipitated by the addition of 30 ml. of 60–80° pet-roleum ether. The suspension is filtered through a 2×12 cm. column of alumina and the column is eluted with 10 ml. of petroleum ether. The petroleum ether is distilled off, and the product is distilled, b.p. 76–77°/0.5 mm.

Deformylation. The reagent should give good service in synthesis by providing a means for the efficient removal of a protective formyl group. Shimizu, Mitsuhashi, and Caspi[11] developed an efficient sequence for conversion of (1) into the formyl enone (3) and then needed a completing step of deformylation to (5). They found such a step in reaction of (3) with tris(triphenylphosphine)chlororhodium (4) to give (5) in good yield. Chromatography of the reaction mixture afforded 17β-hydroxy-Δ^1-

(1)   (2)   (3)

$$\xrightarrow[68\%]{(4)\ \angle(C_6H_5)_3P\angle_3RhCl}$$

$+\ (C_6H_5)_3PO\ +\ \angle(C_6H_5)_3P\angle_2Rh\overset{\overset{O}{\|}}{C}Cl$

(5)   (6)   (7)

5β-androstene-3-one (5) and the two by-products: triphenylphosphine oxide (6) and yellow chlorocarbonylbis(triphenylphosphine)rhodium (7).

Decarbonylation.[12] Aliphatic aldehydes are decarbonylated to the corresponding paraffins according to the following formulation:

$$RCHO\ +\ \angle(C_6H_5)_3P\angle_3RhCl\ \longrightarrow\ RH\ +\ \angle(C_6H_5)_3P\angle_2RhCl(CO)\ +\ (C_6H_8)_3P$$

The reaction occurs at room temperature or in refluxing benzene or toluene and yields are generally in the range 65–90%. The reagent also decarbonylates aroyl chlorides to aryl chlorides ($ArCOCl \rightarrow ArCl$) at relatively low temperatures. Acyl halides of type (1) are converted into olefins:[13]

$$C_6H_5CH_2CH_2COCl\ \xrightarrow[71\%]{\angle(C_6H_5)_3P\angle_3RhCl}\ C_6H_5CH=CH_2$$

(1)   (2)

When olefin formation is impossible, the alkyl or aryl halide is formed.

Angular methylation. Dawson and Ireland[14] of the Calfornia Institute of Technology developed a stereoselective method for the introduction of an angular methyl group which depends upon decarbonylation of an aldehyde by tris(triphenylphosphine)chlororhodium. In an illustrative example, *l*-carvone, with the formula arranged as in (b), was converted by annelation and other appropriate steps into the allylic alcohol (2). Rather than prepare the vinyl ether and submit it to Claisen rearrangement as a means of introducing an angular carbon substituent, Dawson and Ireland applied the amide acetal procedure introduced by Eschenmoser (1964) and described (271–272) under **Dimethylacetamide diethyl acetal.** The amide (3) was isolated

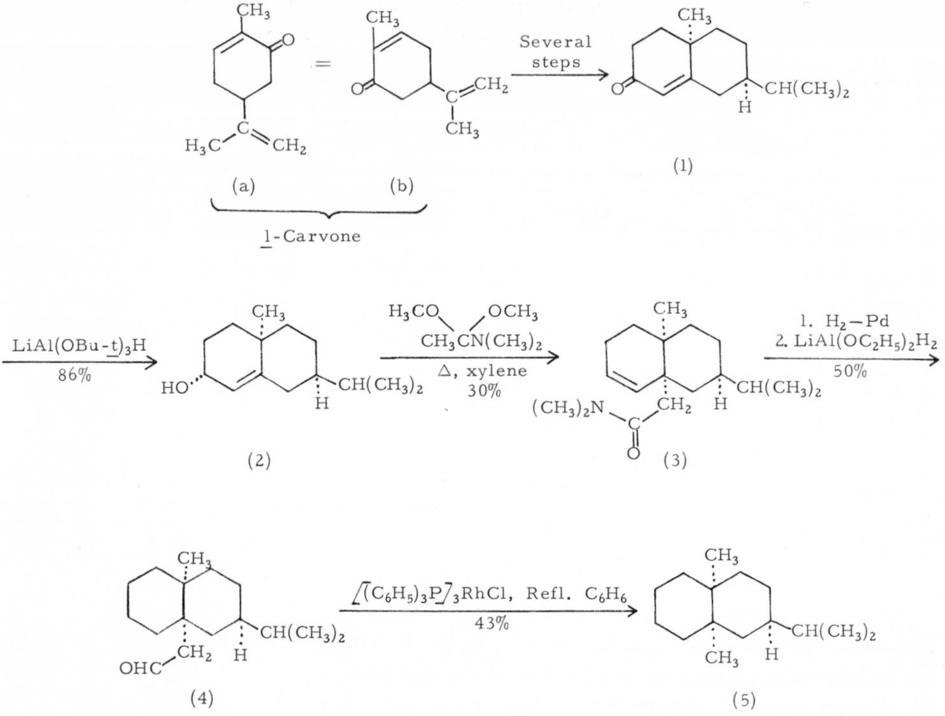

(a)   (b)

1-Carvone

(1)

(2)   (3)

(4)   (5)

as an oil in low yield but was converted by hydrogenation and reduction with lithium diethoxyaluminum hydride into the crystalline aldehyde (4), m.p. 170–173°. Refluxing a benzene solution of the aldehyde (4) with the complex rhodium reagent for 22 hrs. gave a hydrocarbon oil of IR spectrum indicative of the absence of the aldehyde function and with a proton magnetic resonance spectrum showing three additional protons in the methyl region.

Other reactions. Blum *et al.*[15] report that the organometallic complex causes decarbonylation of carbonyl compounds and desulfonation of aromatic sulfonyl chlorides. They noted also that 20-g. samples of ethylbenzene, fluorene, and acenaphthene on being heated with 100 mg. of rhodium complex for 5 hrs. at 130° are oxidized to the extent of 10–60% to acetophenone, fluorenone, and acenaphthenone.

Birch[16] found that the tetralin (1) is oxidized by air in benzene solution in the presence of the complex (5% by weight) to the alcohol (2) in 48% yield with 40% recovery of the starting material. In the absence of solvent and at steam-bath temperature the ketone (3) is obtained in 40% yield with substantial recovery of starting material. The ketone (3) is of interest because it is a key intermediate in an industrial total synthesis of estrone.

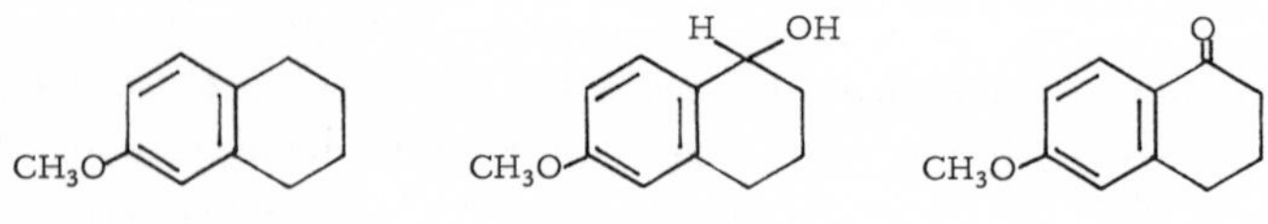

(1)   (2)   (3)

The complex catalyzes the isomerization of 1,4-dienes to 1,3-dienes; the reaction is best carried out in refluxing chloroform (2 hrs., 1% by weight of catalyst).[17]

[1]J. A. Osborn and G. Wilkinson, *Inorg. Syn.*, **10**, 67 (1967)

[2]J. F. Young, J. A. Osborn, F. H. Jardine, and G. Wilkinson, *Chem. Commun.*, 131 (1965); J. A. Osborn, F. H. Jardine, J. F. Young, and G. Wilkinson, *J. Chem. Soc.*, (A), 1711 (1966)

[3]M. A. Bennett and P. A. Longstaff, *Chem. Ind.*, 846 (1965)

[4]C. Djerassi and J. Gutzwiller, *Am. Soc.*, **88**, 4537 (1966)

[5]E. Piers and K. F. Cheng, *Canad. J. Chem.*, **46**, 377 (1968)

[6]F. H. Jardine and G. Wilkinson, *J. Chem. Soc.*, (C), 270 (1967)

[7]M. Brown and L. W. Piszkiewicz, *J. Org.*, **32**, 2013 (1967)

[8]F. H. Jardine, J. A. Osborn, G. Wilkinson, and J. F. Young, *Chem. Ind.*, 560 (1965)

[9]A. J. Birch and K. A. M. Walker, *Tetrahedron Letters*, 3457 (1967)

[10]F. H. Jardine, procedure submitted to *Org. Syn.*, 1968

[11]Y. Shimizu, H. Mitsuhashi, and E. Caspi, *Tetrahedron Letters*, 4113 (1966)

[12]J. Tsuji and K. Ohno, *Tetrahedron Letters*, 3969 (1965); *idem, ibid.*, 2173 (1967); *idem, Am. Soc.*, **88**, 3452 (1966); K. Ohno and J. Tsuji, *ibid.*, **90**, 99 (1968)

[13]J. Blum, *Tetrahedron Letters*, 1605 (1966); J. Blum, E. Oppenheimer, and E. D. Bergmann, *Am. Soc.*, **89**, 2338 (1967)

[14]D. J. Dawson and R. E. Ireland, *Tetrahedron Letters*, 1899 (1968)

[15]J. Blum, H. Rosenman, and E. D. Bergmann, *ibid.*, 3665 (1967)

[16]A. J. Birch and G. S. R. Subba Rao, *ibid.*, 2917 (1968)

[17]*Idem, ibid.*, 3797 (1968)

Trityl chloride [1, 1254–1255, after formula (7)].

Lehrfeld[6a] found that trityl derivatives of carbohydrates can be cleaved in high yield by some commercial silica gels. For example, a solution of 1.000 g. of methyl

2,3,4-tri-O-acetyl-6-O-trityl-α-D-glycopyranoside (1) in 8 ml. of benzene was adsorbed on a column prepared from 100 g. of a Davison grade 12 silica gel, activity grade 1, and the column developed with an additional 170 ml. of benzene. After 16 hrs. at room temperature, the column was eluted with 600 ml. of 10% ethyl acetate in benzene; analysis of the eluate by TLC showed triphenylcarbinol and a trace of starting material. The column was then eluted with 600 ml. of 25% methanol in ethyl acetate. The solvent was removed on a rotatory evaporator and dried in a vacuum dessicator. The residue (553 mg., 98%) was dissolved in a small amount of ether, and hexane was added until the solution became cloudy; needlelike crystals deposited on cooling overnight (81%).

[6a]J. Lehrfeld, *J. Org.*, **32**, 2544 (1967)

Trityl fluoroborate [**1**, 1256–1258, after citation of ref. 5].

Dehydrogenation. Trityl fluoroborate was the most satisfactory reagent found for the dehydrogenation of (1) to the dibenzosesquifulvalene (2).[5a] Yields with chloranil and with NBS–triethylamine were 7% and 1%, respectively.

$$(C_6H_5)_3 C^+ B F_4^-$$
$$30-35\%$$

(1)   (2)

[5a]H. Prinzbach, D. Seip, L. Knothe, and W. Faisst, *Ann*, **698**, 34 (1966)

Tdtyllithium [**1**, 1256, before references].

Tomboulian and Stehower[5] prepared this reagent in quantitative yield by metalation of triphenylmethane with *n*-butyllithium (50–150% excess) in THF or tetrahydro-2-methylfurane as solvent. They recommend that the *n*-butyllithium be prepared from lithium and *n*-butyl chloride in the reaction solvent. If the exchange is carried out at room temperature, excess butyllithium is rapidly consumed by reaction with tetrahydrofurane. With tetrahydropyrane as solvent, tdtyllithium was found to react with benzophenone to form *p*-(diphenylmethyl)diphenylhydroxymethyl-benzene:

[5]P. Tomboulian and K. Stehower, *J. Org.*, **33**, 1509 (1968)

$$NH_2$$

L-Tyrosine hydrazide, $4-HOC_6H_4CH_2CHCONHNH_2$ [bottom of **1**, 1261]. Mol. wt. 195.21. Supplier: A.

Preparation. Tyrosine ethyl ester is treated with freshly distilled hydrazine hydrate; yield 94%.[1]

Resolution.[2] The carbobenzoxy derivatives of DL-proline, DL-alanine, and DL-isoleucine have been resolved by fractional crystallization, in the lower alcohols or water, of the diastereoisomeric salts with L-tyrosine hydrazide. The yield is low in the case of DL-phenylalanine.

[1]T. Curtius, *J. pr.*, [2] **95**, 349 (1917)
[2]K. Vogler and P. Lanz, *Helv.*, **49**, 1348 (1966)

U

Urea [1, 1262–1270].

Effectiveness as a base [1, 1268, after line 2]. In studying the acetolysis of ethyl arenesulfonates, Bartlett and co-workers[23a] wished to add a base sufficiently strong to convert the sulfonic acid produced into an inert sulfonate salt but one that is non-nucleophilic and not able to effect direct displacement (which can happen with sodium or potassium acetate). For this purpose they used urea successfully.

Newman and Lola[23b] observed that, when 3-chloro-3-phenylphthalide (1) is allowed to react with methanol in the cold, the pseudo ester (2) produced on standing in the presence of the hydrogen chloride reacts rapidly by addition of methanol to the carbonyl group to give the normal methyl ester (3). They found that added urea effectively neutralizes the mineral acid and suppresses the reaction of (2) to give (3). This

(1)   (2)   (3)

observation emphasizes the effectiveness of urea as a base for neutralization of strong acids in alcoholic solution. Tetramethylurea is not so effective as urea but it does have some effect and, since it is more soluble than urea in organic solvents, it may prove to be a desirable reagent in certain cases.

[23a]W. S. Trahanovsky, M. P. Doyle, and P. D. Bartlett, *J. Org.*, **32**, 150 (1967)
[23b]M. S. Newman and L. K. Lola, *Tetrahedron Letters*, 3267 (1967)

V

Vanadium oxyacetylacetonate (Vanadyl acetylacetonate), $VO(CH_3COCH_2COCH_2)_2$ [**1,** 1271, before **Vilsmeier** reagent]. Mol. wt. 265.16, m.p. 255°, dec. Supplier: Alfa Inorganics.

Amine oxides. A convenient procedure for the oxidation of a tertiary amine which affords the amine oxide easily in completely anhydrous form is illustrated as follows.[1] A mixture of 23.5 g. of N,N-dimethyldodecylamine (Eastman, 90%),

$$\underset{\underline{n}\text{-}C_{12}H_{25}\overset{\displaystyle CH_3}{\underset{|}{N}}-CH_3}{} \xrightarrow{(CH_3)_3COOH, \ (CH_3)_3COH, \ VO(CH_3COCH_2CO)_2} \underset{\underline{n}\text{-}C_{12}H_{25}\overset{\displaystyle CH_3}{\underset{|}{\underset{\downarrow}{N}}}-CH_3}{O}$$

9.2 g. of *t*-butyl hydroperoxide (Lucidol, 94%), 27 g. of *t*-butanol, and 0.5 g. of van-adium oxyacetylacetonate is stirred and refluxed for 15 min. and then cooled to room temperature. Removal of the *t*-butanol on a flash evaporator (30–40 mm.) gives 21 g. of the amine oxide, m.p. 123–125°, which is triturated with 50 ml. of *n*-pentane, filtered, and dried under vacuum; yield 17.7 g.

[1]M. N. Sheng and J. G. Zajacek, *J. Org.,* **33,** 588 (1968); *idem,* procedure submitted to *Org. Syn.,* 1967

Vinyllithium [**1,** 1273–1274, before references].

Vinyllithium reacts with tetraphenylphosphonium bromide in ether solution to give styrene and triphenylphosphine:[4]

$$[(C_6H_5)_4P]Br \ + \ CH_2=CHLi \ \longrightarrow \ \underset{65\%}{C_6H_5CH=CH_2} \ + \ \underset{80\%}{(C_6H_5)_3P} \ + \ LiBr$$

The reaction is general; thus, if tetra-*p*-tolylphosphonium bromide is used, *p*-methyl-styrene is obtained (61% yield). Isopropenyllithium can be used in the same way.

[4]D. Seyferth, J. Fogel, and J. K. Heeren, *Am. Soc.,* **88,** 2207 (1966)

Vinyl triphenylphosphonium bromide [**1,** 1274–1275, before references].

Synthesis of five- and six-membered cycloalkenes has been achieved by the re-action of vinyl triphenylphosphonium bromide with ketomalonic esters of type (1), $n = 1$ to give 2[(2, $n = 1$): diethyl 3-methyl cyclopentenodicarboxylate].

$$\underset{(1) \ n \ = \ 1 \ or \ 2}{\overset{\displaystyle O}{\overset{\|}{CH_3C}}(CH_2)_nCH(CO_2C_2H_5)_2 \ + \ CH_2=CH\overset{+}{P}(C_6H_5)_3Br^-} \xrightarrow{\ NaH\ }$$

$$[\overset{\displaystyle O}{\overset{\|}{CH_3C}}(CH_2)_nC(COOC_2H_5)_2CH_2\overset{-}{C}H\overset{+}{P}(C_6H_5)_3] \longrightarrow$$

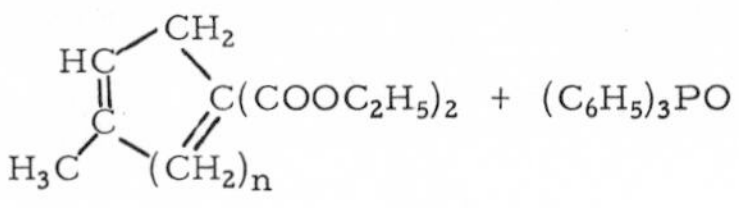

$$(2) \quad n = 1, \quad \text{yield } 69\%$$
$$n = 2, \quad \text{yield } 51\%$$

The reaction fails when $n = 3$.[5]

A general chain extension reaction has been developed[6] with use of vinyl triphenylphosphonium bromide to give an intermediate ylide followed by a Wittig reaction:

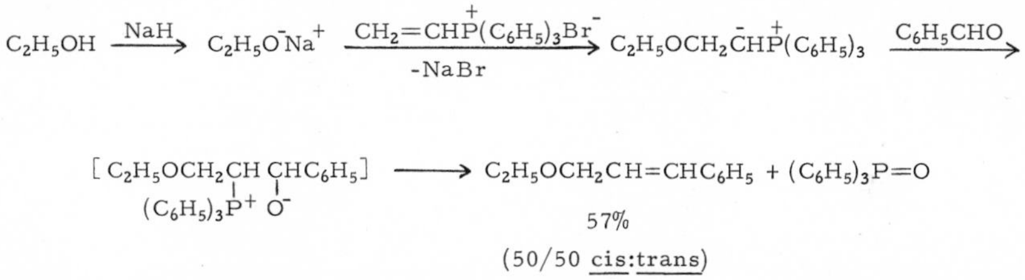

$$[C_2H_5OCH_2CH \underset{(C_6H_5)_3\overset{+}{P} \ \overset{-}{O}}{CHC_6H_5}] \longrightarrow C_2H_5OCH_2CH=CHC_6H_5 + (C_6H_5)_3P{=}O$$

57%

(50/50 cis:trans)

Schweizer and Liehr[7] showed that the reagent reacts with the sodium salt of an α-hydroxy ketone to give a 2,5-dihydrofurane (3), for example the 3-phenyl derivative.

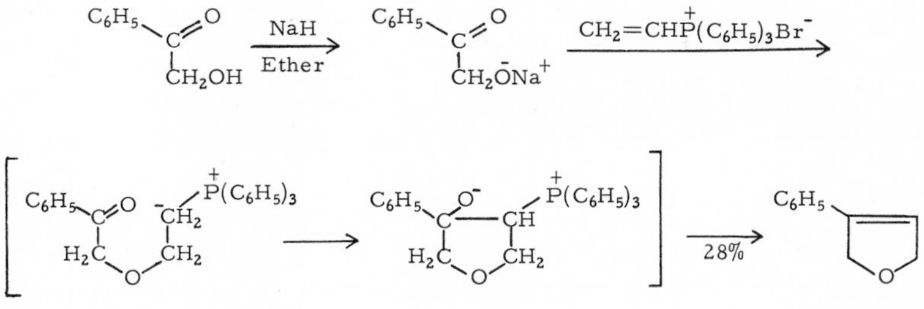

(3)

Schweizer and Thompson[8] prepared 2H-1-benzopyrane by reaction of the sodium salt of salicylaldehyde with the reagent in DMF to give 2-H-1-benzopyrane (4).

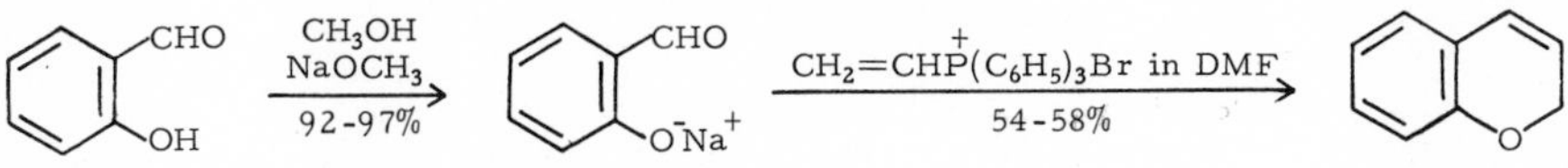

(4)

[5] E. E. Schweizer and G. J. O'Neill, *J. Org.*, **30**, 2082 (1965)

[6] E. E. Schweizer, L. D. Smucker, and R. L. Votral, *ibid.*, **31**, 467 (1966)

[7] E. E. Schweizer and J. G. Liehr, *ibid.*, **33**, 583 (1968)

[8] E. E. Schweizer and J. G. Thompson, procedure submitted to *Org. Syn.*, 1968

X

Xenic acid, H_6XeO_6 [**1**, 1276, before **Zinc**] Mol. wt. 233.35.

Preparation by hydrolysis of either xenon tetrafluoride or xenon hexafluoride.[1]

Oxidizing action.[2] Xenic acid reacts readily with *vic*-diols in neutral or alkaline solution; the products are xenon (gas) and carboxylic acids.

[1]F. B. Dudley, G. Gard, and G. H. Cady, *Inorg. Chem.*, **2**, 228 (1963)
[2]B. Jaselskis and S. Vas, *Am. Soc.*, **86**, 2078 (1964)

Z

Zinc, dust [**1**, 1276–1284].

Zinc dust–acetic acid cleavage of a sulfone [1278, after ref. 19a]. The α-aroyl sulfone is cleaved by zinc and acetic acid in better yield than by aluminum amalgam (57%).[23b]

$$C_6H_5COCHSO_2CH_3 \xrightarrow[78\%]{Zn-AcOH, \ EtOH} C_6H_5COCH_2CH_3$$
$$\overset{|}{CH_3}$$

Zinc dust–mineral acid [**1**, 1279–1280, at end].

Substituted indoles can be reduced to indolenes in satisfactory yield with tin or zinc dust and hydrochloric acid, but the reaction fails with indole itself, which poly-merizes under these conditions. However, the combination of zinc dust and 85% phosphoric acid reduces indole to indoline in 64–69% yield. The method was applied to two substituted indoles.[28a]

Serini reaction [**1**, 1282, after citation of ref. 42]. The activation of 1100 g. of granular 30-mesh zinc with 4.4 liters of concd. sulfuric acid containing 2 ml. of 90% nitric acid and its use in the Serini reaction is described by Rubin and Brown.[42a]

The Serini reaction is actually a general synthetic method. Thus Ghera *et al.*[42b]

found that the Serini reaction was the most satisfactory method for removal of the tertiary hydroxyl groups of the tetrol diacetate (5) to give the diketone (6). The reaction was also used in one step in a total synthesis of the β-amyrin derivatives (9) and (10).[42c] The diacetate (7) was converted into a diketone, which on equilibrium with base gave the more stable epimer (8). Cyclodehydration of the diketone was effected with perchloric acid and acetic anhydride in benzene–acetic acid at room temperature.

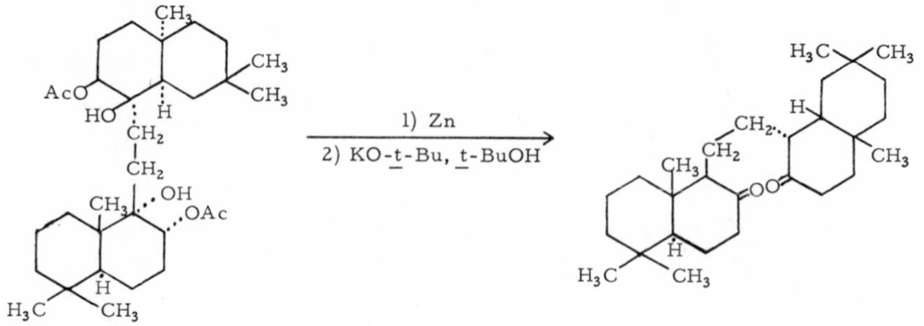
1) Zn
2) KO-t-Bu, t-BuOH

(7) (8)

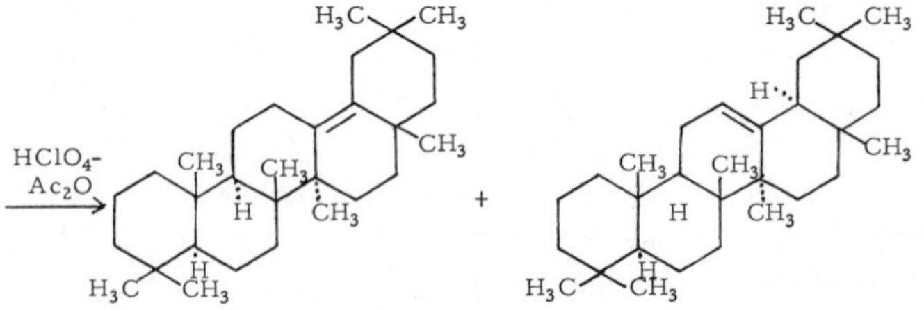
$HClO_4$-
Ac_2O

(9) (10)

Ghera[42d] has now found that the reaction can be applied to acyclic diol acetates and thus affords a general synthesis of aldehydes and ketones. The diol acetates must be pure and activated zinc is essential.

Examples:

$$C_5H_{11}C(CH_3)(OH)CH_2OAc \xrightarrow{62\%} C_5H_{11}CH(CH_3)CHO$$

$$(C_6H_5)_2C(OH)CH_2OAc \xrightarrow{70\%} (C_6H_5)_2CH_2CHO$$

$$C_6H_5CH(OAc)-C(OH)(CH_3)_2 \xrightarrow{64\%} C_6H_5COCH(CH_3)_2$$

C-Alkylation [**1**, 1283, before references]. A Dartmouth group[52] discovered that treatment of an α-bromoketone such as (1) or (3) in benzene–DMSO (10:1) with methyl iodide and zinc dust gives the α-methylketone (2, 4).

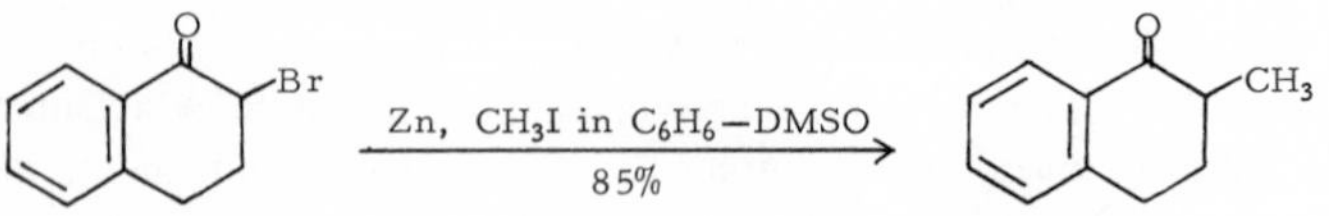
Zn, CH_3I in C_6H_6–DMSO
85%

(1) (2)

(3)   (4)

With some α-bromoketones, self-condensation to a furane overshadows alkylation. Thus α-bromocycloheptanone (5) at a concentration of only $0.016\,M$ reacts chiefly to give the α-methyl ketone (6, 43%), but in a more concentrated solution ($0.28\,M$) gives the furane (7, 58%).

(5)   (6)   (7)

Clemmensen reduction. Japanese chemists[53] have activated commercial zinc powder (Kishida Chem. Co. Ltd.) by washing with 2% hydrochloric acid for 3–4 min., and then washing successively with water, ethanol, acetone, and ether. The powder is then warmed at 90° for 10 min. under reduced pressure.

Unhindered keto groups of steroids are reduced to methylene groups by the reagent in acetic anhydride saturated with hydrogen chloride.[54] Highest yields are obtained with freshly prepared reagent.[53] In addition, α-halo- and α-acetoxyketosteroids are reduced; thus 2α-bromocholestane-3-one affords cholestane in 86% yield. The reaction was discovered in the course of studies on the alkaloid isodaphniphylline.[55]

Synthesis of cumulenes. 1,2,3-Trienes have been prepared in good to excellent yields by dehalogenation of 1,4-dichloro-2-alkynes (obtained from the corresponding 1,4-dihydroxy-2-alkynes by reaction with thionyl chloride). Two reagents have been used apparently with equal success, zinc dust or sodium iodide, both in DMSO at 80°.[56]

$$>\overset{\underset{\mid}{Cl}}{C}-C\equiv CCH_2Cl \longrightarrow\ >C=C=C=CH_2$$

Isomerization of α,β-unsaturated ketones and esters. Schering chemists[57] observed that 6β-bromo-Δ⁴-cholestene-3-one (1) on reductive debromination with zinc in aqueous ethanol is converted into Δ⁵-cholestene-3-one (2), but that some isomerization to the conjugated ketone occurs simultaneously. However, it was possible to obtain the nonconjugated ketone in 25% yield. The cross-conjugated ketone 6β-bromo-Δ¹,⁴-androstadiene-3,17-dione (3) was converted into Δ¹,⁵-androstadiene-3,17-dione (4).

Similarly γ-bromo-α,β-unsaturated esters are converted into β,γ-unsaturated

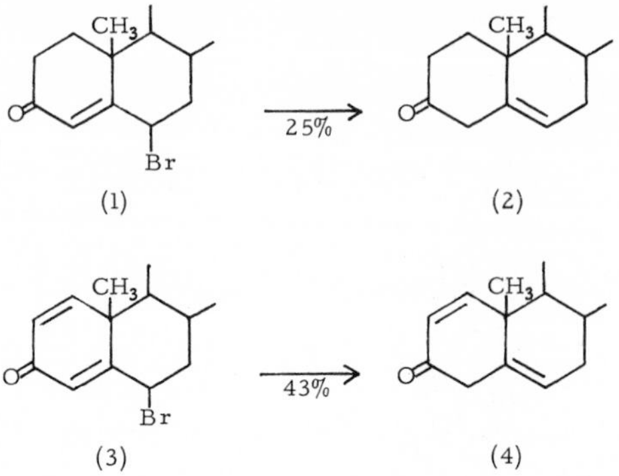

(1)   (2)

(3)   (4)

esters by treatment with zinc and acetic acid.[58] Yields of products are 75–95%. Examples:

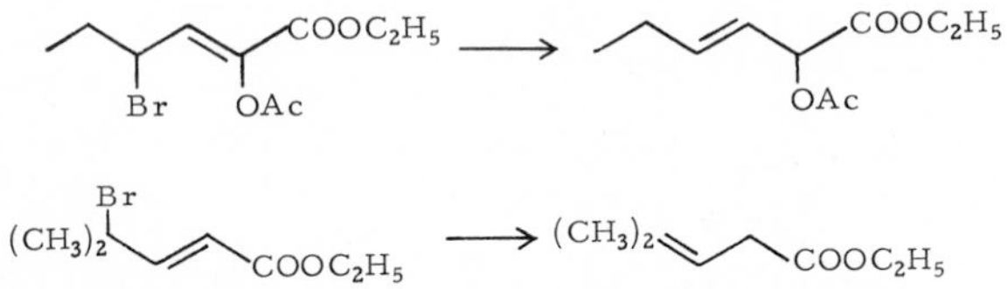

[23b]H. O. House and J. K. Larson, *J. Org.*, **33**, 61 (1968)

[28a]L. J. Dolby and G. W. Gribble, *J. Heterocyclic Chem.*, **3**, 124 (1966)

[42a]M. B. Rubin and A. P. Brown, procedure submitted to *Org. Syn.*, 1967; M. B. Rubin and E. C. Blossey, *Steroids*, **1**, 453 (1963)

[42b]E. Ghera, M. Gibson, and F. Sondheimer, *Am. Soc.*, **84**, 2953 (1962)

[42c]E. Ghera and F. Sondheimer, *Tetrahedron Letters*, 3887 (1964)

[42d]E. Ghera, *Chem. Commun.*, 1639 (1968)

[52]T. A. Spencer, R. W. Britton, and D. S. Watt, *Am. Soc.*, **89**, 5727 (1967)

[53]S. Yamamura, *Chem. Commun.*, 1494 (1968)

[54]S. Yamamura, S. Ueda, and Y. Hirata, *ibid.*, 1049 (1967); S. Yamamura and Y. Hirata, *J. Chem. Soc.*, 2887 (1968)

[55]S. Yamamura, H. Irikawa, and Y. Hirata, *Tetrahedron Letters*, 3361 (1967)

[56]P. P. Montijn, L. Brandsma, and J. F. Arens, *Rec. trav.*, **86**, 129 (1967)

[57]A. L. Nussbaum, G. B. Topliss, T. L. Popper, and E. P. Oliveto, *Am. Soc.*, **81**, 4574 (1959)

[58]C. E. Moppett and J. K. Sutherland, *J. Chem. Soc.*, (C), 3040 (1968)

Zinc, other forms [**1**, 1286–1287, ref. 3]. *Add*: Similarly dibromoketene has been prepared from tribromoacetyl bromide with zinc activated with copper.[3a]

[3a]W. T. Brady, *J. Org.*, **31**, 2676 (1966)

Zinc amalgam [**1**, 1287–1289, before references].

Svensson[9] attempted reduction of the keto group of 3-perinaphthanone-1-car-

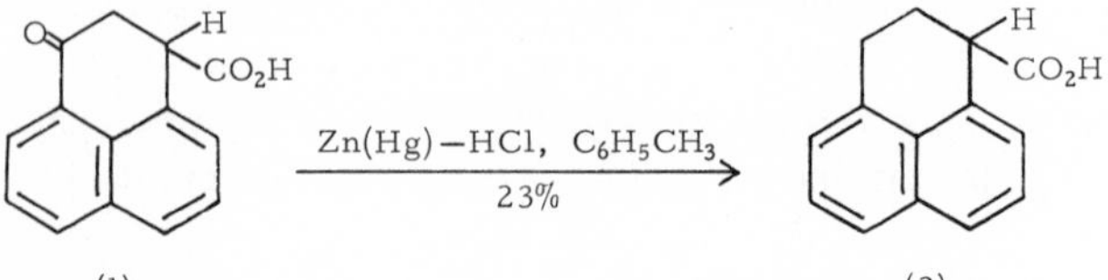

(1)   (2)

boxylic acid (1) by the Huang-Minlon method and by desulfurization of the ethylene-thioketal but without success. He was able to obtain the desired acid (2), if in low yield, by the Martin modification of the Clemmensen method.

[9]T. Svensson, *Arkiv Kemi*, **26**, 27 (1967)

Zinc bromide, $ZnBr_2$ [**1**, 1289, before **Zinc chloride**]. Mol. wt. 225.19, m.p. 394°. Suppliers: Alfa Inorganics, B, F.

Roberts and Mazur[1] reported that treatment of a mixture of cyclopropylcarbinyl chloride and cyclobutyl chloride (approximately 2:1) with zinc chloride in concd. hydrochloric acid (Lucas reagent[2]) gave allylcarbinyl chloride in 46% yield. They also isomerized the corresponding bromides with zinc bromide in 48% hydrobromic acid.

Johnson[3] wished to apply this rearrangement in one step of a stereoselective synthesis of *trans*-trisubstituted double bonds but encountered some undesired isomerization due to the strongly acidic conditions. Anhydrous zinc bromide in ether was then found more satisfactory. Thus the carbinol (1) was treated with phosphorus tribromide in the presence of collidine to give a mixture of bromides (2) and (3).

This mixture on treatment with zinc bromide at 0° gave, in 85–90% overall yield, a product which was essentially the *trans*-dienic bromide (4).

This procedure was used as a key step in a synthesis of racemic juvenile hormone (7).[4] The carbinol (5) was transformed by bromination and rearrangement as described above into the *trans,trans*-bromodienic ester (6). This was converted in several steps into the hormone (7).

[1]J. D. Roberts and R. H. Mazur, *Am. Soc.*, **73**, 2509 (1951)
[2]H. J. Lucas, *ibid.*, **52**, 802 (1930)
[3]S. F. Brady, M. A. Ilton, and W. S. Johnson, *Am. Soc.*, **90**, 2882 (1968)
[4]W. S. Johnson, T. Li, D. J. Faulkner, S. F. Campbell, *ibid.*, **90**, 6225 (1968)

Zinc chloride [**1**, 1289–1292, before references].

Blanc reaction. In carrying out the reaction of *p*-bromotoluene with formaldehyde and a Lewis acid catalyst to obtain the isomeric chloromethyl derivatives for use in a synthesis of methylcholanthrene, Fieser and Seligman[18] fused a mixture of anhydrous zinc chloride with 1% of aluminum chloride and let it cool, added *p*-bromotoluene and paraformaldehyde, and passed a slow stream of hydrogen chloride into the mixture while heating it at 45–50° for 18 hrs. Use of the special catalyst increased the yield about threefold over that obtained with zinc chloride alone.

Preparation of cycloheptane-1,3-dione. Indian chemists[19] have prepared this dione from dihydroresorcinol (1) by conversion into the monoethylene ketal (2) followed by reaction with ethyl diazoacetate catalyzed by anhydrous zinc chloride. They note that the quality of zinc chloride is important; consistently good yields were obtained with material supplied by Riedel-de Haën. The product (3) is converted into the dione (4) by hydrolysis and decarboxylation with aqueous potassium hydroxide.

[18]L. F. Fieser and A. M. Seligman, *Am. Soc.*, **57**, 942 (1935)
[19]R. Selvarajan, K. V. Narayan, and S. Swaminathan, procedure submitted to *Org. Syn.*, 1968

Zinc–copper couple [**1**, 1292–1293, before references].

Synthesis of allenes. A report by Ginzburg[5] that reduction of dimethylethynyl-carbinyl chloride (5) with zinc–copper couple in ethanol affords 3-methyl-1,2-

$$\underset{\substack{|\\ \text{Cl}\\ \\ (5)}}{\overset{\substack{\text{CH}_3\\ |}}{\text{CH}_3\text{C}-\text{C}\equiv\text{CH}}} \quad \xrightarrow{\text{Zn}-\text{Cu, EtOH}} \quad \underset{(6)}{\overset{\substack{\text{CH}_3\\ |}}{\text{CH}_3\text{C}=\text{C}=\text{CH}_2}}$$

$$\underset{\substack{|\\ \text{Cl}\\ \\ (7)}}{\text{CH}_3\text{CH}_2\text{CH}_2\text{CH}-\text{C}\equiv\text{CH}} \quad \xrightarrow[71\%]{\text{Zn}-\text{Cu, EtOH}} \quad \underset{(8)}{\text{CH}_3\text{CH}_2\text{CH}_2\text{CH}=\text{C}=\text{CH}_2}$$

butadiene (6) was confirmed by Hennion and Sheehan,[6] who applied the method to the synthesis of 1,2-hexadiene (8). These authors suggest the following mechanism for the interesting rearrangement:

$$\text{C}_2\text{H}_5-\overset{\frown}{\text{O}}-\text{H}$$
$$\downarrow$$
$$\text{R}-\text{CHCl}-\text{C}\equiv\text{CH} + \text{Zn} + \text{C}_2\text{H}_5\text{OH} \longrightarrow \underset{\text{ZnCl}}{\text{R}-\text{CH}-\text{C}\equiv\text{CH}} \longrightarrow \text{R}-\text{CH}=\text{C}=\text{CH}_2 + \text{C}_2\text{H}_5\text{O}-\text{Zn}-\text{Cl}$$

A more recent example is reported by a British group.[7]

$$\text{CH}_3\text{CHCl}-\text{C}\equiv\text{CCH}_2\text{CH}_2\text{OAc} \xrightarrow[49\%]{} \text{CH}_3\text{CH}=\text{C}=\text{CHCH}_2\text{CH}_2\text{OH}$$

[5]Y. I. Ginzburg, *J. Gen. Chem. USSR*, **10**, 513 (1940)
[6]G. F. Hennion and J. J. Sheehan, *Am. Soc.*, **71**, 1964 (1949)
[7]P. D. Landor, S. R. Landor, and E. P. Pepper, *J. Chem. Soc.*, 185 (1967)

Errata for Volume 1, First Corrected Printing

Page 40, first ref. 1, *for* Inuakai *read* Inukai.

Page 131, *Chloroiridic acid, read:* Supplier: Johnson Matthey Chemicals Ltd.

Page 139, second ref. 2, *read* L. Lábler and F. Šorm.

Page 151, line 4, *read* Reduction.[2]

Page 160, line 2 up, *change* cupric acetate bromide *to* cupric acetate.

Page 166, line 6. *Read* **Cuprous chloride,** Cu_2Cl_2.

Page 183, line 7-8. *Read* each of dihydro and tetrahydro derivatives.

Page 212, line 3 up. *Read:* but not with methyl iodide, boron trifluoride, or sulfur trioxide.

Page 224, line 14. *For* di-*n*-propylcyclopropene *read* di-*n*-propylcyclopropenone.

Page 250. *Read* **Diethyl ethoxycarbonylmethyl phosphonate,** *see* Triethyl phosphonoacetate.

Page 251. Second formulation, over first arrow. *For* $(CO_2CH_3)_3$ *read* $(CO_2CH_3)_2$.

Page 259, line 5. *Read* **Iron enneacarbonyl.**

       last line. *Read:* Structure I is favored by the British group.

Page 290, line 1. *Change* to **Preparation of hydrazones.**

Page 310, ref. 46. *Read:* E. Scoffone.

Page 348, read formulation as follows:

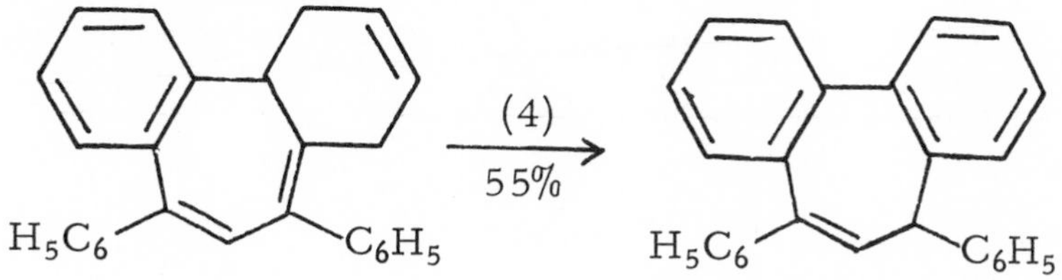

(5)   (6)

Page 389, formula over second arrow: the group to the left *should be* ethyl *not* methyl.

Page 427, ref. 3. *Read* M. Makita.

Page 512, group of four formulas. Place the notation (2) under third formula.

Page 561, formula (2): the N should carry two pairs of electrons: RCON̈:

Page 563, formula (3) *should read* $C_6H_5CF_2CH_2C_6H_5$ and the name (line 6 up) *should be* 1,2-diphenyl-1,1-difluoroethane.

Page 594. Second formula (1): $C_6H_5CH_2CCH_2C_6H_5$

$$\|$$

           NOH

Page 658, ref. 1, *read* M. Akhtar.

Page 685, line 4 up. *Read* triethyl α-bromoorthopropionate.

Page 744. Under *Formylation,* change the second and third formulas to read:

$$\overset{O}{\overset{\|}{HC}}OC_6H_4NO_2\text{-}\underline{p}$$

$$\overset{O}{\overset{\|}{HC}}-\overset{H}{\overset{\|}{N}}(CH_2)_3 \text{ or } {}_4\overset{}{C}HCO_2H$$

$$NH_2$$

Page 1055, ref. 16. *Read* L. Caglioti.
Page 1109, Table 1, *for* Apriotic *read* Aprotic.
Page 1113, line 4, *for* cuprous bromide *read* stannous bromide.
Page 1140, line 9, *for* occurs *read* does not occur.
Page 1166, under *Derivatives*. Change third line of formulas to read:

$$\xrightarrow[80\text{-}90\%]{H_2NCH_2CO_2H-NaOH} HO_2CCH_2C\begin{matrix}{=}NH\\ \diagdown NH_2\end{matrix} \quad + \quad C_2H_5SH$$

Page 1167, third line under Thoria *should read:* In contrast, dehydration of 2-alcohols over alumina.
Page 1187, ref. 4, *read: 81*, 5512 (1959)
Pages 1216-1217. Transpose the two reagents:
Triethyl phosphonoacetate
Triethyl phosphoenol pyruvate
Page 1274, formula following **Vinyl triphenylphosphonium bromide.** Insert plus sign over letter P.
Page 1286, last equation. *Change* C_2H_4OH *to* C_2H_5OH.
Page 1298, *read*: Johnson Matthey Chemicals Limited, 74 Hatton Garden, London, EC1.
Page 1309, line 7 up. *Change* Phenyl sulfur trichloride *to read* Phenyl sulfur trifluoride.
Page 1313. Oxidation reagents, *read* Pertrifluoroacetic acid, Ruthenium tetroxide, Silver trifluoroacetate.
Page 1315. Reducing agents, *read* Sodium hydrosulfite.

Author Index

Page 1321 Akhtar, M.
Allen, D. S., Jr., 814, 986
Page 1329 Caglioti, L.
Page 1334 DeTar, D. F.
Page 1342 Greenwald, R., 318, 1246
Greenwald, R. B., 244
Page 1359 Mokita, M., 427. *Change to* p. 1357, Makita, M., 427
Page 1369 Sahyun, M. R. V., 309, 927
Page 1370 Delete Scaffone, E., 310
Page 1372 Scoffone, E., 266, 310
Page 1378 Tišler, M., 370
Delete ref. 370 under Tishler, M.

Subject Index

Page 1416 Disiamylborane, *57-59*, 201, 262
Page 1426 *Read* Iron enneacarbonyl
Page 1429 Lysine monohydrochloride, *change* 939 to 959

Important Note: M. Guntrum of Eastman Kodak Co. has informed us that *p*-toluenesulfonyl azide (*1*, 1178–1179; *2*, 415–417) is extremely shock sensitive—in fact, in the general range of nitroglycerin. The company is offering as a substitute *p*-carboxylbenzenesulfonyl azide, which is a comparatively safe reagent.

ADDITIONS TO SUPPLIERS

(Fl.)	Fluka AG
(K and K)	K and K Laboratories
(K.-L.)	Koch-Light
(Sch.)	Schuchardt

EGA-Chemie KG, Steinheim, Germany
Fluka AG, Buchs, Switzerland
Hoechst AG Farbwerke
Koch-Light Labs, Ltd., Colnbrook, Buckinghamshire, England
E. Merck AG., Darmstadt, Germany
Riedel-de Haën AF, Seelze bei Hannover, Germany.
Schuchardt, Dr. Theodor, Munich, Germany
Thallium Ltd., Carrow Road, Norwich, England
United States Testing Co., 1941 Park Ave., Hoboken, N.J. 07030

INDEX OF REAGENTS ACCORDING TO TYPES

ACETOACETYLATION: Diketene. Mercuric acetate.

ACETONIDE FORMATION: Acetone. Cupric sulfate.

ACETOXYLATION: Lead acetate, Lead tetraacetate.

ACETYLATION: Acetic acid. Acetic anhydride. Acetic—phosphoric anhydride. Boron trifluoride etherate. Ketene. p-Nitrophenyl acetate.

ACETYLENE ADDITIONS: Hexafluoro-2-butyne. Iodine azide. 1-Iodoheptafluoropropane.

ACETYLENIC COUPLING: n-Butyllithium. Cuprous chloride.

ACID ACCEPTORS: Urea.

ACIDS, STRONG, MINERAL: Fluorosulfuric acid. Hydrobromic acid. Hydrochloric acid. Hydrogen fluoride.

ACTIVE-METHYLENE REAGENT: Dimethylformamide diethyl acetal.

ACYLATION, t-ALCOHOLS: Calcium hydride.

ACYLATION, AMIDES: Thallous ethoxide.

ACYLATION, FRIEDEL-CRAFTS: Methylene chloride.

ACYLATION, KETONES: Sodium hydride.

ACYLOIN CONDENSATION: Trimethylchlorosilane.

ADAMANTANE SYNTHESIS, CATALYST: Aluminum bromide.

cis-ADDITION TO ALKYNES: Diisobutylaluminum hydride.

trans-ADDITION TO ALKYNES: Lithium diisobutylaluminum hydride.

1,4-ADDITION (*See also* Michael reaction. Thiele reaction.): Acrolein. Cuprous chloride. Cuprous iodide. Diethylaluminum cyanide. Difluoramine. Dimethylcopperlithium. Methyl(tri-n-butylphosphine)copper complex. Methyl vinyl ketone. Rhodium trichloride. Sulfur dichloride.

1,6-ADDITION: Sulfur dioxide.

ALDOL CONDENSATION: Lithium diisopropylamide.

C-ALKYLATION: Diethyl oxalate. Dimethylcopperlithium. Dimethyl sulfoxide. 1,3-Dithiane. Lithium diethylamide. Potassium t-butoxide.

N-ALKYLATION: Ethyldicyclohexylamine.

O-ALKYLATION: Acetaldehyde dimethyl acetal. Dimethyl sulfoxide. Pentaethoxyphosphorane.

S-ALKYLATION: Trimethyloxonium fluoroborate. Trimethylammonium. 2, 4, 6-trinitrobenzenesulfonate.

ALLENE SYNTHESIS: Methyllithium.

ALLYLIC ACETOXYLATION: Lead tetraacetate.

ALLYLIC BENZOYLATION: t-Butyl benzoate.

ALLYLIC COUPLING: Nickel carbonyl. Titanium trichloride.

π-ALLYLIC PALLADIUM CHLORIDE COMPLEX: Di-μ-chloro-π-allyldipalladium.

AMIDATION: Hexamethylphosphoric triamide. Polyphosphoric acid.

AMINATION. Dimethylformamide. Tetrakis(dimethylamino) titanium. Trichloramine.

AMINES, HINDERED: 2,6-Di-t-butylpyridine.

ANHYDRIDE FORMATION: Thionyl chloride.

ANION EXCHANGER: Tetraheptylammonium chloride.

ANNELATION: 1,3-Dichloro-2-butene. 2,3-Dimethyl-2-butylborane. 3,5-Dimethyl-4-chloromethylisoxazole. Methyl vinyl ketone. trans-3-Pentene-2-one. Pyrrolidine.

ARNDT-EISTERT REACTION: Diazomethane.

AROMATIC SUBSTITUTION: Cupric nitrate-acetic anhydride. Triethyl orthoformate.

AUTOXIDATION: Potassium t-butoxide. Salcomine.

BAEYER-VILLIGER REACTION: m-Chloroperbenzoic acid. Potassium persulfate.

BANFORD-STEVENS REACTION: p-Toluenesulfonylhydrazine.

BASES: Alumina, *see* *p*-Toluenesulfonylhydrazine. Dehydroabietylamine. 1,5-Diazabicyclo
[4.3.0]nonene-5. 1,4-Diazabicyclo[2.2.2]octane. 1,5-Diazabicyclo[5.4.0]undecene-5. 2,6-Di-*t*-
butylpyridine. N,N,-Diethylglycine ethyl ester, *see* *t*-Amyl chloroformate. 2,6-Dimethyl-
piperidine. Ethanolamine. Lithium diisopropylamide, *see* Diphenylsulfonium isopropylide.
Lithium nitride. Magnesium methoxide. N-Methylmorpholine. Piperidine. Potassium amide.
Potassium hydroxide. Potassium triethylmethoxide. Pyridine. Pyrrolidine. Sodium methoxide. Sodium 2-methyl-2-butoxide. Sodium thiophenoxide. Thallous ethoxide. Triethylamine. Triphenylphosphine, *see* 1-Methyl-2-pyrrolidone.

π-BASES: Tetremethoxyethylene.

BECKMANN REARRANGEMENT: Pyridine hydrochloride. Triphenylphosphine.

BENZYLATION: Dimethyl sulfoxide.

BENZYNE PRECURSORS: 1-Aminobenzotriazole (*see* 1-Chlorobenzotriazole). Benzenediazonium-
2-carboxylate.

BIMOLECULAR REDUCTION: Magnesium—Mercuric chloride.

BIRCH REDUCTION, *which see*.

BLOCKING OF OH-GROUPS: β-Benzoylpropionic acid. *p*-Nitrophenyl chloroformate.

BROMINATION: Boron tribromide. Bromotrifluoromethane. N-Bromosuccinamide. *n*-Butyla-
mine. Cupric bromide. Dibromoisocyanuric acid. Dioxane dibromide. Iodine monobromide.
Iron. Pyridine.

BROMOFLUORINATION: Silver fluoride.

BROMOHYDRINATION: N-Bromosuccinimide.

CARBENE GENERATION: Alumina—Potassium hydroxide. Bis(tribromomethyl)mercury. Bis
(trimethylsilyldichloromethyl)mercury. Bromotrifluoromethane. *n*-Butyllithium. Copper (II)
acetylacetonate. Diazoacetaldehyde. Di-μ-chloro-π-allyldipalladium. Dichloromethyl 2-
chloroethyl ether. Dicyanodiazomethane. *sym*-Difluorotetrachloroacetone. Ethylene oxide.
Methyl dichlorofluoroacetate. Methyllithium. Phenyl (trichloromethyl)mercury. Sodium
chlorodifluoroacetate. Sodium trichloroacetate. Thallous ethoxide. *p*-Toluene-sulfonyl-
hydrazine.

CARBODIIMIDES, DIMERIZATION: Tetrafluoroboric acid.

CARBOETHOXYLATION: Diethyl carbonate.

CARBOMETHOXYLATION: Dimethyl carbonate.

CARBONATION OF ORGANOBORANES: Lithium trimethoxyaluminum hydride.

CARBONIUM IONS: Fluorosulfuric acid.

CARBONYL ADDITIONS: Dichloromethyl(trichloromethyl)lithium. Dimethylsulfonium methylide.

CARBONYLATION OF ORGANOBORANES: Carbon monoxide. N,N'-Carbonyl-diimidazole. 2,3-
Dimethyl-2-butylborane. Hydrogen fluoride—Antimony pentafluoride. Lithium trimethoxyaluminum hydride. Palladium (II) chloride.

CARBONYL CONDENSATIONS: Sulfur tetrafluoride.

CARBONYL PROTECTION: Ethanedithiol.

CARBOXYLATION: CO_2, *see* Methylenemagnesium bromide (iodide). HCO_2H, *see* Adamantane
1-carboxylic acid chloride.

CARBOXY PROTECTION: 4-(Methylthio)phenyl.

CATALYTIC ACTIVITY: Phenyldiazomethane.

CHARACTERIZATION:

ACID CHLORIDES: Diacetyl-trimethyl phosphite adducts. Lithium nitride.

ALCOHOLS: Hexamethyldisilazane. Trichloroacetylisocyanate.

ALDEHYDES: Diacetyl—Trimethylphosphite adducts.

ALDOPYRANOSE DERIVATIVES: Acetaldehyde dimethylacetal.

ALDOSES: *p*-Aminobenzoic acid.

CARBOHYDRATES (CARBANILATES): Phenyl isocyanate.

CARBONYL COMPOUNDS: N,N-Dimethylhydrazine. Ethanedithiol.

DIANILINOETHANES: Triethyl orthoformate.

DIOLS: Phosgene.

FORMALDEHYDE: Tetrahydrophthalazine.

HYDROXY COMPOUNDS: 2,4-Dinitrofluorobenzene.

RESIN ACIDS: 2-Amino-2-methyl-1,3-propanediol. 2,6-Dimethyl-piperidine. Ethanolamine. Piperidene.

CHLORINATION: *t*-Butylhypochlorite. Catechyl phosphorus trichloride. N-Chlorosuccinimide. Cupric chloride. N,N-Diethyl-1,2,2-trichlorovinylamine. Iodobenzene dichloride. Mesyl chloride. Sulfuryl chloride.

CHROMATOGRAPHY: Silver fluoroborate.

CLASSIFICATION OF ALCOHOLS: Trichloroacetylisocyanate.

CLEAVAGE OF:

    ACETALS: Formic acid.

    ACETONIDES: 80% Acetic acid.

    t-AMINES: Phenyl Chloroformate.

    ARYLCYCLOPROPANES: Ceric ammonium nitrate.

    BENZYLAMIDES: Methanesulfonic acid.

    Bismethylenedioxy derivatives: 40% HF, *see* Formaldehyde.

    BLOCKED OXYTOCIN: Hydrogen fluoride.

    1,2-DIOLS: Cobalt (II) acetate.

    EPOXIDES: Boron trifluoride etherate. Lithium diethylamide.

    ETHERS: Acetyl *p*-toluenesulfonate. Boron tribromide. Boron trichloride. Boron trifluoride etherate—Acetic anhydride. Ferric chloride. Methylmagnesium iodide. Pyridine hydrochloride. Sodium borohydride. Sodium iodide.

    KETONES: Potassium *t*-butoxide.

    OXIMES: Ceric ammonium nitrate. Sodium bisulfite.

    PEPTIDES, PROTECTIVE GROUPS: Hydrogen fluoride.

    SEMICARBAZONES: Ceric ammonium nitrate.

    SULFONAMIDES: Naphthalene-Sodium.

COMPLEXES: *d*- and *l*-α-Benzylamine. Palladium (II) chloride. Silver nitrate.

CONDENSATION CATALYSTS: Boric acid. 1,5-Diazabicyclo[4.3.0]nonene-5. 1,4-Diazabicyclo[2.2.2]octane. Magnesium methoxide. Potassium fluoride. Sulfolane. Sulfomix. Trifluoroacetic acid.

CONFIGURATION DETERMINATION: α-Phenylbutyric anhydride.

CYCLIZATION: Boron trifluoride etherate. Ion-exchange resin. Lithium, diethylamide. Mercuric acetate(then sodium borohydride). Methanesulfonic acid. Nickel carbonyl. Polyphosphate ester. Sodium aluminum chloride. Sodium methoxide. Trifluoroacetic acid.

CYCLOADDITION: 1,1-Dichloro-2,2-difluoroethylene. Dichloroketene. Dichlorovinylene carbonate. N,N-Diethyl-1-propynylamine. Diphenylcarbodiimide. *see* Manganese dioxide, oxidation of dihydrobenzenes. *see* 4-Phenyl-1,2,4-triazoline-3,5-dione.

CYCLODEHYDRATION: 1,5-Diazabicyclo[4.3.0]nonene-5. 2,3-Dichloro-5,6-dicyano-1,4-benzoquinone. 1,1-Dichloro-2,2-difluoroethylene. Dichloroketene. Hydrobromic acid. Phosphoryl chloride-Phosphoric acid-Phosphorus pentoxide. Polyphosphoric acid. Thionyl chloride.

CYCLOPROPANE FORMATION. Diethylzinc-Methylene iodide.

DAKIN REACTION: Hydrogen peroxide.

DEACETOXYLATION: Calcium—liq. NH_3. Chromous chloride.

DEACETYLATION: Triethyloxonium fluoroborate.

DEALKYLATION, *t*-AMINES: Phenyl chloroformate.

    PHENOL ETHERS: sodium iodide.

DECARBETHOXYLATION: Sodium cyanide—Dimethylsulfoxide.

DECARBONYLATION: Chlorocarbonylbis(triphenylphosphine)rhodium. Chlorosulfonic acid. Tris(triphenylphosphine)chlororhodium.

DECARBOXYLATION: *t*-Butylhydroperoxide. Copper powder. Dimethyl sulfoxide. Iron.

DECARBOXYLATION, OXIDATIVE: Lead dioxide. Lead tetraacetate. Pyridine-N-oxide.

DEGRADATION, BILE ACID SIDE CHAIN: Periodic acid.

DEHALOGENATION: N,N-Dimethylaniline. Disodium phenanthrene. Naphthalene-sodium. Sodium-*t*-Butanol-Tetrahydrofurane. Sodium telluride. Tin. Tri-*n*-butyltinhydride.

DEHYDRATION: Alumina. Alumina–Pyridine–Diluent (sand). Dicyclohexylcarbodiimide. N,N-Diethyl-1-propynylamine. Dimethyl sulfoxide. Diphenylcarbodiimide. Iodine. Methoxyacetylene. Oxalic acid. Phenylcyanate. Phosphorus pentoxide–t-Amine. Phosphoryl chloride–Phosphoric acid–Phosphorus pentoxide. Phosphoryl chloride–Pyridine. Thionyl chloride.

DEHYDROGENATION: N-Bromosuccinimide. Chloranil. 1,3-Dibromo-5,5-dimethylhydantoin. 2,3-Dichloro-5,6-dicyano-1,4-benzoquinone. Manganese dioxide. Sodium hypobromite.

DEHYDROHALOGENATION: Alumina, see Sulfur tetrafluoride. Alumina–Potassium hydroxide. Cesium fluoride. 1,5-Diazabicyclo[4.3.0]nonene-5. 1,4-Diazabicyclo[2.2.2]octane. 1,5-Diazabicyclo[5.4.0]undecene-5. Dimethylaminotrimethylstannane. Dimethyl sulfoxide. Hexamethylphosphoric triamide. Lithium chloride. Lithium dicyclohexylamide. Magnesium oxide. Potassium t-butoxide. Potassium fluoride. Potassium triethylmethoxide. Pyridine, see Nitrosyl chloride. Silver fluoride. Silver nitrate. Sodium amide. Sodium bicarbonate, see Nitryl iodide. Sodium isopropoxide. Triethylamine, see Sulfur dioxide.

DEHYDROTOSYLATION: Potassium t-butoxide.

DEMERCURATION: Sodium borohydride, see Mercuric acetate.

DEMETHYLATION: Boron trichloride. Chromic anhydride. Ferric chloride. Methylmagnesium iodide.

DEOXIMATION: Iron pentacarbonyl.

DEOXYGENATION: Diethyl phosphonate. 1-Phenyl-5-chlorotetrazole. 2-Phenyl-3-methyl-1,3,2-oxazophospholine. Sodium borohydride. Sulfur dioxide.

DESICCANTS: see Drying agents.

DESULFURIZATION: Hexaethylphosphorous triamide. Methyl iodide. Nickel boride. Nickel catalysts (a) Raney type. Nickel peroxide.

DIAZIRINE–DIAZIRIDINE SYSTEM: Hydroxylamine-O-sulfonic acid.

DIAZONIUM SALTS: Diazonium tetrafluoroborates.

DIAZOTIZATION: Sodium nitrite–CF_3CO_2H–DMSO.

DIELS-ALDER CATALYST: Aluminum chloride.

DIELS-ALDER DIENES: Benzene, see Dicyanoacetylene. Cyclooctatetraene, see 4-Phenyl-1,2,4-triazoline-3,5-dione. Cyclopentadiene ketals. cis-7,8-Dichlorobicyclo[4.2.0]octadiene-2,4, see cis-3,4-Dichlorocyclobutene. 5,5-Dimethoxy-1,2,3,4-tetrachlorocyclopentadiene. Hexachlorocyclopentadiene. Methyl trans-2,4-pentadienoate. $\Delta^{14,16}$-Steroid dienes, see 4-Phenyl-1,2,4-triazoline-3,5-dione. Tetrachlorocyclopentadienone ethylene ketal.

DIELS-ALDER DIENOPHILES: Dichlorovinylene carbonate. Dicyanoacetylene. Diethyl azodicarboxylate. Dimethyl acetylenedicarboxylate. Ethylene, see 5,5-Dimethoxy-1,2,3,4-tetrachlorocyclopentadiene. 4-Methyl-1,2,4-triazoline-3,5-dione. 4-Phenyl-1,2,4-triazoline-3,5-dione. 1,4-Phthalazinedione.

DIENE ADDITION: Rhodium trichloride.

1,5-DIENES FROM ALLYL ALCOHOLS: Titanium trichloride.

DIMERIZATION: CARBODIIMIDES: Tetrafluoroboric acid.
    OF DIENES: Di(cobalttetracarbonyl)zinc. Naphthalene–Lithium. Palladium acetate. Periodic acid. Pyridine–Aluminum chloride. Rhodium trichloride.
    DIPHENYLACETYLENES: Aluminum bromide.

DIMERIZATION, OXIDATIVE: Naphthalene–Lithium. Palladium acetate. Periodic acid.

cis-DIOLS, protection: Phenylboronic acid.

DISPLACEMENTS: Boron trifluoride etherate. N,N-Diethyl-1,2,2-trichlorovinylamine. Dimethyl sulfoxide. Hexamethylphosphoric triamide. Lead acetate. Lithium bromide. Magnesium bromide. Polyphosphoric acid. Tetraethylammonium acetate.

DISPROPORTIONATION: Nickel catalysts.

DRYING AGENTS: Linde 4A molecular sieves. Sodium–lead alloy.

ELIMINATION OF HOR, HOAc: Chromous chloride. Sodium amide.

ENAMINE ADDITION: Trichloroacetic acid.

ENAMINE FORMATION: Tetrakis (dimethylamino)titanium.

ENOL ACETYLATION: Perchloric acid. Sodium hydride.

EPIMERIZATION: Tetraethylammonium acetate.

EPOXIDATION: *m*-Chloroperbenzoic acid. Molybdenum hexacarbonyl. Peracetic acid. Sodium perborate.

ESTERIFICATION: Dimethylacetamide. Dimethylformamide. Diphenyldiazomethane. Molecular sieves. Perchloric acid. Thionyl chloride. Trichloroisocyanuric acid.

ESTERIFICATION, ASYMMETRIC: α-Phenylbutyric anhydride.

ETHERIFICATION: Perchloric acid.

ETHERS→ESTERS: Trichloroisocyanuric acid.

ETHOXYLATION OF KETONES: Diethyl oxalate.

ETHYLATION: Pentaethoxyphosphorane.

ETHYNYLATION: Lithium acetylide.

ETHYNYLCARBINOL ACETATES→ALKYLALLENES: Formic acid.

FAVORSKY REACTION: Silver perchlorate.

FLUORINATION: Diethyl(2-chloro-1,1,2-trifluoroethyl)amine. Fluoroxytrifluoromethane. Perchloryl fluoride. Sodium fluoride.

C-FORMYLATION: Triethyl orthoformate.

O-FORMYLATION: Acetic-formic anhydride.

FORMYLOLEFINATION: Diethyl β-(cyclohexylimino)ethylphosphonate.

FRAGMENTATION, α,β-EPOXYKETOXIMES: *p*-Toluenesulfonylhydrazine.

FRIEDEL-CRAFTS ACYLATION: Aluminum bromide. Aluminum chloride. Diphenylcarbamyl chloride. Methylene chloride.

FRIEDEL-CRAFTS CATALYSTS: Aluminum bromide. Iodine. Iron.

GATTERMANN ALDEHYDE SYNTHESIS: *s*-Triazine.

GRIGNARD REACTION: Acetic-formic anhydride. Dichlorobis(tri-phenylphosphine)nickel. 1,1-Diethoxy-2-propane. Grignard reagents. 1-Iodoheptafluoropropane. Methylenemagnesium-bromide. Methyltri-*n*-butylphosphine)copper complex.

HALOGEN EXCHANGE: Boron tribromide.

HOMOCYCLIC RING CLOSURE: Sodium amide.

HOMOLOGATION: Acrolein. Carbon monoxide. Cuprous bromide–Diazomethane. Ethyl bromo acetate. Ethyl diazoacetate. Methyl vinyl ketone. Phenylthiomethyllithium. Trimethyl phosphite.

HUNSDIECKER REACTION: Thallous ethoxide.

HYDRATION, OLEFINS: Mercuric acetate.

HYDROALUMINATION, ALKYNES: Diisobutylaluminum hydride.

HYDROBORATION: Acrolein. 9-Borabicyclo[3.3.1]nonane.

HYDROCARBOXYLATION: Nickel carbonyl.

HYDROCHLORINATION: Hydrogen chloride.

HYDROCYANATION: Triethylaluminum.

HYDROFORMYLATION: Cobalt hydrocarbonyl.

HYDROGENATION CATALYSTS: Dichlorotris(triphenylphosphine)ruthenium. Iridium. Iridium tetrachloride–Triethyl phosphite. Iridium–BaSO$_2$ or CaCO$_4$. Lithium aluminum hydride. Nickel catalyst, Raney. Palladium hydroxide. Platinum catalysts. Potassium hydride. Trihydridobis(triphenylphosphine)iridium (III).

HYDROGENATION POISON: Quinoline.

HYDROGENATION PROMOTER: Hydrobromic acid.

HYDROGENATION, stereoselectivity: Nickel catalyst, Raney.

HYDROGENOLYSIS: Palladium catalyst. Triethylamine.

HYDROLYSIS: Alumina. Dimethyl sulfoxide. Iron pentacarbonyl. Levulinic acid.

HYDROXYLATION: Lead tetra(trifluoroacetate). Osmium tetroxide. Silver acetate–Iodine. Silver chlorate.

HYDROXYL PROTECTION: *iso*-Butyl chloroformate. 4-Methoxy-5-6-dihydro-2H-pyrane.

INCLUSION COMPLEXES: Thiourea.

IODINATION: *t*-Butyl hypoiodite. Iodine–periodic acid. Iodine monobromide, 1-Iodohepta-fluoropropane. *o*-Phenylene phosphorochloridite.

ISOMERIZATION: Aluminum bromide. Boron trifluoride–Hydrogen fluoride. Dimethyl sulfoxide. Formic acid. N-Lithioethylenediamine. Mercuric acetate. Perchloric acid. Potassium *t*-butoxide. Potassium hydride. Potassium hydroxide. Zinc dust.

ISOMERIZATION, EPOXIDE: Perchloric acid (oleic acid → γ-stearolactone).

ISOMERIZATION, ethynylcarbinols: Formic acid.

ISOTOPIC LABELLING: Dipotassium platinum chloride.

ISOXAZOLE ANNELATION: 3,5-Dimethyl-4-chloromethylisoxazole.

LACTONIZATION: Phosgene.

LEUCKART-WALLACH REACTION: Dimethylformamide.

MALONDIALDEHYDE PRECURSOR: Malonic dialdehyde tetraethyl acetal.

MEERWEIN-PONNDORF REACTION: Aluminum *t*-butoxide.

MEERWEIN REACTION: Cuprous bromide.

MERCAPTANIZATION: Sodium trithiocarbonate.

MERCURATION: Perchloric acid.

METALATION: *n*-Butyllithium. 1,4-Diazabicyclo[2.2.2]octane. N,N,N′,N′-Tetramethylethylene-diamine.

METHYLATION: Diazomethane–Boron fluoride etherate. Dimethylcopperlithium. Dimethyl-sulfonium methylide. Iodine. Methyl iodide. Methyl-(tri-*n*-butylphosphine) copper complex. Silver perchlorate. Simmons-Smith reagent. Sodium hydride.

METHYLATION, REDUCTIVE: Formaldehyde.

MICHAEL ADDITION: Dimethyl acetylenedicarboxylate. Magnesium methoxide.

MILD ACID HYDROLYSIS: Levulinic acid.

MIXED ANHYDRIDE SYNTHESIS: Triethylamine.

MOLECULAR COMPLEXES: Digitonin.

NITRATION: *i*-Amyl nitrate. Nitronium tetrafluoroborate. Potassium amide.

NITRENE GENERATION: N-*p*-Nitrobenzenesulfonoxyurethane.

NUCLEOPHILIC SUBSTITUTION: Hexamethylphosphoric triamide.

NUCLEOSIDE SYNTHESIS: Adamantane-1-carboxylic acid chloride. Bis-(*p*-nitrophenyl)hydrogen phosphate. β,β,β-Tribromoethyl chloroformate.

OIL-SOLUBLE SALT: Tetraheptylammonium chloride.

OLEFIN ADDITIONS: Bromine azide. Bromine chloride. Bromine (chlorine) dipyridine nitrate. N-Bromoacetamine. N-Bromoacetamide–DMSO–Water. N-Bromoacetamide–Hydrogen fluoride. *n*-Butyllithium. Dichloroketene. Dichloromethyl 2-chloromethyl ether. N,N-Dichlorourethane. Dichlorovinylene carbonate. Difluoramine. Ethyl azidoformate. Ethyl bromoacetate. Iodine azide. Iodine isocyanate. Iodine nitrate. Iodobenzene dichloride. 1-Iodoheptafluoropropane. Mercuric acetate. Nitrosyl chloride. Nitrosyl fluoride. Nitryl iodide. Rhodium trichloride. Silver fluoride.

OLEFINS, ISOMERIZATION: N-Lithioethylenediamine.

  MARKOWNIKOFF HYDRATION: Mercuric acetate.

  OLIGOMERIZATION: Di(cobalttetracarbonyl)zinc.

OLEFINS, SYNTHESIS: *n*-Butyllithium. 1,3-Dibenzyl-2-methyl-1,3,2-diazaphospholidine. Dimethyl methylphosphonothioate. Diphenylsulfonium isopropylide. N-Methanesulfinyl-*p*-toluidine. Methylphosphoric acid bis(dimethylamide). Phosphoryl chloride–Stannous chloride–Pyridine. *p*-Toluenesulfonylhydrazine. Triphenyl phosphite.

ORGANOBORANE ADDUCT: Ethyl dibromoacetate.

ORGANOLITHIUM COMPOUNDS, ACTIVATION: Potassium *t*-butoxide.

ORGANOMETALLIC COMPLEXES: Diiron nonacarbonyl. Iron pentacarbonyl. Silver nitrate (olefin complexes).

ORGANOMETALLIC REAGENTS: Bis(tribromomethyl)mercury. Bis(trimethylsilyldichloromethyl) mercury. *n*-Butyllithium. Chlorocarbonylbis(triphenylphosphine)rhodium. Cobalt hydrocarbonyl. Copper(II) acetylacetonate. Di-μ-chloro-π-allyldipalladium. Dichlorobis(triphenylphosphine)nickel. Dichloromethyllithium, Trichloromethyllithium. Dichlorotris(triphenylphosphine)ruthenium. Di(cobalttetracarbonyl)zinc. Diethylaluminum cyanide. Diethylzinc–Methylene iodide. Diiron nonacarbonyl. Diisopropylaluminum hydride. Dimethylaminotrimethylstannane. Dimethyl copperlithium. Grignard reagents. Iron pentacarbonyl. 3-Lithio-1-trimethylsilylpropyne. Lithium acetylide. Lithium dicyclohexylamide. Lithium diethylamide. Lithium diisobutylmethylaluminum hydride. Lithium diisopropylamide. Lithium tri-*t*-butoxyaluminum hydride. Lithium triethoxyaluminum hydride. Lithium trimethoxyaluminum hydride. Magnesium methoxide. Magnesium methyl carbonate. Manganic tris(acetylacetonate). Methyllithium. Methylmagnesium iodide. Methyl(tri-*n*-butylphosphine)copper complex. Molybdenum hexacarbonyl. Naphthalene–Lithium. Naphthalene–Magnesium. Naphthalene–Sodium. Nickel carbonyl. Phenylthiomethyl-lithium. Phenyl(trihalomethyl)mercury. Potassium *t*-butoxide. Potassium triethylmethoxide. Pyridine–*n*-Butyllithium. Salcomine. Silver tosylate. Simmons-Smith reagent. Sodium benzoate. Sodium chlorodifluoroacetate. Sodium dihydrobis-(2-methoxyethoxy)-aluminate. Sodium isopropoxide. Sodium methoxide. Sodium trichloroacetate. Tetrakis(dimethylamino) titanium. Tetrakis[iodi(tri-*n*-butylphosphine)] copper. N,N,N′,N′-Tetramethylethylenediamine. Thallous ethoxide. Tri-*n*-butyltinhydride. Triethylaluminum. Trihydridobis-(triphenylphosphine)iridium. Trimethyl phosphite–Methyl copper complex. Trimethyl (trifluoromethyl)tin. Triphenyltin hydride. Tris(triphenylphosphine)chlororhodium. Trityllithium. Vanadium oxyacetylacetonate. Vinyl lithium.

OXIDATION, ALLYLIC: *t*-Butyl perbenzoate. *t*-Butyl chromate. Lead tetraacetate–N-Bromosuccinimide. Mercuric acetate. Nickel peroxide. Selenium dioxide.

   t-AMINES: CrO$_3$–Pyridine.

   BAEYER–VILLIGER: *m*-Chloroperbenzoic acid.

   BENZYLIC: Palladium acetate.

   CATALYST: Platinum.

   N,N-DIMETHYLHYDRAZINES: Hydrogen peroxide.

   HYDROCARBONS: Lead tetra(trifluoroacetate).

   OLEFINS→γ-LACTONES: Manganic acetate.

   PROPARGYLIC ALCOHOLS: Lead dioxide.

   SELECTIVE OF S-COMPOUNDS: Lead tetraacetate. Perlauric acid.

   VINYLIC: Lead tetraacetate.

OXIDATIVE CYCLIZATION: Cupric chloride. Manganese dioxide. Mercuric acetate.

OXIDATIVE DECARBOXYLATION: Cupric acetate(catalyst). Lead dioxide. Lead tetraacetate.

OXIDATIVE REARRANGEMENT: Dimethyl sulfoxide–Acetic anhydride.

OXIDIZING AGENTS: N-Bromosuccinimide. *t*-Butyl chromate. Ceric ammonium nitrate. Ceric sulfate. Chloramine. *m*-Chlorobenzoic acid. 1-Chlorobenzotriazole. Chromic acid in acetone (Jones reagent). Chromic acid–Manganous nitrate. Chromic anhydride–anhydrous acetic acid (Fieser reagent). Chromic anhydride–pyridine (Sarett reagent). Chromyl acetate. Chromyl chloride. Cobalt (II) acetate. Cupric chloride. 1,3-Dibromo-5,5-dimethylhydantoin. Diethyl azidodicarboxylate. Dimethyl sulfoxide–Acetic anhydride. Dimethyl sulfoxide–DCC (Pfitzner-Moffatt reagent). 4,4′-Dinitrodiphenyl-nitroxide. Ferric chloride. Hydrogen peroxide. Iodine. Lead dioxide. Lead tetraacetate. Lead tetraacetate–N-Bromo-succinimide. Lead tetra (trifluoroacetate). Manganic acetate. Manganese dioxide. Mercuric oxide. Mercurous trifluoroacetic acetate. Nickel peroxide. Nitrobenzene. Nitrogen tetroxide (*see* 4-Phenyl-1,2,4-triazoline-3,5-dione). Osmium tetroxide. Osmium tetroxide–Sodium chlorate. Oxygen difluoride. Periodates. Perlauric acid. Perphthalic acid. Pertrifluoroacetic acid–Boron trifluoride. Potassium ferricyanide. Potassium nitrosodisulfonate. Potassium permanganate. Potassium persulfate. Potassium persulfate–Silver nitrate. Ruthenium tetroxide. Ruthenium tetroxide–Sodium periodate. Salcomine. Selenium dioxide. Silver acetate–Iodine. Silver carbonate. Silver chlorate. Silver (I) oxide. Silver(II) oxide. Silver perchlorate. Sodium perborate. Sulfur trioxide–Pyridine. Tetraethylammonium periodate. Thallium triacetate.

OXONIUM FLUORINATION: Perchloryl fluoride.
OXYGENATION: Platinum catalyst.
OXYMERCURATION: Mercuric acetate.
OZONIZATION: Dimethyl sulfide.

PECHMANN, VON, COUMARIN SYNTHESIS: Hydrogen fluoride, anhydrous.
PEPTIDE ANALYSIS: Phenanthrenequinone. Phenyl isothiocyanate.
PEPTIDE CLEAVAGE: Boron fluoride etherate.
PEPTIDE SYNTHESIS: t-Amyl chloroformate. Bis-(2,4-dinitrophenyl)carbonate. Bis-o-phenylene pyrophosphite. i-Butyl chloroformate. sec-Butyl chloroformate. t-Butyl chloroformate. t-Butyl 2,4,5-trichlorophenyl carbonate. Copoly(ethylene-N-hydroxymaleimide). N,N-Diethyl-1-propynylamine. Di-(p-nitrophenyl)sulfate. Ethoxyacetylene. N-Ethoxycarbonyl-2-ethoxy-1,2-dihydroquinoline. N-Ethylbenzisoxazolium fluoroborate. Ethyl chloroformate. N-Ethyl-5-phenylisoxazolium-3′-sulfonate. N-Hydroxysuccinimide trifluoroacetate. Methyl-morpholine. 4-Methylthiophenol. p-Nitrophenol. Oxalylchloride. Pentachlorophenol. Pentamethylbenzyl chloride. t-Pentyl chloroformate. Phenacyl bromide. Polyhexamethylene carbodiimide. Tetraethyl pyrophosphate. 1,2,4-Triazole.
PEPTIDE SYNTHESIS, CARBOXY PROTECTION: 4-(Methylthio)phenol. Pentamethylbenzyl chloride. Phenacyl bromide.
PEPTIDE SYNTHESIS, N-PROTECTION: Acetic–formic anhydride. Adamantyl chloroformate. Benzylthiocarbonyl chloride. t-Butoxycarbonyl-N-hydroxysuccinimide ester. t-Butyl azido-formate. t-Butylcarbonic diethylphosphoric anhydride. t-Butyl fluoroformate. t-Butyl-oxycarbonyl fluoride. t-Butyl pentachlorophenyl carbonate. t-Butyl 2,4,5-trichlorophenyl carbonate. Carbobenzoxy chloride. 3,5-Dimethoxybenzyl p-nitrophenyl carbonate. [2-(Diphenyl)isopropyl]phenyl carbonate. t-Pentyl chloroformate.
PEPTIDE SYNTHESIS, SH-PROTECTION: Acetamidomethanol. Benzylthiomethyl chloride. Benzyl-trimethylammonium chloride.
PEPTIDE SYNTHESIS, SOLID-PHASE: Ion-exchange resins.
PHENOLS, REDUCTION: 1-Phenyl-5-chlorotetrazole.
PHENYLATION, ANIONS: Diphenyliodonium chloride.
PHOSPHORYLATION: α-Bromocyanoacetamide. Di-(2,2,2-trichloroethyl)phosphorochlororidate. Pyrophosphoryl tetrachloride. Sodium methyl phosphorazidate.
PHOTOADDITION: Ethyl azidoformate.
PHOTOBROMINATION: N-Bromoacetamide.
PHOTOCHEMICAL SENSITIZER: Michler's ketone.
PHOTOCHLORINATION: t-Butylhypochlorite. Dichlorovinylene carbonate. see Lithium dicyclo-hexylamide. see Tetrahydrophthalazine.
PHOTOCYCLIZATION: Chromyl acetate. Tetrachloro-cyclopentadienone ethylene ketal.
PHOTOCYCLOPHILE: Dichlorovinylene carbonate.
PHOTODECOMPOSITION: Diiron nonacarbonyl. Iodine azide.
PHOTOELIMINATION OF N₂: 2-Diazopropane. Iodine azide.
PHOTOISOMERIZATION: Cyclopentadienone ketals. Mercuric oxide. see Nickel carbonyl.
PHOTOREDUCTION, under p-Boronobenzoic acid, see 1,8-Naphthalylnaphthalene. Sodium sulfite.
PHOTOSENSITIZER: Benzophenone (see 2-Diazapropane). Methylene blue (see Formamide). Michler's ketone.
PI-COMPLEXES: Silver nitrate.
PINACOL REARRANGEMENT: Potassium t-butoxide.
POLONOVSKI REACTION: Acetic anhydride.
POLYMERIZATION CATALYST: Aluminum chloride.
POLYMERIZATION-CYCLIZATION OF α, ω-DIHALIDES: Disodium acetylide.
PROTECTION:
    AMINO SUGAR: Diphenylphosphorochloridate.
    CARBONYL GROUP: Ethanedithiol.
    CARBOXY GROUP: 4-(Methylthio)phenol.
    CYSTEINE GROUP: Acetamidomethanol.

HYDROXYL GROUP: Adamantane-1-carboxylic acid chloride. β-Benzoylpropionic acid. Ethyl vinyl ether. 4-Methoxy-5,6-dihydro-2H-pyrane. p-Nitrophenyl chloroformate.

Δ⁴-3-KETOSTEROIDS: Pyrrolidine.

PYRROLE: t-Butyl azidoformate.

SH: Acetamidomethanol. Benzylthiomethyl chloride. Silver nitrate π-complex.

PROTEIN SEQUENCE ANALYSIS: Malonic dialdehyde tetraethylacetal.

PUMMERER REARRANGEMENT: Iodine, oxidation.

Δ²-PYRROLIDINE SYNTHESIS: Methyl vinyl ketone.

PYRYLIUM SALTS: t-Butyl chloride.

QUASI-FAVORSKI REACTION: Silver perchlorate.

RADICALS: Bromine azide. n-Butyllithium. Cuprous acetate. N,N-Dichlorourethane. 4,4'-Dinitrodiphenylnitroxide. Iodine, oxidation. Iodobenzenedichloride. Manganic tris(acetylacetonate) Potassium t-butoxide. Potassium ferricyanide. Potassium nitrosodisulfonate.

REARRANGEMENTS: Aluminum bromide. Calcium carbonate. Dimethylthiocarbamyl chloride Dimsylsodium. 1,3-Dithiane. Lithium diethylamide. Manganese dioxide. Methyl vinyl ketone, 4a → 5a. Michler's ketone. Norbornene. Perchloric acid. Pinacol-type: see Potassium t-butoxide. Potassium t-butoxide. Silver perchlorate. Thallium triacetate. Triethyloxonium-fluoroborate.

REDUCING AGENTS: Aluminum hydride. Bis-3-methyl-2-butylborane. n-Butyllithium–Pyridine. Calcium borohydride. Chloroiridic acid. Chromous acetate. Chromous chloride. Chromous sulfate. Copper chromite. Diborane. Diborane–Boron trifluoride. Diborane–Sodium borohydride. Diethyl phosphonate. Diimide. Diisobutylaluminum hydride. Dimethyl sulfide. Hexamethylphosphorous triamide. Iridium tetrachloride. Lead. Lithium alkylamines. Lithium aluminum hydride. Lithium aluminum hydride–Aluminum chloride. Lithium–Ammonia. Lithium diisobutylmethylaluminum hydride. Lithium–Diphenyl. Lithium ethylenediamine. Lithium–Hexamethylphosphoric triamide. Lithium hydride. Lithium triethoxyaluminum hydride. Lithium tri-t-butoxyaluminum hydride. Nickel-aluminum alloy. Pyridine–n-Butyllithium. Sodium amalgam. Sodium–Ammonia. Sodium borohydride. Sodium borohydride–BF₃, see DDQ. Sodium dihydrobis-(2-methoxyethoxy) aluminate. Sodium hydrosulfite. Sodium telluride. Stannous chloride. Tin–HBr. Tri-n-butyltin hydride. Trimethyl phosphite, see Dinitrogen tetroxide.

REDUCTION METHODS: Bimolecular: Magnesium–Mercuric chloride.

   BIRCH REDUCTION (which see).

   ETHYLENETHIOKETALS: see Ethanedithiol.

   MEERWEIN-PONNDORF REDUCTION: see Aluminum t-butoxide.

   PHENOLS: Diethyl phosphonate.

   REDUCTIVE DEBROMINATION: N,N-Dimethylaniline.

   REDUCTIVE METHYLATION: Formaldehyde.

   STEREOSPECIFIC R OR S: Lithium aluminum hydride-3-O-benzyl-1-2-O-cyclohexylidene-α-D-glucofuranose complex. α,β-Unsaturated ketones: Li (or K) in hexamethylphosphoric triamide and ether.

REFORMATSKY REACTION: Aluminum.

RESIN ACIDS: Piperidine.

RESOLUTION: p-Boronobenzoic acid. d-10-Camphorsulfonic acid. Di-p-toluoyl-L-tartrate, see Hydrazoic acid. Iodobenzenedichloride. d- and l-α-Methylbenzylamine. 1-Phenylethanesulfonic acid, see 1,3-Dibenzyl-2-methyl-1,3,2-diazaphospholidine. (+) and (−)-α-)2,4,5,7-Tetranitro-9-fluorenylideneaminooxy)-propionic acid.

RING EXPANSION: Hydrazoic acid. Iodine isocyanate.

SALTS, OIL-SOLUBLE: Tetraheptylammonium chloride.

SANDMEYER REACTION: Cupric chloride–Nitric oxide.

SAPOGENINS, ACETOLYSIS: Pyridine hydrochloride.

SCHMIDT REACTION: Hydrazoic acid. Sodium azide.

SECOSTEROID ACETYLENIC KETONES: p-Toluenesulfonylhydrazine.

SOLVENT EFFECTS: Dimethyl sulfoxide. Hexamethylphosphoric triamide. Mercurous trifluoroacetate. Methylene chloride. N-Methylmorpholine. 1-Methyl-2-pyrrolidone. Tetrahydrofurane.

SOLVENT EXTRACTION: Tetramethylene sulfone.

SOMMELET REACTION: Hexamethylenetetramine.

STOBBE CONDENSATION: Hydrazoic acid.

SULFATATION: Sulfur trioxide–Pyridine.

SULFONATION: Sulfur trioxide–Dioxane.

SYNTHESIS (OR PREPARATION) OF:

ACETYLENES, DIENES, ENEYNES: 3-Lithio-1-trimethylsilylpropyne.

ACID BROMIDES (CHLORIDES): Catechyl phosphorous tribromide (trichloride).

ADAMANTANE: Aluminum bromide.

ALDEHYDES: Dichloromethyl methyl ether. p-Dimethylaminobenzaldehyde. Dimethyl sulfide. Lithium tri-t-butoxyaluminum hydride. Nickel catalysts, Raney type. Sodium nitrite–CF_3CO_2H–DMSO. Titanium tetrachloride. Triethyl orthoformate. Trimethylamine oxide.

α-ALKOXY KETONES: BF_3-etherate.

ALKYL AZIDES: Tetramethylguanidinium azide.

ALKYL HALIDES: Difluorotriphenylphosphorane. Sodium borohydride.

ALLENES: n-Butyllithium. Methyllithium. Olefin → allene Phosphorus tribromide.

AMIDES: Hexachlorocyclotriphosphatriazine.

ANHYDRIDES: Methoxyacetylene. Phenyl cyanate.

1-ARYLCYCLOPROPANOLS: 1,3-Dichloroacetone.

ARYLHYDRAZONES: p-Carboxybenzenediazonium chloride.

1H-AZEPINS: Iodine isocyanate.

AZIDE SYNTH.: p-Toluenesulfonyl azide.

AZIRIDINES: N,N-Dichlorourethane. Ethyl azidoformate.

2H-AZIRIDINES: Iodine azide. Lithium aluminum hydride.

BIARYLS: Thallium (I) bromide.

CARBAMATES: N-Carbonylsulfamic acid chloride.

CARBANILATES: Phenyl isocyanate.

CARBODIIMIDES: Phosphorus pentoxide-t-Amine.

CARDENOLIDE AGLYCONE: Diethyl cyanomethylphosphonate.

CAROTINOIDS: Alumina.

4-CHLOROBENZOFURAZANE: Sodium azide.

β-CHLOROGLYCOSIDES: Aluminum chloride.

COUMARINS: Hydrogen fluoride, anhydrous.

COUPLED ALLYLIC PRODUCTS: Nickel carbonyl.

CUMULENES: Methyllithium. Sodium amide. Zinc dust.

ω-CYANO ACIDS: Formamide.

CYCLIC KETONES: 1,3-Dithiane.

1,3-CYCLOHEXADIENES: Methyl trans-2,4-pentadienoate.

CYCLOPHANES: 1,3-Dithiane.

CYCLOPROPANE ESTERS: Ethyl(dimethylsulfuranylidine) acetate.

CYCLOPROPANES: Dichloromethyllithium. Trichloromethyllithium.

CYCLOPROPANONES: Diazomethane.

CYCLOPROPENONES: Phenyl(trihalomethyl)mercury.

p-DIACETYLBENZENE, see Hydriodic acid.

DIARYLCYCLOPROPENONES: Phenyl(trihalomethyl)mercury.

DIAZIRIDINES: Chloramine. Hydroxylamine-O-sulfonic acid.

DIAZIRINES: Difluoramine.

DIAZO COMPOUNDS: p-Carboxybenzenesulfonyl azide. p-Toluenesulfonyl azide.

DIENES: Cuprous chloride.

1,5-DIENES, 1-ENE-5-YNES: 3-Lithio-1-trimethylsilylpropyne.

β,β-DIFLUOROSTYRENE: Sodium chlorodifluoroacetate.

trans-1,2-DIHYDROPHTHALIC ACID: Sodium amalgam.

gem-DIMETHYLCYCLOPROPANES: 2-Diazapropane.

DISULFIDES: Diethyl azododicarboxylate.

ENAMINES: Tetrakis(dimethylamino)titanium. Titanium tetrachloride.

β-EPOXYKETONES: Nickel carbonyl.

EPOXYQUINONES: Sodium perborate.

ESTERS FROM OLEFINS: Ethyl bromoacetate. Ethyl dibromoacetate.

FURANES: DMSO-derived reagent (c): Dimethyloxosulfoniummethylide. Ethyl diazoacetate.

FUROXANES: Dinitrogen tetroxide.

HETEROCYCLES: t-Butylisocyanide. N,N'-Carbodiimidazole. Cyanogen bromide. Dimethyl acetylenedicarboxylate. Dimethylformamide–POCl₃. Hydrazine. Phenyldiazomethane. Phenylhydrazine. Phenyl(trihalomethyl)mercury. Polyphosphate ester. Sodium aluminum chloride.

IODIDES: o-Phenylene phosphorochloridate.

ISOCYANATES: Catechyl phosphorus trichloride. Trimethylchlorosilane.

ISONITRILES: 2-PHENYL-1,3,2-oxazophospholine.

β-KETOALLENES AND α,β-UNSATURATED KETONES: Isopropenyl methyl ether.

KETONES: 2,3-Dimethyl-2-butylborane. Iron.

β-KETOSULFONES: Dimethyl sulfone.

MERCAPTANS: Sodium trithiocarbonate.

METACYCLOPHANES: Phenyl(trihalomethyl) mercury.

METHYL CYCLOHEXYL KETONE: Methyllithium (and cyclohexanecarboxylic acid).

METHYL KETONES: Methyllithium.

NITRILES: Chlorosulfonyl isocyanate, Hydroxylamine hydrochloride.

NUCLEOSIDES: Adamantane-1-carboxylic acid chloride. Bis-(p-nitrophenyl)hydrogen phosphate.

NUCLEOTIDES: Isobutyl chloroformate.

cis-9-OCTADECENYL BROMIDE: Magnesium bromide.

OLEFINS: see Olefins, synthesis.

OLIGONUCLEOTIDES: β-Benzoylpropionic acid.

OXIRANES: Dimethyloxosulfonium methylide (DMSO-derived (c)).

α-OXO ESTERS: Lithium bromide.

PARACYCLOPHANES: Aluminum bromide.

PHENAZINES: Nitrobenzene.

PHENOLS: m-Nitrobenzenesulfonyl peroxide. Trimethyl borate.

POLYUNSATURATED KETONES: Isopropenyl methyl ether.

PYRAZOLES: Phenyl(trihalomethyl)mercury.

PYRIDINES: 3,5-Dimethyl-4-chloromethylisoxazole.

PYRROLES: 2,5-Dimethyltetrahydrofurane.

PYRYLLIUM SALTS: t-Butyl chloride.

SPIROCYCLOPROPANES: Simmons-Smith reagent.

STEROID RING A: 1,3-Dichloro-2-butene.

STEROIDS: 3,5-Dimethyl-4-chloromethylisoxazole. Ethyl vinyl ether.

SULFONES: Polyphosphoric acid.

SULFOXIDES: Periodates. Perlauric acid.

TETRAZOLES: Tetramethylguanidinium azide.

THIOPHENOLS: Dimethylthiocarbonyl chloride.

TRIBENZAMIDE: Lithium nitride.

TRICHLOROMETHYLBISTRIFLUOROMETHYLCARBINOL: Trichloromethyllithium.

TRIPHENYLPHOSPHAZINES: Molecular sieves.

TROPONE: Silver fluoroborate.

TROPYLIUM SALTS: t-Butyl chloride.

α,β-UNSATURATED ALDEHYDES: Potassium fluoride.

YNAMINES: Cupric acetate.

TAYLOR-McKILLOP REACTIONS: Thallous ethoxide.

THIELE REACTION: Acetic anhydride. Acetic phosphoric anhydride. Boron trifluoride etherate. Perchloric acid. Sulfuric acid. Zinc chloride.

TRANSESTERIFICATION: Molecular sieves.

TRANSPOSITION OF KETO GROUPS: *i*-Amyl nitrate.

TRAPPING: Aldehydes: 1,2-Dianilinoethane.

    ALLENES: 1,3-Diphenylisobenzofurane.

    CARBENE: Cyclohexene.

TRICHLOROMETHYLATION: Sodium trichloroacetate.

TRIMERIZATION OF ALKYNES: Aluminum chloride.

TROPYLIUM SALTS: *t*-Butyl chloride.

VILSMEIR REACTION: DIETHYL AZODICARBOXYLATE.

VINYLIC SUBSTITUTION: N-Bromosuccinimide.

WATER SCAVENGER: Titanium tetrachloride.

WHITE DEAMINATION: Dinitrogen tetroxide.

WITTIG REACTIONS: Carbomethoxymethylenetriohenylphosphorane. Cyclopropyltriphenylphosphonium bromide. 1,5-Diazabicyclo[4.3.0]nonene-5. Diethyl cyanomethylphosphonate. *p*-Diphenylphosphinobenzoic acid. Diphenylsulfonium isopropylide. Diphenyl triphenylphosphoranylidenemethylphosphonate. Ethyl(dimethylsulfuranylidine)acetate. Ethylene oxide. Hexamethylphosphorous triamide. Methoxymethylenetriphenylphosphorane. Methylenemagnesium bromide (chloride). Simmons-Smith reagent. Sodium 2-methyl-2-butoxide.

WOLFF-KISHNER REDUCTION: Hydrazine.

WURTZ-LIKE COUPLING: Lead, pyrophosphoric. Tetraphenylethylene.

ZIEGLER CYCLIZATION: Lithium diethylamide.

AUTHOR INDEX

SUBJECT INDEX